The Body

BY ANTHONY SMITH

Jambo
High Street Africa
Sea Never Dry
Blind White Fish in Persia

THE BODY

by Anthony Smith

WALKER AND COMPANY

NEW YORK

Foreword

There are problems in writing a book of general science. Strict scientific writing requires wholesale qualification, and no generalizations are acceptable; every statement is therefore beset with qualifying appendages. General scientific writing demands generalizations, and most of the qualifying precision has to go by the board. It cannot be otherwise. Without this seeming disregard for the truth, a contentious nightmare soon results—human beings produce babies; female human beings produce babies; female human beings 15 to 50 years old produce most babies; most female human beings between 15 and 50 can and do produce most babies; assuming fertility, prowess, and desire from their mates, most female human beings between 15 and 50, although both younger and older have been plentifully recorded, can be fertilized and most of these women will successfully produce babies, although a number of the offspring will be stillborn, this number varying according to race, area, age. . . . The nightmare is readily accessible and has to be avoided without falling foul of gross oversimplification.

Science has precise meaning for most of its words, even such ordinary words as average, mean, median, normal, and mode. To follow such precision into the more casual everyday world, which happily blurs their respective meanings, can be disastrous. Strictly, on an average, human beings possess fewer than two ears. The actual number of ears per person, bearing in mind those born without ears and those who have earlessness thrust upon them, must be a figure like 1.9999. Similarly, science may contend that an average family has 2.4 children. Plainly, absolute accuracy cannot be the sole guide.

Common meanings can be extremely troublesome. Man is a mammal. Mammals are animals. Man is not an animal. The word "man" is often awkward. Man stands upright on two legs. Man cooks food and hunts. Man has babies. Even human temperature is no one thing. "Normal" is usually 98.4 in Britain, 98.6 in the United States, and 37 on the continent of Europe. When does an embryo become a fetus? Some say at eight weeks, but others hate the words and talk only of the products of conception. A mother uses no such phrase and refers to her "baby" even before it has been born. And is it all right to talk of white races but not of black races? Must American Negroes be called Negroid, and must Americans from Europe follow suit and be called Caucasoid? Early attempts to respect current usage and common understanding have led, on occasion after occasion, to my own prejudices riding determinedly and roughshod over the opinions of others.

Perinatal mortality, infant mortality, and neonatal mortality all refer to dead babies, but a neonate, for example, is a baby less than four weeks old, whereas an infant is less than a year old. Most people do not talk of infants and certainly not of neonates; instead they talk only of babies, and let them become children at some indefinite age. However, the words "baby" and "child" are almost as meaningless in their imprecision to some people as the word "neonate" is meaningless to others. Both sides have to be respected, and babies have to be qualified.

Even the word "England" demands extreme caution. It ought to be feasible to use the word to refer to "the English," but facts solely from the whole of England are very rare. More commonly, they come from England and Wales, or from England, Wales, Scotland, and Northern Ireland. Very rarely do facts relate to the entire British Isles. The Americans can also be confusing (although they never match the British in such inanity) by having to specify whether they mean the contiguous states or the United States.

Science is written (usually) in grams, cubic centimeters, liters, and degrees Centigrade. English-speaking people prefer ounces, cubic inches, pints, and Fahrenheit. To add to the problem, English-speaking people from Britain have a different pint from the American one, and are happy to give their weight in stones, a procedure that confounds most Americans. I have a further conviction that most people are wonderfully vague about nearly all weights and measures. An eight-week embryo weighs about one-fifth of an ounce, or some 6 grams. Does either weight really indicate anything other than extreme lightness? At eight weeks a mother's uterus contains one ounce of amniotic fluid. What is that? A thimbleful, an eggcupful, or a teacupful? Therefore, whenever I have felt the precise units of measurement to be particularly meaningless, I have tried other methods. An eight-week embryo, for example, has to be 600 times heavier to be an average baby seven months later. There is a danger

that such circumlocution can annoy (and I was once extremely irritated
to be told that a missile's nose cone flying through the air was as hot as
Regulo 7 on my oven) but the intention is to clarify, however unsatisfactory the result may be.

A final point is that scientific articles give a source for every stated
fact. The customary procedure is to insert numbers in appropriate positions in the text and give the actual reference at the foot of each page
or article. I have not done this, mainly to relieve myself of the burden this
would entail, but partly because such annotations (e.g. "4. Orie, N.G.M.,
De Vries, G.A. Kikstra, A. *Am. Rev. resp. Dis.,* 1960, *82,* 649.") have
limited appeal. However, I have tried to give sources whenever their who,
when, and where seemed particularly important, even though I have very
rarely mentioned the journal, let alone the volume or page number.

If any of these personal prejudices, mannerisms, and preferences fails
to achieve its object of making more sense out of the subject matter, I
apologize here and now for the irritation they will surely cause.

Contents

CONTENTS

It is highly dishonourable for a reasonable soul to live in so divinely built a mansion as the body she resides in altogether unacquainted with the exquisite structure of it.

Robert Boyle

Before I came here I was confused about this subject. Having listened to your lecture I am still confused. But on a higher level.

Enrico Fermi

Introduction

"These, gentlemen, are the opinions on which I base my facts." No one is certain who originally made this statement but, without doubt, it should be written again and again, and especially at the outset of any work that professes to be objective. Facts do indeed speak through an interpreter and are subject to his wishes. The facts in this book, culled from a bewilderment of sources, have been influenced by three major contentions.

The first is that man is no isolated being. Admittedly, it is over a hundred years since the modern theory of evolution was first propounded, and few people today accept the simplicity of Adam and Eve's creation, but the human species is still considered most distinct. There is mankind on one side and animal life on the other; there is Homo sapiens, and there are all the beasts of the field and birds of the air. Given any opportunity, I have been happy to break down this barrier. Man is just another bit of biology, and therefore much of the animal kingdom is entirely relevant to his body, to his mechanism of sperm transfer, to his sex ratio, to his brain, to his sense of smell. He is not an isolated piece of creation, like a meteorite that has flown in from somewhere else. He is a part of terrestrial evolution, and facts about animals can make sense of facts about him. To my mind the menstrual cycle (which affects women and apes) has to be compared with the estrous cycle (which affects most other mammals). Even so, this is not a book about animals. It is a book about the human body, and animals are used to lend emphasis, to clarify, and to illuminate whenever they can.

My second main contention concerns the collection of facts. I have used an extremely wide net in the belief—and hope—that most of the subjects would benefit. It is possible to deal with hemophilia in a strictly

[1]

biochemical fashion and discuss the missing clotting factor most academically, but it is preferable—according to this second contention—to describe Queen Victoria's knowledge of this affliction as well and to show its ramification throughout her family. There is the straightforward human stomach, and there is also the remarkable tale of the French-Canadian whose stomach was permanently open to view. There are twins, and there are also cases of twins where each of the pair is the offspring of a different father. There are forceps deliveries, and there is the roguish and un-Hippocratic story of their development. Behind every aspect of the body there are relevant but more indirect facts that can be most enlightening. What about inbreeding and the famous men who have been products of cousin-cousin marriages? What about speaking and those who—like Einstein—wait until the age of four before saying anything? The stories are best told, according to this contention, by mixing the direct with the indirect.

Thirdly, because medical men are primarily interested in medicine, the curing of ailments, and the preservation of health, most medical books concentrate on disease and on breakdown. This book does not totally disregard such failure, but regards a pumping heart as more interesting than a heart failing to pump. Sometimes, the manner of a breakdown can be exceptionally revealing on its own, just as hemophilia has much to say about inheritance; but, in general, function is given greater space than malfunction. At the same time, the classical precision of medical jargon, quite another language to most of us, is avoided if there is a convenient way of avoiding it.

These, then, are the three principal contentions. Each is relevant to every chapter of the book, but on page 37 is a further introduction called "On Reproduction" to explain why some two-thirds of this book is concerned with procreation. Between these two introductions are three chapters, dealing with evolution, race, and population. They are a rapid attempt to set the scene. There are some 3.3 billion people living today of the species Homo sapiens whose body this book is about. They are all products of evolution, as is every other living creature, and the first chapter (the hastiest of all) runs through the biological events of the geological epochs until, in this Quaternary period, mankind dominates the scene. The second chapter discusses the differences within our species, for, most blatantly, we are not born equal. And the third chapter enlarges upon our actual population numbers, what they used to be and what they will soon become. Anyone alarmed by the magnitude of this book and wishing to skip a section could well pass over these first three chapters. Then, much like the sudden presence in that garden of Adam and Eve, the chapters on the male and the female will be abruptly encountered.

After the gamut of reproduction has finally been played, leading from fertility through growth and eventually to senility and death, the subsequent chapters (starting on page 304) discuss those bodily systems that cannot be brought under the all-embracing title of reproduction. Finally (on page 485), there is a chapter on radiation. There is a factor "L" used by certain scientists to indicate the length of time after a civilization has acquired the means of self-annihilation before it uses those means. Happily, mankind is still living, but the subject of radiation is highly germane to our well-being, whether the particles come in small or large doses, and is therefore included. A postscript and an index conclude the book.

❧ 1 ❧

Evolution

The Origin of Life · The Fossil Record ·
Mammals · Primates · Man

*If we could first know where we are and whither we are tending, we
could better judge what to do and how to do it.*

Abraham Lincoln

The Origin of Life

When Charles Darwin, chivied into print by similar thinking from Alfred
Russel Wallace and championed afterward so forcibly by Thomas Henry
Huxley, finally caused the world to think about evolution, the world
was part bewildered, part horrified by the idea. Within a few decades
the horror diminished, mainly because there was reconciliation with
the contradictory story in Genesis; but the bewilderment still thrived.
However many facts of evolution are absorbed, however many fossils
are seen, strata examined, books read, and whatever evidence is accumulated, the scale of the evolutionary epochs remains as lengthy and vast as
ever. The blindness of evolution and its lack of purpose, coupled with
the constant change and the eternal urgency of life, add to the incompre-
hensibility. It has gone on for an immensity of time, and it is happening
now as it was in the beginning. It is small wonder that Darwin shook
the world.

The word "million" is partly to blame, for all the epochs, eras, and
geological periods are numbered in millions of years. The figure is
difficult to absorb. A day, for instance, rushes by and is rapidly replaced by another. We live many days. We peer into history and feel
a great sense of time, of passed days, passed years. The Elizabethans
lived in the remote past, and remoter still were men like the Normans,
or King Alfred, or Charlemagne, or the Emperor Hadrian, or Christ. Yet
Christ, who is so deeply embedded in the past, lived only some 700,000

[4]

days ago. To go back a million days means going back to the eighth century B.C., before even the Greeks and the Romans had started on their glory and their grandeur. A million days is an eternity of time. The evolutionary era is a matter of thousands of millions of *years*.

The fossil record starts being clear only in the Cambrian rocks. These extremely ancient deposits were being laid down at the beginning of the Paleozoic era, some 600 million years ago. Yet the living creatures of that time, incorporated within those rocks as fossils, include many forms of crustaceans, of mollusks, of worms, and of echinoderms—like the starfish. Such animals, although primitive from our standpoint, are highly advanced and specialized if viewed from the time when life began as some distant protoplasmic form. The earliest recorded fossils are about five times more ancient. Some have been observed in a kind of Australian quartz, a substance thought to be 2.7 billion years old. Others, notably bacteria, have been found in South African sediments called black chert; their age is reputed to be 3 billion years. If these sediments have been accurately dated and if one bears in mind that these bacteria were found associated with some threads of organic material, the start of life was presumably much earlier. And the start of this planet, whose turbulent birth had to settle down before life of any kind was possible, was thought to have occurred 5 or 6 billion years ago. Life began sometime after the Earth itself had been formed, and sometime before those most antique of fossils had been laid down. In short, there has been life—and evolution—for much more than half of this planet's existence. Such a quantity of continuing biological change is both hard to visualize and to accept.

A refusal to accept the idea of evolution's blindness added to the turmoil surrounding Darwin. Genesis is clear. Its story of creation is simple. Besides, it was all over in a week. There was a purpose, the making of night and day, the separation of sea and land, the creation of fish, flesh, fowl, and finally man. Evolution has no purpose. The predator seeking out the prey has no greater objective than the grass growing, the rain falling. If there seems to be a purpose in evolution, said Sir Julian Huxley, it is only an apparent purpose. "It is just as much a product of blind forces as is the falling of a stone to earth or the ebb and flow of the tides. It is we who have read purpose into evolution, as earlier men projected will and evolution into inorganic phenomena like storm or earthquake."

Sir Julian wrote that in 1942. This positive and didactic clarity was not so easy in 1859, when Darwin's book *The Origin of Species* was published, or even in 1871, when he published *The Descent of Man*. Man's evolutionary origin had only been implied in the first book. It was asserted cogently in the second; hence the furor. Since then, religious beliefs and scientific opinion have managed to coexist more peacefully in most minds. Nevertheless, this lack of evolutionary purpose, coupled with the eternity of its purposelessness, is a difficult pill for many to swallow. The most disquieting conclusion is that mankind, gifted and skilled, is the product of those innumerable millennia of random biological activity. Somehow Shakespeare arose from the primeval ooze of this planet, from its mud, from the ebbing and flowing, from all those eons of unrecorded time.

Dr. G. H. Haggis, who has written and speculated about the origin of life, points out that the sudden appearance of a man in a world of one-celled organisms would be highly improbable, but his gradual evolution entirely conceivable. Similarly, the sudden appearance of a cell in a world of small molecules would be improbable, but the evolution of small molecules to larger molecules, and then to an aggregate of molecules, is conceivable.

Some experimentation along these lines is possible. If a mixture of the gases thought to have been present in the Earth's early atmosphere (hydrogen, methane, ammonia, water, carbon monoxide, hydrogen sulphide, etc.) are suitably encased, and if a spark—as with lightning —is made to pass through them for a time, a variety of large molecules will be formed. Some of these large molecules will even be amino acids, the raw materials from which proteins are made. Even so, the presence of raw materials does not immediately lead to the existence of the finished product. Other conditions, and other mixtures, coupled with more energy from electrical storms, or from the sun, would have been necessary. Larger and larger molecules would then have been formed, and somehow the cell would have resulted from all this random activity. Quite how this happened naturally is not even a matter for speculation because far too little is known about the cell, and how amino acids and proteins are coordinated to form a living organism. Only when this mechanism is at least partly understood will conjecture be possible on the origin of the living cell in all the molecular bewilderment of the planet's early days. William Shakespeare did arise from the primeval ooze—somehow.

A paradox about those very early years concerns oxygen. This vital commodity has plainly been in existence at a fairly fixed level for many hundreds of millions of years. Life, in the form of most animals and plants, could not have been generated without substantial oxygen in the atmosphere. Yet, the origin of life would have been impossible, or so current theory has it, had oxygen been abundant. Had it existed, the chemicals needed for incorporation in the infant organisms would have been promptly oxidized. No other planet in our solar system has our abundance of oxygen. Instead, as may be revealed in space exploration, some of them could possess gas mixtures highly relevant to the early days of the planet Earth. The other planets probably do not have a form of life upon them; but they may have a form of chemistry which is germane to that existing here, say, 5 billion years ago.

The Fossil Record

Evolution becomes interesting after the period of the Cambrian rocks, a mere 600 million years ago. The pre-Cambrian picture is extremely sketchy and remarkably unclear. With the start of the Paleozoic era and the Cambrian period, paleontology becomes possible. (Geologists have divided time into three eras. Each of these is divided into periods, and each period then divided into epochs.) The Cambrian period lasted about 100 million years. It was a time solely for invertebrates. Nothing that had a backbone existed, but practically every major invertebrate grouping, creatures with hard external skeletons, such as the arthropods, or creatures with no skeletons at all existed at this evolutionary dawn.

The vertebrates first came into being during the subsequent period, the Ordovician (roughly lasting 60 million years). These were, in general, part fishlike, part tanklike, and their armor plating looks highly impressive in their fossil forms. The true archaic fishes began in the next period, the Silurian (of 40 million years), and at the same time the plants and the arthropods (the jointed-limbs—insects, spiders) invaded the land. Next came the Devonian period (of 50 million years), the age of the fishes. These were abundant mainly in fresh water but also in salt water, and they lived with the first trees and the earliest amphibia. The first vertebrate invasion of the land was then taking place. The Carboniferous period (80 million years) saw a flowering of those trees into the coal forests, a great expansion of those amphibia, and the arrival of the reptiles. The Permian (45 million years) saw the reptiles take over from the amphibia. At this point in time, geologists draw a line and call it the end of the Paleozoic era. It totals 375 million years, lasts for over half of the clear fossil history of this planet, and covers the change from the invertebrates to the reptiles. At the end of it, poised like some lizard all ready to go, the great reptilian empire is about to flourish.

The Mesozoic era lasted for the next 155 million years. Its three periods are the Triassic (45 million years), the Jurassic (45 million years), and the Cretaceous (65 million years). The whole era can be called the age of the reptiles. They flew in the air, swam in the sea, and either ran about on land or wallowed in swamps. In the Jurassic era they were dominant. Great forms like diplodocus, eighty feet from head to tail, gorged their way through the vegetation. At sea the ichthyosaurs were powerful carnivores of the time, and in the air pterodactyls flew. Yet it was in the Jurassic era, with so much reptilian activity on every side, that the first mammals evolved about 180 million years ago. Certainly not then the dominant species, their triumph did not begin until the reptiles were on the wane at the end of the Mesozoic era. Why the all-powerful reptilian world collapsed so dramatically is a matter of conjecture. Perhaps they were too specialized at a time of too rapid change. Perhaps the new, cunning little mammals, warm-blooded, furry, and producers of living young, were able to displace them from their comfortable niches in the ecological world.

The word "dinosaur" now implies an implacable and monstrous inability to change, and some defense of the reptiles is therefore necessary. Reptiles did flourish and dominate for 155 million years. They still thrive as crocodiles, lizards, turtles, tortoises, and snakes, some 300 million years after the first true reptiles made their appearance. The mammals have so far dominated for only 70 million years, and man himself is far, far younger. He has lived as the species Homo for perhaps 2 million years, and he has dominated as Homo sapiens for only a few hundred thousand. The reptile age of the Mesozoic was vast by comparison.

The third great geological era is the Cenozoic, the age of mammals. It is divided unequally into the Tertiary period (of 70 million years) and the Quaternary (of one million or so years). The main subdivisions or epochs of this time are, in order of antiquity, Paleocene, Eocene, Oligocene, Miocene, Pliocene, Pleistocene, and Recent. The first five are major quantities of time, the latter two extremely short, with Recent being shortest of all. It has been only in the Recent epoch of the Quaternary period of the Cenozoic era of geological time that man has made his mark.

Mammals

There is a prime and basic difficulty about our classification of the mammal group. Their characteristics are distinct and well-known—warm blood, hair (rather than scales), lactation, care for the young, and viviparity (or live births rather than the production and hatching of eggs). But such characteristics do not lend themselves to fossilization and to easy recognition in the fossil form. Instead, the paleontologists have been forced to take more interest in the mammal's skeletal conditions, such as the presence of several bones in the lower jaw (a reptilian characteristic) or only one (as in the mammals).

Nevertheless, the picture is clear. The first mammals were small creatures, mainly flesh-eaters that preyed only upon such modest meat as grubs, insects, and worms. Much like modern shrews, they lived privately for millions of years before the near extinction of the reptiles permitted their freedom and their ramification. Then, like the reptiles before them, they spread over the land (elephants, mice, lions, squirrels), into the sea (seals, whales, sea cows), and into the air (bats). Out of this stock were to evolve the primates, yet another stage en route to man.

Primates

The primate group has its roots in the first days of the Cenozoic, at a time when the last of the dinosaurs were dying out. Undoubtedly, some of the very early shrewlike mammals living even earlier in the reptile age had taken to the trees. It is highly probable that these tree-living creatures gave rise to the primates, for such a life is entirely compatible with the characteristics which distinguish the primates from the bulk of the mammalian stock—the improvement of visual acuity, the deterioration of smell, the development of limbs for grasping, the forelimbs for investigation, and an expansion of the brain for the agility and coordinated skills necessary for an active treetop existence. Coupled with these characteristic features and seemingly paradoxical is a great lack of specialization. On the ground the mammals tended to concentrate on running, on digging, on hopping, on one particular activity, and on eating only a small range of foods—like the anteaters' ants or even the lions' raw meat. The early primates had simple teeth, which allowed them to deal with a wide selection of foods; there was little specialization in other parts of their body and they could survive in a wide variety of circumstances. Many mammals cannot do so, and perish when their precise habitat is suddenly changed. To adjust to a changing world is extremely important.

Broadly speaking (and here I am indebted to Professor Le Gros Clark's summary), the primates are distinguished by:

1. A generalized limb pattern with a primitive five-fingered and five-toed arrangement (contrast the hoofed mammals on two digits per limb or the horse, which stands on only one).
2. Free mobility of the digits (most primates have feet almost as skilled as their hands, although man does not).
3. The replacement of claws by nails.

4. A shortening of the nose (with the loss of interest in smell, although primates that took to the ground once more tended to develop long noses, e.g., the baboons).
5. Good eyesight, with varying degrees of binocular vision (only possible when both eyes have moved to the front).
6. Teeth with a wide variety of tearing, biting, and chewing possibilities (the basic insectivore stock that gave rise to the primates had sharp teeth without the blunt cusps of the normal primate molars).
7. A steady expansion and elaboration of the brain (mainly the cerebral cortex).
8. A small number of offspring, either twins or singletons; a long gestation; and a long period of nursing.
9. A habitat within or very near the tropics. (Man is the great exception.)

Man

Unfortunately, the evolution of mankind is not a clear-cut course of events. The horse, for example, or the elephant tells a definite evolutionary story, well supported by a good fossil record; not so mankind. Instead, about 1,000 fragments of fossil bone have been found that form part, somewhere or other, of the patchwork ancestry of the genus Homo. There is certainly not unanimous agreement about their piecing together. Inevitably, much of the trouble stems from mankind's introspective devotion to his own past. Had the Piltdown fake, where the lower jaw of an orangutan and a skull of a man were forcibly linked, been of some other creature, the interest in the discovery would have been marginal, and the subsequent revelation of the fake would have been of equally slight concern. Also, wherever facts are few and evidence is lacking, theories multiply. Whole treatises have been prepared on a fragmentary find, and a wealth of argument was once based upon nothing more than a single tooth of Peking man. (Most of the argument was entirely vindicated when more of this man came to light.)

It is very easy to distinguish man from his nearest living relatives, the anthropoid apes such as the gorilla and the chimpanzee. It is far less easy to distinguish man's ancestors from the ancestors of those anthropoid apes. Briefly and sweeping aside many contrary views, a sort of man emerged about 2 million years ago, and modern man (Homo sapiens) appeared about 500,000 years ago. Nothing is firm about these assessments, and they change almost annually. Even so, by dinosaur standards, man's life on Earth is extremely short. There are only 100,000 generations at most between the New Yorker and those earliest individuals of the species Homo. There are only 25,000 generations between today's men and the first men who could be called modern, the first representatives of Homo sapiens. There is even less time, say 2,000 generations, between the first cave painters and us.

Coming down from the trees and becoming terrestrial was a hazardous undertaking. To move upright and rather slowly in a world of fast-moving herbivores and agile carnivores exposed all the weaknesses of the unspecialized ape, our ancestor; but the descent to ground level also taxed his latent ingenuities. The new skills, made possible by a versatility of hand and arm and by many of the characteristics developed for tree-living, were to save him. He could invent things. He could manipulate objects to his advantage. He could fashion sticks and stones. He could provide himself with something more useful than a claw. The new terrestrial life meant a change to a more carnivorous existence, to hunting, to a greater need for tools and weapons. Finally, and with its ancestry back in an arboreal world, there existed the social organization of mankind, the community, the cooperation of activity, the communication of information, the lengthy period of time available for learning by the young.

No one knows where man's ancestors lived throughout this vital time. Initially, with inevitable myopia, European scholars assumed Europe to have been the location. The discoveries of Peking and Java man then directed attention eastward. Nowadays, supported by some exciting finds, the continent of Africa is thought to be a likely spot. Southern and eastern Africa in particular have been favored with some exceptionally diligent and determined investigators, among them Dr. L. S. B. Leakey, of Olduvai Gorge.

It had been known for 20 years before he went there that the Olduvai Gorge was a good fossil area. It was another 28 years before the first hominid remains were discovered in that hot, arid, lonely, and fascinating valley, a scar through the Serengeti plains of Tanzania etched out to reveal the remains of 150 extinct mammals—and then man. Leakey insists that the two score teeth, the bits of four skulls and three jaws, and a few other bones and bone fragments from seven individuals, to which the name Homo habilis has been given, are parts of the earliest known representatives of mankind. Standing erect, some four feet high, with an advanced foot, a less well-developed hand, and a brain about half the modern size, this individual is the center of current controversy. Is he an early man or merely an australopithecine, one of a large group of ape-men too primitive and too early to be called man? Many anthropologists believe Leakey was overhasty with his use of the word "man," and consider such a human creature did not exist for another million years or so. The controversy is by no means settled. Olduvai Gorge, which undoubtedly has more to offer, may well be the place to provide the answer, but, if the gorge fails, there is always the rest of Africa or the rest of the world.

The principal attraction of Homo habilis is that he does possess several features that bridged the gap between the ancient apes (who possessed some human features) and the far less ancient men (who possessed some ape features). Whether Homo habilis be called an ape-man or a man-ape is obviously excellent material for perpetual argument. Evolution, it should be remembered, is the gradual merging of one type into another type or types, and taxonomy is the ruthless classification of the resulting types. The student of any evolutionary line is therefore torn both ways, toward rigid classification and toward a breaking down of that classification. Is it man-ape or ape-man, primitive australopithecine or Homo habilis, an aberrant offshoot or direct descendant, a missing link or just a fragment from the past?

The Homo habilis supporters justify his importance by saying he had:

1. A brain capacity of 680 cc., halfway between the australopithecines and Homo erectus (of whom more soon).
2. A skull rounded more like man's than the australopithecine skull.
3. Man-type teeth.
4. A capable hand, although not a modern one.
5. A modern collarbone.
6. An advanced (or human) form of foot.
7. Many stone tools associated with his own fossil remains.
8. Animal bones found near his own, which indicated both that he hunted and cracked the bones open for their marrow.

Moving on in time means moving toward greater agreement and a much more advanced type of individual. Homo erectus is a blanket term for many fossils found in strata sometimes a million years old, sometimes much less old. Java man, Peking man, and others tend to get lumped together into this group. Walking upright, with a thick skull, a heavy jaw, a cranial capacity of 1,000 cc. or so, capable of hunting and using fire, these creatures were undoubtedly human. Later on, and moving from the Middle Pleistocene to the Upper Pleistocene, Homo erectus yields to modern man. By no means are all or any of these modern men our ancestors. Neanderthal man, although big brained and a burier of his dead (occasionally) and although active in much of Europe, Asia, and Africa only 70,000 years ago or less, was definitely not our ancestor.

Quite suddenly, and entirely replacing the Neanderthal remains, appears Cro-Magnon man, with a modern skull and a fondness for art (Neanderthal man never drew anything). Cro-Magnon man appeared on the scene in Europe, having apparently come from the East about 40,000 years ago, right in the middle of the last great ice age. Mankind had been making things for 2 million years but Cro-Magnon was the first artist. From 40,000 to 10,000 B.C., he painted cave walls and carved bones, and he was even making limestone statuettes (all buttocks and breasts) 30,000 years ago. Artistic man had therefore arrived.

The line habilis (perhaps) to erectus (probably) to sapiens had, somehow, been drawn. The blindness of evolution had finally created a species capable of dominating the entire planet, capable even of leaving the planet, of traveling to other worlds. The few amino acids mingling in that primeval ooze had finally led to man, the species with the wit and skill to organize the resources all around him. Well over a million species exist today. Each is the culmination of an evolutionary line, but, for each one existing today, there must have been hundreds of evolutionary lines that led nowhere except to extinction. There were hundreds of millions of evolutionary lines, therefore, and then the creation of man. Quite suddenly, out of 4 billion years of random biological activity, appears a species with the means to control his own fate.

❧ 2 ☙

Race

Racism · Racial Classifications · Jews ·
Negroes · Brain Size · Superiority and Purity ·
A Biological Necessity? · The Scientific Conclusions

The human race, to which so many of my readers belong. . . .
Gilbert Keith Chesterton

"In today's world anybody's weakest chapter," wrote Paul Bohannan
in the *Scientific American,* "is the chapter 'On the Concept of Race.'"
At this stage in this chapter I am happy to agree. He argues that no
reader can face the subject dispassionately, even if the writer can present
it so. The word is hideously loaded. As jokes about Jews are almost
forbidden by society to non-Jews, so the word "race" almost implies
racism if it is not dismissed almost as soon as it is brought forward.

Racism

Mussolini said, "Race is a feeling not a reality." Lancelot Hogben wrote
that geneticists believe anthropologists know what a race is, ethnologists
assume their racial classifications are backed up by genetics, and politicians believe that their prejudices have the sanction of both genetics and
anthropology. Actually, none of them, he adds, has any grounds for such
beliefs. We all use the word "race" to suit our prejudices and our feelings.
"But" wrote John Stuart Mill in 1848, "of all the vulgar modes of escaping
from the consideration of the effect of social and moral influences on the
human mind, the most vulgar is that of attributing the diversities of contact and character to inherent natural differences." Had he been able to
foresee some of the vulgarity attained in the subsequent century, his
Principles of Political Economy would have boomed even louder.

To some degree, racism began its course only in the nineteenth century. The first Negro arrived in the New World a mere two years after Columbus, but he was not a slave. Countless Negroes were never slaves, but the antislavery agitation assisted in the creation of an irremediable linkage between "slaves" and "Negroes." The argument posed in *The Origin of Species* (published only four years before the Emancipation Proclamation in the United States) did have a loophole for those wishing to escape the horror of a common anthropoid ancestor: there may have been evolution of ape-men, but, if this were true, the black men would be nearer the takeoff point than the white. This argument is still held by many today who believe that the African Negro became Homo sapiens relatively recently.

Parenthetically, it should be added that many a scientific wrangle over race has nothing to do with racism. Carleton S. Coon is a professor of anthropology whose most famous book is called *The Origin of Races*, and he has revised another called *The Races of Europe*. Other scientists abhor the word. Sir Julian Huxley repudiated it in 1936. Ernst Hanhart says there are "no true races" in man anyway. L. S. Penrose, of London, says that he sees no virtue in the apologetic retention of the term. "The biological view of race has been more misused and distorted than perhaps any other scientific conception," writes Thomas F. Pettigrew, of Harvard, in his book *Profile of the Negro American*. In general, scientists prefer the term "ethnic group" because (as summarized by Ashley Montagu) it emphasizes distinguishability, it does not indicate status, it suggests cultural influence, and it eliminates "obfuscating emotional implications." However, the word "race" still exists. So does racism.

Foundations of the Nineteenth Century, by Houston Stewart Chamberlain, sounds innocuous enough, but this book, published in 1910, was one of the first racist tracts. Kaiser Wilhelm II of Germany called it his favorite book and bought many copies. John Oakesmith purloined a phrase (from Sydney Smith) to name it "the crapulous eructations of a drunken cobbler." Anyway it followed an *Essay on the Inequality of the Human Races* (in four volumes) by Count Joseph Arthur de Gobineau, a French antirevolutionary of the mid-nineteenth century who held that the Revolution's "egalitarian philosophy was the hopelessly confused expression of a degraded rabble," and it was followed in its turn by the innumerable efforts of today. Typical among these is *The Biology of the Race Problem,* by Dr. Wesley Critz George, the writing of which was commissioned by Governor George C. Wallace, of Alabama, in 1962. It admits that some Negroes are intelligent, but likens them to the Trojan horse. Let in some and you let in the lot, with an aftermath like that of Troy. Dr. George, drawing on facts from Latin America, has decided that miscegenation is the root of evil there, for its people are an assortment of whites, Indians, mestizos (part-white, part-Indian), Negroes, and mulattoes (part-white, part-Negro). He cites Brazil as an example, for, despite her lavish natural resources, she is unable even to feed herself. "There is no advanced civilization in any area where there has been a high degree of absorption of Negro genes. Nowhere in the world have the Negroes demonstrated that they have the creative capacity to make a civilization." Etc., etc.—with a few occasional comments about some disastrous crossings in the dog world.

Rough things can be written about the Negroes. Rough things can be written about all groups. "It has been said against the African Negroes that they never produced a scientist; but what kind of scientist would he be who had no weights and measures, no clock or calendar, and no means of recording his observations and experiments? And if it be asked why the Negroes did not invent these things, the answer is that neither did any European, and for the same reason—namely, that the rare and perhaps unique conditions which made their invention possible were absent." That was a quotation from Lord Raglan. This is one from Cicero: "Do not obtain your slaves from Britain, because they are so stupid and so utterly incapable of being taught that they are not fit to form part of the household of Athens." The Emperor Claudius was just as trenchant in his assertions that the inhabitants of Britain were no good. Nevertheless, despite the rejection of any belief in innate racial superiority and despite attempts at an objective assessment of superiority ("facts never speak for themselves," writes Professor Montagu, "but always through an interpreter"), it can never be argued that men are born equal. It is also undeniable that groups of people do exist. There are Negroes and Eskimos and Pygmies. There are still Bushmen, and there were Tasmanians until 1876. Mankind is of many kinds, but just how many is virtually anybody's guess.

Racial Classifications

Scientists, normally all in favor of useful classifications, are quite unable to agree about the species Homo sapiens, of the subfamily Hominae, of the family Hominidae, of the superfamily Hominoidea, of the suborder Anthropoidea, of the order primates. Theodosius Dobzhansky, professor of zoology at Columbia University, concludes from this disagreement that there must be some basic fault in the methods of description and classification. The more carefully human observations are studied the less clear-cut the races become.

Taxonomy really began in 1740 with Carolus Linnaeus, the Swedish prince of classifiers. Since then over 2 million species of animals and plants have been described, most of which are insects and one of which is man. Linnaeus contented himself with four variants: European, American Indian, Asiatic, and African. Thirty-five years later J. F. Blumenbach, an early anthropologist, divided man into a spectrum of five: White (Caucasian), Yellow (Mongolian), Black (Ethiopian), Red (American), and Brown (Malayan). Back in the eighteenth century classification was simpler partly because fewer groups of men had been discovered. By 1900 the age of exploration was over, everything was more complex, and Joseph Deniker distinguished six groups with twenty-nine smaller classifications:

Woolly hair, broad nose
   Yellow skin   Bushmen
   Dark skin   Negrito, Negro, Melanesian
Curly or wavy hair
   Dark skin   Ethiopian, Australian, Dravidian
   Tawny white skin   Assyroid
Wavy brown or black hair, dark eyes
   Clear brown skin   Indo-Afghan
   Tawny white skin   Arab or Semite, Berber, Littoral European, Ibero-Insular
   Dull white skin   Western European, Adriatic
Fair, wavy or straight hair
   Reddish white skin   Northern European, Eastern European

Straight or wavy hair, dark eyes
   Light brown skin   Ainu
   Yellow skin   Polynesian, Indonesian, South American

Straight hair
   Warm yellow skin   North American, Central American, Patagonian
   Brownish yellow skin   Eskimo
   Yellowish white skin   Lapp, Turkish or Turko-Tatar
   Pale yellow skin   Mongol

In 1934 Egon von Eickstedt reduced everything to three major stocks: white, black, and yellow (Shem, Ham, and Japheth?). He called them Europiform (or Leucoderm), Negriform (or Melanoderm), and Mongoliform (or Xanthoderm). Not surprisingly, these names have never caught on, and preference is given to Caucasoid, Negroid, and Mongoloid for the big three. What was surprising was that von Eickstedt's subdivisions (eight, nine, and twelve, respectively) added up to twenty-nine, the same as Deniker's total, but their subdivisions were quite different.

Recently there has been a retrenchment. (This often happens with classifications. First there is one type, then far too many, and finally, a reasonable few.) A modern American anthropologist, S. M. Garn, thinks nine are sufficient. These are:

1. American Indian
2. Melanesian-Papuan (New Guinea to Fiji)
3. Micronesian (most Pacific Islands north of the equator)
4. Polynesians (the rest of the Pacific, including New Zealand, Hawaii, and Easter Island)
5. Australian
6. Asiatic (a huge group, including the Filipinos, Japanese, Eskimos, Mongolians, and Tibetans)
7. Indian (all of that subcontinent)
8. European (including North Africa and the Near East)
9. African (south of the Sahara)

But even Garn, having trimmed the races to this extent, admits these groups are "neither fully discrete nor internally uniform." He indicates that six of his nine groups could easily be split into thirty-two, making thirty-five in all.

Garn's division was published in 1961. Five years earlier, W. C. Boyd, another American, and a professor of immunochemistry, had made much use of blood groups and reached a total of thirteen groups, namely:

a. Early European
b. Lapps
c. North West Europeans
d. East and Central Europeans
e. Mediterraneans
f. Africans
g. Asians
h. Indo-Dravidians
i. American Indians
j. Indonesians
k. Melanesians
l. Polynesians
m. Australian Aborigines

At first glance, this may seem a different grouping; but if all Boyd's Europeans (a. through e.) are banded together to form Garn's number eight, there is remarkable similarity between these two recent assessments of major groups. In other words, there are about nine human types, subraces, infraspecies, or subdivisions, give or take a group or two.

Jews

A word is necessary here about the Jews. They do not appear (or should not) in anyone's grouping of the human races. There is no such thing as a Jewish physical type (Montagu), and there is not, nor was there ever, anything remotely resembling a Jewish race or ethnic group. The conventional picture of a Jew, short, dark-eyed, a Shylock nose, greasy skin and hair, thick lips, is neither universal nor confined to Jews (think of Armenians). Chinese Jews look Chinese; 45 percent of Polish Jews have light eyes; 18 percent of Hungarian Jews and 51 percent of Jews in Rumania have fair hair, and many from all countries have red hair. Most certainly, Jews are not a race. George Sacks, who wrote *The Intelligent Man's Guide to Jew-Baiting,* 1934, said in that book that the Jews are a race only because others consider them a race. In fact, they are a socioreligious (Huxley and Haddon) or a quasinational (Montagu) group. "Antisemitism is so profoundly irrational," writes Anthony Barnett, a zoologist at Glasgow University, "that it can hardly be made the subject of a straightforward biological discussion."

Negroes

Negroes (or Africans, or Congoids) appear, or should appear, in everybody's grouping of mankind, but the definition of a Negro is not easy. Melanesians also have woolly hair, dark skin, and a broad nose. Many included within the Negroid camp, such as Bushmen, have much lighter skins than many Indians and Australians. Definitions can become tortuous, but comparisons are easier. A lot of work has been done on this subject in the United States. The characteristics of the whites (who mostly come from West Europe) and the blacks (mostly from the Gulf of Guinea) have been compared and the following conclusions reached. The American Negro has a slightly narrower, longer, and shorter head; a smaller braincase (by about 50 cc.—but more on this later); a wider gap between his eyes (pupil to pupil); a lower hairline on the forehead; a broader nose with a lower bridge; a more jutting (prognathous) jaw; thicker lips; a shorter external ear (pinna); a shorter torso (by 1¼ in.); a shallower chest; a smaller, narrower pelvis (female Negroes have hips 21 mm.—.83 in.—broader than Negro males as against a 10 mm.—.39 in.—difference among whites); a longer leg (by 2 in.); a similar stature, but greater weight; and of course a darker skin. (Pigmentation increases until puberty—reaching its maximum by the age of 15—and then decreases, less rapidly, after the age of 35.) Typical Negro hair is more frizzy and less profuse, having fewer follicles and less growth. There are more sweat glands (reasonably enough), and Negroes have slightly larger teeth.

There are also differences that do not exist between black and white Americans. Professor Montagu has listed them. There is no difference in intelligence (despite an abundance of funds set up to prove a difference); the brain looks the same; suture closure, or cessation of skull growth, is similar; nose cartilage is similar, although the Negro's has often been alleged to be more primitive; the Negro forehead does not slope more (it just looks that way due to the jutting jaw); the Negro hand is not longer, only the fingers are; there are no disharmonies between pelvic outlet and baby's head in mulatto births (a strong racist assertion); the Negro eye is not larger, but often looks so due to its less angular orbit; and, finally, the Negro penis is not larger. This particular story is nearly 200 years old, dating from that pioneer anthropologist Blumenbach, who saw "an Aetheopian with a remarkable genitory apparatus." Whereas he, the scientist, only wondered whether this prerogative was "constant and peculiar to the nation," many others for reasons of their own have assumed it to be the case. Professor Montagu is adamant. It is not.

Brain Size

A difference in brain size has naturally been used in anti-Negro literature. Major R. W. Shufeldt, M.D., writes that "The Negro brain is undersized with a cranial capacity of 35 fluid oz. as against 45 fl. oz. for whites. Also the cranial bones are dense and unusually thick, converting his head into a virtual battering ram. . . ." Few agree with his figures. Also, brain size and intelligence are not related. The average male capacity is between 1,300 and 1,500 cc. But 1,050 to 1,800 cc. is still considered normal. Two writers, Anatole France and Ivan Turgenev, are frequently spoken of in this regard because the Russian's brain was exactly twice the size of the Frenchman's—2,000 to 1,000 cc. (Despite the constant references, I could find no indication why their capacities were recorded. Most people are just buried and, although not forgotten, not measured either.)

The brain of the average European male is 1,450 cc. (The female brain is about 10 percent smaller in most populations, and therefore around 1,300 cc. in Europe.) This European average dwarfs the anthropoids, such as the chimpanzee (400 cc.), the orangutan (420 cc.), and the gorilla (543 cc.). It is also bigger than many fossil men, such as Australopithecus africanus (600 cc.), Telanthropus (850 cc.), and Sinanthropus (1,043 cc.). And it is bigger than some modern men: Australian aborigines (1,246 cc.), Veddas—cave-living people of Ceylon (1,285 cc.)—and Andaman Islanders (1,264 cc.). In other words, there does seem a certain logic in the order thus far. But Eskimos, some southern Africans, Mongols, Japanese, and American Indians have brains of larger capacity than the Europeans. (I have here left out the actual capacities, for these vary between different authors, although the trends are similar.) Bigger still are the brains of Neanderthal man, the thickset people who buried their dead but knew no art and fashioned only simple stone implements. Their capacity was about 1,550 cc. Yet 100 cc. bigger than *their* brains (and therefore 200 cc. bigger than modern Europeans) were the brains of the cultured Cro-Magnon, who made the cave paintings of Europe and who seemed to have killed off, absorbed, or survived better than the Neanderthal men. Again there exists, in part, a certain logic, for Cro-Magnon was undoubtedly brighter than Neanderthal, but was Neanderthal brighter than we are today? It is assumed instead that, because brain size and intelligence do not correlate precisely, they did not always do so. In short, to borrow a statement from N. A. Barnicott, of London University's anthropology department, "Although increase of brain size is a notable feature in earlier phases of Hominid evolution, the significance of brain volume in relation to mental functioning is by no means clear."

Superiority and Purity

Whatever anybody says in any piece of polemics about race, there are always two dominant questions, whether spoken or unspoken, whether answered or not. The first asks about racial superiority and the second about mixed breeding.

Racial superiority tends to be uppermost, with intellectual prowess at the top. The fact that Negroes are more likely to get sickle-cell anemia, less leukemia, more diabetes, fewer "blue" babies, far less hemophilia, and less color blindness does not really concern people (although these points fascinate scientists). It is intelligence that is disturbing. Hitler and some Germans may have been horrified by the success of American Negroes (Jesse Owens, in particular) at the 1936 Olympic Games in Berlin, but the Americans were jubilant. Today, American Negroes are three times more successful in athletics than their population size would suggest, and no one complains. But there was nationwide interest in the results of a huge and famous investigation carried out by the United States Army into its recruits. The so-called "Alpha and Beta" tests were given to 1,726,000 men, and Negroes scored unmistakably worse than whites. Only much later was it pointed out that, while southern Negroes scored badly, northern Negroes, on average, scored more than southern whites. As Otto Klineberg has said: "It is apparently not 'race' but environment which is the crucial variable." Philip Vernon, of London University's Institute of Education, has said ". . . it is unprofitable to investigate racial difference in intelligence . . . because intelligence . . . is always the interaction between genetic potentialities and environmental pressures, and because intelligence is no one thing, but rather a name for a group of overlapping skills. . . ." J. B. S. Haldane said at a Ciba symposium: "I do not believe in racial equality, though of course there is plenty of overlap; but I have no idea who surpasses who in what."

This overlapping is a vital concept. Just as American Negroes are shorter than American whites—by 2 mm.—so may there be an intelligence difference between them by the intellectual equivalent of those 2 mm. Height is, of course, easy to measure. Intelligence is not. "But even," writes Dr. Anthony Barnett, "if future investigation does show a correlation between intelligence and physical characteristics, every large human group will overlap every other in the distribution of intelligence." Every lot will have people both high and low, idiots and geniuses, mental dwarfs and mental giants. Hence, intelligence tests will never justify discrimination against any group. "But so far," writes Professor Montagu, "if there are any inborn mental differences associated . . . with the different mental groups, then science has been unable to discover them."

Mixed breeding is the second emotional firecracker. In one sense, the question has no right to exist. Mankind is a heterogeneous assortment, and were it being viewed unknowingly by a biologist, he would consider mixed breeding impossible. The physical differences between, say, a Hottentot (short stature, yellowish and loose skin, big steatopygous rump, peppercorn hair) and a Nordic European are far greater than many animal species that look more alike yet cannot breed. As it is, the "Reheboth bastaards" of South Africa, the results of Hottentot and white matings, are taller and more vigorous than both parental stocks. Groups of normal creatures, unlike man, are kept apart genetically, even if they occupy the same territory, partly by having a set of signals to communicate with their own kinds. "There is little desire," says Professor Carleton S. Coon, "for them to interbreed. But man," he adds, "communicates by speech." We learn one another's languages. We do interbreed. Wives have been traded or captured, and men have frequently traveled alone without any compunction about mating only back home. So, he concludes, despite racial differences, that is how we are still one species.

Is further mixed breeding beneficial? Even though the word "pure" can hardly be applied to the mixed ancestry of everyone of us ("Man has always been a mongrel lot," says Professor Dobzhansky), ought efforts to be made to prevent further impurity? The largest mixed racial groups are in South Africa, in the southern United States, in South America, and in certain Polynesian islands, notably Hawaii. South Africa has laws against further mixing, the southern United States had them until very recently, but the other two areas do not. Before the June 12, 1967, U.S. Supreme Court decision that declared miscegenation laws unconstitutional, there were 15 states that had laws prohibiting marriage between whites and Negroes—Alabama, Arkansas, Delaware, Florida, Kentucky, Louisiana, Mississippi, Missouri, North Carolina, Oklahoma, South Carolina, Tennessee, Texas, Virginia, and West Virginia. Sentences for breaking this law varied between thirty days' and ten years' imprisonment. Evidence for breakdowns in fitness (equivalent to some of the disastrous cross-breeding of dogs, where they have been fashioned with legs of insufficient length to keep their stomachs off the ground) has not been found. Heterosis (or hybrid vigor—well-known among breeders of plants and animals) has even been claimed, as in the case of the offspring of the Polynesian women who lived with the *Bounty* mutineers.

Unfortunately, as G. A. Harrison stresses in the book *Human Biology,* "no really systematic studies have been undertaken of human hybridization." Its consequences are, to all intents and purposes, unknown. "Confronted with this lack of evidence," says Professor Stern, of the University of California at Berkeley, "the conservative will counsel abstention, since the possible ill effects of the breakup of races will not be reversible." "The less conservative," he adds, "will not raise their voice against racial mingling since, from a long-range point of view, it is probably bound to occur anyway." There is also the argument that in today's world the half-caste is frequently an outcast. Most mixing is in defiance of social convention. Therefore, the half-breed may suffer and may in consequence attain less than his racial peers. "After all," says the American geneticist W. E. Castle, "attainments imply opportunities as well as abilities." In other words, it is society, not genetics, that can kill that hybrid vigor.

To summarize, no biologically harmful effects have been discovered following mixed marriages, but scarcely any real (objective) work has been done to find them. However, so long as prejudice exists, social harm will always be at work, hindering, thwarting, and stopping.

A Biological Necessity?

Particularly in the past it was considered that racial strife of whatever form was merely a manifestation of man's vital and necessary aggression, of his competitive struggle to live. It caused his castigation of other groups, his dislike of aliens, foreigners, savages, "wogs." This resentment still found its supporters when it bubbled over into war. In 1912, General Friedrich von Bernhardi, who had been a young Uhlan officer at the Siege of Paris, wrote: "War is a biological necessity; it is as necessary as the struggle of the elements in nature; it gives a biologically just decision, since its decisions rest on the very nature of things." Two years later the war began that led to 8 million dead on the biological battlefield. The Nazi war, started a mere 21 years later, which was to kill 50 million in its five years, had a racist creed behind it. "A nation," wrote Alfred Rosenberg, the official spokesman, "is constituted by the predominance of a definite character formed by its blood, also by language, geographical environment, and the sense of a united political destiny. These last constituents are not, however, definitive; the decisive element in a nation is its blood."

The final say should be given to Voltaire: "As long as people believe in absurdities, they will continue to commit atrocities."

Here are three facts that touch more lightly on the subject. First, there are even racial bedbugs: Cimex lectularius is the white man's bedbug, and Cimex rotundatus is the black man's (the two species even have different chromosome numbers). Secondly, as Charles Darwin first pointed out, lice that decide to move from Hawaiians on to English sailors die before the week is out. And thirdly, in a book entitled *The Natural Superiority of Women,* it has been pointed out that everything ever said of any "inferior race" has also been said of women.

The Scientific Conclusions

There have been two major and definitive statements on race by UNESCO, each drafted by an international team of scientists. Both are some 1,500 words long, and I will quote from the second, which was published in September, 1962. Among its fourteen authors were J. B. S.

Haldane, Theodosius Dobzhansky, Sir Solly Zuckerman, Sir Julian Huxley, Professor Harry Schapiro, and Professor Ashley Montagu.

1. Scientists are generally agreed that all men living today belong to a single species, Homo sapiens, and are derived from a common stock. . . .

2. Some of the physical differences between human groups are due to differences in hereditary constitution, and some to differences in the environments in which they have been brought up. In most cases, both influences have been at work. . . .

3. National, religious, geographical, linguistic and cultural groups do not necessarily coincide with racial groups, and the cultural traits of such groups have no demonstrated connection with racial traits. . . . The use of the term "race" in speaking of such groups may be a serious error, but is one which is habitually committed.

4. Human races can be, and have been, classified in different ways by different anthropologists. Most of them agree in classifying the greater part of existing mankind into at least three large units. . . . So far as it has been possible to analyse them, the differences in physical structure which distinguish one major group from another give no support to popular notions of any general "superiority" or "inferiority" which are sometimes applied in referring to these groups. . . .

5. Most anthropologists do not include mental characteristics in their classification of human races. . . . It often happens that a national group may appear to be characterised by particular psychological attributes. The superficial view would be that this is due to race. Scientifically, however, we realize that any common psychological attribute is more likely to be due to a common historical and social background, and such attributes may obscure the fact that, within different populations consisting of many human types, one will find approximately the same range of temperament and intelligence.

6. The scientific material available to us at present does not justify the conclusion that inherited genetic differences are a major factor in producing the differences between the cultures and the cultural achievements of different peoples or groups. . . .

7. There is no evidence for the existence of so-called "pure" races. . . . No biological justification exists for prohibiting intermarriage between persons of different races.

8. . . . . We wish to emphasise that equality of opportunity and equality in law in no way depend, as ethical principles, upon the assertion that human beings are in fact equal in endowment.

9. We have thought it worth while to set out in a formal manner what
    is at present scientifically established concerning individual and
    group differences:—
    a. In matters of race, the only characteristics . . . (effective) as a
        basis for classification are physical.
    b. . . . no basis for believing that the groups of mankind differ in
        their innate capacity for intellectual and emotional development.
    c. Some biological differences between human beings within a single
        race may be as great or greater than the same biological differ-
        ences between races.
    d. Vast social changes have occurred that have not been connected
        in any way with changes in racial type. . . .
    e. There is no evidence that race mixture produces disadvanta-
        geous results from a biological point of view. The social results
        of race mixture, whether for good or ill, can generally be traced
        to social factors.

~§ *3* §~

Population

Past · Present and Future · Urbanization ·
Immigration · Prediction

Be fruitful, and multiply, and replenish the earth, and subdue it.

Genesis 1:28

Only a scientific people can survive in a scientific future.

Thomas Henry Huxley

The time has already come when each country needs a considered national policy about what size of population, whether larger or smaller than at present, or the same is more excellent. And having settled this policy, we must take steps to carry it into operation.

John Maynard Keynes

I would suggest that it is time to consider a fifth freedom—freedom from the tyranny of excessive fertility.

Sir Dugald Baird

In Mauritius in the year 1900, 37 babies were born for every 1,000 people on the island. In the year 1966, the figure was still 37 babies per 1,000. Yet, during this century, Mauritius has been in the grip of a powerful population explosion, the like of which the island has never known before. No more babies are being born, but far fewer babies are dying. An intensive postwar DDT campaign on the island against malaria was so successful that infant mortality fell from 150 to 50 per 1,000 in ten years. Hence the phenomenal expansion, the sudden transformation from stability to rapid growth, the "explosion."

Any student of bacteria, or mice, or rabbits, or practically any creature, is amazed at the constant repetition of the word "explosion" in this context. Given good conditions, bacteria will double their numbers in twenty minutes, quadruple them in forty, and octuple them in an hour. Humanity is raising a shrill alarm because it has suddenly reached a state where its numbers will double in the next thirty years. Mice,

[27]

needing only three weeks to produce a litter of ten or so, take about as many days as man now takes years for a doubling to occur. Even large animals, such as horses, or cattle, or the huge blue whale, are sexually mature in two or three years and can double their numbers far faster than man. The word "explosion," used to describe a duplication over three decades, is hardly accurate. A growth rate of 2 percent in many countries, or 3 percent in the most rapidly growing, is precisely equivalent, arithmetically, to the growth rate of money invested in unrewarding companies. It is even lower than the annual increment of money invested governmentally, and nobody calls that explosive. Nevertheless the word demonstrates mankind's concern at his swelling numbers, which are more like the inexorable expansion of rice grains in water than a great big bang.

Past

"We have been god-like," said the historian Arnold Toynbee, "in the planned breeding of our domesticated plants, but rabbit-like in the unplanned breeding of ourselves." Until advances in death control had advanced sufficiently to cause a need for birth control, we were entitled to be as rabbitlike as the rabbits. No one knows, but men on earth at the time of Christ are thought to have numbered about 250 million, most of them in Asia. How many men there were before then is, naturally, even more obscure. They probably numbered only about 30 to 50 million before the discovery of agriculture, but there was then a slow, slow climb over the millennia to reach that figure of 250 million. The start of towns, of farming, of animal husbandry, must all have been associated with expansions of population in various areas at various times; but disease and wars and poor food and the lean years were powerful obstacles to any major flowering of the human race. Despite modest technological and medical progress, they prevented any further doubling of the human population for the next 1,600 years. It was such a delicate advance that one wonders why it did not retreat, and why the birth rate was *just* a match for the death rate.

Present and Future

The delicacy stopped in the middle of this millennium. There were about 500 million people on earth in the year 1600. The British figure then was about 5 million (according to G. M. Trevelyan). The North American figure was about one million. Suddenly, the situation rapidly altered. There were 1 billion people in the world by 1850, 1.5 billion by the turn of the century, 3 billion by 1960 (some say 1962), and there will almost inevitably be 6 billion by the end of this century. The four doublings since Christ will have taken some 1,600 years, 250 years, 90 years, and 30 years, respectively, to bring the human race from a scattering of 250 million people to 4 billion people by 1980. All finesse has gone from the balance of birth versus death. In some of the Asian, Latin-American, and African countries, the life expectancy for a newborn child has been rising recently by one year per year. A medieval birth rate has been combined with a twentieth-century death rate. There has never been a time quite like the present in the whole history of the Earth.

Even the huge figure of 6 billion by the year 2000 may be an underestimate. If the fertility rate of the 1960s continues at the same pace and if the mortality rate continues to decrease in similar fashion, A.D. 2000 will be welcomed in by 7 billion people. This figure, calculated by the United Nation's demographers, just might be realized, but most estimates hover between 5.3 and 6.8 billion for the turn of the century. Three times as many people, therefore, will welcome the twenty-first century as welcomed the twentieth century back in 1900.

To try and stir the conscience of the world, the propagandists in favor of a less warrenlike approach to breeding hammer home their message in varied fashion. They tell us there are 65 million more mouths to feed every year, that this annual enlargement is more than the population of the British Isles, that it represents the population of New York City appearing almost every six weeks, or the combined populations of Poland and Spain every year. The present annual increase means 180,000 more mouths to feed every day, 7,500 more every hour, 125 more every minute, two more every second. Two people die every second, but four babies are born, and these two extra mouths are the remorseless tick-tock addition to the world's bulging population.

To put it another way, the unyielding growth also means that more people are starving today than at any time before. (Even if everyone at the time of Christ had been starving they would represent only 7 percent of today's population, and no one believes that 93 percent of today's people are adequately fed.) The rate of 4 percent annual increase in food production, required to abolish malnutrition within the next 15 years, has not been achieved by any underdeveloped country. (This is not suddenly making two rice grains grow where one grew before, but every year making 104 grow where 100 grew before.) The agricultural production per head in Asia is now less than it was before the war. Despite improvements in education, there are more illiterates in Asia than there were ten years ago. Nehru once said that

every problem in India has to be multiplied by 400 million. Each year
that number goes up, by 10 million or so, and had he been living in
1967 he should have said by 500 million. Even Alice was told in her
fairy-tale world that it was necessary to run twice as fast actually to get
anywhere. A further difficulty is that a rapidly expanding population is
swamped with children, who eat well but do not—in general—support
families. In countries with a 3 percent growth rate half the population
is under 15. In Britain less than a quarter is under 15. In the United
States, the figures for the 1960 census put those under 15 at 31 percent
of the population.

In 1950 Sir Julian Huxley, who has never been one to pull his
demographic punches, warned that the world population was probably
increasing by 0.8 percent a year, perhaps by 1 percent. By the end
of the century, he said, the global population would be 3 billion. Within
a dozen years that total had been reached. Revised estimates now put
the world increase at 1.9 percent a year. Asia's growth rate is 2.7
percent, and there will be 4.4 billion Asians in A.D. 2000 as against
today's 1.8 billion. Even this huge increase is proportionately overshadowed by the Latin-American growth rate. In 1800 two men out of
three on this planet were Asians. By the year 2000 only half the population will be Asian, mainly because the Americas as a whole will then
possess 13.5 percent of the world's people, whereas in 1800 they possessed 2.8 percent. The overall growth rate today in Latin America is
3 percent, with some countries reaching 3.5 percent. Such an expansion
means a doubling in twenty years. It hardly emulates the bacterial
twenty minutes, but it is revolutionary for mankind.

The last four decades of this century will bring the facts home to
everyone. Between the years 1960 and 2000, Latin America will acquire
3.6 times as many people; Africa and Asia three times as many; East
Asia 2.3 times; Oceania, North America, and the Soviet Union two
times; and Europe one-third more than today's number. Every four years
man is now adding as many people to his planet as were existing in all
five continents when Christ was born. To put it yet another and final
way, about as many people will have reached adulthood in the twentieth
century as reached adulthood during the whole of the first Christian
millennium.

Urbanization

Coupled with the explosion of numbers there has been an "implosion"
toward the towns. Instead of pushing outward and making new frontiers,
like the pioneers of North America, mankind has been concentrating

on the crowded areas. He is doing this at an even faster rate than he is breeding. The world growth rate is less than 2 percent. The town and city growth rate is 4 percent, and it is even 8 percent in some rapidly developing countries. In 1960 one-quarter of the world's people were living in towns of 20,000 or more inhabitants, and they are continuing to crowd themselves together. In a place like Monaco there are 40,000 people per square mile. Each person therefore has on average only 75 square yards, or a plot of ground slightly less than 9 yards long and 9 yards wide. In London and its home counties there are 2,733 people per square mile, but in a place like French Guiana there is one person per square mile. Such emptiness is beaten by Antarctica, with 2.3 million square miles and not a soul as resident population.

All the signs are that the world's cities will grow larger and larger, that the world's population will increasingly forsake its age-old role of agriculture, and that the world's empty places will remain empty—unless tremendous governmental pressures are exerted. In 1950 only a fifth of the world's population was living in towns. By 1960 one-quarter was living in a town. In Latin America half the people live in towns, and in the United States the proportion is two-thirds. The World Health Organization reckons that only 10 percent of us will actually be working on the farm by A.D. 2000, and the lure of the towns will continue. São Paulo in Brazil leaped from 1.3 million people in 1940 to 3.8 million in 1960. Santiago de Chile went from 952,000 to 1.7 million in the same time. It is small wonder that town planners often make a poor job of good accommodation for such invasions—2,400 more people a week in São Paulo *every week* for twenty years.

Immigration

Population mobility has always been thought of as the great pressure-relief valve for crowded areas. Certainly the Atlantic steamers took millions to the New World, notably in the nineteenth century. The people of Ireland, made desperate by starvation, emigrated in such numbers as to leave the mother country not just with a reduced pressure but with a small fraction of her former population. Even so, despite the exodus of human traffic, and the beckoning fingers of a whole new continent, the number of people leaving Europe for the New World since 1850 has been estimated at only 30 million. But the number of new people being added to the world's population is 65 million a year, or more than the total emigration from one country to another during the past 150 years. So much for a solution through immigration. Were some magic to happen and were Antarctica to blossom like the warm prairie fields of the Midwest, the new lands would be of only marginal assistance to the overcrowding problem. Before very long the frozen sixth continent would have a population hazard of its own, and the rest of the world would have benefited from no detectable easing of pressures.

Besides, unlike the Irish, most people do not move. Not long ago in England many people had not been outside their county. In the United States many have never seen the sea (I was amazed to discover the truth of this when staying in Nebraska). The Isle of Man, not far from busy Lancashire and often thought of as a spot primarily for low-tax retirement, keeps most of its citizens to itself. A 1961 census showed that some 67 percent of the people on the island had actually been born there.

The New World is still the great recipient of the footloose, but there is no longer an open door. For the past eighty years potential immigrants to the United States have been either barred or subjected to restrictive quotas (based on race and nationality). Great Britain used to have a quota of over 65,000 annually, and recently has only been making use of about half its allocation. Italy had a quota of 5,666 and Greece of 308, and both quotas were easily consumed. In a law effective as of July, 1968, these national prejudices are to be curtailed. The Western Hemisphere will be able to send 120,000 persons to the United States annually, with a 20,000 maximum for any country. The rest of the world will be able to send 170,000 annually. This immigrant total of 290,000 is a sizable number of people if thought of in terms of boatloads. It is minuscule when set beside the world's problem, because the world adds that number to its population every 39 hours. Besides, the United States itself is making its own contribution: the population, 200 million in 1967, is expected to reach 265 million by 1985 and 300 million by the turn of the century.* If all quotas are taken up, there will have been 6 million new immigrants between now and 1985, but 60 million more native-born Americans to outnumber them.

For years Britain had been a country that lost more people than it received, a net exporter of population. Suddenly, in the mid-1950s, the traditional role was reversed. By 1961–62, there were 225,000 more immigrants than emigrants. Coupled with the rising birth rate this meant a population increase of 504,000 in twelve months. On July 1, 1962, the Commonwealth Immigrants Act came into operation, an act designed to check the immigrant flow, which at that time came primarily

* The Department of Commerce has a census clock in Washington. Every 13½ seconds one American is added to its total.

from the West Indies but also from Pakistan. There was much criticism of this act, because it chiefly hindered the entry of black and brown Commonwealth citizens.* Nevertheless, Britain was then receiving more immigrants per year than the relatively empty United States, and more than were comfortable for an already well-populated island.

The one thousand or so islands that make up the British Isles will be even more crowded in the years to come despite the curtailing of immigration. The 54 million of today will, forecasters say, reach 75 million by A.D. 2000. For England and Wales the 1966 figure of 48.1 million will increase to 54.5 million by 1981, and 66 million by 2001. To fit another 18 million into an area as crowded as England and Wales within the next 34 years is a forbidding thought, but even this increase may be an underestimate. These projections are up on the estimates made only a year beforehand. Within 12 months the forecasted population for 1981 had gone up 1½ percent, and for 2001 by 4½ percent. Queen Elizabeth II already has about ten times as many subjects in Britain as had her predecessor Elizabeth I. Will King Charles III have 15 times as many? When is it going to stop?

Prediction

As a futuristic digression various calculations have been made about the whole planet's potentialities. One set has been worked out by Dr. J. H. Fremlin, of Birmingham University. He has divided progress into stages. Briefly they are:

Stage 1. Proper agriculture, using roofs over cities plus the oceans as growing areas, would permit seven doublings of the existing population, or 400 billion people 260 years from now.

Stage 2. The plants and animals eaten in the twentieth century would be replaced by more efficient converters, e.g., plankton instead of fish. Ten more doublings would therefore be permitted, or 3 trillion people by the year 2330. There would be 1/30 of an acre per person.

Stage 3. Satellite reflectors, bringing energy to the poles, abolishing night and bringing equatorial conditions everywhere. 15 trillion people by A.D. 2410.

Stage 4. Direct synthesis of all foods and use of waste products: one quadrillion by A.D. 2640.

* The act has certainly been a barrier. That 1961–62 figure of 225,000 for the net migration increase was down to 17,000 by the year 1965–66.

Stage 5. With two people to every square meter there would be problems in keeping the planet cool, but there could be ways and means
of losing heat . . . 12 quadrillion people by A.D. 2760.

Whether futuristic whimsy of this sort proves to be wide of the mark
or not, it is highly relevant that such predictions do not have to
probe very far into the future before our current and customary methods
of living become hopelessly upset. Dr. Fremlin's forecast does not
peer at some Jurassic age of future time but keeps itself within the
third millennium The year A.D. 2760 is only as far in the future as the
year A.D. 1160 is in the past; only as many years as lie between Henry II
of England and Elizabeth II.

Phenomenal doublings of the population are inevitable unless either the
death rate goes up or the birth rate goes down. As no one advocates
an increase in the death rate and as the prospects of huge population
increases are alarming in most countries, attention should consequently
be focused on birth control. Yet, both internationally and nationally,
next to nothing is done about the control of the birth rate (more on this
under Contraception). Only in 1965, after many years of inaction on this
score, did the World Health Organization resolve that advisory services
should be given on medical and public-health aspects of family planning.
Most countries hope that contraception will be readily available for
all and that their citizens will be reasonably sensible in planning their
families. The technique is much like fostering education solely by printing cheap textbooks without any compulsory schooling. Even countries
with determined family-planning programs are not in control of the
situation. At the 1965 United Nations' conference on world population in Belgrade, it was stated that ". . . not one of the major fertility
declines in the Western World was the result of an organized program
of birth control by a governmental agency. It resulted from individual
decisions. . . ."

Not too much is known about these individual decisions. Similarly,
no one seems to know why in the late eighteenth century the British
population, for example, suddenly began to increase so sharply.
Of course, population increase is quite different from birth-rate increase,
and in Britain in 1870 the birth rate started to go down even though
the population was still leaping up. No one is too sure about that
birth-rate decline, particularly as the widespread use of contraceptives
in Britain developed almost entirely after 1910. The availability of good
contraceptive methods is plainly not the answer. The slump in the

birth rate that paralleled the lean years of the early 1930s was not marked by any change in contraceptive use. In France, where contraceptives were used less, the birth-rate fall between the wars started even earlier.

Why? Why did the United States reach a peak in 1957 (with 125 births per 1,000 women of child-bearing age) and then fall steadily (to fewer than 100 births per 1,000 women in 1966), making the rate almost identical to the lowest years of the Depression? Why did Britain continue to have more and more babies until 1964 (its highest birth rate for 17 years) and only then begin to slacken its puerperal pace?

Theories abound for both rises and falls, indicting social prestige, economic aspects of the family, women's status, education, the likelihood of a child's surviving childhood, and available birth-control devices. Interaction among these and other factors helps to distort the picture still further; higher education may mean having more children —but later, causing a greater number of children per family but an actual fall in the population growth rate. If average family size is four but average parental age is 30, the population increase is almost identical with that caused by parents aged twenty who have only three children per family. This calculation is extremely relevant to India, where the average maternal age of a first birth is 16½. India would be far better off if this could be raised to the European average, which is about 22 years.

Also economics is no one thing. The Institute of Life Insurance in New York has calculated that today's cost of rearing one child from birth to eighteen, for a family with an income of $6,600 a year, is $23,835. The cost, therefore, of rearing the average family of 3.2 children is $76,272, and this figure does not include the cost of a college education. In less wealthy countries children cost less, and right at the opposite end of the scale is an Indian village, where it is cheaper to have a child than to prevent it by contraception. Although infants are a liability to start with, they ought to be an asset to their country (and their parents) on reaching adulthood. Some countries, only too aware of all the openmouthed liabilities and uncertain of the eventual assets of their vast population, have calculated the value of preventing a birth. Figures varying from $250 to $500 have been quoted. Normal family planning is thought of as the prevention of an unwanted pregnancy; governmental family planning should perhaps be aimed at preventing or discouraging *wanted* pregnancies.

Japan presents the most striking modern story concerning population control. In 1945 a "Eugenic protection law" suddenly permitted abortion and family planning in a Japan equally suddenly bereft of an empire and desperately short of land space. The birth rate fell from 34 per 1,000 people to 18 per 1,000 between 1948 and 1959. Even so, the Japanese confounded the planners in 1965. During that year births were up 6 percent over the previous year. The reason, according to the Health and Welfare Ministry, is simple, and due to the firehorse. Girls born in 1966 (or 1906), both years of the firehorse, will be so domineering that no self-respecting bachelors will wish to marry them. In 1906 there was a big birth drop. In 1965 many couples wanted their children born before the time of ill omen—hence the sudden rise in births.

Thomas Robert Malthus, born on February 17, 1766, a cleric, a denouncer of Rousseau, and a gloomy prophet of inevitable overpopulation, is so far having his predictions proved woefully accurate. He contended that population numbers would increase geometrically, while food production would only rise arithmetically. Consequently, he saw little hope for mankind, only failure. "Any attempt," he wrote in 1798, "to check the superior power of population will produce misery or vice." Today population is indeed growing faster than the food to support it. Malthus did not distinguish between mankind and animals in their power to breed excessively and inexorably. "I can see no way in which man can escape from the weight of this law which pervades all animate nature." Until now, mankind's willingness to breed without much concern for the consequences does put it in the animate or rabbitlike class. The Communists, for example, do not regard Malthus as a progressive and forward-looking thinker; they bluntly call him a reactionary. However, it is up to mankind to call him a false prophet and to prove that the first species with the power to arrange its own destiny actually does so.

Dr. I. J. Good, the Oxford scientist who once prefaced a book by saying that its intention was to raise more questions than it answered, has expressed his own particular and extremely final view of the present growth of people. "Should the population continue to expand at the current rate it will only be 3,500 years before we shall have converted into people all the matter that can be reached during that period."

~⧉ 4 ⧉~

On Reproduction

My main assertion in this book is that reproduction deserves most emphasis. Mother Nature, the eponymous heroine of all natural history, certainly insists that everything is secondary to survival, not of the individual but of the species. Without the ability to reproduce, there can be no biological survival. Without the ability to reproduce in a manner that induces change, there can be no survival in a world of constant change. Reproduction is uppermost, and all internal systems of excretion, respiration, and so on are ancillary to it. "What are people for?" asked Sir Julian Huxley in another context. They are, like every other living thing, to survive, to change, to reproduce.

Reproduction has a wider scope than mere replication. Unlike some berserk factory that cannot alter its own output, that pours out identical scrubbing brushes or crankshafts in a relentless stream, biological reproduction is more than the mere creation of offspring. It is the creation of induced change. It is also development. It is maturity. And then, first for individuals and then for species, it is senescence, it is death. The old must be prepared to die to make way for the new. If there is not death there is not change; instead there is stability, and that way lies extinction. "Qu'est ce que la vie?" asked Claude Bernard. "La vie, c'est la mort."

Therefore reproduction is all-pervasive. It is the egg. It is the growth of that egg. It is puberty. It is the manufacture of another ovum. A chicken, said Samuel Butler, is an egg's way of making another egg. Rather, a chicken is an egg's way of making, from time to time, a slightly different egg. Reproduction has to change its chickens in order to have the ability to change its eggs, and it must get rid of earlier examples. Therefore reproduction has to include postmaturity, old age, death, and decay; immortality has no place in a changing world.

Just as fundamentally, reproduction is also the creation of sex. Human beings may revel in sex—or currently revel in talking about it

[37]

—but only rarely do they ask themselves why there should be two sexes. After all, put at its crudest, the existence of two sexes does complicate creation. Why should there not be one? Why should we not all be mother figures who bud off infants, much as any hydra makes two grow where one grew before?

The fact that there are two human kinds can, of course, never be forgotten. Apart from the primary distinctions between male and female, there are the secondary characteristics, the type of hair growth, of stature, of shape, of fatness. And there are what can be called tertiary characteristics. Women have a different suicide pattern from men. They live longer. They have a different proportion of red blood cells. Their ulcer tendencies are not like men's. Their brains are lighter. Fewer of them are conceived; fewer of them are stillborn.

The differences between man and woman are by no means confined to the chapters distinguishing the male and female reproductive systems. So, both reproduction and the existence of two sexes spread a wide net. All in all some three-fifths of this book is encompassed by reproduction in the broad sense of that word. Its breadth, to my mind, includes not just the basic entities of sperm and egg, but of conception and infertility, of implantation and contraception, of pregnancy and delivery, of twins and malformations, of maternal and infant mortality, of lactation and puerperal fever, of growth, development, and size, of circumcision and castration, of puberty and adolescence, of sex crimes and marriage, of mating, of the proof of paternity, of inheritance, inbreeding, and incest, of family size and population, of the menopause and old age, of suicide and death.

To kill oneself, or not to conceive, or to have the infertility of castration thrust upon one—these are quite as crucial to reproduction as stillbirths and abortion. To be genetically unfit means a failure to reproduce —from whatever cause.

The word "sex" does not indicate reproduction; it includes male and female. The system of sexual reproduction arose extremely early in evolution—no one has any idea when—but it has been of paramount importance because it has commendable advantages. At first sight it might seem that other systems, and there are many, have more to be said for them. With sexual reproduction only one sex can produce offspring, and it cannot produce those offspring without the intervention of its nonproductive sexual partner, the male. With asexual reproduction the offspring can be manufactured as soon as the adult is ready to make them; every adult is therefore a producer, and no delay is necessary while waiting for, finding, cajoling, stimulating, and mating with a partner. Asexually, one makes two, or two hundred as the case may be, and the two or two hundred become four or forty thousand as soon as they are ready to do so. Many lower animals and plants breed in this fashion and do indeed multiply most rapidly, but mere multiplication is not entirely desirable. Individual insects or bacteria or protozoa can produce a population explosion entirely on their own account, but their teeming descendants have nothing but numerical superiority on their side. They are all carbon copies of their solitary ancestors; they have strength in numbers but not in diversity.

Sexual reproduction gives that diversity. Instead of receiving all genetic material from a single parent, as in asexual reproduction, sexual offspring receive half from each parent. In other words, they cannot be carbon copies of either parent, but must be different from both of them. This may or may not be a good thing in immediate terms, but the reproduction of dissimilarity is extremely advantageous in the long run. Instead of producing those satisfactory and teeming copies, it leads both to superior and inferior offspring. Mother Nature has most casual maternal characteristics, for she considers the 99 inferior offspring who die quickly a fair price to pay for one exceptional infant. What does it matter if the herd is cut to pieces by a predator, provided that one escapes due to an exceptional turn of speed?

Assuming that the successful escaper finds a mate, the offspring are likely to possess something of that swiftness even if the mate is normal; but—and this is a second major advantage of sexual reproduction— there is a chance the mate will also be exceptional to some degree. Any offspring from these two will then be the product of a particularly advantageous combination. This can never happen with asexual reproduction; there can be no such thing as a combination, advantageous or otherwise.

Human beings can only reproduce sexually. There have been claims for virgin births (see pages 73–75), but the occurrence, whether believed or disbelieved, is certainly irregular. Not so with many animals. From the perpetually asexual (as with many simple forms) to the perpetually sexual (as with man) there is a wide, ambivalent range. Earthworms, for example, are hermaphrodite in that they always possess both male and female organs; but they still have to mate with other worms. During these encounters the two worms exchange sperm. Later on, each worm will use the stored foreign sperm (certainly not its own, as that would defeat the object) to fertilize its own eggs. Some creatures, such as the oyster, are not truly hermaphrodite, but regularly alternate from Hermes to Aphrodite, from male to female. Others become female only in adversity, when short-term numbers are more advantageous than long-term adaptability. Still others, such as the slipper limpet, change their sex according to the first individual of their species that comes their way; if the newcomer is male, the original limpet becomes a female. Some segmented worms are male at one end of their body, female at the other end. And some males of other species actually live inside their females or are attached equally parasitically to the outside—the ultimate gigolos, to use a phrase from the zoologist Martin Wells.

Having such diminutive masculine forms also seems the ultimate compromise: the male provides the genetical advantages of sexual reproduction and yet does not consume half the available food supply. In fact, such dwarf males are rare. Odder still, considering that most males in most species are capable of fertilizing many females, the sex ratio between male and female is customarily 1:1. Even in species that favor harems and have single bulls serving a score of females, such as seals, there is still parity; do not forget all those other bachelor seals in the backroom who are frustratedly just as male as the active bulls. A beehive contains only one mature female but dozens of mature males.

Whenever the 1:1 ratio of male to female is significantly different in the animal kingdom, an overwhelming preponderance of males is a more probable cause of the disunity. There must be advantages in making sure that every female is found by a mate even at the risk of having an unnecessary number of unproductive males occupying the same ecological niche, consuming the same food, and competing in a sense with the females they never serve. Those bachelor seals eat fish just as determinedly as the females, who will at least be producing more pups for the community, even if half those pups will be just another crop of males.

Reproduction by means of two distinct sexes, the paramount system, has certainly dominated evolution for hundreds of millions of years. Whereas lower forms make use of it, but can breed asexually, the higher forms can only use it. Nevertheless, despite ubiquity, despite its history and indispensability, the sexual distinction is incomplete. No male is wholly male; no female is wholly female. Not only do human males, for example, possess breasts and frequently experience transient, small-scale changes in them during adolescence, but both females and males possess hormones to some degree that, given the opportunity, can develop both forms of sexual system. Sex reversal is common among many animals; something similar can even happen with man, with woman. This is not homosexuality, nor transvestism, nor intersexuality; it is a change of sex. The two sides, so crucial to reproduction, so vital to our society, so integral a part of us, are not so far apart as we generally imagine. The Gender Identity Clinic of Baltimore, for example, proclaims a general dictum that ". . . if the mind cannot be changed to fit the body, we should consider changing the body to fit the mind." Any Martian inspecting this planet, having comprehended our bisexual arrangement, would be astounded to learn of the slender distinction between the two sides of the sexual fence.

Perhaps it is to that Martian that I bequeath this book. He would, one hopes, be primarily interested in the species man. He would not, I hope, be initially as interested in our diseases as in the organism itself, how it multiplies and grows, how it feeds and achieves its energy. He would be told of evolution and would then know that mankind is really another animal, however much mankind wished to distinguish itself from other forms. Therefore, and this I fervently hope, he would like the approach to be biological and to see man as quite the most intriguing and exciting of all the animals here on Earth; but, first, he would have to know how it all began. Only then, having examined evolution and having received a broad picture of humanity, would he start to learn about its reproductive system. As with Genesis, he would start with male and female.

ᦷ 5 ᦷ

The Male

Means of Sperm Transfer · The Penis · Potency ·
Aphrodisiacs · Spermatozoa · Testicles · Ejaculation ·
Sperm Prints · Nomenclature · Mating Time · Sexual
Offenses · Homosexuality · Castration · Circumcision

Means of Sperm Transfer

The penis is the accessory organ used for the transfer of sperm. Low down
in the animal kingdom and in water-living forms there is no need for such
an organ. Both sperm and eggs are liberated into the water, where fertilization occurs. The new forms are truly independent right from the
start. As soon as either shelled eggs or viviparity is involved, with the
mother producing either a shelled form or a free-living form, both of
which have already been fertilized, there is need for sperm transfer.
Somehow or other, she must receive the sperm fairly near the start of
the operation, and the father must be capable of giving them to her. The
average human couple may consider this interchange an extremely elementary procedure, but occasionally they should spare a thought for
sharks, for whales, for porcupines, for seven-ton elephants, for giraffes,
and for tortoises; the mechanics of sperm transfer does have its problems.

Male sharks and rays have a pair of claspers, extensions of their pelvic
fins, that are stiffened by the skeleton. Each pair has tubelike folds of
skin along which the sperm travel, and the claspers can be inserted
into the female cloaca (a combined vent for feces, urine, and reproductive
products possessed by many of the lower vertebrates; it is Latin for
"sewer"). Various other vertebrates are much more haphazard about the
process, merely presenting cloaca to cloaca, with the proximity helping
the sperm to get across. Most birds—ducks and geese are exceptions—
have no specific organs of copulation, although it is thought that their

ancestral forms were not so lacking in this respect. Many reptiles, the group from which birds evolved, do have a special organ. Snakes and lizards have hemipenes; at the right moment these are turned inside out, extruded, and then inserted into the female. Various other reptiles, such as crocodiles and turtles, do have an organ that seems to be the true forerunner of the mammalian penis and therefore merits the same name.

The Penis

It is in the mammals that the penis is most highly developed. Nevertheless, the mere possession of a copulatory organ is inadequate for copulation. It has to be made capable of insertion into the female.

Such insertion is made possible both by increasing length and rigidity. Neither of these is necessary at times other than copulation, and the penis is normally a more flaccid and reduced organ. There are very many variations within the mammals concerning this reduction. The penis may disappear from view completely, it may be made to fold, to retreat within a special sheath, or merely to remain completely external but shrunken. A cold external temperature can cause this shrinkage to be even more marked. Erection is achieved when the organ is engorged with blood. Suitable nervous stimulation, whether directly physical or merely mental, starts this process. The penis's dorsal vein is compressed, thereby restricting the blood's outlet. At the same time, the muscular coating around each arteriole (or miniature artery) is relaxed, and so is the spongy tissue that forms much of the penis. Hence, with a greater area to occupy, the blood distends the penis. Similarly, due to the continued pressure from the heart and a smaller venous outlet, the pressure within the penis is built up and rigidity follows. (An analogy is a water hose. Provided the end is open, water will flow smoothly along the hose. When it is sealed, the water pressure will distend and stiffen the hose. The hydraulics of both hose and penis are the same.) Full engorgement of the human penis can be most rapid. It may occur within three to five seconds from the start of stimulation. The average final length is 6¼ in., with its diameter at the base 1½ in. According to R. L. Dickinson, author of *Human Sex Anatomy,* there is relatively little difference in penis size as compared with body height and weight differences.

Naturally, with animals and with the great size differences that are involved, there is considerable variation in the process of erection and retraction. Usually, the penis is concealed when at rest within a fold of skin in the lower abdomen known as the preputial sac. The penis, for example, of a bull, a stallion, or an elephant is customarily invisible. To determine the sex of humans at a glance when they are naked is easy, but it is not so with many animals, despite their nakedness; the genital organs can be totally invisible. For a long time the sex of London Zoo's giant panda, Chi-Chi, was unknown. Only after the animal had been several years at the zoo was it definitely pronounced to be a female. It was frequently held in the past that the hyena must be hermaphrodite because all hyenas appear externally similar.

Sometimes, as in most monkeys and apes, the preputial sac is less effective, and the penis is only partly hidden. Or, as in man, the tree shrews, and certain bats, such a sac is absent, and the penis is then said to be truly pendulous. Occasionally, as with bulls and guinea pigs, the normal penis is longer than the sac into which it retreats. In these cases the retracted organ folds conveniently into an S-shape. With very large animals, the penis naturally has to be very large to be effective in sperm transfer. In the boar it is 18 in., in stallions 30 in., in bulls 3 ft., in elephants 5 ft., and in the blue whale—the largest animal there has ever been—it is 7 to 8 ft. long.

Many animals, but not man, possess a bone in their penis. Known as the os penis, or baculum, it can be of bone or cartilage or a bit of both. Presumably it helps in the acquisition of rigidity. Presumably, too, such a bone was possessed by the ancestors of mammals because its present distribution is so widespread. All carnivores (dogs, cats, seals, bears), insectivores, bats, rodents, and primates (except man) have one. Man, the ungulates (hoofed mammals), most marsupials, and whales do not have one. The shape of the bone among those that do is itself highly variable, far more so than any other bone. A femur, whatever the animal that walks on it, always tends to look like other femurs. Not so the os penis. Professor A. S. Romer, of Harvard University, who writes exemplary zoological textbooks, has said that it may be "a plate or a rod of varied form—straight, bent or doubly curved; round, triangular, square or flat in section; simple, pronged, spoon-shaped or perforated; long or short." As an examination query for a student, the bone has a host of confusing possibilities.

The tip of the penis, cone-shaped in man, also varies greatly. It may be in two halves, as in some marsupials, or single, as in all other mammals. It may be extended into a long, threadlike part, as in the ram. It may be covered with spiky protuberances, as in rodents, carnivores, and insectivores. It may, as in some primates, be very small. In man it occupies about one-quarter of the total penis length, it is the most sensitive part, and normally (without circumcision) it is covered by a fold of skin called the prepuce.

Potency

The ability of the human male to achieve erection and to produce sperm continues in time long after the human female has met her menopause. One American survey showed that over 90 percent of men still had "erectal potency" at the age of 50, over 80 percent at the age of 60, over 70 percent at 70, and even 25 percent at 80. These proportions do not necessarily indicate the ability to achieve orgasm. The survey, carried out by A. C. Kinsey and his colleagues, also indicated that the American male of 50 was still having an average of about two orgasms a week, and of 70 about one a week. As for sperm production, this probably continues at a diminishing rate until the time of death. The mechanism of erection and ejaculation can, like presumably every other bodily function, go wrong. Ejaculation, for instance, can become retrograde. The sperm, instead of being ejected correctly, can be shot backward into the bladder at the moment of orgasm. Erection can also become permanent. Known as priapism, the condition has a multitude of causes, some sinister, some merely inconvenient. For a long time it has been observed that erections can be caused by severe injuries to the spinal cord. Fatal injury to the cord caused by judicial hanging can have the same effect.

Aphrodisiacs

Many societies, including our own, have great faith in the ability of certain substances to arouse sexual appetite and performance. The beliefs of other societies are pooh-poohed, such as the belief in rhinoceros horn; but there is a general feeling that aphrodisiacs do exist. The beetle Cantharides, which is used to make "Spanish fly," is said to be one of them. Certainly this concoction, also used by animal breeders, does act as an irritant and some irritation is caused in the genital area, perhaps stepping up the flow of blood to this area; but such action by no means implies improvement of prowess or desire. Similarly, there is yohimbine, (or johimbe) from the yohimbine tree of Africa, and phosphorus, caffeine, and strychnine. Great faith has been attached to all of them, yet little satisfactory scientific evidence exists. According to *Patterns of Sexual Behavior,* by Clellan S. Ford and Frank A. Beach, there is no real evidence to indicate "that any pharmacological agent is capable of directly increasing the individual's susceptibility to sexual arousal and capacity for sexual performance." There may well be such an agent, they admit, but there is not one known as yet.

The greatest faith of all is attached to alcohol. "Lechery, sir, it pro-

vokes and it unprovokes;" says Shakespeare's Porter in *Macbeth,*
"it provokes the desire, but it takes away the performance." Scientists,
however, will admit only that it unprovokes social inhibitions, thereby
releasing desire from its customary cage. Otherwise, alcohol is a sexual
depressant that interferes with the capacity both for erection and for
orgasm. In large amounts neither is possible. Alcoholics may be totally
impotent. Drugs such as morphine and heroin reduce sexual excitement and activity, and abrupt withdrawal of these drugs from addicts
can lead to frequent erections and ejaculations in males and to
orgasms in women.

The most bizarre addition to the list of reported aphrodisiacs, bearing
in mind its current status of warm, gentle goodness, is cocoa. The
Aztecs of Montezuma's Mexico said their drink chocolatl was a sexual
reviver, and the Spanish priests believed them. For over a century,
cocoa had resplendent fame as a violent inflamer of the passions, and
then it quickly subsided into its present role. Sir Hans Sloane holds the
credit for the final indignity accorded to the Mexican brew when he invented milk chocolate. A drink fit for the halls of Montezuma became a
cozy nightcap for the old world.

Spermatozoa

The first man to see bacteria and protozoa, the first to see red blood
corpuscles, and the first to describe the insect's compound eye was also
the first man to see spermatozoa. Living a simple life as a rich merchant
of Delft, Antony van Leeuwenhoek spent much of his life constructing
his own microscopes, grinding his own lenses, and then looking through
them at the far more miniature world beyond them. His microscopes
looked more like draftman's compasses than optical instruments, but
they could magnify by some 160 times. Therefore, they could unblock
much of the invisible world beyond the normal reach of the human
eye.

It was in 1677 that he and his friend L. Hamm looked at human
semen, and saw minute objects swimming in it. The Royal Society of
London was then very new, having been formed the moment political
stability and Charles II returned to England, but it was the leading scientific society in the world, and the Dutch microscopist sent it a letter
detailing his findings. Simultaneously bearing in mind the fact that
human semen might be considered an indelicate subject for discussion,
he begged the Royal Society not to publish his findings should it consider them either obscene or immoral. The Royal Society found them
fascinating and published without delay. The existence of human
spermatozoa has therefore been known for almost 300 years.

The existence of human seed had already been assumed in many societies for countless centuries. In fact some considered the male seed to be all that was necessary, bar a little nourishment from the mother, for the production of the next generation. A contrary view held, for example, by many Australian tribes is that intercourse has no relation to pregnancy. It is all a matter of spirits, not semen. The ancient Greeks held that the mother of a child was no real parent to it, merely a nurse to the young life that had been sown in her. The Egyptians had also held that the father alone is the author of generation. Aristotle, in the fourth century B.C., could not quite accept these earlier views and gave rather more credit to the mother. The embryo was attached, after all, for nine months to the mother's uterine wall, and therefore could be receiving not only nourishment but other influences.

It was up to the greatest polymath of all time, Leonardo da Vinci, to give the mother full credit. "The seed of the female," he wrote, "is as potent as that of the male in generation." And he came to this conclusion after examining the offspring of a white Italian woman and a black "Ethiopian" man. The children were neither black nor white, for both male and female inheritance had decided the mixed outcome. The remarkable part of this story, as in so many others, is not so much that one man saw the light, but that so many had failed to see it. It must have been common knowledge, if not in the Italian Middle Ages at least in any Egyptian century, that blacks crossed with whites produced a broad spectrum of browns. Leonardo was employing no microscope to see what could so conspicuously be seen by everyone else.

Nevertheless, spermatozoa needed an optical aid to become visible. They are minute. A micron is a thousandth part of a millimeter, and there are 25 millimeters to the inch. The sperm head is 2.6 microns in diameter, 4.6 microns long. The tail is the longest part, twelve times longer than the head, or 50 microns, or 1/20 mm., or about 1/500 in. Its thinness means that the fatter but smaller head is always easier to detect. Within this head, despite its minute volume, is all the tightly packed nucleoprotein of the chromosomes that are the male factors of inheritance. Within it is all that the father contributes to his offspring. When joined with the maternal chromosomes (and they are no bigger), all the information exists, all the nucleoprotein coding, for the next generation. That the offspring will be a vertebrate, will be a mammal, will be a human, will be a type of human, and will have both paternal and maternal characteristics—all these are ordained by the miniature bundle of chromosomes. And the masculine contribution to that bundle, precisely half—give or take a fragment of chromosome No. 23—is all contained in an active, motile, invisible, flagellating sperm with a head measuring 2.6 by 4.6 microns. One wonders why the Royal Society did not dispatch Leeuwenhoek's letter about the microscopic human seed back to Delft on the grounds not of indecency but of incredibility.

Each human sperm is formed in about 46 days. It is fashioned within one of the two testicles and from a fragment of the tubular convolution —some say a mile long—of sperm-making cells within each testicle. It is a progressive manufacture. Upon the tubular membrane are cells called spermatogonia. These divide to form spermatocytes. These then divide, and each division marks a change as well as duplication, to form spermatids, and they then divide to form spermatozoa.

During this process the normal cell complement of 46 chromosomes has been changed to 23, following the so-called reduction or meiotic division when spermatocyte becomes spermatid. At fertilization, when 23 fuse with 23, the normal complement for a human cell will again have been restored. Whereas the male production line is producing perhaps a couple of hundred million sperm a day, the female is maturing just one egg a month. Similarly, while a male may produce some infinite number around a million million in his lifetime, the female ovary actually sheds only some strictly finite number of eggs, like 400, and no more, in her reproductive lifetime. Both egg and sperm contain the same amount of genetic material. Therefore the male's production swamps the female's, although both male and female contribute a precisely equal amount of what is actually used to form the next generation.

Testicles

Human testicles are strangely placed. No one designing an organism, having packed every internal organ within the confines of the body cavities, would be content with an extramural position for the vital testes. The whole future generation of the species hangs not by a thread, but is certainly less secure than with some internal system. Most animals do have an internal system. Only in the mammals do the testes (or testicles) migrate from their original position up near the kidneys. The movement happens in early life, long before birth. However, there is great variation within the mammal class about where, when, and how this happens.

In some species it does not happen at all, and the testes remain in their original place somewhere near the small of the back. In other species they move down to the bottom end of the abdominal cavity, but still remain within the body, and in some (as in man) they move into a pair of pouches known as the scrotal sacs or scrotum. A male human baby almost always has his diminutive testes, which will not produce sperm until puberty, within his scrotum by the time he is born. (There is a widespread but false belief that the testes do not descend until puberty.) In humans the testes stay in the scrotum, or should stay there, for life; but this weakness in the defenses of the abdominal wall means that the testes can move inward, and parts of the intestine, for example, can move outward as in inguinal hernia.

In no species is such a hernia either an acceptable or regular occurrence, but in many species the testes do migrate with the seasons. When unwanted they return to the abdomen. During the breeding period, they move again into the scrotum. This annual movement hammers home the point that, for many creatures, the testes must be external to be effective. Certainly, the outside scrotum is at a lower temperature than the internal abdomen, and, certainly, temperature does seem to be involved; but the reason and mechanisms are much less clear. Rats have been made infertile by wrapping their scrotal sacs in cotton wool, and there is even a fertility theory that the breeziness of the kilt is better for men than the restrictive confines of undershort and trouser.

It is difficult to see why sperm grow best at different temperatures for similar species. Why do some marsupials have internal testes when some do not? Why do the whale and the armadillo, for example, have them internally when their lives have so little comparison, and why are some scrota firmly—and warmly—attached while others (as in most carnivores, and horses, and cattle, and many monkeys and man) are loose and pendulous?

Incidentally, there is even variation in the position of the scrotum among animals. In man it lies behind the penis. In marsupials it may be in front, and in gibbons it may lie alongside the penis. In bats the scrotum may even be behind the anus. Some birds carry that matter of temperature still further by lowering their whole body temperature when sperm are being produced. For example, the house sparrow is normally at 110°F. Its night temperature, when most sperm are being produced, is 104°F.

Dimensions are also highly variable. In man each testis is about 2 in. long, 1 in. wide, and less than 1 in. thick. They stay that size throughout the seasons. With hibernating animals they shrink and then regrow. So too with animals having a definite season of sexual excitement. As man has no sexual respect for the seasons, sperm production is continuous. When formed, each spermatozoon is complete with its head, neckpiece, middle piece, and tail—but this tail is without movement. Nevertheless, each sperm has a long way to go—over a foot— before it even enters the female. Initially it is jostled along by the production of subsequent sperm until it reaches the epididymis. (Almost all biological names make classical sense despite their appearance. This one is from two Greek words meaning "on" and "testicles.") Within this small lump of tissue, which does indeed sit on the testicle, the sperm mature, become motile, and wait—for this is the main sperm storehouse. Both fertility and motility of sperm can last for several weeks, but if they are not ejaculated during their lifetime, the sperm degenerate and eventually liquefy.

Ejaculation

If they are to be emitted, the long journey is accomplished very quickly. To begin with, they travel up the thin vas deferens, the tube that is surgically cut during male vasectomy castration. This initial journey is longer than strictly necessary because of the original migration of the testis. Instead of leading straight to the penis, the tube leads up and over another tube leading from the kidney to the bladder, and can only then descend in the general direction of the penis. (Like a cat trailing a length of wool caught around a paw, the wool will indicate any backtracking in its path. Similarly, the apparently random detour of the vas deferens behind the bladder positively indicates the original location of the testis.)

Having made this loop, the tube then meets with the seminal vesicles. These produce a yellow fluid, which forms much of the semen and which mixes with the sperm on its journey. The mixture then passes through the prostate gland, and this adds its complement of secretion, a thin fluid that gives semen its characteristic smell. The next addition to the mixture is from the small bulbourethral glands. And that is the lot. The resultant assortment of liquids and sperm, between 2 cc. and 7 cc., 90.3 percent water, is then ejaculated down the urethra along the penis and into the female vagina. Swimming energetically at half an inch or so a minute, the spermatozoa, perhaps 200 million of them, perhaps more, set about achieving their goal. From this huge armada of an assault, only one individual sperm will be successful.

Various niceties of coordination and timing have to be achieved during the headlong flight of orgasm. The urethra is the tube used by both urine and sperm. Therefore, a sphincter has to be closed to prevent sperm from being shot into the bladder or urine being mixed disastrously (for urine is spermicidal) with the sperm. Removal of the prostate gland, a fairly frequent operation in the aged, usually destroys this sphincter. Therefore retrograde ejaculation—into the bladder—will result at least partially. The normal ejaculation process is a refinement of ordered coordination. The muscle coatings of that original epididymis, of the vas deferens, of those seminal vesicles, and of the prostate all contract, shrinking the available volume and forcing the sperm and semen toward the final urethra. And when they reach it, a wave of contraction from the muscles around it, the bulbo-ischio-cavernosus, shoots those few vital cubic centimeters straight out of the penis.

The haste of orgasm is succeeded by the haste to reach the egg. Human sperm have a short life. If still in the vagina after an hour they cease to move. If they are within the uterus or cervix, they live longer, perhaps 25, perhaps 40 hours. In any case, 48 hours is generally reckoned to be the limit. The sperm have to swim upstream because the normal uterine flow is toward the vagina; but if the woman has an orgasm as well as the man, the uterus, or so many scientists believe, suddenly contracts and then relaxes, thus helping to suck up the semen toward the Fallopian tubes, where fertilization will take place. Female orgasm is not necessary for fertilization. It is believed that without its aid the sperm will reach the tubes within an hour, although possibly within minutes if orgasm helps.

There is no attraction by the egg, if egg there be at the time, for the sperm. They cannot detect its proximity, but can start the process of fertilization only if an actual encounter is made. This then involves digesting away the egg's outer layer. Many sperm help in the task by liberating the necessary enzyme (called hyaluronidase merely because much of that outer layer contains hyaluronic acid). Once digested, the egg is exposed and ready for fertilization by a single spermatozoon.

There is not such continuous haste in all species. Fertilization can often take place months after copulation. Female bats can store sperm, and so can various reptiles. The female rattlesnake is often mated in the autumn, although ovulation will not occur until the spring. The record lack of urgency that I could find, and presumably the record length of life for viable sperm as well, was of a snake that produced fertile eggs in captivity five years after the last possible copulation. The only way of improving upon this record is to freeze the sperm artificially. Semen banks, used in the artificial-insemination departments of animal husbandry, store sperm for long periods at $-79\,°C.$, or colder. Thus, a bull's semen can be used long after the bull himself is dead. For some obscure reason different semen from different bulls responds either well or badly to the technique. And human semen responds (so far) even less well to lengthy periods in the deep freeze, although techniques for conserving it are improving.

Sperm Prints

That hint of a difference in character between sperm from different individuals is supported by what have been called "sperm prints." Fingerprints are well known; sperm prints less so. Nevertheless they exist, for all individuals tend to produce sperm with varying degrees of abnormality. And they tend to produce these abnormalities in fixed ratios. There may be twisted heads or double tails or immobile flagella or any one of a wide variety of deformities, and they are produced by cells that, presumably, cannot make them otherwise. Hence, the constancy of their mistakes; hence, the ability of a scientist examining sperm through a microscope to match one collection of deformed sperm with a similar collection from the same man. The number of items that can be left with impunity at the scene of the crime is steadily decreasing.

Another major difference is in the fertilizing power between individuals. The various possible disabilities of the human sperm are mentioned in the chapter on fertility, but all males tend to become infertile if their ejaculations are too frequent. Remember that it takes 46 days to make a sperm; the available stock can be quickly consumed. Determined virility can lead to unintended infertility if production is not permitted to keep pace with demand. At the other end of the virility scale is impotence. This too can mean infertility, despite an abundance of sperm. Generally, it is manifested in one of three main ways. The first is an inability to achieve an erection, either at all or for sufficient time—often associated with alcoholism. The second is an excessive ability to ejaculate sperm, possibly the moment erection is achieved and before penetration is possible. The third and rarest is an inability to emit sperm: erection is achieved, but ejaculation does not follow.

Nomenclature

Once again there is a problem of names. A quite remarkable aspect of our society is that there is no word both universally acceptable and accepted for the sexual act. There is no equivalent of "to eat" or "to drink" for the equally basic function of sperm transfer. Instead our plethora of blunt or evasive terms, including scientific, euphemistic, and street-corner phraseology, has to be used according to circumstance. Coitus, copulation, intercourse, intromission, make love, sleep with, go to bed with, fornicate, stuff, couple, fuck, prod, poke, mate, mount, lay, knock up—all have their uses, but in closely confined contexts. Animal husbandry has words of its own. To serve is the general description, but stallions cover, dogs and cats mate, bulls bull, and rams tup. The Bible, the law, the newspapers, the antenatal clinics, science, literature, the messroom, and the general populace have their individual preferences. Consequently, there is much scope either for misunderstanding or for total inarticulation when different cultures meet and wish to discuss this subject. The same is true for defecation and excretion. I well remember a fellow schoolboy's insistence to a nurse that, so far as he knew, he had never opened his bowels in his life. "What on earth are they?" he protested.

Mating Time

Whatever word is used, mankind is also odd in restricting most of its sexual activity to the time customarily reserved for rest and least physical activity. Man is a diurnal, a daytime creature, and yet most sexual play is in most human societies at night. Contrarily, the Chenchu of India believe nocturnal intercourse to be dangerous, producing blindness in a child. The anthropoid apes, just as diurnal as man, keep the night for sleeping; all their sex activity is in daylight. Nocturnal animals keep the day for sleeping and have their sex activity at night. Daytime birds (most birds are diurnal) mate during the day. Night birds, such as the owls, mate at night. A. C. Kinsey and others suggested that human males prefer light, whether at night or not, whereas human females like the dark. (Kinsey, incidentally, so much a student of human sex, was originally an entomologist, primarily concerned with wasps and with the intricacies of their sex.)

Mankind is also one of the few species whose mating continues throughout the year, and with even fewer restrictions than most. The female can be receptive to the male virtually always and not solely— as with so many animals—during the short periods when in estrus (in heat).

There are various taboos about when and where human sexual intercourse is forbidden, many allied to the belief that it weakens the male. For the rest of the time, according to C. S. Ford and F. A. Beach, "in most of the societies on which information is available, every adult normally engages in heterosexual intercourse once daily or nightly." For American couples Kinsey reported a slightly lower frequency, four times a week when 15 to 20 years old, three times a week by the age of 30, twice a week at 40, and once a week at 60. Naturally, these average figures contain considerable individual differences. In every age group from 15 to 60 there were men who reached orgasm at least ten times a week.

In the animal world there is less regularity of behavior. There is usually a mating season, possibly with all the masculine activity confined to only a few of the males, as in seals. Or there may be several estrous cycles for the female in one year, with each estrous female mated by several males before the period passes. Females in estrus seem, in general, to be insatiable. Males are likely to find that the sexual capacity of the available females exceeds their own.

With animals the sexual act is often markedly brief. In the bull and ram it lasts a few seconds. In the stallion slightly longer. In chimpanzees it is less than ten seconds on average, rarely more than fifteen. In the elephant, aided by an independently mobile penis, it is less than thirty seconds; in the boar perhaps several minutes. In felines, such as lions and cats, it may be seconds; but for canines, such as dogs and wolves, it may be far longer. They can become locked, as the penis swells to its maximum size only after insertion; premature attempts at unlocking can cause actual injury. Mice can continue for twenty minutes or so, producing perhaps 200 thrusts during that time.

In humans the time can vary widely. Generally, it takes longer for the female to achieve orgasm than for the male, and the time of coitus may be controlled by the masculine ability to restrain his climax in the hope of coinciding with hers. An American survey (by R. L. Dickinson and L. Bean) concluded that 9 percent of couples took more than thirty minutes from intromission to ejaculation, that 17 percent took fifteen to twenty minutes, 34 percent five to ten minutes, and 40 percent less than five minutes. Mae West, in a more personal survey, recounted a possible record in her autobiography—a man "called Ted" made love to her for fifteen hours. He later said "he was both astounded and pleased at his own abilities."

The Balinese, although unkindly forbidding sexual intercourse to the sick and malformed, conveniently believe that a hurried lovemaking will result in a malformed baby. Female orgasm, although unnecessary for conception, is important in a well-adjusted sexual partnership, but many women never experience it. It is unbelievable that the characteristic of a feminine climax is confined to the human species, but female animals do not in general appear to reach a similarly blatant pinnacle during coitus. The male's mounting climax and fulfillment is usually only too easy to observe. Equivalent behavior in the female is markedly absent. Ford and Beach, from whose *Patterns of Sexual Behavior* so many of these facts have been culled, suggest that the clitoris may be a clue. This organ, highly sensitive and directly equivalent (or homologous) to the male penis, usually causes great sexual excitement when stimulated. It so happens that if the penis is inserted into the vagina from the rear, with both male and female facing the same direction, the clitoris is less likely to be stimulated by the penis—hence, according to the theory, a lack of sensation and, possibly, an inadequate stimulus for orgasm. All mammals except man favor rear entry. Mankind, although wildly experimental in positioning, generally favors a face-to-face encounter. Such a position, with its method of entry, does generally lead to stimulation of the clitoris, and most human females experience orgasm.

The clitoris hypothesis is admitted by its authors to be "highly speculative." Perhaps female animals experience orgasm, but less demonstratively than their frantic partners. Or perhaps the human female is curiously unique in her climactic ability.

Sexual Offenses

Sexual offenses come most properly under the general heading of "male reproduction" because it is so much simpler for a male to offend the law in western society, whether the law is justified or not. Penalties can be severe for any male convicted of rape in the United States or Britain. For a female accused of raping a male the act is not a specific crime; she may be convicted only of an indecent assault. The New York law also would not convict her of rape, but it would be an assault. The Institute of Sex Research in the United States put the situation bluntly by saying (in the book *Sex Offenders*): "If a man walking past an apartment stops to watch a woman undressing before the window, the man is arrested as a peeper. If a woman walking past an apartment stops to watch a man undressing before the window, the man is arrested as an exhibitionist."

The main law in Britain is the Sexual Offences Act of 1956. C. J. Polson, in *The Essentials of Forensic Medicine,* summarized the various crimes within its scope. They can be grouped as:

a. Intercourse by force, intimidation, false pretenses, or the administration of drugs to obtain or facilitate intercourse
b. intercourse with girls under 16
c. intercourse with defectives (now called "severely subnormal persons")
d. incest
e. unnatural offenses
f. indecent assaults.

Rape, which does not have to include the emission of sperm, although this can help to provide proof of the crime, comes under group a. Under group c—intercourse with defectives—there is scope for quite unintentional guilt. An usherette at a Glasgow movie house once took her mongoloid daughter to her theater and seated her. During the performance the daughter had intercourse with a man who afterward denied all knowledge of her deficiencies, particularly as the theater had remained dark throughout the encounter. He was later convicted, but later still the conviction was quashed. Under group *b,* particularly with increasingly early puberty and the increasing ability of young girls to appear older than their years, many males must be victims of their own assumptions and the girls' appearances. As a kind of proof, babies are born every year to many mothers of 13, sometimes 12 years old, sometimes 11. As nine months have to be subtracted to reach the actual date of the offense, making their ages probably 12, 11, and 10, the girls are jumping the gun to a considerable degree. Nevertheless, it is their male consorts who are found guilty. The act of 1956 does not recognize "consent" by any girl until she is 16, although it does recognize the difference between girls who have reached their teens and those who have not. Intercourse with a girl over 13, but under 16, is only an offense. Sexual intercourse with a girl under 13 is a felony, a crime subject to severe punishment. Only boys over 14 are considered capable of rape—in England. In Scotland there is no such watershed; theoretically all boys there are capable of rape. According to the interpretation of New York's new penal code, there are no male age limits in two categories of rape. They are sexual misconduct—including rape without consent, deviate intercourse without consent, sodomy, and necrophilia—and first-degree rape, which involves forcible compulsion, incapacity of consent by reason of physical helplessness, or intercourse with a female younger than 11. Nonetheless, a person younger than 16 "is not criminally responsible for conduct," although those between the ages of 7 and 16 are subject to juvenile delinquency proceedings.

The 1956 act was supplemented by the Indecency with Children Act of 1960. This makes a criminal of any person who, without committing an assault, "invites a child to handle him or otherwise behaves indecently towards a child under 14." If the girl is under 13 and the man tries sexual intercourse he can get seven years' imprisonment. If his assault is merely "indecent," he can get five years.

Incest is defined as sexual intercourse between a man and his granddaughter, daughter, sister, or mother, or between a woman and her grandfather, son, brother, or father. The practice must be commoner than the few facts indicate, and information about most incestuous indiscretions is likely to remain within the family circle. The cases that reach the courts usually involve a father-daughter relationship or one between brother and sister. Sex crimes, in general, are on the increase, so far as the courts are concerned. In 1938 there were about 5,000 in Britain. In 1945 there were almost 10,000. In 1960 there were 20,000, a fourfold increase in 22 years. However, as a yardstick, there was more than a fivefold increase during the same period for crimes of violence. Their total jumped from 3,000 to 16,000.

Newspapers give considerable coverage to any association between the murder of a child and sexual motives. In fact a child has only to be reported missing for the assumption to arise that its naked and assaulted body will be found a few days later; but in 1964, for example, thirty children were murdered during the year in Britain. Of these crimes, two were unsolved, 27 had been committed by relatives (almost always the parents), and only one was committed by someone unrelated. In summing up the subject, the *British Medical Journal* estimated that about four children a year are killed for sexual reasons. Offenses by strangers make the most headlines, but most detected sexual acts with children are committed by relatives or friends. Children should therefore still beware of strangers, but statistically, they are far more likely to be harmed either by friends and relations, particularly their parents, or by accidents. Sexual murders of children are outnumbered by ordinary child murders, and both are quite outnumbered by road accidents involving children and by accidents children bring upon themselves.

Homosexuality

Facts on homosexuality tend to be obscured by society's attitude to it. Estimates on the number of males who are homosexual vary between 3 and 5 percent. A round figure frequently quoted for Britain is 500,000. Under particular conditions, such as prison camps, the proportion rises. A. C. Kinsey and his associates in their survey of sexual behavior state that 40 percent of adult American men and 13 percent of women had experienced homosexual contact to the point of orgasm. Greater proportions had experienced homosexuality to some degree. Male homosexuality is generally more common than lesbianism, both with man and animals, although Bryan Magee, in his book *One in Twenty*, says there are nearly one million lesbians in Britain (the title refers to the number of men he believes to be homosexual).

On average, homosexuals (and this means male from now on) have more brothers in their families than heterosexuals have. The normal average of families is 106 boys to 100 girls, while the homosexual average is 119 boys to 100 girls. Lesbians have more sisters than the average. Mothers of homosexuals are older than average, and homosexuals also tend to appear late among the family births. (These last two facts may seem to be a rewording of the same phenomenon, but both are quite distinct.) Homosexuals have no detectable chromosome abnormality, and are therefore nothing like the intersexes. Despite much current opinion, homosexuals do not have an excess of feminine features. They are as physically capable of fathering children as heterosexuals. There is no necessarily clear-cut line between the two. Many men can be both, with preferences verging one way or the other.

Most homosexuals are not, as is commonly supposed, interested in young and prepubertal boys. The proportion of criminal homosexual acts to known offenses must be phenomenal. Estimates vary from 2,500:1 to 30,000:1. Societies still have and have had totally different attitudes toward homosexuality, ranging from complete acceptance to complete intolerance. The Greeks put it on a high plane. The Romans regarded it in a more basic fashion. The higher primates frequently engage in it, whether in zoos or not. No one knows whether it has a genetic cause or not. E. Maurice Backett, to whom I am indebted for many of these facts, wrote in 1964, "Most biologists would put heavy bets upon the environment as the main contributor in the production of homosexuality."

Theories about this contribution, although similarly obscured by society's attitude to homosexuality, are plentiful. The men's mothers have been called demanding, overprotective, domineering, seductive, and inhibiting. Their fathers have been described as weak, indifferent, absent, hostile, abusive, or rejecting. In general, positive characteristics are ascribed to the mother, weaker ones to the father. The family as a whole is often said to be rigidly puritanical. Of course, there are exceptions even to this broad spectrum of suggested possibilities. Countless mothers must be protective and fathers indifferent without the son becoming homosexual. And homosexuals must arise from the most well-balanced families. Such exceptions appear with monotonous regularity in every biological generalization, and of course they cannot be forgotten. Nevertheless, the general picture is of an ill-balanced parental situation, with the mother highly emotional. It seems likely, says Backett, that a son subjected to a relationship so charged becomes disturbed by, or horrified at, the "implicit sexuality of the relationship, and tends thereafter to renounce the female as an object of his sexuality."

Can homosexuals be treated? Can they be helped to revert to normal heterosexuality or to adjust themselves satisfactorily to their problem? Backett says attempts have not been "strikingly successful." A *British Medical Journal* editorial in 1965 said treatment for the established homosexual was "frequently ineffective," although the journal was then jumped on by one physician, who said he had converted 16 out of 32 patients to heterosexuality. Plainly, the task is not easy and must depend on the degree of homosexuality, the willingness to cooperate, and the desire to revert to heterosexuality.

The recent pressures in Britain (notably the Wolfenden Report*) to revoke the Criminal Amendments Act of 1885, which could put a man in prison for a private homosexual act with another man, have been successful. Homosexual acts between consenting adult (over 21) males are no longer punishable in Britain due to a new law of July, 1967. Soliciting, pimping, homosexual brothels, and homosexual acts with minors (under 21) are still punishable. Lesbians, however, were not included in the 1885 act, and there is a story that Queen Victoria had a royal hand in this omission. The original wording of the law embraced both male and female homosexuals. She refused, allegedly, to countenance the idea of lesbianism, and so struck them out before signing.

During discussions for changing the law, Dr. Keith Simpson, the forensic pathologist, said that "homo" and "queer"† had become almost playful epithets and that homosexual practices were "rotting the fabric of the arts as well as the more solid principles of family life." It is often said that there is no law against practicing lesbians because they cause no serious social problem. There is a counterargument that many problems of homosexuality result solely from the laws imposed by society.

Most private homosexual acts remain private. A minute minority, bearing in mind the half-million British men who are said to be homosexuals, become known to the law. In the five years from 1955 to 1959 the number of "unnatural offences known to the police" was 761. In the previous five-year periods, beginning with 1935 to 1940, the figures were 117, 201, 309, and 680. Though small, the numbers were increasing, although this may only reflect increased police diligence. (Such figures are not available for the United States at large. Even the *Uniform Crime Reports* of the F.B.I. do not have a category for "unnatural offenses.") No one knows whether the homosexual population is also increasing. As with hanging, no one knows whether relaxation in the law will be followed by a higher rate of offenses because of the greater tolerance. It is just one more unknown in a subject steeped in unknowns.

Finally, homosexuality is not intersexuality. In the chapter on inheritance the various types of intersex are mentioned, such as the male hermaphrodites, the pseudomales, and the female pseudohermaphrodites. These physical intersexes, or between-sexes, may be due to abnormal chromosomes or abnormal glandular development; but there is no simple relationship between them and abnormalities of human sexual behavior. A homosexual cannot be seen to be a homosexual merely

* *Report of the Committee on Homosexual Offences and Prostitution,* 1957.
† Other names once listed by *Time* magazine were fairy, nola, pix, flit, fag, faggot, agfay, fruit, nance, pansy, queen, she-male, mary.

from his chromosomes. Physically, he or she is usually a typical specimen of his or her sex; it is only the behavior that is abnormal.

Castration

The word "eunuch" comes from two Greek words meaning to guard the bed. It was to frustrate any sexual intentions on their part that so many men suffered this indignity. Nevertheless, such intentions may not be halted if the operation is done too late. One suspects that many a eunuch, castrated after puberty, had quite a merry time in the harem because neither desire nor performance need be diminished by the total lack of sperm. If the testicles are cut off before puberty, the boy is never affected by all the changes of puberty. His voice does not break. No hair grows in the masculine places, such as the face and the chest. His pubic hair grows in a feminine fashion. His body acquires fatty deposits like a girl's, and his muscles are weak. He may grow very tall, although this seems to depend upon the growth spurt and the precise time of castration. His skin will always be pallid. Despite all this, despite the absence of the hormone testosterone, which is produced in the testicles, claims have been made that some early castrates have been able to produce erections, some even to copulate. They are the exceptions. Most prepubertal castrations are not followed by any form of sexual competence.

The story is different with adult castrates. Their voices have broken. They are already the shape of a man. They know about sexual desire. Their penis, assuming this part is retained, is of a normal size. And many of them, with a total lack of testicles and of sperm and with a withering of various sexual accessories like the prostate and the seminal vesicles, will maintain normal desire and potency for decades after the operation. Their sexual activity will be satisfactory, and ejaculations of a sort will be possible. Other men, influenced perhaps by an assumption that castration is followed inevitably by a cessation of previous sexual activity, do find that desire and capacity both wane fairly rapidly. A third group claims desire but an inability to satisfy it. Castration can, reasonably enough, be a psychological trauma, producing various consequences in its wake, but its direct physical manifestations are very slight, save the overriding effect upon reproduction.

The Chinese and various other Eastern groups were not generally content to give their eunuchs any chance of sexual potency. They performed a total removal of the genitals with a hallowed operation involving one deft stroke of a sickle-shaped knife. The urethra, the tube leading from the bladder, was then plugged. The wound was bandaged, the victim ate nothing, and the pewter plug was removed after three days. A city called Ho-chien-fu, near Tientsin, had the honor of producing most of the eunuchs for the imperial court, and the practice has not been confined to days of old. Even in this century, a European physician in Hong Kong was introduced to "an irascible Chinese gentleman from the north." He proved to have no external genitalia, and his urethra was found with difficulty in a great mass of scar tissue. He admitted the operation had been performed on him at the age of 12, and his home had been "near Tientsin."

Eunuchs, one might have thought, would have been ideal not just as harem guards, but in those professions that demand the absence of sexual activity, such as the Roman Catholic Church. In fact, they are banned from ordination. The Law of Moses stated that eunuchs could not enter into the sanctuary, and Leviticus even considered that castrated animals should not be permitted as sacrifices. The Greek Orthodox Church (and I am indebted to Dr. Charles W. Lloyd's book on human reproduction for this account) did not accept this discrimination against eunuchs, but the Roman Catholic Church, according to legend, felt that anyone elected pope should prove that his genitalia were intact. A special chair was fashioned, an example of which is in the Louvre, that had a horseshoe-shaped seat, much like the old birthstool, upon which the pope would allegedly sit. The cardinals would pass by, checking the papal possession and proclaiming, *"Testiculos habet et bene pendentes."* I failed to learn when this particular adjunct to the initiation ceremony was dropped. Or even whether the tale is strictly accurate. If it is true, how on earth did Pope Joan get elected? Or is she totally apocryphal?

Circumcision

Any mother wishing her child to retain his prepuce "would be well advised to maintain permanent guard over it until such time as they both leave the hospital." So said Dr. W. K. C. Morgan in 1965. This British physician practicing in the United States was expressing concern at the "rape of the phallus," the habit of circumcising newborn males with routine indifference. He has a hard task ahead of him if he intends altering the present attitude toward circumcision. It is as old as the hills (Egyptian male mummies were all circumcised). It is supported by religions (with the Bible and the Koran constantly haranguing the uncircumcised). It is practiced in innumerable societies (where there are puberty rituals or merely traditional mutilation). It is advocated by large segments of the medical profession (who refer to greater hygiene, less cancer of the penis for circumcised men, and less cancer of the

cervix for their wives). It is promoted actively and doggedly by many
women, who have no valid reasons for their prejudice, save conformity,
tradition, and, some say, a desire to influence masculine characteristics.
It is also a remunerative procedure for many of those who carry out the
operation. Any crusader fighting so formidable a battery of opinion,
prejudice, and custom is going to have a very long crusade.

He will also find the enemy very determined. Considering the insignificant size of the newborn foreskin and considering its relative
unimportance, the arguments for and against its retention generate
great heat. In Britain, the operation is less frequent than it was between
the wars. It is hard to find out the actual incidence, but I suspect fewer
than half the modern crop of babies suffer this age-old mutilation. In
the United States, it is being carried out as fervently as ever, often two
to three days after birth. In Britain, when it is done, it is usually done
a little later. With Jews it is virtually as important as it has always
been. In Britain many parents find their request for a baby's circumcision bluntly refused by hospitals. In the United States, says Dr.
Morgan, most hospitals have an insatiable urge to remove it.

In Britain it is often held to be an archaic procedure, and Sir James
Spence in 1950 proclaimed this view in a delicious letter to a colleague.
"If you can show good reason why a ritual designed to ease the penalties
of concupiscence amongst the sand and flies of the Syrian deserts should
be continued in this England of clean bed linen and lesser opportunity,
I shall listen to your argument; but if you base your argument upon
anatomical faults, then I must refute it. The anatomists have never
studied the form and evolution of the preputial orifice. They do not
understand that Nature does not intend it to be stretched and retracted
in the Temples of the Welfare Centres, or ritually removed. . . ." On
the other hand, and on the other side of the Atlantic, to quote from
a representative textbook, it has been "almost universally recognized
that circumcision is a valuable procedure." Someone must be right.
Or at least more right than the others.

There are facts; but there is also disagreement about their interpretation and difficulty about their acquisition. One major problem associated
with questionnaires is that a wife is often confused about her husband's
penis, and the husband, too, is often at fault. In a survey, in Buffalo,
New York, one-third of the men who said they had been circumcised
were wrong, and one-third who said they had not were equally wrong.
The women were even more inaccurate. A fact generally agreed upon
is that cancer of the penis is virtually eliminated by circumcision. This
cancer is common in many primitive countries but not in the United
States or Britain. There were 259 deaths attributed to it in the United

States in 1964. England and Wales have 300 to 400 cases a year. To counter this long-term reason for circumcision are various other reasons, mainly short-term, such as the pain it presumably causes the child, the ulcers more likely to occur on the circumcised, the increased risk of infection—some hospitals have banned the operation on this account alone—and the possibility of death. Dr. Morgan cites 15 deaths in Britain a year as attributable to circumcision (although this was based upon a statement in 1949).

Another fact is that nuns (never) and Jewish women (hardly ever) get cancer of the cervix. Admittedly, nuns are different from other women in the community in many ways—no intercourse, no contraceptives, no children—but Jewish women are generally similar to others save that most of them are married to circumcised men. Another difference is that Jews are supposed to follow the Niddah ritual, or abstention from intercourse for a week or more after menstruation begins, but some Jewish groups are very lax about this. Also the Jewish freedom from cervical cancer varies geographically; North African Jews are not so free.

Does the foreskin, and in particular the smegma, the glandular secretion that collects under it, help to cause either cancer of the penis or cancer of the female cervix? No one knows, but many want to know, particularly as cancer of the cervix kills about 5,000 women in England and Wales every year, and killed 8,111 in the United States in 1964. Why should most Jewish women, notably those from central and eastern Europe, evade it so successfully? Is it that Jewish standards of hygiene are higher? There are bacteria that live on smegma. Perhaps they, less rife in cleaner people, carry the carcinogen that does the harm? Existing evidence suggests that a clean foreskin is no more harmful than no foreskin. At present, according to an editorial in the *British Medical Journal,* "There is no case for recommending circumcision rather than hygienic measures to adults as a means of preventing cervical cancer." The same article was more in favor of circumcision for babies "when advice on hygiene is unlikely to be followed."

A further argument frequently cited—one suspects mainly by women —for removing the foreskin is that the tip of the penis lying beneath it, the highly sensitive part called the glans penis, becomes less sensitive when exposed to the daily abrasion of clothing. Hence, and there is some support for this argument, the circumcised male can take longer to reach his orgasm, thereby being more likely to coincide with his slower partner.* Sometimes, but rarely, there is a straightforward call for

* Although *Human Sexual Response,* by William H. Masters and Virginia E. Johnson, reports no difference in glans sensitivity between circumcised and uncircumcised males.

circumcision. Phimosis, for example, is a condition that can affect infants and is caused by the foreskin's blocking the flow of urine. Balanitis, an inflammation beneath the foreskin, can occur at any time. Nevertheless, when compared with the daily slaughter of foreskins, such complaints are extremely rare.

❦ 6 ❧

The Female

Reproductive Anatomy · Estrus · Ovulation · Menstruation ·
Sex Determination and Virgin Birth ·
Menopause and the Change · Circumcision

The male's reproductive function is to manufacture sperm and then transfer them to the female. The female's function is to receive the sperm, produce the egg, provide protection and nourishment for the developing form, and then expel it from her body. There is some economical duplication of function: the vagina acts both as a receptacle for the sperm, then as the birth canal for the offspring 266 days later. Uneconomically, there are two ovaries and two Fallopian tubes, when one of each would do. The human female has an undeniably more complex reproductive role to play than the male, but her basic reproductive anatomy is no more complex than his.

Reproductive Anatomy

Equivalent to the male testes are the female ovaries. They are slightly smaller than the testes when both are fully grown, and they lie internally roughly three inches on either side of the midway point between vagina and navel. This human similarity in the size of the testis and ovary is odd, bearing in mind their totally different approach to the identical task of producing germ cells for the next generation. The male testis does not really begin its manufacturing abilities until puberty; thenceforth, sperm are produced in their millions. The female ovary has all its eggs at birth—a dozen or so years before puberty. Moreover, by the time puberty is reached, there are far fewer than there were at birth. Women live on their capital, while men start with nothing and then produce in abundance. It is generally reckoned that a newborn female has 200,000 to 400,000 ova in her ovaries but, by puberty, the number

[65]

has shrunk to about 10,000. Of that smaller figure, only about 400 will actually be shed as mature eggs from the ovaries. Only one in a thousand of the original supply (or fewer if the woman has a lot of babies) will have a chance of being fertilized. A normal man manufactures far more sperm every second than a woman produces mature eggs in her lifetime.

Basically, the female reproductive anatomy is in the form of the letter "Y." At the extremities of the two top arms are the ovaries. Leading from them, and forming the two arms of the Y, are the Fallopian tubes. They are sometimes called the oviducts or uterine tubes or ovarian tubes, and they are very thin. They are able to be so thin because the egg that will pass along them is a speck 1/10 mm. across and just about visible to the human eye. Where these two tubes join at the center of the Y is the uterus. Traditionally called pear-shaped, and roughly pear-sized, this muscular lump of tissue will house and nourish any future baby, swell enormously, and then expel the child. Unlike a pear it lies with the stalk pointing downward. This thinner end of the pear is the cervix, the neck of the womb. It virtually seals off the diminutive cavity of the uterus, but it changes its shape dramatically and effectively in the last hours before birth. After the cervix, and forming the bottom leg of the Y, is the muscular tube of the vagina, the connecting link with the outside world, the receiver of sperm, the exit passage for the baby.

The symmetrical arrangement of two ovaries leading to a united or single vagina is the rule, but just occasionally there have been cases of total symmetry, i.e., two ovaries leading through two uteri to two vaginae. With such a system two quite different pregnancies have been known to occur, each with different conception times and different delivery dates. The basic simplicity of the female anatomy is paralleled by that of the male, but, unlike the male system, which is consistent throughout its postpubertal life, the female system has its cycles. Quite apart from the cyclical program of a baby's gestation, there is the cycle of egg production, the cycle of menstruation, and the finality of the menopause.

Estrus

As processes, these need independent elaboration. Before that, and in order to emphasize some of the peculiarities, a look at the systems of animals is germane. After all, to criticize it bluntly, the human system allows successful matings only for a couple of days a month, there is no coordinated mechanism causing more frequent copulations at this time, there is no general indication of ovulation, there is all the unpleasantness of the time both before and during menstruation, and the whole system packs up long before the woman herself is likely to die.

Most mammals, unlike humans and various other primates, follow the ritual of the estrous cycle. (Estrus is the noun, estrous the adjective.) It is characterized by a time when the female is in heat, when she most attracts the male, and when she will mate with him. It is also characteristically coordinated with ovulation—the production of an egg or eggs. Sometimes the egg appears spontaneously, as in rats, mice, and whales, but sometimes the very act of mating, as in rabbits, cats, mink, and ferrets, causes ovulation. The cat needs three matings for ovulation to occur, and the egg is produced 26 hours later. Spontaneous ovulation, not dependent on coitus, is the more common process. The sexual attraction that goes with it and assists in the coordinated arrival of sperm and egg is usually followed by a period of repulsion, when the female will have nothing to do with any male, and the males are not attracted by the nonestrous females.

Since the majority of animals are sexually ruled by the behavior of the estrous cycle, it is usually the female who calls the tune; either she welcomes mating or she does not, and her consorts just take the opportunity when it is there. In a few species, the males also have seasons of their own, known as the rutting season; the males are not sexually inclined until they are rutting. Camels, elephants, and deer are examples.

Some creatures carry their sexual seasons still further. In the mole and spotted hyena, for example, the vagina closes up at the end of each cycle. Hence the old countryman's idea that female moles can be found only in the spring and that African notion that hyenas are hermaphrodite. Neat coordination of ovulation with mating can go wrong; for instance, rabbits, cats, cows, and horses can be in heat during pregnancy. Subsequent matings are, of course, useless, as the uterus is already occupied, but in the hare it can lead to what is called superfetation. With this animal it is a regular occurrence. Matings can successfully occur three days before delivery of the gestating litter. This means, for the wild hare, that litters can be born every 39 days even though the actual gestation period is 42 days. Rats and mice, although producing litters very rapidly, cannot quite emulate the hare's ability to jump the gun. However, they do achieve estrus within 24 hours of the birth, and if mating then follows, it cannot be said that much time has been wasted.

For a long period, it was thought that no difference existed between a woman's menstruation and the ovulation of animals in estrus. After all, a bitch, say, loses blood when in estrus, and so does a menstruating woman every month. In fact, the two things are quite distinct because ovulation occurs *between* menstruations and not at menstruation. This particular manifestation, so different from the traditional estrous cycle, occurs in apes, monkeys, and a few shrews, as well as in humans. By the time human or monkey menstruation occurs and when the uterus is shedding its prepared surface, the ovulated egg has long since died and withered away. Estrus and ovulation go together: menstruation and ovulation do not. As menstruation occurs in the higher mammals and is certainly a development subsequent to the estrous pattern, the method presumably has advantages, even though they are not strikingly apparent.

The menopause, or complete cessation of female reproductive ability, appears to be confined solely to womankind. It is true that animals in the wild have little chance to live to a ripe and infertile old age and that animals in zoos are not truly representative of their kind, but study of both shows that there is no stage in the animal world comparable to the human menopause. Animals definitely do breed less as they get older, but there is no climacteric similar to that of the human female. Rather, as with men, their powers gently lessen as they grow more senile.

As a system, the human reproductive method could plainly be improved. A compensation is that, as intercourse is so casually geared to fertilization, there is much more desire and opportunity for it than with animals whose estrous cycles forbid, prevent, or discourage any sexual behavior for large portions of every year.

Ovulation

The production of one egg occurs in one ovary at a time, apparently from each ovary at random. The female egg is produced in a much more complex fashion than any sperm. For one thing, it has lain dormant since before birth, and therefore is probably 20, possibly 40 years old before its sudden awakening. Although one egg is shed regularly some two weeks after the start of menstruation, the mechanism of its shedding has started a few weeks before that menstruation. During this procedure, the chosen egg is surrounded by a swelling bundle of cells. Known as a Graafian follicle, this bundle slowly enlarges within the ovary. Containing just one egg, the follicle is almost ½ in. in diameter 14 days after the start of the menstrual period.

Usually, just one follicle from one ovary is ready then, but two may have developed. When this has happened, there is a possibility of two-egg—or dissimilar—twins being initiated. Their two eggs may have come from one ovary or one from each; it is also a random procedure. Anyway, whether two follicles are ripe, or merely one, they move to the edge of the ovary. Then, because of the increasing pressures within them, they burst and the eggs are liberated. This is ovulation. It takes place usually 13 to 17 days after the start of the menstrual period. It can create slight pain, called *mittelschmerz,* and this pain has been the cause of many an appendix operation when doctors, not realizing the monthly regularity of its appearance, have confused it with appendicitis. Ovulation is associated with a change in temperature, and the precise time of ovulation can thus be assessed, but most women remain quite unaware that one follicle 10 mm. in diameter has ruptured and has freed its solitary egg.

The egg itself, having waited so long within the ovary for its crucial hour, suddenly has very few hours to live, probably no more than 48, possibly no more than 24. The preceding period of inactivity could well have been 24 *years* or even 48 *years,* but suddenly the length of time when it is ripe for fertilization is extremely brief. If an encounter with sperm does not occur, the egg will become infertile and deteriorate. By then it will have passed along the few inches of Fallopian tube and will have reached the small cavity within the uterus. From there, at the next menstrual flow, the unused and aged egg will be flushed out of the system.

The follicle that produced the egg has a greater role to play than the mere production of that egg. It secretes hormones, initially estrogen, then progesterone. The chemistry is complex, but the tasks of the hormones are basically straightforward. Estrogen, which comes from the ovary itself, gives rise to estrous behavior and prepares the vagina for mating. Progesterone supports the changes going on in the uterus—all the hopefully receptive preparations for the embedding of a fertilized egg. Each disrupted follicle is thus continuing to care for its solitary egg after that egg has escaped.

The care persists—assuming no fertilization and no pregnancy—for 12 to 14 days. Known by then as the corpus luteum, the follicle has grown further in size and has poured out its hormones; then it stops doing so. The uterus, suddenly deprived of the vital chemicals for its preparatory changes, suffers menstruation. And the follicle, without any further need for its activities, suffers degeneration. However, should there be fertilization and should there be a successful implantation of the developing egg, the follicle will then continue to produce hormones. The uterus and its prepared receptive layer have to be suitably maintained, and progesterone has to be manufactured to maintain that suitability. So the follicle grows, and the large yellow object it has become remains vital to the continuance of the pregnancy. Eventually, when the placenta has grown and is itself producing hormones for its own maintenance, including progesterone, the old follicle will degenerate. This happens about halfway through pregnancy. By then the carefully nurtured egg, cared for, cast out, and then more distantly supported, is a fetus of sizable proportions.

Menstruation

These days, in societies where pregnancy is an exceptional event rather than the inevitable rule, most follicles do not have pregnancies to care for. More frequently, they degenerate and trigger off menstruation. They do not cause it so much as they suddenly fail to prevent it. Whether this is a tautology or not, menstruation is undoubtedly a bizarre phenomenon. Some have called it a paradox and a puzzle, a seemingly useless procedure, inexplicable, wasteful, and disturbing.

The menstrual cycle begins at puberty. The outward manifestation of blood flow takes many girls completely by surprise. Some surveys indicate that about one-third of the women in Britain have received no premenstrual counseling, and the appearance of the blood is the first they learn about the menstrual cycle.

The flow is symptomatic of the end of the cycle, not the beginning. Days earlier, the menstrual cycle had started on its monthly course. The innermost layer of the uterus is called the endometrium, and initially it is very thin—about a millimeter. Then it thickens. Within its substance various glands and arteries also lengthen and enlarge, and by the time of ovulation, normally some eight days after the earlier menstrual bleeding has stopped, the endometrium is about 3 mm. thick. For girls having their first menstruation, this preliminary process is likely to take longer than normal.

Whether for the first or any subsequent menstruation, the glands within the endometrium, which secrete a mucus, become straight and tubular. During the next 14 days, these glands become more convoluted, more like concertinas than tubes. The endometrium containing them continues to thicken, and soon reaches 5 mm. (1/2 cm., 1/5 in.). Roughly midway through these 14 days any fertilized egg will have been implanted. It takes about a week after ovulation before implantation occurs. The egg will both have implanted itself and will also have been implanted by the uterus, for the process is mutual; both developing egg and welcoming uterus assist in the embedding. Should no implantation occur, there will be menstruation. The bloody disruption is the product of a frustrated womb, which has not experienced implantation that month. The menses are the outward sign of the internal changes.

With the sudden stopping of the flow of progesterone, cut off by a finally disillusioned follicle, the uterine preparations abruptly end. The top section of the endometrium is shed; the 4 mm. carefully built up in the preceding three weeks are discarded. Not all of this layer is shed at once, but patches here and there. It is not really known what causes the shedding; perhaps blood to the area is cut off temporarily, causing the endometrial cells to die, and is then made to flow again, causing some of the blood loss but coming too late to reprieve the dying endometrium. In any case, four to five days after the start of the shedding, all the carefully prepared layer has been affected. Together with blood and a lot of mucus, the discarded endometrium is exuded, first from the uterus, then from the vagina. The average blood loss in each period is 40 milliliters, or less than 1/10 pt., but it may be five times as much, or a fifth as much. The range of variation in this and other aspects of menstruation is considerable.

No woman is absolutely regular. The "monthly" period may have a normal cycle of between 19 days and 37, although 28 days is an average interval. Usually, the more average the length of the period, the more fertile the woman. The irregular lengths of time are generally between ovulation and the preceding menstruation; there is far greater constancy between ovulation and the succeeding menstrual bleeding. When the cycle is finally over, the endometrium starts to grow again. And once again, assuming no pregnancy, it will be shed only to start to grow all over again. Dr. George Corner, of Princeton, has called menstruation "an unexplained turmoil in the otherwise serenely coordinated process of uterine function, a puzzling paradox whereby a normal function regularly displays itself by the destruction of tissues." For the average woman, the paradox will irritatingly happen about 440 times in her lifetime, if she has no children, and about a dozen times fewer for each child. Its regularity will end finally with menopause. But before that, she will have learned that there is more to menstruation than those merely physical changes regularly taking place within her uterus.

Premenstrual syndrome, cyclical syndrome, and premenstrual tension are names given to the host of complaints experienced by many women (some say 75 percent) in the few days before menstruation begins. These include headaches, irritability, tiredness, nausea, and aching joints. A survey at a women's prison in London completed shortly after World War II showed that "93 percent of female crime was committed during the premenstrual phase." Other surveys have shown that well over half of accidents in the home occur in the premenstrual week and that women driving cars at this time are more likely to be involved in road accidents. Millions of working days are lost from the premenstrual cause.

Physiologically, the main general difference occurring is water retention, often by as much as 6 to 7 lb. (or three-quarters of a gallon). This is caused by progesterone. The edema, or liquid swelling, may be too diffuse to be noticed, or it may manifest itself in the face, the ankles, the breasts, or the abdomen. Perhaps the edema directly affects the brain, which would help to explain many of the symptoms. Oddly, women who suffer premenstrual tension seem to have little or no pain during the menstrual flow, and conversely, women who suffer a painful flow—dysmenorrhea—rarely suffer premenstrual tension. There is a rough justice in the arrangement.

The retention of water is taken many stages further by those animals that possess sexual skin. Although not a feature of human beings, such skin is part of many nonhuman primates, of which the mandrill, with its blatant coloring, is a good example. Some monkeys have their sexual skin around the vulva, some around the anus, some on the face. It starts to swell with the start of each cycle and reaches a peak of size and coloration at ovulation. In fact, the sexual skin may by then be so swollen that it incorporates one-sixth of the animal's total body weight. After ovulation the balloon collapses, the water is suddenly lost through the urine, and the color recedes. The cycle will then begin all over again. As a digression, one can speculate upon the possible changes in human behavior if the human female had been endowed with a similarly blatant demonstration of her fertile hour.

The other important change during the menstrual cycle is temperature. It provides guidance to the timing of ovulation. In the days preceding ovulation, when the uterus has once again started on the task of preparing the endometrial layer, a woman's temperature remains reasonably constant, but tends to get slightly lower as ovulation day approaches. Then, roughly 14 days after the preceding menstrual bleeding began, there is an abrupt but brief drop of .2°F. to .4°F. below the normal temperature. This is considered to indicate the crucial hour, the bursting of the follicle and the liberation of the long-imprisoned egg. To make slightly more of a landmark in the temperature chart, this small and brief depression is followed by a larger and longer rise, the so-called "thermal shift." Temperatures vary from woman to woman, but a typical temperature pattern may start at 98°F., fall slowly to 97.8°F. in the early days of the cycle, fall abruptly to 97.6°F. at ovulation, rise to 98.5°F., and stay in that vicinity until a day or so before the next menstrual flow. It will then fall to about 98°F. again. Should it not fall at the next menstrual flow, this can be an indication of a successful pregnancy.

Apart from indicating ovulation, and when couples urgently desiring a child should best have intercourse, a woman's temperature chart can also indicate either normality or abnormality. Faulty ovulation, faulty progesterone quantities, and other defects can be inferred from a faulty temperature rhythm. There should, on average, be a difference of .9°F. to 1.3°F. between the highest and the lowest temperatures of the cycle. The best day to have intercourse for those couples who want a baby is the day of the thermal shift; some 50 percent of conceptions are thought to occur on that day. The remaining 50 percent occur either slightly before or slightly after that vital time.

Sex Determination and Virgin Birth

Brief reference has to be made to two of the oldest of old wives' tales.

There are two ovaries, and offspring are of two sexes. Hence, it was almost inevitable that a theory should arise connecting the two. Whether the right ovary produces boys and the left girls, or the other way around, varies from place to place, but neither tale has a whisper of validity. The male sperm are the sole arbiters of the offspring's sex. The female eggs, whether from left or right ovary, are identical. The only way a determined feminist could advocate a mother's influence over the sex of her offspring would be to produce a new theory. As only sperm can carry the essential maleness for boys, the new theory would have to suggest that the mother's egg or the Fallopian tubes were less eager, on occasion, to receive either the male-determining sperm or the female-determining sperm. Such a theory would find few backers. On the other hand, no one knows why far more boys are conceived. Is it because far more male-type sperm are produced? Or because male sperm are swifter? Or because the female-type sperm are tolerated less happily by the women they are invading? Although the sperm are the arbiters, women may have some influence in the matter after all.

The importance of sperm is also crucial to the possibilities of parthenogenesis, or virgin birth, the second of the oldest old wives' tales. The ability of an egg to divide on its own, and to produce a normal adult of either sex, without the initial assistance of the fertilizing sperm, is a common occurrence in many of the lower animals, but it is highly improbable, to say the least, that virgin birth should occur in the higher and highest animals. However, several claims have been made by womankind.

The onus upon such women is to prove the nonintervention of any male. Parthenogenetic eggs, which have started to develop by themselves, have been found in human ovaries, and it would be hard for anyone, male or female, to assert categorically that virgin birth is totally impossible, but what becomes particularly difficult to suggest, assuming that such a freak of nature as a virgin birth did happen, is that the offspring might be a male. Females possess two X chromosomes as their sex chromosomes. Males possess one X and one Y. This minute difference controls the sex of offspring. All normal women have 44 chromosomes in each cell plus two X chromosomes. All normal men have 44 chromosomes in each cell plus one X and one Y. The difference between a chromosome arrangement containing two X's and one containing one X and one Y is clearly visible under the microscope.

Each male is bound to receive his X from his mother, for she has nothing else to contribute, and his Y from his father. Had the father contributed an X instead, the offspring would have been XX—therefore a girl, and not a boy. As females are XX any sudden and unfertilized egg development must lead to an XX. The vital male chromosome cannot be conjured up from nowhere. Hence, virgin births, should they occur, would produce females solely. The most famous virgin birth of all time, Jesus, was awkwardly a male, but in this instance, bearing in mind the complex role of the Holy Ghost, it is plainly out of step for biologists to continue to assert the importance of such a thing as a Y chromosome. The manner of Jesus' birth must be a matter of belief, not of microscopy.

In November, 1955, London's *Sunday Pictorial* asked women who had reason to believe there had been no father for their child to come forward. It was stressed that the baby would have to be a girl who bore a striking resemblance to her mother in looks and gestures. Nineteen parthenogenetic claims were made to the newspaper, and these were sifted and investigated. Eleven of them were negated even in the preliminary interview because the mothers were under the impression that an intact hymen inevitably indicated a virgin birth. After further sifting, other reasons reduced the original nineteen to one. Mrs. E. Jones and her 11-year-old daughter, Monica, were then subjected to a still more critical examination.

Their blood, saliva, and tasting powers were all examined, and attempts were made to graft skin from each to the other. The results were that blood, saliva, and tasting powers were almost identical, but the grafts did not take. The panel of doctors who helped with the investigation made special mention of the fact that Mrs. Jones made her claim before she could have known about the tests to which she and her daughter were to be subjected and before she could have known of the results and extreme similarity of the blood groupings, etc. In June, 1956, the *Sunday Pictorial* stated that, after six months of investigation, the results were consistent with a case of virgin birth. Professor J. B. S. Haldane disagreed. He said the evidence led to the opposite conclusion —that the child in fact had a father. His wife, Dr. Helen Spurway, wrote —in the *Daily Worker*—that the mother's claim was disproved. Nevertheless, it was, I feel, a brave and interesting attempt by a mass-circulation newspaper to use its enormous readership in an attempt to solve a scientific riddle.

Menopause and the Change

At one end of a woman's reproductive life is puberty; at the other lies the menopause. One marks the beginning, the other the end. Known also as the "climacteric," after the Greek word for the rung of a ladder, it is an inevitable step in every woman's life, provided she reaches the requisite age. Just as the age of puberty is relentlessly becoming lower these days, the age for menopause becomes higher. Those who have examined the ancient literature on the subject believe that reproduction used to end at 40. By the middle of the last century, it was ending, on average, at 45. Now, certainly in most of Europe, the median age of menopause is 50. One recent report even gave an average of 52.

Therefore, in the last hundred years, with the age of puberty falling from 15½ to 13, and with the time of the menopause rising from 45 to 50, the reproductive span has stretched from three decades to nearly four. No one knows for sure why either end is stretching, but better food and better conditions are probably relevant. Although the age of 50 is the current average, this change of life can occur at 38 or 39 at the lower end of the scale and extend as far as 55, though rarely higher. Oddly, one of the best recent books solely dedicated to this subject, and published in 1956, is called *Women of Forty*. There is no relationship between the age puberty is reached and the age the menopause occurs; if a girl reaches puberty early, there is no greater likelihood of her reaching menopause early.

Although it emphatically changes a woman's reproductive ability, the menopause does not necessarily change either sexual ability or sexual appetite. For some, the impossibility of an accidental conception steps up enthusiasm. Similarly, for others, the change induces a last-fling feeling and an increased determination to enjoy sex while they can and while their mates are ready and willing to gratify them. Sometimes desire simply increases as a direct physical consequence of the menopausal changes. More often, there is a loss of libido, of lust, and the change is frequently an excuse to stop sexual relations that were never too happy. However, there is no reason, given satisfactory sexual compatibility, why the cessation of egg production should be accompanied by a cessation of coitus.

No woman can tell which menstrual period is going to be her last. Should she keep diligent record of her changing cycles, a gynecologist ought to be able to give her a good guess; but for most women the realization that the last menstrual bleeding of their lives has occurred will come only when no successor follows. Whether or not each last twitch from a dying reproductive system is the final effort is of less concern to the woman experiencing this change than is the cessation of the symptoms accompanying it.

Many of these are extremely unpleasant. They include hot flushes, headache, giddiness, obesity, nervous instability, itching, and insomnia. The flushes can range from a temporary blushlike manifestation to frequent and long-lasting effects often accompanied by excessive sweating. Whether drenched by day or soaked by night, the woman can be left cold, exhausted, and thoroughly fed up with the whole business. Coupled with the other symptoms and with various emotional feelings of inadequacy, unattractiveness, and depression, the menopause can be a dismal experience. Some people have harangued the researchers for doing so little to ease this inevitability, to make the change something less cataclysmic. There is much to their complaint. Common unromantic ailments do not make glamorous research.

Although there is so much on the debit side, there is also contrary evidence that the change is not generally severe. To counter those reports, which state that "75 percent of all women suffer distressing symptoms at the climacteric," there are others from equally reputable sources stating that "70 percent to 90 percent of women experience no symptoms materially interfering with general health or with domestic or social activities." Both quotations are taken from the *British Medical Journal,* and both may be accurate, although the general implication may be otherwise. It all depends, as C. E. M. Joad used to say, on what you mean by the words being used. Dr. M. E. Landau, who wrote *Women of Forty,* stated that "for most women menopausal discomforts are too trivial to demand the attention of a doctor, and can be dealt with by the patients." She also writes that if sexual response was good before the menopause, it will be as good after it, or better. There is general agreement that those least susceptible to menopausal troubles are the emotionally well-balanced women who are healthy, whose marriages are good, and whose families are entirely satisfactory.

The detectable physical changes may be sudden or gradual. Menstruation may stop without warning. Or it may continue regularly, but produce less and less. Or it may be irregular, but with an even flow. Or it may be regular, but with an uneven flow. In other words, the change rings all possible changes. Those women, usually plump, who go to hospital with a stomach ache and come out a week later with a brand-new, totally unsuspected, full-term baby have often been assuming that the nine-month-long cessation of menstruation, coupled

with the marked weight increase, has merely been another manifestation of the "change." The error can be made by women who have had
babies before. A more trivial error is to blame upon the menopause
events that are taking place independently of it, which are more a feature
of increasing years than decreasing ovulation.

The internal physical changes are primarily a gradual atrophy of
the reproductive organs. First on the list are the ovaries, each of which
becomes smaller. Their Graafian follicles, which earlier were the protective containers of solitary eggs, disappear, and the unused eggs disappear along with them. In their place, fibrous tissue is formed. No
longer are corpora lutea produced, and no longer do the ovaries manufacture their internal secretions. The hormones, created elsewhere,
which used to galvanize the ovaries into their regular cycles of activity,
are still being created by those other glands, but the ovaries no longer
respond. Their day is over. Similarly, the Fallopian tubes, no longer
having eggs to transport from ovary to uterus, become smaller and
shorter, and they lose their surface layer of epithelial cells. The uterus
itself, with no more childbearing ahead of it, also atrophies under the
influence of the menopausal changes. It hardens and shrinks, possibly to
one-quarter of its former size, and loses its original rounded shape.
The vagina also shortens slightly, narrows, and loses some of its
elasticity. The breasts lose some of their glandular contents and therefore wither, but such atrophy may be accompanied by a compensatory
deposit of fat. The urine becomes markedly different in its hormonal
content.

The internal changes are unlikely to be as vexing as outward and
visible signs. Certain male characteristics may manifest themselves,
especially beard growth, particularly at the mouth's corners. Many of the
troubles can be alleviated by the administration of hormones, and
the finality of menopause can be delayed and delayed if need be. The
old rhythm of menstruation can be artificially perpetuated, and many
thousands of American women are doing so, but hormones are more
frequently used in attempts to lessen some of the unpleasantness of
the change. Tranquilizers and sedatives are generally thought to be
preferable to hormone treatment. Although headaches are common at
this time, one benefit is that migraines are nearly always cured by the
menopause. An evil to offset this good is that menopausal women are
more prone to become diabetics. That such an association exists is
proved when a dose of estrogen is added to the necessary insulin, for
it promptly reduces the insulin requirements. Estrogen is the hormone
manufactured by the developing follicle. Without an active ovary, these
egg-bearing follicles do not develop, and neither does their estrogen.

The actual chemical relationship between estrogen and diabetes is both complex and unclear.

Some women get fatter at menopause. Once again, the causes are complicated and interrelated. Sometimes a woman just allows herself to get fatter by caring less about diet, but sometimes the decreasing estrogen, which is associated with a decrease in energy output, is not coupled with a decrease in food intake; the woman just eats what she has always eaten but gets fatter. The reduction in estrogen is also linked with a thinning of the skin, and with osteoporosis. The latter can occasionally be serious, with pain and general demineralization of the bones, but such long-term changes, although initiated by the menopause, are not what is normally thought of as part of the menopausal syndrome. It is the short-term manifestations, the flushing and so on, that are most typical.

Unfortunately, although short term, the menopause is no sudden matter. Women can have troublesome symptoms for several years or just for months or not at all. Those who are unlucky have a longer time to reflect upon this further blatant inadequacy of the human system. It seems so unnecessary, and it appears to be peculiar to the human species. It causes an upheaval, and it certainly has no equivalent in those animals that live long enough for their reproductive systems to wane.

And just to confuse the issue still further, there are cases on record of women who have conceived after an apparent menopause. Unlike the women who have confused a new pregnancy with the menopause, these women suffer an absence of menstruation and *then* become pregnant. No one knows precisely when ovulation ends for any woman. A generalization is that it has finally stopped within a year or two of the end of menstruation.

Circumcision

Many of the emotive words so closely allied with the reproductive system, such as castration, sterilization, and circumcision, are immediately allied in most minds with the male system. Yet females can be castrated (by removal of their ovaries), sterilized (by cutting the Fallopian tubes*), and circumcised. The extent of the operation varies from place to place. In Australia, for example, one aborigine group removes both the clitoris and the labia of its young girls at puberty; all the men subsequently have intercourse with the newly circumcised.

In northern Africa various other forms of mutilation have been, and

* Known as salpingectomy.

presumably still are on occasion, carried out. Apart from the excision of either clitoris or both labia, there is also infibulation. Basically this is the sewing up of the vulva in very young girls, leaving only a small hole for the passing of urine and for the effluent of menstruation. When the girl is married, the hole is enlarged, and is totally opened shortly before the birth of any child. After delivery, the infibulation is again performed. Besides being sewn together, the vulva can also be held together with special clasps or with thorns. Evidence that such operations are still performed was shown when a Sudanese woman was examined at an English hospital in 1962. She was then in the middle of a pregnancy, although her vagina was exceptionally small, totally preventing normal intercourse. The infibulation had been done in 1951 when she was 11, and somehow she became pregnant after her marriage eleven years later. The surgeons restored her vagina to normal, and the subsequent delivery of a boy was entirely satisfactory. The girl later admitted that, although the procedure was illegal, female mutilation was still the rule in certain high-class Muslim families.

Fertility

The Infertile Couple · Insemination · Age, Ardor, Mood ·
Hormone-stimulated Fertility · The Case of the
"Strange Males"

Give me children or else I die.
Rachel, Gen. 30:1

Only half of humanity is responsible for the next generation. The other
half plays no part in reproduction, and therefore fails to pass on any of
its genetic material. Members of this second, unreproductive half fail
either because they die too soon, or have chosen not to have children, or
because they have not been able to have children. In evolutionary terms
this half can be called genetically unfit. To have 50 percent of humanity
classified as "unfit" is considerable, but Professor L. S. Penrose, of London, has added up the various classes of unfitness to reach this total. Some
15 percent of humanity die even before birth, and therefore can play no
part in reproduction. These miscarriages, etc., have to be included, for
they are failed human beings just as much as a baby or child who has
died. Some 3 percent of humanity are stillborn, another 2 percent die
shortly after birth, and another 3 percent die before maturity. Of those
that reach maturity, 20 percent do not marry, and 10 percent marry but
remain childless. Reproductively speaking, 50 percent drop out of the
race in each generation. Only 25 percent of our grandparents' generation
were responsible for the current generation, and only 12 percent of our
great-grandparents' contemporaries. When Cain slew Abel and put him
out of the running, he was also inadvertently establishing the pattern
of 50 percent.

On the other hand, nothing like 50 percent in many other species are able to reproduce, to produce the next generation. One million fish eggs, laid and fertilized, may all start development, but only a couple of mature specimens may survive. Most bachelor seals, living in a harem-ridden world, will die before having the strength and cunning to possess a single wife, let alone a harem. And a 2-percent neonatal mortality rate—the human figure—must be uniquely low in the entire animal kingdom.

A further anomaly of mankind is the small number of offspring produced by each fertile male. A man is considered highly fertile if he produces ten babies in his lifetime. A male seal will produce triple that number in a year. A good bull, in these days of artificial insemination, can be made to serve 40 to 50 cows from each ejaculation, with a 60-percent success rate expected. Rams can serve 30 to 40 ewes from one ejaculation, stallions 8 to 12 mares, and boars 2 to 4 sows. A good human male could doubtless be made to serve comparable numbers of women, and even without artificial insemination he could, if society and custom permitted, be enormously more potent than he is. After all, to be an average father it is necessary only to fertilize an egg on two or three occasions, and in a lifetime of hundreds—or, more probably, thousands —of ejaculations.

The Infertile Couple

About one in six of all marriages is sterile. Despite a strong male belief to the contrary, it is just as frequently a deficiency in the husband that causes the sterility as in the wife. An inability to conceive after, say, two years of marriage does not necessarily indicate infertility. There is much that can be done for the infertile couple, and it has been found that only 35 percent of such couples are hopelessly sterile. Incapacities such as azoospermia (complete absence of sperm) make for such sterility. Other, more common male defects are oligospermia (low sperm content in a given volume of semen), asthenospermia (too few sperm capable of movement), and spermatic dysplasia (high proportion of abnormal sperm). By no means can males sit back and assume that the female, with the greater role she has to play, must be at fault.

Nonetheless, there are very many ways in which the female can fail. She may not have eggs to produce, or she may not be able to produce them because of a cyst on her ovaries. Her uterine tubes may be blocked, or her uterus may be diseased or absent. Her hymen may be intact. She may be rejecting the semen. Or she may be incapable of receiving her husband's penis. The last defect may be a combined one; as is a failure to practice intercourse at the right time or an overfrequent indulgence. Finally, by no means is every case of infertility understood.

Some women have an incompatibility with their husbands, but can be fertilized easily by others. In many cases, there should—by all the signs —be fertility, but there is not. Conversely, when couples have been considered infertile, the wife has suddenly become inexplicably pregnant, despite a defect and despite fidelity.

Much can be done for the infertile couple, both by advice and by surgery. The advice can be mainly concerned with instruction about body temperature and the way in which it suddenly rises at the time of ovulation, because conception can of course only occur when an egg exists to be fertilized. This time has to be known if it is going to be aimed for, whether naturally in normal intercourse or unnaturally in artificial insemination.

Insemination

If the husband is sterile or incapable of inseminating his wife or does not wish to—because of some hereditary defect—then AID (artificial insemination by a donor) can be the answer. (AIH, with the husband himself as the donor of the sperm, is much rarer.) The results of AID are good, with 30 percent of women conceiving in the first month, 18 percent in the second month, and 18 percent in the third, or 66 percent in three months. This may increase to 70 or 80 percent after six months. Insemination has to be done at the right time, paying due respect to the temperature shift. Dr. Walter Williams, an authority on this subject, is insistent on many points. For example, both husband and wife should give evidence of a harmonious marriage, they should be in complete agreement about the sperm donor's suitability, and the husband should actually assist in the operation. The donor, chosen from a description of 10 to 15 men by the couple, should give the sperm shortly before the operation. He should always remain anonymous, even to the couple. He should look like the husband, be of the same race and of unquestioned integrity, and be between 20 and 35 years old. He should neither be sexually promiscuous, nor indulge in excesses of any kind. His moral qualifications should be of the highest order, and he should be either a university student or a graduate. Medical students are frequent donors. Afterward, it is best if the woman is treated by a doctor who is unaware of the cause of her pregnancy and assumes the husband to be the true father.

No laws have been passed about AID. "It is highly improbable," says Dr. Williams, "that courts of law will be turned into an instrument to bastardise children born in wedlock to a legally married woman." The Roman Catholic Church, whose own laws make even an examination for infertility a more difficult procedure, by insisting that sperm are collected only from the vagina, is against AID. The practice is unnatural, says the church, and therefore to be condemned. Most Jews do not object, but orthodox Jews require rabbinical authority. Protestants do not object, holding that adultery always signifies extra-marital sexual relations, and although AID is undoubtedly unnatural, few can believe it to be adulterous.

As human sperm does not have to be delivered immediately from donor to recipient, and as it can now be kept in a frozen state at least for months, one wonders about the future morality of insemination. The University of Michigan has already reported the successful use of some human sperm after its storage for 2½ years. Will society be content to let go this one chance of "positive eugenics," of selective breeding? Will it initiate rules that the donors must be a master race? Would Americans today be happy to accept George Washington's sperm, were it available in the deep freeze, and make the first president the real father of his country? Whose sperm today should be frozen for posterity? Worse still —and Brave New World gets nearer—should imbecile sperm be kept to sire workers for the monotonous labors inevitable in any community until automation finally relieves us of these duties?

Age, Ardor, Mood

Even though males have no menopause or its equivalent and they retain their powers of fertility into their advanced years, an older man is not statistically an ideal father. Not only do fetuses from him die more frequently in the uterus, but more babies die at birth if conceived by aging fathers. It is widely believed, notably among males, that prowess and fertility go hand in hand. But excellence in prowess can lead to nothing in fertility, as the requisite number of sperm may not exist in each skilled but depleted ejaculation. With old people, whose produc-tion is tending to fall off anyway, a mimicking remembrance of youthful ardor can also decrease fertility quite unnecessarily and below the level for a successful conception. Such overtaxing of the system may be an explanation of the prompt manner in which many women conceive shortly after adopting a baby. The adoption may follow years of failure, followed abruptly by the arrival of two babies—one adopted, one conceived. There may previously have been a fervent amount of sexual activity, which was then relaxed, therefore permitting greater fertility.

On the other hand, when pregnancies are undesired with equal fervor, and when rape has taken place, they still happen. Emotion does not seem to play a powerful part. Nor, strangely, does chronic underfeeding. In those parts of the world of perpetual food shortage, conceptions are never in short supply. (Perhaps even noise is important. Professor Bernhard Zondek, of the famous Aschheim-Zondek pregnancy test, reported from Israel in 1966 that rats and rabbits copulated just as frequently in noisy surroundings, but their fertility was much impaired—until the noise ceased.)

Hormone-stimulated Fertility

Infertility is not normally associated with multiple births; but it has been recently. Quintuplets, sextuplets, and septuplets are blue-moon cases, all very rare and pounced upon by the world's press; but on Tuesday, July 27, 1965, a woman gave birth to quints in New Zealand. The press was delighted. Two days later quints were born in Sweden; the press was amazed. Earlier, Munich had been amazed when quints and sextuplets had been born within three weeks. Sweden had had an earlier encounter when septuplets had been born both in August, 1964, and February, 1965. Behind this spate of multiple births was a new technique for bringing fertility to certain infertile women. It was also plain that the technique had not been completely mastered.

This story begins in 1958, when Professor Carl-Axel Gemzell, now of Uppsala University, and his team reported that they had brought ovulation to several young women who had not been menstruating. The women's production of the correct hormones had been at fault. They were given extra FSH, the follicle-stimulating hormone produced by the pituitary gland, which ripens some of the cells in the ovary and stimulates them, to produce an egg or eggs. In 1966 Gemzell summarized the situation. Half of the one hundred infertile women chosen for the new procedure had become pregnant, and of those pregnancies half had been multiple—twins or more. Other researchers, such as Dr. Arthur Crooke, of Birmingham, were concurrently trying to make the dosage more accurate, in its quantity and timing, because the dividing line between no pregnancy and a multiple pregnancy was apparently slim. The quantity of pituitary extract had to be correct for each woman.

An added difficulty was obtaining a supply of pituitary extract. It is recovered either from mortuaries or the urine of older, postmenopausal women. Either the whole pituitary gland is taken from a dead woman, or the FSH substance is taken from the urine of women whose pituitaries are still producing it and who are past childbearing age. Nuns have been particularly helpful. Either ten whole glands from the dead or a month's supply of urine from the living is necessary for one course of ovulation treatment. Nevertheless, despite the supply and dosage difficulties and the awkward multiplicity of the offspring, the work opens up exciting possibilities for the help of an important type of infertility. Previously, and I quote from a textbook published only in 1962, it had been written, "There is, as yet, no known medical treatment to promote ovulation."

The Case of the "Strange Males"

About the strangest story of all in recent research into infertility is the case of the "strange males," as it was called. It has nothing to do with man, so far as is known. It has to do with mice, but there is just a possibility that it has a moral for humans. Dr. Hilda Bruce was working at the National Institute for Medical Research in London, when, by chance, she discovered the "strange male" phenomenon. Some normal female mice, which had been normally mated, were moved to a new cage. Such females, already pregnant, were expected to follow the traditional pattern of rejecting all further male advances. Generally, further acceptance comes only after the litter has been born. However, the traditional apple cart was upset. Within the new cages were new and strange males. Promptly the females all mated again. Their original pregnancies vanished, and their offspring were emphatically sired by the strange new males and not by their earlier mates. Dr. Bruce had therefore opened up an extra dimension to conceptions and had shown that smell was a crucial factor. The mice not only recognized one another by smell, but also were able to distinguish between one type of mouse and another. The more curious the smell of the newcomer, the less likely the female mouse was to maintain her original pregnancy.

The moral for humans? Well, so little is known about those first chancy days of pregnancy and what causes a developing embryo to implant itself firmly that women may be mimicking those female mice. No grass grows where many people walk, say the Scandinavians. Mate too soon afterward with a strange male, and the original short-lived pregnancy may quietly wither away. The hypothesis is highly unlikely, but the case of the "strange males" was also totally unexpected.

~ 8 ~

Contraception

Historical Ideas · The Birth Controllers · Religious
Opinion · Today's Situation · The Pill · IUD's ·
Sterilization

There was a young woman who lived in a shoe.
She had no children: she knew what to do.
Quoted in *The Malthusian*, September, 1906

Mary Mother, I believe, without sin thou dids't conceive.
Mary Mother, still believing, let me sin without conceiving.
attributed to Lord Byron

Mankind has had some idea of what to do about birth control for millennia. Yet, in its modern sense, it is less than a century old. The even more modern notion of having clinics to dispense information is less than half a century old, and the Church of England did not give any blessing to the limitation of parenthood until 1930. The story of the contraceptive pill did not begin until the 1950s, nor did the idea gain much acceptance until the 1960s. Therefore, despite a history stretching back to the world's first medical tracts, most of the progress in attitudes and techniques is recent.

Historical Ideas

Both the Petri (or Kahun) papyrus of 1850 B.C. (use crocodile's dung as a pessary, place honey in the vagina) and the Ebers papyrus of 1550 B.C. (sit astride a burner producing fumes of wax and charcoal) gave recommendations. Earlier, the Chinese had suggested the consumption of minerals, such as mercury and lead, to offset conception. Both ideas, taking pills with a metallic base and using materials with a multitude of effects (including spermicide and womb-contraction), were to last

[86]

for thousands of years. No one seemed short of ideas. Catch a wolf, kill it, boil its penis, and add some hair, wrote Albertus Magnus (1193–1280) in his *Book of Admirable Secrets.* Use pessaries of cabbage, colocynth pulp, pomegranate skin, ear wax, elephant's dung, and whitewash, wrote Rhazes of Baghdad in 882. (Plainly spermatozoa encountering such a chemical battery of conflicting properties cannot have benefited from their presence.) Use rock salt, said Ali Ibn Abbas in the tenth century. Use alum, said Avicenna a few years later.

The world's herbalists plucked apparently at random from the plant kingdom. On the list are rosemary, pea, yarrow, asparagus, barrenwort, ivy, marjoram, white poplar (all used somewhere in Europe), thistle (North America), green coconut (Pacific islands—there is a seeming inevitability about this particular choice), and pineapple (Malaya). According to B. E. Finch and Hugh Green in *Contraception Through the Ages,* it is extraordinary that no natural contraceptive was found in so many centuries of testing and tasting. The American Indians came nearest to success with the plant Lithospermum ruderale (the chemistry of the substance involved has not yet been worked out).

The world's folklore was naturally steeped in suggestions. Pliny the Elder (in the first century A.D.) cited instructions for dissecting a spider, mixing part of it with a deer's skin, and attaching all of this to a woman before sunrise. The complexities of such recipes presumably added to the trust in them. In Russia they collected menses (from menstruating women), cooked them, and then listened for the sound of weeping children to indicate sterility. In modern Egypt, in a less gruesome but more courageous practice, women have lain between railway lines, faceup to cure sterility, facedown to prevent pregnancy. The passing train is the effector.

Sperm have also met with physical barriers for centuries. Sponges, suitably soaked with honey or wine, were put into the vagina. Aetius of Amida recommended half a pomegranate. The Arabs of the year 1200 suggested using the right testicle of a wolf, partly because it would help to stop sperm if wrapped in oil-soaked wool and partly because such an insertion would lessen feminine desire. Distraction of this kind, particularly at the moment of coitus, was often held to be effective. The Chinese in 1100 B.C. recommended Kong Fou—for the girl. At the exact moment she should draw a deep breath and think of other things. Soranus said the woman should hold her breath, then get up quickly, squat, and sneeze. Avicenna felt that ejaculation should be followed by the woman's leaping backward seven times, sneezing all the while, if conception was not desired. Sheaths also have an ancient history, although much of the spur for their use was the fear of venereal disease rather than conception.

Some Romans used animal bladders, but the real inventor seems to have been Gabriello Fallopio, the sixteenth-century Italian whose name was given to the Fallopian tube or oviduct. His sheath was a modest thing of linen, fashioned to fit over only the tip of the penis.

The dominant mystery of the whole sheath saga is the origin of the name "condom." There is no mention of this word in Britain in the seventeenth century; then it suddenly blossoms all over the place in the first twenty years of the eighteenth century. Spelled first as condum, then condon, then conton and condom, the word has no known derivation. Suggestions are that it comes from the Persian *kemdu* (a kind of haggis of grain), or from the Gascony town of Condom, or from an English physician or colonel. Neither John Evelyn nor Samuel Pepys mentions such a man; neither do the medical or military lists. Perhaps, having made the invention and given his name to it, the man could no longer tolerate such a name with such a fame.

Giovanni Jacopo Casanova de Seingalt called them *redingotes d'Angleterre,* or English riding coats. Some time later, the English retaliated by calling them French letters. Casanova also favored a gold ball, two-thirds of an inch in diameter. Inserted into the vagina, it theoretically acted as a sperm barrier and was undoubtedly cheap after the initial capital outlay. Nevertheless he approved "of the overcoat that puts one's mind at rest." So did James Boswell, who makes frequent references to his "armour." And armor many considered it to be, effective but insensitive. The arrival of rubber in the nineteenth century meant that equal effectiveness could be achieved with far greater sensitivity. The current European giant in this fertile field is the London Rubber Company, which also owns Schmidt, Inc., of New York, coleader in the United States with the Youngs Rubber Company, also of New York. It started in 1916 in one room at the back of a tobacconist in Central London. By 1960 the company was producing more than 2.5 million sheaths a week.

The Birth Controllers

Other important pioneers in contraception include Walter John Rendell, Dr. Friedrich Adolph Wilde, Dr. Wilhelm Mensinga, and Dr. Ernst Gräfenberg. In 1880 Rendell opened a pharmacy in Clerkenwell for pessaries based on quinine; they were extremely successful. Dr. Wilde, of Germany, invented the rubber cap in the 1830s; but Dr. Mensinga, also of Germany, popularized it. The Mensinga diaphragm reached England via Holland, and en route became known as the Dutch cap. Dr. Gräfenberg was experimenting with "rings" in Berlin in the

1920s, and was thus bringing up to date various ancient ideas. These intrauterine devices, known today as IUD's have had a controversial history, but are gradually finding increasing favor. (For a fascinating account of the story of birth-control propaganda, its promoters and detractors, read *The Birth Controllers,* by Peter Fryer.) The battle really began in the first half of the nineteenth century. Francis Place (1771–1854) was the first propagandist and Richard Carlile (1790–1843) fought for the freedom to discuss and publicize all forms of opinion. Dr. Marie Stopes's birth-control clinic, the "first in the British Empire," was opened on March 17, 1921. Among its patrons were Arnold Bennett and Dame Clara Butt. Two years later, Margaret Sanger, America's pioneer in the birth-control movement, opened the Margaret Sanger Research Bureau in New York.

Quite apart from all physical aids to contraception, there is also coitus interruptus and the safe period. The former, mentioned in the story of Onan (Gen. 38), has undoubtedly been used by millions for millennia, despite its obvious dissatisfactions and its failure as a method among those whose desire, timing, and self-control do not match. It was only in 1930 that scientists in Austria and Japan (B. Kraus and D. Ogino) discovered almost simultaneously that a maternal egg was regularly released from an ovary 12 to 16 days before the start of menstruation. Ordinary mortals had known ages beforehand about the safe period, about rhythm, about the likeliness of contraception on certain days, but they had not known the precise reason for such timing. Soranus in the second century said coitus should not take place at certain times if children were undesired. The ancient Hebrews said that a woman was "unclean" for 14 days after the start of menstruation. Hence, the clean time came at a time of maximum chance for conception.

Religious Opinion

The present Roman Catholic attitude, which approves only the "safe period" method of contraception, really stems from 1931. In 1930, Pius XI's Encylical on Marriage stated that any frustration of the natural power to generate life was against God's law. The following year another encyclical added that married people were not acting against the order of nature if "they make use of their rights . . . even though no new life can thence arise on account of circumstances of time. . . ." The advisory council on Roman Catholic marriage gives the following tongue twister of a clarification about these circumstances of time: "First fertile day is found by subtracting nineteen from the number of days in the shortest recorded cycle, and the last fertile day is found by subtracting ten days from the longest cycle the woman has ever recorded. This formula gives at least ten possible fertile days in the middle of the menstrual cycle. And the greater the difference between the shortest and longest cycles, the greater the number of possible fertile days." Two main troubles with such a method are that many women (about one in four) are wildly erratic with their periods, and all women tend to be erratic for the first few periods after the birth of a baby.

Other religions have other ideas. Jews customarily forbid methods of contraception for males, although extreme orthodoxy forbids any form of contraception except abstinence, and extreme unorthodoxy tolerates any contraceptive behavior. Muslims, following a fatwa issued by the Grand Mufti in 1937, are allowed to take any measures by mutual consent to prevent conception. In India, according to Jawaharlal Nehru in 1960, there is no major organized group opposed to family planning. Orthodox Hinduism demands abstention on certain days. The Church of England was against the birth-control movement throughout its most difficult years and was supported by, for example, *The Sunday Express:* "John Wesley was an eighteenth child. Birth control would have deprived the world of Wesley." Many others with a similar view drew up long lists of the famous who had been born well down the family order and whose births would have been frustrated by family planning.

Today's Situation

Britain's Consumers Association has lately surveyed contraception. It interviewed 1,500 people married between 1930 and 1960. Main methods used were condom (reported by 49 percent); withdrawal, i.e., coitus interruptus (44 percent); safe period (16 percent); diaphragm (11 percent); suppositories (10 percent); douche (3 percent). Some people reported using more than one method; hence the total is more than 100 percent. Apart from withdrawal or the safe period, which are free, the cost of a year's contraception varies widely. Assuming a hundred uses annually, at the time of the survey the use of condoms can cost £7 a year—or much less, the use of a diaphragm plus a spermicide is about £2 a year, and a washable sheath is about 10s a year. The oral contraceptive, a recent development, is more expensive, about £7 to £9 a year. These prices may not seem unwarrantably high to the western world, but in rural India all prices are high, and hence there is much enthusiasm for the relatively negligible price of the modern intra-uterine devices. Even then, the few pennies are greatly added to by the need for reasonably expert insertion. It was Dr. S. Chandrasekhar, then professor of sociology at the University of California, who wrote in

1961, "Shocking as it may seem, in many rural areas the cost of having a baby would be cheaper than the price of birth control equipment." This single statement hammers home the overpopulation problem with one quick and resounding stroke.

The Consumers Association report was published in 1963. It concluded that no brand tested was, if used alone, a certain way of preventing conception. Earlier, Dr. A. S. Parkes, President of the British Institute of Biology, had said, "Contraceptive methods are so crude as to disgrace science in this age of spectacular technical achievement." Perhaps the 1960s will be known as the age when contraception no longer disgraced it. Three lines of attack made remarkable strides in the first half of this decade. They were the pills, the loops (or other shapes), and surgical sterility.

Nevertheless, even in the 1960s, some of the old reaction against birth control still festered in various guises. Even in 1965, only one British medical school compelled students, during their six-year course, to attend a Family Planning Association clinic for instruction. In France, birth-control propaganda is now permitted, but sale of birth-control devices is still restricted (and yet it has been estimated in France that 50 percent of all pregnancies end in abortion). In late 1961, a birth-control clinic in New Haven, Connecticut, was forced to close down after only nine days, and it took almost four years for the order to be rescinded. United States tobacconists and gas stations still sell more contraceptives than chemists, and in 1965 28 states still had laws on their books limiting contraceptive advertisements or sales outlets or the spread of information. The unmarried girl in Britain still finds it extremely difficult to get contraceptive advice. The old battle for more knowledge about contraception, first called birth control in 1914,* later called family planning, is not yet over. A few more skirmishes are yet to come, but the pill, the loop, and surgery have all made significant and independent advances. Science is at last leaping ahead from the regime of English overcoats, American tips, and Dutch caps. It is about time.

The Pill

The advance of the pill has been extremely rapid. In 1955 Dr. Gregory Pincus, an American research director, spoke at the Fifth International Conference on Planned Parenthood in Tokyo. His subject was the inhibition of ovulation in women who had taken progesterone or norethynodrel. Ten years later, his few female volunteers had been replaced by 10 million women.

* A phrase coined by Margaret Sanger, who died in 1966 at the age of 82.

An important step in making the transition from the few to the 10 million was the intensive trial undertaken in Puerto Rico in 1957. By 1962, according to the Family Planning Association's clinics, 3,536 women in Britain were taking the pill; by 1963 it was 13,760 and 44,000 by 1964. By 1966, the estimates were 800,000 in Britain, over 5 million in the United States, and 2 million in the rest of the world. Barriers against the pill are coming down all the time.

The pill, which should strictly be called a tablet, had become big business. By 1966 there were 15 different types on the British market. In the United States, where an even higher proportion of women take an oral contraceptive, the advertisers have been busy pushing their new products. "Simple setting, built-in 'memory' recording, push-button ease, crush-proof tablet protection, safety from small children, plus the look and feel of a fashionable compact . . . this is what she will like about it." Long, delicate feminine hands, plainly ready for bed, stroke the latest offer. "It costs no more . . . offers much more." In the June 18, 1965, issue of *Medical World News* there were 70 pages of advertisement, of which 13 were for oral contraceptives only. The remaining 57 covered everything else. Considering the number of other pills and products on the medical market, such concentration upon the new idea is phenomenal.

Inevitably, there were doubts about the pill. Dr. John Rock, the American Roman Catholic whose name is linked with that of Dr. Pincus as developer, was recently scornful of these wrongful notions. The right pills taken in the right way, he stressed, *do* prevent ovulation (it had been said that they did not always do so). In *no way,* he said, do they act as an abortifacient (it had been said that they cause an abortion if started when an unknown pregnancy already existed). They in *no way* act as a condom by preventing sperm from entering the womb (some had argued that they were sperm killers, not ova preventers). There is *no* relationship, he continued, except perhaps a favorable one, between the pills and cancer of the female organs (fear of a cancerous side effect had initially been strong). *No* association has been found with thrombosis (a few women taking the pill had died of thrombosis, but not in greater numbers than is normal for their age group). The pills *can* bring out symptoms and side effects similar to those encountered in pregnancy. The pills are *not* dangerous. They do *not* postpone the menopause. Dr. Rock was most emphatic. So too was the special committee set up by the Food and Drug Administration. In August, 1966, it reported finding "no adequate scientific data, at this time, proving these compounds unsafe for human use." Like similar reports from Britain and the World Health Organization the report warned there was no proof they were safe even though there was no proof they were unsafe.

During a recent B.B.C. broadcast, Dr. Gordon Wolstenholme, director of the Ciba Foundation in London, said, "I consider that Dr. Pincus's pill was one of the most risky and foolhardy measures ever to be put into general use, particularly against an undeveloped people such as the Puerto Ricans. The fact that it has come off is quite remarkable." On a later occasion, he amplified this point. "It was a bigger risk among the Puerto Ricans, not so much because they could not appreciate the risks as because if anything went wrong the emotional racial reaction would have been overwhelmingly strong. Nevertheless, Pincus accepted the responsibility, he introduced all possible safeguards and controls, and I admire him immensely for doing it. In the history of this century I have a feeling that the introduction of the pill will turn out to be one of the most responsible things done by any one individual."

It has already been one of the most rapid advances. From a few women to nearly 10 million in ten years is outstanding. I could find no precise reference made, almost understandably, to any prediction for the next ten years.

Despite the pill's success no one is yet completely sure how oral contraceptives do their trick. It is, to quote the recurring phrase, "not yet fully understood." Attempts are also being made to make the pill a monthly dose, rather than—as at present—for 20 to 21 days in each month. By 1965, a monthly injection had been devised. By 1966, an annual pill was being mentioned, perhaps lodged beneath the skin, demanding a positive step and its removal to become pregnant. By 1975, judging by past progress, a single pill taken every year by hundreds of millions of women does not seem impossible. And scientists are already predicting a postcoital, or morning-after, pill, surely the most convenient arrangement of all. In fact, scientists from Yale University's medical school told the American Fertility Society in 1966 that a pill had been developed that could be taken a week after sexual relations and still prevent implantation—the week-after pill.

IUD's

It never rains but it pours. Scarcely had the pill started on its remarkable career than it had a rival. In 1959, only two years after the Puerto Rican trials had begun, two important papers were published, by an Israeli and by a Japanese. Both reviewed recent progress and thinking on intrauterine devices. For centuries humanity had been inserting metallic objects into the vagina, notably of animals, in the hope of preventing conception. (Camel pregnancies were particularly unwelcome during any long and dangerous journey, and their prevention was extremely important.)

Then, after World War I, Dr. Ernst Gräfenberg, working in Berlin, made the procedure more scientific. He inserted coils of silver or gold wire into the wombs of hundreds of women who did not wish to conceive. His results were good, but others trying his methods were less successful. The women bled or did conceive or aborted their fetuses; and the method fell quickly out of favor. The two 1959 papers drew attention again, and favorably, to the idea of "Gräfenberg rings," to the intra-uterine devices (or IUD's) and work began in many countries. All kinds of shapes were devised and inserted and the results noted. By 1964 a large conference in New York summed up the situation. The five shapes then available were the Zipper nylon ring, the Hall-Stone ring (stainless-steel wire in a coil), the Lippes loop (a plastic snakelike coil), the Birn-berg bow (a plastic figure eight), and the Marguilies spiral (a plastic Catherine-wheel shape with a long tail).

All of them are cheap to make (just a penny or two). All permit fertility to return as soon as they are removed. All discourage conception when correctly in place, although none is completely effective. And all are inserted right up in the uterus. (The procedure is much easier if the woman has already had a baby.) A minority of women find that their loop/ring/spiral is ejected. Sometimes another type will stay; some-times it will not. Also these devices cause bleeding in a minority of women. And a very small minority conceive, with the device being worn at the time of birth or, very rarely, remaining within the womb even through-out all the turmoil of parturition. Someone else has to do the original insertion, and that someone—according to one report—can place 60 to 75 in position a day. About 80 percent of them will still be in place by the end of the year. (Gräfenberg's original metallic rings had to be changed annually. Plastic can perhaps stay forever.)

An important point, particularly for underdeveloped countries at last able to see a device suitable for their threadbare pockets, is that a man without medical qualifications can be taught to do the inserting. South Korea, for example, plans to have a million inserted between 1965 and 1970. Other countries are equally eager, and the World Health Or-ganization estimated in 1966 that a million of the world's women had already been fitted with IUD's. By the beginning of 1967, the East Asia Office of the Population Council was predicting that the number of Asian women alone to be fitted with an IUD would be 3 million before the end of the year.

How do they work? Once again, no one is sure. Somehow, the presence of this shape within the uterus either prevents sperm and ovum from meeting, or prevents the egg from implanting itself within the uterus by hurrying it too quickly down the Fallopian tube, an answer that most opinion leans toward. Is the device therefore causing a very early (one-week-old) abortion or causing the egg to be too immature to be fertilized? Dr. Eleanor Mears, a British family planning expert, says this is a philosophical rather than a medical matter. At what point does life begin? And can an embryo be aborted even before it has been implanted?

A panel set up by the British Council of Churches' advisory group on sex, marriage and the family came to the convenient conclusion that biological life became human life when the embryo was implanted and attached to its mother. Thus the devices can destroy only biological life. The group could see no objection to their use. Will these devices overtake the pill's formidable success? Judging by South Korea, which is certainly not going to pay for the million women to have the pill (at a cost of $14,000,000 *every* year), the low price will be decisive. A Chilean, having noted that there is occasionally trouble after insertion, thought that 230 women would require hospital treatment (for pelvic inflammation) in the first year if 100,000 women were fitted with devices. But he added that 5,000 of those 100,000 women would need hospital treatment (for abortion difficulties) if the devices were not fitted. Prevention is not only better, but cheaper and easier than the cure.

The ring may also help to solve the problem of the sacred cow, one of the most formidable aspects of religious tolerance. There are 176 million sacred cows on the loose in India. Their castration is about as unthinkable to the Hindus as their slaughter. So an American research scientist, long stationed in India, fitted 18 cows with plastic spirals, and was pleased with the result. Whether cows or people or both make use of contraception, the result will be the same; there will be more food for the remaining millions. India's overpopulation and starvation problems must be aggravated by the 176 million hungry, useless, ownerless, and wretched sacred cows.

Sterilization

Finally, there are sterilization and pills for men. Both ideas can make males tremble for their virility, for their maleness. Both smack of castration, of the swift blow with two bricks or one knife. Despite primeval emotions, which undoubtedly exist, many males are bringing themselves up to date on the facts, and are being sterilized or taking pills.

At the International Conference of Endocrinology held in London in August, 1964, a figure of 100,000 American males a year was quoted. *Time* magazine estimated in January, 1965, that 1.5 million Americans had by then been voluntarily sterilized. The operation, therefore, can now be considered commonplace (and is permitted in 47 states). It is known as vasectomy, takes about fifteen minutes, and can be done with a local anesthetic. Each of the two tubes called the vas deferens is cut, and the ends are tied off. As these tubes carry the sperm from each testis up into the body, the sperm can no longer travel. Hence there is ejaculation, normal libido, normal capacity for intercourse—but no sperm. Should a man change his mind, and wish for more children, he can ask for the tubes to be rejoined. As yet, this operation (reversible vasectomy, or vasovasotomy) has not always been successful, but it is more often than not. An extra difficulty, nothing to do with the surgery, is that 27 states have legalized sterilization of mental defectives, and 12 states can sterilize certain groups of criminals. Therefore the surgeon has to know just who is being made fertile once again.

In Britain the operation is very rare. For a long time, there was argument about its legality, as an Act of 1861 seemed to forbid it, but its lawfulness is now more securely established. In India, supported by the government with a modest bonus for each sterilized man, vasectomy is catching on fast. It is hoped there that 2.5 million men a year will be sterilized, but even this huge figure does not match the 10-million-a-year increase in population. In the United States, although three states prohibit it (Connecticut, Kansas, and Utah) and although it was associated with compulsory operations on mental defectives and criminals, the simple technique of preventing males from unnecessary fertility while retaining virility is obviously seen to have merits. Female castration, or salpingectomy, is not quite so simple, but is fairly common as an operation. However, the arrival of both pills and IUD's is unlikely to advance its popularity.

At that 1964 London congress on endocrinology, Professor Warren Nelson, of New York, spoke of male contraceptive pills and experiments with them upon prisoners in the Oregon and Oklahoma state penitentiaries. Four groups of chemicals and twelve specific compounds had been tried by them. All did their work by attacking the actual manufacture of spermatozoa. Once again, there was no loss of libido or performance—only sperm. And the sperm came back within five weeks after the last pill had been taken. An advantage of the system is the need for only one pill a month. A disadvantage is that, as with many modern drugs, some of these pills become troublesome and produce unpleasant symptoms when in contact with alcohol. Therefore, the chemicals, these dinitropyrroles, will have to be examined to find out which part affects the sperm and which reacts with the alcohol. But there will certainly be effective once-a-month contraceptive pills on the market for men within five years, said Professor Nelson—in August, 1964.

As an antidote to these success stories here is one from Dr. S. Chandrasekhar with a different note to it, one of despair. He devised a ready reckoner, a safe-period necklace to inform women simply when to abstain from intercourse. The beads were to be moved once a day; there were green and red beads, red for abstention, green for go. First troubles came at night, for red and green are then identical. The inventor put on square beads for abstention, round for indulgence. He also made it a one-way necklace as women had pushed them wrongly. The inventor relaxed, but the troubles poured in. Women refused to wear the necklaces, resenting wide publicity of their very personal rhythms. Orthodox women would not touch the beads during their periods, and others had to push the beads for them. Those others forgot to do so. So did many of the women themselves, orthodox or not, and some women seemed not to believe that merely pushing the beads would keep them free from pregnancy.

Dr. Chandrasekhar then dropped his idea of the good, simple, safe period reckoner and admitted temporary defeat. Mother India had won.

Sir Dugald Baird has spoken of the fifth freedom, the freedom from the tyranny of excessive fertility. Oxfam, the charity devoted to the relief of famine, decided in 1965 to amend its policy of giving money only for food and food production by supporting family-planning projects as well. The World Health Organization, which had been rebuked by over 30 countries in 1952 for proposing to give family-planning advice, discovered at a meeting in 1965 that the situation had almost entirely changed. Even the observer from the Vatican then gave general support to the memorandum that sparked WHO's revolutionary, new thinking. Carlile, Place, Sanger, Stopes, and all the rest would have been amazed by the suddenness of the world's changed attitude.

Will the actuality be equally sudden? Will the good news percolate down to the deeper layers where most people live? I am thinking of a report about a desperate Mexican girl, already with nine children, who entered a clinic for advice. If another child came, she said, she would kill herself. The girl, a Roman Catholic, was informed about the rhythm method. Her flood of tears suddenly flowed even faster. "How can I try that? I haven't had a menstrual period since I got married."

9

Marriage

All men are equal—but the women aren't.

Anonymous

All women should be married, and no men.

Benjamin Disraeli

The dread of loneliness being keener than the fear of bondage, we get married. For the one person who fears being thus tied there are four who dread being set free.

Palinurus, *The Unquiet Grave*

Within the animal kingdom there is a great assortment of forms of association and relationship, but generally a consistency of behavior within each species. Some species find a mate for life, some for the season, some just in passing. Some find no mate, such as those fish that liberate sperm and ova into the sea at random. Some have many mates, such as the bull seals. Some have their mates fastened to them, as in the case of the dwarf males who resemble appendages rather than partners. And some devour their mates after intercourse. There are myriad systems; but normally—at least—there is consistency within each species.

With the single human species, there is far less conformity. There is both polyandry and polygyny, the two forms of polygamy. There is marriage with or without choice by the partners involved. There are marriages that are totally indissoluble, and there are marriages with every stage of solvency from totality down to the most casual and temporary pairings. Some societies never expect the pairings to last. Even in some that do, the pairings can be brief—the current record number of divorces in the United States is sixteen, held by both a man and a woman. Some widows have been traditionally expected to follow their husbands even through the barrier of death; some, as in India today, are not expected to marry again; some, such as 7 percent of America's widows, manage to find another mate and remarry. Due to the different interpretations by different groups of these human partnerships, it is hard to equate one country's idea of marriage with another's, and to compare statistics. Even in modern societies, various forms of association blur the picture, but the state does not recognize any marriage its officials and representatives have not themselves authorized.

In Britain, marriage, even as the state understands it, is booming. Despite a widespread unwillingness to conform, despite the tax imposition upon earning partners who get married (in Britain it pays to cohabit rather than get married; in the U.S. it is the other way about), despite the removal of so much stigma from illegitimacy, marriage is a far from outmoded custom. In 1965, the seventh successive year of increase and the highest total since 1949, there were 371,000 marriages in England and Wales. The spring is still a good time, with March the top month; September is customarily second, October is third, and January is usually least favored. Since 1935, the average age of bachelor bridegrooms has been falling. In 1965 their average age was 25 and that of spinster brides was 22 years, 8 months. In that year both bride and groom were under 20 in 24,000 (6.4 percent) of the year's official pairings; ten years earlier the number of such teen-age marriages had been one-third of 1965's level. Teen-age girls give birth to 8 percent of the country's children, and a quarter of these are illegitimate. Early marriage is frequently hastened by a premature pregnacy, and 68 percent of all girls who marry when less than 20 years old have produced a baby within 12 months. In the past, the women either worked or got married; at least, that was the custom. Today one-third of British wives go out to work, and they form over half of the female labor force. Marriage in the U.S. is also on the up and up: in 1966 there were more than ever before except in the two freak postwar years of 1946 and 1947.

Divorces are also booming. Over 43,000 petitions were filed in Britain in 1965, the record number apart from the two exceptional postwar years. Decrees always lag behind the filing of petitions, and a record 38,000 decrees were made absolute in 1965, 22,000 granted to the wife, 16,000 to the husband, and there were 56,000 children of these dissolved marriages. Divorce rates were about twice as high for women married before they were 20 as against those married at 20 to 24. Nevertheless, despite this divorce boom, 93 percent of British marriages do endure, and 59 percent of those reaching the courts have lasted ten years. Two-thirds of divorced people remarry and one-third of all divorced couples have no children. Only 7 percent of children born in England and Wales are born to parents not married at the time, but over 20,000 children are adopted annually although over a quarter of these go to couples where one or both is a natural parent of the child.

With women living so much longer than men, and with the gap between the lengths of their lives growing steadily longer in the Western world, the problem of widows is growing. In the 1890s the American wife outlived the husband in 56 percent of families; now she does so in 70 percent of families. What had been a patriarchal society and what is now often said to be a matriarchal society is becoming a widowed society. Men leave their money to their wives, and their wives live on—wealthily. Women collect 65 percent of all legacies in the United States. They are thought to own 60 percent of all stocks and bonds, 65 percent of all savings, and 40 percent of all houses. Taking everything else into consideration, American women, many of them elderly, are thought to own 70 percent of the country's assets.

By no means are all widows rich, or even the majority; widowhood is a time also of great financial hardship made harder by society's attitude to the old. The increasing number of widows, who are now widowed at an average age of 59, means a growing number not just of rich or poor old women but of lonely old women. Remarriage is difficult, partly because of the modest number of available males. Dr. Victor Kassel, who practices in Salt Lake City, Utah, thinks polygyny should be permitted for all men over 65 provided that their additional spouses are also over 65. (Polygamy means more than one mate; polygyny means more than one wife.) At least loneliness might be reduced were such vintage cohabitation to be encouraged. In England and Wales, with a perennial housing shortage, 12 percent of the houses are occupied by just one inhabitant, and a very large percentage of these are the homes of old, lonely, and unhappy widows; in years to come, more and more of the population will be widows.

In India the widows are an even greater sociological problem. Most widowers remarry, but society frowns on the remarriage of widows. Hence, as Indian women often die young and do not in general have the longevity of the American female, there is a great shortage of girls. Men seeking marriage or remarriage have to take younger and younger brides in a country where the ceremony is a quasireligious duty. "I am not old enough to be a virgin" is a remark attributed to an English girl, but many young Indians could say the same on their wedding day. Child marriages, i.e., for males under 18 and girls under 15, are forbidden and punishable under Indian law, but the 1951 census revealed innumerable lawbreakers. Although government officials collected the facts for the census and although one might have expected some reticence at declaring illegal marital states, the final figures revealed that there were (at least) 2,833,000 married boys, 6,118,000 married girls, 66,000 widowers, and 134,000 widows all between the ages of 5 and 14. In that same year, only 6 percent of Indian females over 15 were unmarried; equivalent percentages for unmarried females over 15 in the United Kingdom and the United States were about four times as high. By 1967 the Indian government was even considering a ban upon all marriages of females under 21. One wonders for the success of any such scheme in a country with 134,000 widows not yet 14, and where—as already reported—the current *average* age of first childbirth is 16½.

Although the English are not allowed to vote until they are 21, and although they cannot join the Army until 17, English girls are allowed to marry (and care for any subsequent children) at 16—provided their parents have given consent to the marriage. There have been moves, notably by a committee recommending change to the British Medical Association, that young people in England and Wales between 18 and 21 should be able to marry without parental consent. Pope Paul VI in 1966, relaxing the situation still further, authorized local bishops to permit the marriage of boys at 15 and girls at 13 whenever the circumstances were exceptional. Certainly, the age of puberty is decreasing in western society, and, certainly, the custom of younger marriages is growing; therefore society's laws will—probably slowly—be made to follow suit. Shakespeare's Juliet was 13 when she longed for Romeo, and today's problems of marriageable ages were then accurately summed up. "Younger than she are happy mothers made," said Paris. "And too soon marr'd are those so early made," added Capulet.

✺ 10 ✺

Pregnancy

The Signs · Tests for Pregnancy · Embryology · Fertilization ·
Ectopic Pregnancies · Rate of Development · Ectoderm,
Mesoderm, Endoderm · The Calendar of a Pregnancy ·
The Puzzles of Pregnancy · Its Normality ·
The Placenta · The Umbilical Cord · Abortion

No woman knows precisely when one of her eggs has been fertilized. At present she has no means of knowing, no signs, no symptoms, nothing. She may be stepping onto a bus, for all she knows, when sperm actually meets ovum and a new life has been begun. And she may be stepping onto a bus again, for all she or anyone else knows, when that fertilized egg takes the first positive and vital step of dividing into two. Finally, she is equally unaware when, some six days after fertilization, the round bundle of divided and dividing cells settles down from its apparently haphazard and mobile existence and implants itself securely within the receptive wall of the uterus.

A week later she misses the normal start of menstruation, a firm pointer toward the activity of which she has been ignorant—although some women claim an ability to be aware from a markedly early date. By then, 14 days after it began, the minute embryo is already on its way, many hundreds of cells in size, with its sex decided at the moment of fertilization and with a phenomenal rate of growth and development both behind and before it. A week later, when menstruation has been missed for a week and when maternal doubts are growing into certainties (if they have not already done so), the embryo within has a lump of heart, and the rudiments of brain and eyes and limbs budding from its surface. The new life is then one-tenth of an inch long.

Perhaps a week later still, and four weeks from the silent undetectable start of the explosive spurt of growth stemming from that single cell, the mother will be given official confirmation of her state. Within her the small streak of humanity, curved, a quarter of an inch in length and with traces of all organs developing, is still a minute and delicate thing. Yet, 238 days from then and 3,000 times heavier, it is due to be born as a viable, loud, independent, and single-minded human being.

The Signs

Most women suspect or know because:

1. Their expected menstrual flow does not happen (amenorrhea), although it can fail to happen for a host of other reasons (such as menopause) and can even seem to happen in a modified fashion during the first month or two of pregnancy.
2. They (some two-thirds of them) have "morning sickness," either the feeling or the actuality, which is not necessarily confined to the morning. This can start soon after the first missed menstruation and is usually over a couple of months later.
3. They feel abnormally tired and can and do sleep longer than usual. Sleepiness can and does occur in early pregnancy when the actual physical burden is nothing, compared with what it becomes in late pregnancy.
4. Their breasts start to tingle or itch, and swell (by the second or third month). The thin fluid of colostrum can be expressed from the breasts even at this stage. The areola darkens and its glands become more noticeable.
5. They have to empty their bladder more frequently.
6. They can feel the fetus moving (the quickening) by the eighteenth or twentieth week. At the same time the fetal heart (ticking like a watch at 140 beats per minute) gives emphatic proof.
7. They, particularly brunettes, acquire a dark line running down their navel. Their forehead and cheeks can also darken—the "mask of pregnancy"—and their vulva becomes darker and bluish.
8. They get bigger. The enlarging uterus is out of the pelvis at the end of the third month.
9. They get heavier.

It is one or more of the first five that usually sends a girl along for medical confirmation. Certain of the signs can be caused by occurrences other than pregnancy (such as tumors). A whole group of the signs can be nothing more than false pregnancy (or phantom pregnancy, or pseudocyesis); this is usually confirmation not only of a glandular derangement but also of a frantic desire to have children. It often leads to all the subjective symptoms of pregnancy as well as weight gain, abdominal enlargement, and breast changes. To some degree it can even happen with men.

Tests for Pregnancy

Medical examination means partly taking note of all the symptoms, partly checking the obvious signs (they are what someone else sees; symptoms are what a patient has), and partly making tests, which, by the frequent use of a variety of animals, smack more of the Middle Ages than a modern laboratory.

The signs include inspection of the breasts for any changes and of the skin and genitals for any discoloration and a manual examination of the abdomen for any clues about the uterus within. The laboratory tests make use of rabbits, mice, rats, and toads. The time these tests take and their reliability depend upon which test is being used, but most of them exploit the fact that the hormone called chorionic gonadotropin abounds in the blood and, more conveniently, in the urine of pregnant women. It is produced by the pituitary gland, and the amount produced steadily increases with pregnancy for some 90 to 100 days. Thereafter, its level decreases, but the later detection of pregnancy, with swelling abdomens and increasingly active fetuses, requires a less subtle procedure. The old laboratory examinations underline the fact that human hormones are not rare and unique chemicals in some rigid class by themselves, but can have wide-ranging and powerful effects on many members of the animal kingdom. After all the toad is not even a mammal—by a long way.

The first hormone test to be used—it formed the basis for all the others—is called Aschheim-Zondek. It employs immature female mice. Urine from the woman under test is injected into the mice, and 100 hours later they are slaughtered and their ovaries examined. If these have been made mature, the woman is pregnant. In the Friedman test, virgin doe rabbits are used. Once again human urine is injected, and within 48 hours the rabbit ovaries are examined. Again, activity there means pregnancy. Yet another test uses rats in similar fashion. The strangest test of all makes use of the South African clawed toad (Xenopus laevis). Called the Hogben test, it necessitates the injection of concentrated urine into the female amphibian. Within 15 hours, the toad will spawn 50 to 200 eggs.

All these tests have a high degree of accuracy, 95 percent or thereabouts. Although they are intriguing, particularly the last one, they do take time. This delay and the complexities will be their undoing. In the past two years a rash of less time-consuming alternatives has been proclaimed. Urine and the same hormone are still involved in most of them, but not the living animals. To quote from three claims made in 1965: the first "takes two minutes, gives no false positives"; the second "requires only three minutes to be performed and interpreted"; the third shows up a pregnancy "within ninety-six hours following a missed menstrual period."

In other words, miss a period, become suspicious, visit the doctor, give some urine, flick through a magazine, and get the answer while you wait, all within, say, three weeks of the successful mating. It is quick. Even so, three weeks is a long period in the development of an embryo. A litter of mice would have been born in that time. And a human, although having 245 intrauterine days to go, is in quite an advanced state at three weeks, not in size but in differentiation.

Embryology

The study of an embryo's development is a hideously complicated subject. It starts off simply enough with that solitary, scarcely visible, and recently fertilized egg. It then steadily embroils itself in greater and greater knots. Every organ and every part of every organ and every nerve and blood vessel leading to every part of every organ has to be accounted for. It is small wonder that books on embryology are so generally decried.

Imagine, for an analogy, writing the family history of some English settler in Virginia, a contemporary of John Rolfe. First he takes a wife, and they beget children. Their children's activities and characteristics must next be described and so must those of the grandchildren, whose activities and characteristics cannot be the same. And each succeeding generation, with more descendants, greater differentiation, greater dissimilarity, greater complexity—all leading one to the other, all interwoven, all intermingled, must all be described. The Virginia couple become a people, a population, a country. As in some grotesque Russian novel, every character is playing a part at every stage. To my mind, embryological books have a perfect right to be as bad as they like, for the human baby, stuffed full of organs, brimming over with reflexes and instincts, more chemically complex than any laboratory, is no simple egg. Its development is a bewilderment all its own.

In the beginning, as it was with the Virginia pair, events are concise and straightforward. The female ovum (sometimes called the oocyte) is serviceable only for 12 to 24 hours after leaving the ovary, and the male sperm (or spermatozoon) is effective only for 48 hours. Therefore fertilization is only possible when the arrival of sperm coincides reasonably accurately with ovulation, with the entry of an egg into the oviduct. There is usually only one egg (dissimilar twins disprove this rule) and there are initially 400 million sperm in the 3.9 cc. of the average male ejaculation. Many are necessary, as weak sperm counts are rarely fertile, but only one can fertilize the egg. (An exciting exception to this is dispermy when two sperm both—somehow—fertilize one egg.) Many of the one sperm's companions have previously helped to detach the ovum's outer layer, and the solitary sperm then moves forward into the ovum, losing its tail in the process and swelling its head. Twenty-three chromosomes have met 23 chromosomes to form the central part of a single egg. The long chain of events, hardly any of which is understood, that leads to the birth of a baby has begun. It is not even known why that union of two half-cells to form a single cell is the trigger for the abundant cellular multiplication in the months to come.

Only very recently has the early life of a human being been seen at all. Sperm were first observed in 1677 by Antony van Leeuwenhoek, but the first human egg cell was not seen until 1930. Experimental union of human sperm and egg was not seen until 1944. And one of the biggest mysteries of all, the appearance of a human being in its first few days of life, when it is nothing more than a blackberry jumble of cells, remained a mystery for a long time. Only in 1952 was the first free blastocyst seen, the first human being ever to be observed before implantation in the uterine wall. That individual was less than a week old.

Even today very few have been discovered, despite constant searching. A recent triumph, announced in September, 1965, from the Vanderbilt University School of Medicine, was a photograph of the nuclei of both ovum and sperm, lying side by side, with the sperm's discarded tail lying nearby. This was found after washing out the contents of a woman's oviduct, which had been surgically removed for other reasons. Similar surgical operations have been primarily responsible for providing the means for some understanding of mankind's earliest hours and days. Women about to suffer the removal of their generative organs have sometimes agreed to have intercourse beforehand and to note the time, so that any discovered conception is accurately dated.

Fertilization

The first step of all, the passing of the egg from ovary to oviduct, is one of the least well understood. Normally, there is a gap, almost as if the egg were expected to jump from the ovary to the funnel-ended tube. It is thought that the funnel becomes erect, thus lessening the gap, but no one knows. It is known however that the egg can fail to make it and so pass by error into the abdominal area, and even grow there after having been fertilized. Assuming instead that the egg does reach the oviduct and the sperm's arrival is synchronized, some evidence shows that it may take the sperm only an hour to reach the egg. (As they live for longer, this does not mean that fertilization must occur in an hour or so.) Fertilization is the union of the two nuclei, of the two sets of genes, of the father's sex-determining genes for the offspring (it is either male or female from that moment), of the father's and the mother's dominant characteristics, and of the interaction of both their genetic influences. So much of the human-to-be has been decided already that it is mainly a matter of development right from the start of the fertilization stage.

Having united, the next step is to divide. Although sperm and ovum are so different, the two cells from the first cell division are virtually the same. (An analogy is mixing a glass of water with a glass of ink, and then dividing the mixture.) It is thought that the unification and then the division takes 30 hours. The human form is then still pinpoint sized, measuring roughly .1 mm. across. Its two cells, to judge from studies in the laboratory, do not divide again simultaneously. There is first a three-celled and then a four-celled stage, possibly reached 50 hours after the start. (Two days gone; 264 still to go.) At the end of the third day, the form is composed of 12 cells and has probably reached the diminutive (at this time) cavity of the uterus, having left the long thin oviduct (or Fallopian tube, or uterine tube). How the developing group of cells moves along the oviduct is another obscurity, complicated by such facts that the time taken to do so is equal in the pig and mouse, even though the embryo pig's journey is 40 times longer. Multiplication is now proceeding apace, and 58 of 107 cells have been counted for two human blastocysts, thought to be 4 and 4½ days old, respectively.

The next really crucial stage for this free-floating object, which apparently has every chance of just floating straight out of the uterus— and must do so on occasion—is to attach itself to the walls of the uterus. This is called implantation, or embedding, or nidation, and no one knows how it happens, whether the embryo digests its way into the uterus or whether a niche is prepared for it by the uterus, or whether it is a bit of both. (A clue is that the embryo can become attached elsewhere, as in ectopic pregnancies, which happen away from the uterus and the normal sites.) Anyway, the attachment probably happens between 5½ and 7 days after the start. This seems late for such a necessary and positive step, but scarcely later than the mouse (4½ to 5½ days), which is born a little over two weeks afterward, and the guinea pig. Later still are many other creatures, such as the macaque monkey (tenth day), the cat (fourteenth day), and most ungulates (even later).

The cavity of the uterus—now small and minute relative to its final pregnant size—is filled with salty and sugary fluid. Presumably, the multiplying embryo takes some form of nourishment from it. Once implantation has begun and the embryo sinks into the specially receptive layer of uterine wall, the process for the acquisition of future nourishment via the placenta can begin. It is the loss each month of this receptive layer, the weeping of the womb, that is the basis of menstruation, the monthly "curse." (Incidentally, although I could find no kind of date for the change, the "curse" used to be called the "blessing" because another four weeks' grace—of *not* being pregnant—had been granted.)

Ectopic Pregnancies

Before carrying on with those embryos happily implanted in the correct uterine fashion, I would like to digress to those far less happily implanted in a bewildering assortment of other spots, the so-called ectopic pregnancies. They can be within the Fallopian tube (the commonest place), down at the bottom end of the uterus (very rare), on the ovary itself, or even within the abdomen just attached to some organ like the large intestine.

Not surprisingly, nearly all these pregnancies fail, and they kill about 25 women in Britain a year. One difficulty is that they can be outstandingly hard to detect. (The obstetrician Elliot E. Philipp says no wrong diagnosis is made more often and no condition is more often missed than ectopic pregnancy.) It is estimated that a general practitioner will meet about five or six in his lifetime, for they occur once in roughly 350 pregnancies (although more frequently with Negroes and older mothers). Sometimes they can have a secondary implantation, by bursting through the narrow confines of the oviduct and settling down somewhere else.

For most women, severe pain is an early indicator that something is wrong, and for nearly every woman a laparotomy (opening up of the abdominal cavity) will put things right by showing the surgeon the cause of the trouble and extent of the damage. For very few women, such an operation will show the surgeon not a six-week embryo (a frequent time of trouble with tube ectopics) but a well-developed fetus capable of survival. One such baby, weighing 4 lb., 6 oz., was born in this fashion in England in 1965. The mother had felt no pain for 7½ months, and she then had the operation two weeks later. Even normal weight can be achieved outside the uterus. In India, also in 1965, a 7-pound baby was found after laparotomy to be lying free in the peritoneal cavity. In both cases the mothers (and babies) were well after the strange delivery and even stranger pregnancy. Yet one misplaced fetus is nothing compared to other pregnancy errors. For instance, a three-month-old boy in Hong Kong had three fetuses removed from his abdominal cavity after his mother had become suspicious of his swelling condition. Of the three fetuses one was 2 in. long and well formed.

Rate of Development

Now back to normality and normal implantation within the pear-sized uterus. There are several general points to bear in mind during any discussion on development. The first is the speed of differentiation. Most mothers tend to regard nine months as long, while the weeks go wearily by, as leaves come and leaves fall. It is indeed long, and for the bulk of the time the fetus has just been growing; but actual differentiation, or the original distinguishing of its various parts, is phenomenally rapid. The fetal heart is usually beating by the 25th day. And by the end of the eighth week, the creature looks human; it has all the major external features (eyes, ears, mouth, limbs, toes) and the main internal organ systems. But, and this is the second general point, the human object is still minute. When the heart starts beating, it does so within a pea-sized creature less than ¼ in. long. By the eighth week, when liver, pancreas, kidneys, and so forth are all distinguishable, the new life is not even 1½ in. long (or less than two joints of an adult finger). It still weighs next to nothing. Even by the end of the third month, when differentiation is virtually complete, the young human being weighs less than an ounce.

The third general point is that cell division and growth rate have slowed down by the time of birth to a fraction (2 percent) of the fastest rate. The first cell division takes place after 30 hours, the next 20 hours later. Thenceforth, growth and division proceed apace but, although the newborn baby has some 2 billion cells, there have been only 29 cell generations between fertilization and birth. The second generation is two cells, the third is four cells, the fourth is eight cells, the fifth is 16 cells, the tenth is 500 cells, the twentieth is 500,000 cells, and twenty-nine will give the baby's formidable total. (It is the same mathematical enigma as was used by the legendary individual who asked, as a reward for some legendary deed, to have a grain of wheat for the first chessboard square, two for the second, four for the third, etc. His host, delighted by the apparent humility of the request, concurred greedily, and ordered the grain. Since a chessboard has 64 squares, the request soon proved itself inordinately demanding.)

So, too, with human replication. With two divisions taking place in 50 hours and only 29 necessary, the initial rate does not have to be maintained. The three general points therefore are:

1. Differentiation occurs very rapidly.
2. It occurs when the embryo is very small.
3. The rate of growth after birth is nothing compared with growth before it.

To get from one translucent cell to 2 billion in nine months is fantastically rapid when set against a baby's growth from some 7 lb. at birth to about 28 lb. eighteen months to two years later, or to approximately 140 lb. eighteen years later.

As I have said, embryology is a hideously complicated subject. It tends to get bogged down in its own convolutions right from the start. Therefore, instead of mimicking customary descriptions of development, I shall give the briefest possible general picture and then outline specific events week by week in calendar form.

The egg divides to become two cells. Those two divide, and soon there is a bunch of cells (a morula). The bunch then develops a hole in the middle (the blastocyst stage) with more cells at one end, and the whole thing becomes implanted in the uterus. So much for the first week—and for simplicity. The situation now becomes fraught. Not all the blastocyst cells become the future human being. Some, by growing into the uterus, become placenta. Some become yolk sac, a relatively large (in early days) but yolkless and vestigial structure that can be forgotten. Some become amnion, the protective and liquid-filled balloon that surrounds the developing form. And only some become the human being.

Ectoderm, Mesoderm, Endoderm

From the lump of cells at one side of the blastocyst three layers begin to develop. To begin with, they are vague, but they are crucial in all development (whether human or right down the animal tree). When they first appear they are flat, something like the layers of a cake. They are called ectoderm, mesoderm, and endoderm (some embryologists prefer to spell this third layer as entoderm). Initially, the three of them lie on top of one another, but the flat cake has to become a circular cake, with ectoderm spreading to meet ectoderm, with endoderm at the center, and mesoderm the jam between the inside and the outside. Right from the beginning one end is the head, and the other is the tail.

The first complication of this three-layer tube is that the outer layer —the ectoderm—forms an extra tube, a swelling that runs from front to back, from head end to tail end. From this swelling will grow nervous tissue, the brain, the spinal cord, and all nerves leading from them. From the rest of the outer ectodermal layer will grow, reasonably enough, all outer skin. From the inner, endodermal layer will grow the inner-most organs, such as the lining of the digestive tube and the organs linked to that tube. From the middle layer will grow the middle things, such as muscle and bone. A human is really no more than a complicated worm, with an outer skin, with a gut running through the middle, and with various extras such as muscles and bone and blood vessels in between. But even during its early days—two weeks after conception—the human plainly does not look like any worm. It has already started to distinguish itself from the basic formula.

After the three layers are firmly in place, with a head and a tail and the nerve tube running from one end to the other, the parts of the body begin to manifest themselves. Buds appear, little local swellings become apparent in certain areas of tissue, and they grow. They become limbs or organs, like the liver or glands. If endodermal, like the liver, they grow into the area of the mesoderm but they do not grow through the outer and skin layer of ectoderm. Some of the skin layer, such as the nervous tissue, grows deep down from the skin and ramifies to every part of the body. Cut yourself anywhere, and you will cut ectoderm and then mesoderm, but only if you stab yourself in the area of the vital organs will you meet tissue from the original internal layer of endoderm. The tasks of these three primeval and distinguishable layers, all formed so early in development, are quite finite in the formation of a human being. Briefly, here are some of their end products to indicate the basic pattern of the body's outer, inner and intermediate layers.

ECTODERM (the outer layer)—outer skin, nails, hair, sweat glands, eye lens, mouth lining, tooth enamel, lining of nose, salivary glands, and all nervous tissue.

MESODERM (the middle layer)—muscle, bone, cartilage, inner skin, blood vessels, kidneys, and connective tissue.

ENDODERM (the inner layer)— lining of esophagus, stomach, and intes-tine, liver, pancreas, bladder, lining of lungs, and glands such as thyroid and thymus.

A customary belief about human development is that the embryo passes through all the evolutionary stages of fish, amphibian, reptile, and primitive mammal before emerging as a proper human being. This is not so, despite the fact that every human being is a direct descendant of creatures from these zoological groups. But it is true that there are many similarities in the early development of each group. Plainly each egg, then each two-cell stage or the later morula, or blastocyst, looks much like another and later similarities also exist.

During the fourth or fifth week, a series of grooves, for example, appears within the human embryo (pharyngeal pouches) on the rudimentary throat walls. Were this a fish embryo, these structures would become gills; but in a human embryo, they develop instead into other organs. (Hence the statement that man does not pass through a fish stage.) The first pouch becomes part of the middle-ear cavity. The second forms the basis of the palatine tonsil. The third becomes parathyroid gland tissue, and the basis of the thymus. The fourth becomes the superior parathyroid gland, and the fifth pouch becomes the ultimobranchial body, a vague and little understood object, but emphatically not a gill.

Similarly, although the human embryo has a short stub of tail for a while and it is precisely similar to the short stubs that become tails in many other species, the human stub only forms the basis of the human coccyx. Mankind does not travel up the trunk of the animal tree with each new embryo; it just makes use of a similar cellular differentiation which in the past has led to all the branches of that tree.

The Calendar of Pregnancy

So much for the general story. Now to the calendar. It starts with fertilization. The practice of referring to pregnancy as a period of 280 days or ten lunar months considers the pregnancy to have begun at the start of the last menstruation. This calendar assumes instead that it begins two weeks later—with fertilization. It also assumes, as a further indicator of time's passing, a fertilization date of January 1. Therefore the start of the last menstruation was approximately two weeks earlier, i.e., December 17.

First week (1st to 7th day—Jan. 1 to 7)

Fertilization. First cell division (after 30 hours). Whether dissimilar twins are to be born is now established. Cell mass moves along the four inches of oviduct and becomes a hollow blastocyst en route. Enters uterus (third to fifth day). Implantation occurs (sixth to seventh day).

Mother is probably unaware of the situation. Customary menstruation is not due for another week. Uterus still weighs about 2 oz.

Second week (8th to 14th day—Jan. 8 to 14)

Bleeding may very rarely occur (on the 13th day) as a result of increased blood flow to the implantation site, but it may be confused with menstruation, which is due at the end of this week. Embryo is now plate-shaped, with hundreds of cells, some of which will form the true embryo and some structures like the yolk sac, umbilical cord, placenta, and amnion. The yolk sac and amnion are the first to be formed. Whether identical twins are to be born is usually established at about this time.

Third week (15th to 21st day—Jan. 15 to 21)

Embryo 1/10 in. long and pear-shaped. Neural tube formed. Menstruation is now overdue. Morning sickness and nausea can start. So can breast tenderness. Primordial germ cells, which will eventually produce the cells that produce the sperm and eggs, are already present but the embryo's sex cannot yet be determined. Both eye and ear start development by the 18th day.

Fourth week (22nd to 28th day—Jan. 22 to 28)

Embryo ¼ in. long. Heart (1/10 in.—although more a tube than a heart) starts beating on 25th day, and a circulatory system of a sort exists. Tongue has started to form. Limb buds appear on the 26th day. The yolk sac, often said to be useless as its function is not known, is now as big as the embryo (but will grow little more, although it will never quite disappear). Umbilical cord still very rudimentary. Mother can now often be given medical confirmation of her state and given a date 238 days ahead.

Relative size increase is never again so great as in this first month. The embryo is now 10,000 times larger than the egg. Also the extent of physical change is never again to be equaled.

Fifth week (29th to 35th day—Jan. 29 to Feb. 4)

Heart now pumping frequently. External ears start taking shape. Arm buds differentiate into hand, arm, and shoulders (on the 31st day). Finger outlines appear (on 33rd day). Foot still a flat and budding protruberance. Nose and upper jaw start to form. So does stomach Embryo ½ in. long.

Sixth week (36th to 42nd day—Feb. 5 to 11)

Tip of nose visible (37th day). Eyelids begin to form. Five separate fingers. Toe outlines appear. Marked skeletal growth, but still of cartilage. Stomach, intestines, reproductive organs, kidneys, bladder, liver, lungs, brain, nerves, circulatory system are all being actively developed. Embryo ¾ in. long.

Seventh week (43rd to 49th day—Feb. 12 to 18)

Embryo one inch long. Stomach already produces some digestive juices, and liver and kidney have started functioning. Muscular reflexes can work (as can be shown experimentally, but nothing yet felt by the mother). Outer and hearing part of the ear almost complete. Upper and lower jaw very clear. Mouth has lips, something of a tongue, and first teeth showing up as buds. Thumb markedly different from fingers. Heel and toes are defined. First true bone cells appear. Circulatory system is now effectively operational.

Eighth week (50th to 56th day—Feb. 19 to 25)

A sort of neck is now visible. The head of the embryo is very large compared with the rest of the body. The uterus is now about 4 in. long and wide and deep. The corpus luteum, which produced the egg, is now about the size of the original ovary. The ovary itself has not grown. The corpus luteum will continue to grow until it becomes almost the size of a hen's egg. It will then regress, having fulfilled its hormone-producing role.

Ninth week (57th to 63rd day—Feb. 26 to March 4)

Embryo is often called fetus after this time. (Some call it fetus after fifth week, embryo after third week, ovum before that. Some don't care, and just talk about "products of conception.") Sex of individual can be detected externally. (Until now, organs have appeared similar even to expert scrutiny, although chromosomal assessment of sex possible under the microscope.) Head is ¾ in., and is half crown to rump length (i.e., total length of fetus minus the legs). Footprints and palmprints are now indelibly engraved for life. Spontaneous movements occur, and eyelids and palms are sensitive to touch (as shown by reflex squinting and gripping attempts). Nails start to grow. Dissimilar twins start looking dissimilar. Eyelids close over the eyes for the first time, and eyes still look outward rather than forward. Amount of hormone chorionic gonadotropin (used in pregnancy tests) now reaches its maximum level. Eighth and ninth weeks are generally considered best time for abortions, for "terminating pregnancies vaginally."

Tenth week (64th to 70th day—March 5 to 11)

Quarter stage reached on 66th day (but fetus will have to multiply its weight over 600 times in the remaining three-quarters of pregnancy).

Mother's average weight gain is now 1 lb. (But this *average* can be misleading, as many women can lose weight in first three months, and many begin gaining weight from the start.) Weight of placenta is less than 1 oz. but may be four times heavier than the fetus. Uterus weighs 7 oz. and contains 1 to 3 oz. of amniotic fluid. Breasts have increased in size, some say by about 2 oz. ("No one," said one gynecologist, "has been enthusiastic enough to cut a breast off, and weigh it. What is certain is that women have either let their brassieres out to the full by now, or bought themselves a larger size.") Commonest time for miscarriages is at tenth week, i.e., time of third missed period. The second most common time is at the sixth week, i.e., time of the second missed period. It is much rarer for miscarriages to occur at time of fourth missed period.

11th to 14th week (71st to 98th day—March 12 to April 8)

Many more reflexes are possible, such as frowning. Thumb can be moved to the fingers. Swallowing starts. If foot is tickled (experimentally), the whole leg will be withdrawn. Two halves of palate fuse together. Vocal cords completed. Urination has begun (and urine is removed with regular renewal of the amniotic fluid). Swallowed amniotic fluid can be digested. Sperm cells or egg cells exist. Uterus moves up out of pelvis and can be felt, especially in thin people. At 12th week fetus's crown-to-rump length is 2¼ in., and crown to heel is 2¾ in. Its weight is ¾ oz.

End of Development Period, even though the developed form weighs so little. Start of Growth Period. (Growth has of course been considerable in first three months, but in subsequent six months fetal growth is from less than 1 oz. to 7½ lb.)

Fetus and placenta roughly equal in size. Heart pumps fifty pints a day. Sex of individual now physically definite, as organs clearly distinguishable. Uterus halfway between pubic bone and navel. By this month, the placenta is producing the hormone progesterone in sufficient amount to maintain pregnancy. This job was formerly done by the ovary's corpus luteum.

15th to 18th week (99th to 126th day—April 9 to May 6)

Growth of head hair starts. Eyelashes and eyebrows also begin. Nipples appear. Nails become hard. Heartbeat can be heard externally by listening to the mother's abdomen. The separate heartbeats of twins should be detectable with a stethoscope. Mother starts feeling fetal movements (the quickening) although certain movements had started less obtrusively six weeks before. Thin women may notice movements earlier than normal or fat women. So do women not having their first child.

Fetal hiccups also occur. By now, amniotic fluid (which has been steadily increasing) is over ½ pt. Placenta weighs 6 oz. (at 18 weeks), amniotic fluid 9 oz., and uterus 20 oz. Halfway time.

Fetus's crown-to-rump length is 6 in., and crown-to-heel length is 9 in. (approximately half that of the newborn baby). Its head is now only one-third of total body length. The fetus's weight is 11 oz. (approximately one-tenth of a newborn baby). Mother's weight gain (at 18 weeks) is 9 lb. (or 12 times that of fetus). Her breasts may have gained ½ lb. in weight by now, and colostrum may be expressed from them. Usually breasts do not increase much in size between the 12th and 20th weeks. Customarily breast growth is at the beginning and end of pregnancy, rather than the middle. The mother is now putting on 1 lb. a week, and will do so for the next two months; thereafter, the weekly gain will fall slightly. If fetus is aborted at this time it may possibly survive but, if it does, probably only for a few minutes.

19th to 22nd week (127th to 154th day— May 7 to June 3)

Eyelids can and do open. Premature life now possible, although infant only size of a large man's palm. It can now grip firmly with its hands (although some degree of the grip reflex was seen 12 weeks earlier). Lanugo, the hairy growth on arms, legs, and back, appears. This is generally seen on premature babies, but has normally gone by birth. The fetus's face is red and wrinkled, although fat is now being deposited. Uterus at end of month is up to the navel, but height varies according to the mother's posture. Fetus crown-to-rump length is 8 in., and crown-to-heel length is 12 in. (Leg length is gradually becoming relatively more important.) Weight is 1 lb., 6 oz.

23rd to 26th week (155th to 182nd day—June 4 to July 1)

Many prematures (strictly called immature until the 28th week) of this age are able to live. Volume of amniotic fluid is perhaps 1½ pints, but after 30th week may either not increase or even decrease to allow fetal growth. Head hair may grow long (although many babies are born bald). Most of lanugo disappears. Thumb-sucking may become a frequent habit. Umbilical cord has reached maximum length. At end of period uterus is 2 to 3 in. above the navel. Fetus crown-to-rump length is 9 in., crown-to-heel length is 14 in.; weight is 2 lb., 11 oz.

27th to 30th week (183rd to 210th day—July 2 to 29)

Three-quarter stage reached during the 29th week (and existing weight needs to be multiplied 2½ times in remaining quarter of pregnancy). Chance of survival if born is now better. Fingernails reach fingertips (and may actually need cutting at birth). Fetus (generally) settles into head-down position. Earlier acrobatics cease. Fat is being deposited and smooths out the skin.

Mother's average weight gain is (at 28th week) about 19 lb. (or nearly six times that of baby). Her breasts have increased by about 14 oz. Placenta weighs 15 oz. (at 28th week). Fetus is now four times heavier than placenta. Uterus is halfway between navel and lower end of breastbone and weighs 2 lb. Its height above the navel may fluctuate as the baby's head does or does not fit into the mother's pelvis. This fitting in (or engaging) usually comes later. Efforts to rearrange breech presentations are often made now, sometimes as late as 32nd week. Fetus's crown-to-rump length is 10½ in., crown-to-heel length is 16 in. Weight, 3 lb., 12 oz., is half final weight (this 3 lb., 12 oz., is very much an average figure. The biggest babies at this time may be twice the weight of the smallest).

31st to 34th week (211th to 238th day—July 30 to Aug. 26)

Premature babies of this age are reasonably handsome (less like pink old men) as body is rounded and skin is smooth. Crown-to-rump length is 12 in., crown-to-heel length is 17½ in., weight 5 lb., 1 oz. Most airlines do not like women to fly after the 33rd week (with five weeks to go) for long-distance flights or after 34th week (four weeks to go) for short trips.

35th to 38th week (239th to 266th day—Aug. 27 to Sept. 23)

Heart pumping 600 pints a day (although blood content only slightly over ½ pt.). Growth usually stops for each individual shortly before its birth, but by then weight of that original fertilized egg has been increased 5 billion times. Now, and in the next 20 years, weight has to increase only 20 times. Mother's average weight gain is now 27½ lb. (but may be nil or 60 lb.). Breasts have gained about a pound. Maternal surface area has increased by 1½ sq. ft.

Uterus, now 14 in. long, reaches highest point a couple of weeks before birth. It weighs 2¼ lb. (or some 20 times original weight). Placenta weighs 1½ lb. at term, and is 7 in. to 9 in. in diameter. Baby's crown-to-rump length is 13 in., crown-to-heel length is 20 in. Head is now a quarter of total body length. Weight at 38th week is highly variable, but an average for white communities is 7 lb., 4 oz.

The Puzzles of Pregnancy

There are several major mysteries in all this development. They concern, first, the ability of the human body to contain this explosive growth within one section of it without having the growth urge disastrously affect the mother's body as a whole. The second is the maternal ability to produce and tolerate a "foreign" being, an immunological puzzle of extreme proportions. A third mystery, which I shall describe first, is the mother's weight increase; she puts on more than can readily be accounted for.

It is easier to take an average woman and her weight increase, rather than those others who swell up by 60 lb. or those who have babies without increasing their weight at all. An average woman who is not dieting overtly during pregnancy puts on 27½ lb. And the same average woman expels a baby of 7 lb., 4 oz., a placenta of 1 lb., 7 oz., and amniotic liquid of 1 lb., 12 oz. Her uterus has gained over 2 lb. Her breasts have increased by 14 oz. She has 2 lb., 12 oz. more blood, and 2 lb., 10 oz. more extracellular water within her. All this adds up to less than 19 lb. It therefore leaves almost 9 lb. unaccounted for. Plainly, the extra weight must be somewhere, whether in fat or maternal stores of other kinds, but such deposits are difficult to measure even though they weigh more than the baby that caused them. For instance, some of the fatness of many pregnant women disappears fairly soon after birth, but it is not known whether this lost fatness was fat or just extra blood in the skin or just extra water. The subject of weight gain is by no means completely understood.

The immunological puzzle is presented by the fact that mother and child are two unique people, even though attached. As with all people (except identical twins), they are not able to exchange skin grafts with each other because of vigorous resistance from both sides, and yet a fetus is grafted onto a mother by the placenta for the best part of a year. Sir Peter Medawar, director of the National Institute for Medical Research in London, has suggested that the fetus's privileged position (in not being destroyed by the mother and sloughed off like some skin graft) is due to one or all of three things:

1. The placenta's lack of antigenicity (or ability to reject "foreign" tissue).
2. The fetus's anatomical isolation from the mother.
3. The pregnant woman's immunological inertia (or general acceptance of foreign tissue).

Having posed these three attractive possibilities, Sir Peter then counters:

1. The placenta is antigenic.
2. There is no question of anatomical isolation for the placenta and its fetus.

3.   There is ample evidence that the pregnant mammal is not immuno-
      logically inert.

In other words, a valid conclusion is that pregnancies are impossible—
or that some additional research needs to be done urgently to restore
one's faith in the system.

As for growth, it is the mother's own endocrine system that is
responsible for successfully harboring the enlarging embryo. Growth
stimulants pour from her pituitary glands, and yet she does not grow.
Her own structure does not change. The only parts to enlarge are those
that need to enlarge. When the effects of pregnancy are finally over,
say, a year after it all began, the mother is certainly the same height,
virtually the same weight, and only marginally altered by the experience.

Its Normality

Is pregnancy a more normal state for a woman than nonpregnancy?
Just as the curse of menstruation was called a blessing, was it a rare
event in former times prevented from regular occurrence by repeated
pregnancies? Presumably, the answer to both questions is yes. Girls
would become pregnant before they were even full-grown, as is so
frequent in India today, and regular pregnancies would then relentlessly
follow. As soon as the repressive effects of each pregnancy and the
subsequent breast-feeding began to wear off and as soon as ovulation
and menstruation started again, the time for a new pregnancy would
have arrived.

The interval between each, between one birth and the next fertilization,
was perhaps six months. Children would then have been born every
15 months. Within 20 years, 16 offspring would have been born. For
12 out of those 20 years, therefore, the mother would have been
pregnant, and she may not have experienced a single menstruation
during the whole time. The production of, say, 13 children in 20 years
is still not an uncommon event in many parts of the world, and used
to be common in Britain. Even this rate, whether the babies grow up
or not, means that the mother is pregnant half the time, and is possibly
breast-feeding a child the other half. The average mother of today
produces two to three children and cannot compare her experiences
of motherhood to those women who scarcely experienced anything
else.

Apart from the obvious changes during the pregnant state (which
could be called a reversion to normal, bearing in mind that traditional
regularity of childbirth), there are others less obvious. The heart output

rises by a third. Heartbeat goes up and more blood is pumped with each beat. Pressure in certain veins, such as those in the leg, becomes high (sometimes giving rise to trouble with varicose veins and hemorrhoids). The heart increases in size and changes its position. The flow of blood to the kidneys rises considerably, as does that to the skin, sometimes making hands "clammy" and the days feel unaccountably hot. (A certain Mme X of France made gynecological history by having white and insensible fingers that became normal in pregnancy; it was her first sign of another conception.) Although the bladder becomes more active in getting rid of water during pregnancy, an early sign is also increased thirst. The bladder's flow and general rate of excretion are not what might be expected. They are greatest in early pregnancy, when the embryo is smallest, and least or even below normal toward the end, when the mother may be more than 25 lb. heavier.

Pregnant women may get special cravings (or pica). A B.B.C. broadcast in 1957 solicited 991 craving stories, of which 261 were for fruit, 105 for vegetables, 187 for other special foods, such as pickles, 35 for coal, 17 for soap, 15 for disinfectant, and 14 for toothpaste. The oddities are true pica. One explanation is desire for taste, as all sweet, salt, sour, and bitter things have less taste during pregnancy.

Also, during pregnancy there is more of the clotting chemical fibrinogen in the blood, although there is no rise in the incidence of thrombosis. Respiration is increased, by breathing more deeply, not more frequently. The sensation of shortness of breath (which is not backed up physiologically by any actual shortness) may exist more often when sitting down than when moving about. There are more fats in the blood during pregnancy. Also, the average woman can then do less work, for she has more weight to shift about. Consequently, she feels less efficient, but it is not known whether her actual efficiency for some given and accustomed task has been lowered. Her area has, on average, gone up from 17 to 18½ sq. ft. by the end of pregnancy. Practically everything she takes can cross the barrier between her and her child, such as all gases, alcohol, barbiturates, all antibiotics, and tranquilizers. The effect of smoking is to produce smaller babies (by up to 7 oz.). According to the Food and Agricultural Organization of the U.N. a woman needs 80,000 more calories to produce a baby, 300 more per day. Other experts call this excessive and say that, by changing her activities slightly, by sleeping a little more each day, a woman can easily cut that amount in half. Greater changes will decrease her extra requirement entirely. Generally, the reaction of investigators is astonishment at the minute amount of food a woman needs to produce a healthy child.

Although pregnancy is now considered to be an abnormal state of affairs in contrast with former days, the very normality of today's pregnancies is questionable. Countless women resent the idea of that average 27½-lb. increase and wish for an average baby without an average increase. So they diet. Such behavior was notable in the 1920s, when increases of not more than 14 lb. were desired. One man who aimed at this maximum with 119 mothers achieved anything from a loss of 20 lb. to a gain of 41 lb.

Today's unnatural habits also include taking iron, although, according to Hytten and Leitch, in *The Physiology of Human Pregnancy,* there is "no convincing published evidence that a normal pregnant woman is at an advantage if she takes extra iron." Other customary extras are vitamin preparations, such as folic acid, more calcium or more diuretics (which step up urine excretion), and countless pills, stimulants, sedatives, hypnotics, antibiotics, and alcohols, virtually all of which cross the placental barrier to affect baby as well as mother. The modernity of today impinges upon the modern child long before it is born. And, finally, no child is born anywhere without some man-made strontium 90 already within its bones. It has encountered and entered the nuclear age long before its birth.

The Placenta

The placenta has been mentioned frequently. It has the apparent contradictory role of keeping mother and fetus apart, and yet it is permeable to everything the fetus needs from the mother. It does not let her blood through, and the two blood systems never meet; but oxygen, salts, and nutrients (plus all those medications) pass through the barrier. Initially there was curiosity about how the oxygen in the mother's blood was transferred to the fetal blood. Now it is known that fetal blood is different and has a greater affinity for oxygen. Hence, the ready diffusion of that gas from one to the other. Conversely, the fetus gets rid of its waste products by having a lesser affinity for them; so they pass through rapidly to the mother's side.

The word "placenta" means a flat cake, and a flat-cake shape it is, 1 in. thick and 7 in. in diameter for most of the pregnancy. The side facing the fetus is smooth, with the umbilical cord (usually) coming from a spot between its center and its edge. The side of the placenta toward the mother, together with the uterine wall facing it, is a thick pile of protuberances. This increases the interchange area between fetal and maternal circulations. Although the placental cake has a surface area on the smooth side only of some 40 sq. in., the contortions of its rougher side increase this area to 140 sq. ft. (the floor area of a fair-size room).

Gases, foods, and drugs permeate from one system to the other throughout this huge area. So can antibodies, which will help the new offspring for a time to ward off certain diseases already experienced by the mother. So can some bacteria cross the barrier. So, on occasion, can cancer cells. And then, quite suddenly, when pregnancy ends, the whole delicate arrangement comes to an end as the placenta is sloughed off and ejected summarily about 20 minutes after the birth.

In the wilds of nature the placental afterbirth, rich in blood and tissue, is eagerly consumed by any scavenger. Hospitals have generally considered it as valueless waste. Now it is being collected because gamma globulin can be extracted from it. Essentially this substance contains the blood's antibodies and can therefore help those in need of greater immunity. Europe's largest producer of gamma globulin is L'Institut Mérieux in France. Since 1955, it has collected placentas on a worldwide scale. France has been supplying 150,000 a year, but the rest of Europe has been making its contributions since the institute provided 800 strategically placed refrigerators in maternity units of other countries. Truckloads of frozen afterbirth are then driven to France, and by 1965 over 47 tons of placenta a month were being collected, or about a million placentas a year. The institute is now looking eagerly eastward and hopes to benefit from India's population expansion by relieving that parturient continent of its rich-blooded placentas.

The Umbilical Cord

The outstanding anatomical variant in the production of a baby is the length of its umbilical cord. In fact, it is about the most remarkable variant in the whole baby. Some babies are admittedly born bigger than others, some pelvic girdles are narrower, some cervices rounder, skulls sharper, abdomens fatter, and so on; but the amount of variation is held reasonably in check, presumably by the power of evolution and natural selection. The umbilical cord, the one and only link between mother and fetus, is—to put it facetiously—as long as a piece of string. From 7 in. to 4 ft. is considered normal. Much shorter cords have been known and much longer ones; but to have the long normal cord seven times longer than the short normal cord is a highly abnormal anatomical situation.

All of this cord growth is completed before the 28th week of pregnancy. It then stops. Every cord has a helical, or screwlike, form which is fully established by eight weeks. About three-quarters of cords have a left-handed twist, and the number of twists (as few as four and as many as 29 have been counted) bears little relation to the length of the cord.

Boys, on average, have cords a couple of inches longer than girls. Very short cords are less than one-third of the length of the fetus; a very long cord may be three times the length. There is no correlation of cord length with the mother's weight and height, with the length and weight of the baby, with the duration of pregnancy, with the number of offspring born from the same womb, with age, with the placenta's weight, or with anything, apart from the fetus's sex. Long cords get themselves curled around the neck of the fetus fairly easily, and may even put two, three, or four coils around it. Percentage occurrences of such loopings have been recorded as 22 percent, 3.2 percent, 1.4 percent, and 0.1 percent for one, two, three, and four loops. Strangulation is likely only when the cord has coiled itself around the neck and is short as well. Fortunately, those cords long enough to coil are rarely short enough to strangle. Even though the cord is firmly attached at both the fetal and the placental ends and has no knots to start with, it can have one or more by the end of pregnancy. Presumably a coil has slipped right over the baby to make the knot. Fortunately, again, the knots do not give trouble unless pulled tight, notably during birth, and only the long cords get knots in them.

A particularly dreaded form of cord trouble is known as prolapse. Part of the cord slips down from the uterus before birth and may even appear externally from the vagina before anything else. It occurs once in perhaps 300 pregnancies, although more frequently with twins, but is highly dangerous because it can asphyxiate the baby within. Part of the cord gets caught, or compressed, or wedged in the maneuvers of birth, and its blood supply then slows down or stops. Each cord has two arteries and one vein, and normally about 1/7 pt. a minute runs each way. Any blockage cutting off all that maternal oxygen for long is likely to be disastrous. Some 35 percent of babies who encountered cord prolapse used to die as a result. Ten years ago it was believed that 1,750 babies a year in England and Wales were killed by this one cause. Even today, many stillbirths are caused by prolapse, and many live births suffer permanent damage as a result of the temporary lack of oxygen. Some spastics can blame the transitory complication for their lifelong handicaps.

A perennial argument with the cord is when to cut it. The problem does not arise with animals because herbivores usually tear it and carnivores chew it. Humans used to let it be, at least until the placenta was ejected (usually within twenty minutes), until the seventeenth century. The practice then began of cutting it and tying it off, leaving a short stump. Today's practice is to leave it slightly more than an inch long. The lump of cord dries out quickly and falls off naturally within a couple of weeks, probably in eight days. If the tying or clamping of the stump has been badly done, the new baby can bleed to death very quickly (which happens to about one baby in 1,000).

The argument in favor of delaying the cord cutting is to permit more of the blood left in the placenta to pass into the baby. In the old days, when sitting positions were the rule for labor (most of the early civilizations appear to have done it this way), there was more chance for the placenta's blood to flow down, assisted by gravity. With an uncut cord the blood could then enter the baby. With a cord hygienically clamped with stainless steel almost the moment it appears, the blood can do nothing of the sort. Dr. P. Vardi, of Budapest, for instance, has recently been advocating a method of using more of the placental blood. The new baby is kept between the mother's legs until the placental afterbirth arrives. This is then placed in a plastic dish and held a foot above the baby. The new life is therefore charged with extra blood for two minutes. Dr. Vardi estimated that it gains 80 to 90 ml. in this fashion. As the average fetal blood capacity at birth is otherwise 310 ml. (less than ½ pt.), the proportion gained is not inconsiderable. Even without Dr. Vardi's technique, delayed clamping of the cord for, say, five minutes can well augment a baby's blood volume. Incidentally, a final use for the umbilicus, properly used, is a first-class and ready-made transfusion medium for any new baby in need of extra blood.

Thereafter, the navel remains primarily as something allegedly contemplated for countless hours by those who find trancelike introspection rewarding. There also remains, forever, the debate whether artists should or should not have given one to Adam. Or, for that matter, to Eve.

Abortion

Any offspring has a legal right to a separate existence as soon as it has reached the 28th week of gestation, according to Britain's Infant Life Preservation Act of 1929. On the other hand, many people consider any arbitrary date totally wrong. By the 28th week the young human being, powerless but sucking its thumb, is no less human than any full-term baby. Even during the third month of gestation, when nearly all enforced abortions take place, the fetus that is so summarily aborted still is and always has been a miniature human being. According to the last United Nations conference on world population, some 30 million of these undeveloped lives, or one in five of all pregnancies, are bluntly stopped every year. Over 80,000 fetuses a day are expelled and dumped behind a bush, in a hole, down the lavatory, or in some antiseptic container in some antiseptic hospital. Abortion has been called "the greatest epidemic of all time."

The world's countries have very different ideas on the problem. In the main they are not content with the existing situation, and Britain has been about as muddled as any of them. Until 1803 the law permitted medical abortions, provided quickening had not begun (which is usually in the fifth month). Nineteenth-century recommendations congealed in 1861 as part of the Offences against the Person Act. Section 58 decreed that "every woman being with child who, with intent to procure her own miscarriage, shall unlawfully administer to herself any poison or other noxious thing, or shall unlawfully use any instrument or other means whatsoever with the like intent, and whosoever, with intent to procure the miscarriage of any woman, whether she be or be not with child, shall unlawfully administer to her or cause to be taken by her any poison or other noxious thing, or shall unlawfully use any instrument or other means whatsoever with the like intent shall be guilty of felony." The maximum penalty for both the aborted mother and abortionist was imprisonment for life.

There was much play over the word "unlawful" as it implied the possibility of a lawful use of instruments, a lawful administering of poison. Nevertheless, various judges made it clear that a defense based upon this reasoning was not available to the professional abortionists. The whole lawfulness question was clarified by the act of 1929. This act, more on the side of the mothers than the babies, said abortion was lawful if done "in good faith and for the purpose only of preserving the life of the mother." No law yet concerned itself with the health of the mother. One big step forward in this direction was taken in 1938 with a famous trial. Aleck Bourne, a distinguished obstetrician, performed an abortion without a fee on a girl of 14 who had been raped. He was subsequently acquitted on the grounds that continuation of the pregnancy would have risked the girl's mental and physical health.

The clarity of the ruling in this test became less clear the following year. Norman Birkett, chairman of the two-year-old Interdepartmental Committee on Abortion, then pointed out that the judge's ruling in the Bourne case was not binding upon judges of the High Court. Juries attending similar cases might be directed by the judge "on somewhat different lines." Several people tried to allay the fear that such acquittals were not always to be expected, even if it was clearly shown that the mother's mental and physical health had been at stake. In 1960 Professor T. N. A. Jeffcoate, of Liverpool University, wrote that no doctor need fear the consequences of the law "if, after proper consultation with colleagues, he terminates a pregnancy which he honestly believes is causing or is likely to cause significant harm to the physical or mental well-being of his patient."

The present situation is fraught with problems, with hypocrisy, with unpleasantness. It has been estimated that 50,000 to 150,000 abortions are carried out annually in Britain. (The generally accepted estimate of abortions annually in the U.S. is above one million.) Either one in 18 or one in six or even more of all conceptions are crudely halted. Most of the abortions are illegal, the back-street abortionist is still in business, and the highly qualified abortionist in Britain is still content to take £150 a time. Nineteen percent of all doctors removed from the Medical Register are expelled because of criminal abortion (the number lies second to the 26 percent removed for adultery and improper conduct). Several million pounds must change hands every year for abortions (if there are 100,000 and, say, £60 is an average fee for each). Nevertheless, populations can only be controlled by infanticides, abortion, or contraception. According to some, the most widely practiced of these three methods is certainly not infanticide, not even contraception, but abortion.

Before the recent reform a woman in Britain could succeed in getting a lawful abortion if she admitted a label of mental unbalance. This raised some disturbing questions. Would the label catch up with her whenever her medical history was called for (perhaps by immigration officials, prospective employers, insurance companies) from then on? Was it right to consider only the mother's condition? Ought it not to matter what kind of child it would be, perhaps hideously deformed, perhaps totally unwanted? Ought it not to matter if the child had been subjected to German measles during its early days, making its chance of a defect perhaps as great as one in two? Finally, a girl under 16 was required by British law to have the baby she conceived but she could not, by law, get married. While there is no national equivalent position for the U.S., in the state of New York, for instance, she can marry as young as 14 (with the consent of her parents and of a judge of the Family Court). She cannot, however, have an abortion performed legally unless her life is in danger. (Before the new penal code of September 1, 1967, an abortion could be performed if the life of the fetus was in danger!)

In England and Wales, as well as in the United States, abortion has been one of the two leading causes of maternal death; the other is pulmonary embolism. In England and Wales, abortion deaths were 135 for the three years 1958 to 1960 and 139 for 1961 to 1963, but it is thought the figures were short of the real total; roughly 50 deaths a year is the general assumption. In the United States, the most recent annual figure —for 1964—is five times that. According mainly to the official *Reports on Confidential Enquiries into Maternal Deaths in England and Wales,* about 60 percent of the abortions or miscarriages causing death were criminally induced, and at least half the criminals were the mothers themselves. Even so, assuming an annual 100,000 criminally induced abortions, this meant a maternal mortality rate of .3 deaths per 1,000 illegal abortions.

There have also been some deaths from legal abortions. For the three years 1961 to 1963, there were five such deaths in England and Wales, but the figure has little meaning when unaccompanied by the number of legal abortions. It is occasionally stated that it is statistically safer for a mother to have a legal abortion than to have a child. This may be true, but statistically it is safer for a mother to have a child than an illegal abortion, whether induced by herself or another. (Facts from other countries do not necessarily back up this generalization. In 1966, the *British Medical Journal* carried a report from Scandinavia that legalized abortion mortality varied from .35 up to .9 per 1,000, and that in at least 30 cases per 1,000 abortions there were serious but not fatal complications.)

The abortion controversy was most actively debated in Britain in recent years due to the efforts, now successful, to amend the law. *The Lancet*'s correspondence columns were more active than most. "I do not like to perform the operation, and those who assist me like it even less. I can think of no comparable operation in which normal tissue is removed and that tissue is a potential new individual." "As prevention is not a disease, its prevention is not a proper object for a medical service." "Is the present hesitancy to recommend or carry out abortion due to the profession's deep regard for the preservation of life or to uncertainty in the profession about the present state of the Law in the United Kingdom?" "No woman wishes to have an abortion. Either she desires a child or she wishes to avoid a pregnancy." "I have strong objections to emptying the womb for social reasons, and in this I am probably among 95 per cent of my colleagues in gynaecology who practise in the National Health Service." On therapeutic abortions: "One of the few agreed facts on abortion is that it can never be 'therapeutic' to the foetus except in the sense that euthanasia is 'therapeutic.'" "Ultimately the only way to abolish illegal abortions would be to make it legally possible to terminate any pregnancy. If this is not acceptable illegal abortions will continue." Early in 1967, the Royal College of Obstetricians and Gynaecologists and the British Medical Association issued a joint statement on abortion. This made the point that it should be lawful "for a registered medical practitioner to terminate pregnancy if, in good faith, he considers it to be either in the interests of the physical or mental health of the mother or because of the risk of serious abnormality of the foetus. In deciding whether termination is in the interests of the health of the mother the doctor is entitled to take into account the total environment of the mother, both actual and reasonably foreseeable."

In the United States, where 44 of the 50 states, as in the New York case, still consider the sole legal ground for abortion to be that a pregnant woman would otherwise die, strong recommendations have been made for changing the laws.* For instance, in 1965, the American Medical Association's Committee on Human Reproduction recommended that licensed physicians ought to be able to terminate pregnancy if they could reasonably establish that there was substantial risk that the continuance of the pregnancy would gravely impair the physical or mental health of the mother; or there was substantial risk that the child would be born with grave physical or mental defect; or the pregnancy resulted from legally established statutory or forcible rape or incest.

On October 25, 1967, Britain's House of Commons gave final approval to a bill reforming the abortion law. It permits an abortion if two physicians agree that a continued pregnancy would threaten the life of the woman; would be injurious to her physical or mental health; would produce a child who might "suffer from such physical or mental abnormalities as to be seriously handicapped"; or would injure any of the pregnant woman's existing children, mentally or physically. At the time of approval, the British bill was described as superior to the new Colorado state law passed earlier in the year. The Colorado law makes it necessary for a panel of three physicians to agree that the pregnancy would result in the mother's death or a serious or permanent impairment of her physical or mental health; that the pregnancy had resulted from rape or incest; or that the baby would be deformed.

Attention to the defective risks has been drawn by Britain's Eugenics Society. Its honorary secretary wrote in 1965 about various severe human ailments, and the chances of their inheritance.

CLASSICAL ACHONDROPLASIA, epiloia, multiple polyposis of the colon— a one-in-two risk that the affected parent will pass it on to a child.
CLASSICAL HEMOPHILIA and Duchenne muscular dystrophy—a one-in-two risk for sons and a one-in-two risk that daughters will be carriers.

---

* As elsewhere, the abortion laws in America have little relation to reality. One million induced abortions are thought to take place annually, and 1 percent are induced in hospitals. Even of this small percentage, the majority are probably not in strict accordance with the law, according to Dr. Robert E. Hall, president of the Association for the Study of Abortion.

CYSTIC FIBROSIS of the pancreas—if parents already have one affected child, there is a one-in-four risk for further children.

MATERNAL RUBELLA (German measles)—if the mother gets it during the second half of first month of pregnancy, the risk of some defect for the child may be 50 percent.

Therefore, the chances are high that these and many similar complaints may be transmitted from parent to offspring. Many parents may accept the odds and welcome any form of child. Many may not.

What happens in other countries? Sweden has a reputation for liberality (much publicized when Mrs. Sherri Finkbine, of Phoenix, Arizona, traveled there in 1962 to be relieved of a fetus that had been subjected to thalidomide). Sweden passed a liberalizing act in 1946 that tolerated abortions if there was a defect in the mother, a risk of severe defect in the child, a social "weakness" in the mother, a humanitarian reason (as with rape), or an "emergency" reason. In 1939, there had been 439 legal abortions in Sweden and a suspected 20,000 illegal ones. After the war and the passing of the new act there was a steep rise in legal abortions, 5,503 in 1949, reaching a maximum of 6,328 in 1957. Since then the numbers have dropped. The law, although more liberal than in many other countries, is by no means totally relaxed. Nearly all foreign girls traveling hopefully to Sweden return home still pregnant, and in 1965 many Swedish girls were discovered to be going to Poland for abortions. Sweden's national board of health has appointed a committee, presided over by a judge, to study the necessity of further liberalization. After all, it is still estimated that from 10,000 to 20,000 illegal abortions occur in Sweden every year.

In Latin America, where the situation is not helped by the attitude of the Roman Catholic Church toward contraception, abortions are illegal but common. In Chile there is, the authorities estimate, one illegal abortion for every two live births. Complications following these abortions are responsible for filling a quarter of the maternity beds in the National Health Service hospitals. In Denmark, according to its government commission for sexual education, there are 20,000 abortions a year (and the population is only 4.5 million). In Japan, where the accent has been on population control since the American occupation authorities said that 80 million was the maximum population the land could support, abortion has been very common. Professor Shiden Inoue, of Nanzan University, has said that 80 percent of Japanese women with at least one child have experienced abortion, and most gynecologists in the country were financially dependent upon abortion income.* In the early 1960s legal abortions in Japan outnumbered births.

Eastern European countries also have liberal laws. Hungary has 131 abortions for every 100 live births. East Germany has just revised its laws to permit abortions if the mother's health is endangered, if she is over 40 or under 16, if she has had four children at an average interval of less than fifteen months, if any pregnancy starts within six months of the previous birth, if there are already five children, if the pregnancy results from a crime, or if the child is expected to have a serious abnormality. Only the first and the last had been considered legal before.

Oddly, Rumania announced the banning of abortion at the end of 1966. The first Communist country to take this step said a new law would permit interruption of pregnancy only in very rare cases. Yugoslavia, with liberal abortion laws (one Zagreb hospital in 1966 recorded 4,500 live births and 3,000 abortions), has been expressing concern at the falling birth rate and is now trying to cut down the number of legal abortions.

In Britain, abortion statistics are as nothing compared with the estimated abortion rate. In 1950 there were 103 women officially recorded in the year's register as having had abortions that resulted from criminal interference. In 1955 there were 66 British women thus registered, 62 in 1960. Since it is estimated that there were 300 or so abortions a day, the official register is woefully misleading. Of the offenses for procuring abortion known to the police (according to Keith Simpson's *Forensic Medicine*), which totaled about 200 a year, the number of people committed to trial was about one a week. In other words, there were 2,000 abortions a week, and one trial.

Habitual criminal abortionists usually make use of instruments (such as bougies or curettes) to initiate abortion. Although instruments are the most consistently successful method (according to Simpson), the method of interference is beset with dangers, such as fatal shock, air embolism, instrumental injury, and sepsis. Women themselves are more varied in their efforts to dislodge pregnancies. They try drinking gin or gin with iron filings, hot baths, skipping, riding horses, bicycling, lacing themselves tightly, or falling downstairs. Violence of this sort is rarely effective. A woman once deliberately fell 25 feet and, although she died 24 hours later, the 2½-month fetus stayed put. A man once knelt on a woman's abdomen and then trampled on her back. He later used scissors —but the baby was born when due. In 1963 a pregnant woman was

* Japan's prime minister asked the health ministry in 1967 to tighten abortion laws after it had been revealed that a Japanese physician was offering easy abortions to patients from the United States: "Simply let her fly to Tokyo, and leave the rest to us."

struck by lightning on a Welsh mountainside. and was temporarily knocked out. Naturally, this case was no deliberate attempt at abortion, but the fetus happily survived the incident. Even women in iron lungs or in a coma have delivered healthy children (as with the screen actress, Patricia Neal).

Women are a frighteningly determined lot on occasion. C. J. Polson, in *The Essentials of Forensic Medicine,* has listed some of the methods. Instruments, apart from normal medical equipment designed for other purposes, include knitting needles, hat pins, pokers, paint brushes, or just fingers. Then there is slippery elm bark, an ancient household remedy (this is self-lubricating in that a jellylike layer is formed on it by any available moisture). There are also vegetable poisons, such as saffron, juniper, rue, brook, and laburnum. In World War II, potassium permanganate (generally used as a disinfectant) was much in vogue, for it was frequently recommended by United States servicemen. Long before they arrived in Britain, and after they went, there were preparations like Dr. Reed's Extra Strong Female Pills and Widow Welch's. Keith Simpson says women who abort after taking drugs are more likely to be doing so because they have been made gravely ill by the toxic effects rather than by any abortifacient value in the drugs.

Without doubt legislation on abortion will soon change in many areas, as it has already in Britain. Without doubt the medieval procurer of abortions should be put out of business. Better contraception will inevitably lead to fewer unwanted pregnancies, and relaxation of laws will inevitably take more women away from those back streets. Preventing conceptions is better than aborting them, and aborting them legally is better than illegally. If that world estimate of 30 million abortions a year is either correct or incorrectly high by ten, twenty, or thirty times, the problem is still monumental.

ৰ্ণ 11 ৯

The Time Before Birth

Gestation Length · Legal Pregnancies · Animal Pregnancies ·
Labor: First, Second, and Third Stages ·
Presentation · Uterine Crying

Gestation Length

There is much similarity between a weather forecast and the expected day of a baby's arrival. It is eagerly noted down and even believed in a way; but rarely does it become precise reality. "The eighth of December," says the doctor. "Ah, the eighth of December," repeats the mother-to-be sitting before him. "The eighth of December," she informs her mother on the phone. In fact only 5 percent of babies actually arrive on the forecasted date.

The average period between fertilization and birth is generally calculated at 266 days, or eight and three-quarter calendar months. A traditional method of arriving at the date of birth is to add 280 days to the start of the last menstruation. These 280 days are often said to be the length of human gestation mainly because the date of the start of the last menstruation is a commendably positive date. Another method of assessing the birth date, which also cares little about individual variation, is to add 273 days to the day on which the last menstruation ended. If irregularity in calendar months is casually forgotten, and if the last menstruation began on the first of the month, and if it is assumed that the flow ended a week later on the eighth, then the magic date is also the eighth, but nine months further ahead. The round figure of 280 days is also ten lunar months, or around ten times the average menstruation period of 28 days. Despite efforts to complete this happy circle by finding a correlation between the length of the period and the length of gestation, none has been found.

Two hundred and eighty days, or ten lunar months from the start of the last period, or eight and three-quarter calendar months, are therefore the rules surrounded on both sides by all the exceptions. Apart from premature babies, which are born at least four or five weeks before expectation, there are many babies just born early. From 240 days onward the babies are not actually considered premature (with an arbitrary definition of 5½ lb. or less) whatever the mother, caught unaware by the event, may think. Some babies of only 32 weeks (224 days) weigh those 5½ lb. and are born normally a full 56 days before the doctor's computed forecast.

After 280 days (and still with no sign of activity) no one is greatly concerned for a while; but, when that while has passed, thoughts of inducing labor become more positive. By the time another month has passed beyond the forecasted date, the pregnancy is generally agreed to be abnormal. One woman is on record who, twice in succession, had pregnancies of over eleven lunar months (308 days). At the traditional time of ten lunar months she felt labor pains, but these then subsided and did not manifest themselves again for another month. It would seem from this one case as if the long-forgotten menstruation period had something to do with the onset of labor.

Two hundred and eighty days is too firmly rooted as the hallowed pregnancy time in Europe for it to be treated with less respect, although the bull's-eye is rarely hit and women steadily pepper the target on either side of it. In the United States the mean for white women is 279 days for male offspring and 279.9 for females, and yet 12 percent of the mothers wait for over 300 days before producing their child. The Negro gestation times are shorter, being 273.3 days for male offspring and 274.7 days for females. Negro babies are smaller, and so the shorter time seems reasonable. But children in India are smaller still, and they take longer to appear, 285.6 days for boys and 286.6 for girls. Both birth weight and gestation length are racial characteristics in India, and not a direct cause of harsh living, because they are consistently low and long among the well-to-do and among Indians living abroad.

With all groups of humanity everywhere girls are carried, on average, a day longer than boys. This is just as basic for Homo sapiens as the fact that males die off more rapidly from conception onward.

Legal Pregnancies

The longest pregnancies on record are reported not in the annals of medicine, but of law. Men, such as husbands, have frequently wished to prove that they could not have fathered a certain child as they were else-where/at sea/abroad throughout the vital time. The law, aware that pregnancies can exceed 280 days, has never been prepared to accept the plea of a man who is absent for 281 days before the birth—or even 300. But back in 1802 a man was considered guiltless who had been away for 311 days. Nowadays, pregnancies are (legally) getting longer. It is not good enough to have been at sea for only ten months, and then disown a brand-new baby on stepping ashore. In 1921, with the case of Gaskill v. Gaskill, the husband was petitioning for divorce on the grounds of his wife's alleged misconduct because Mrs. Gaskill had produced a baby 331 days after he "had had access to her." Mr. Gaskill lost his case. In 1947, with the case of Wood v. Wood, Mr. Wood had been away for 346 days, but he still lost. With Hadlum v. Hadlum in 1949 the period of absence, or length of presumed possible pregnancy, was 349 days—or almost one year. The court had accepted that such a lengthy pregnancy, over two months longer than the traditional forecast, was possible. Mr. Hadlum was assumed to be the father. (I have read of one birth after 360 days, but there was no supporting evidence.)

A similar legal judgment has to be made in cases of doubtful legiti-macy after the husband has died. Is the child the dead man's or has it been born too late for this possibility to be acceptable? Some countries have fixed dates. In Germany the law recognizes the legitimacy of a baby born 302 days after the husband has died. In France it is 300 days. A mere twenty days on top of the 280 is very different from the 349 days of Hadlum v. Hadlum. Presumably a difference is that if money is to be inherited only by legitimate offspring, many a young widow might hurry to become pregnant in order to secure more loot for her (illegitimate) successors.

Animal Pregnancies

Animals, as might be expected, vary enormously in their gestation time. At one end is the elephant, which produces its infant after 23 months, while the whale, larger and with larger offspring, takes about a year. At the diminutive end of the scale are the marsupials, the mammals of Australasia and, in part, of South America. Marsupials do not develop placentas, as most mammals do, and so cannot emulate their incubation system. Instead they rely upon different systems.

The opossum is typical. Its young are born when less than two weeks old. These primitive things, more like miniature slugs than young opossums, do not pass out through the vagina. Instead they travel along a rupture in the skin, the pseudovaginal canal. At the end of this, and when confronted by the open air, they have to squirm, wriggle, and make

AVERAGE GESTATION TIMES OF VARIOUS SPECIES

	No. of Days	*Usual No. Born*
Golden hamster	16	6–7
Mouse (laboratory)	19	8–12
Rat	22	6–8
Rabbit	31	6–9
Hedgehog	35	4–7
Polecat	40	6–8
Ferret	42	6–9
Mink	50	3–5
Fox	51	4–6
Cat	56–64	4–6
Dog	58–63	3–7
Guinea pig	63–70	3–4
Lion	107	4
Tiger	107	4
Pig	113	12 (8–16)
Chamois	140	2
Goat	150	2
Sheep	150	1–3
Monkey	150–180	1
Fallow deer	250	1–3
Man	266	1
Cattle	280	1–2
Buffalo	300	1
Roe deer	310	2
Camel	315	1
Horse	336	1
Llama	340	1
Badger	352	2
Ass	365	1
Zebra	400	1
Elephant	700	1

their way for three long, hairy inches from the canal to the pouch. The pouch is security, and also a supply of nipples. Each fetus clamps itself on a nipple and then relaxes until weeks and weeks of growth have passed. Finally it unclamps and becomes a more independent form. It remains in the pouch for as long as necessary, turning to the milk supply whenever thirsty and viewing the world from its kind of external uterus. There is much to be said for the system.

Human eggs, once successfully initiated and implanted, grow throughout their gestation or development. Some other forms conceived at a convenient time have their growth delayed so that they can be born also at a convenient time. Seals, for instance, come ashore for any length of time only once a year. Their pups are then born, and shortly afterward each cow is mated by a bull for next year's pup. (Customary nomenclature frequently goes haywire in the animal kingdom.) One whole year for the development of a seal seems unreasonable when you think that large dogs, very similar creatures biologically, have gestation times of nine weeks rather than eleven months. Some bats employ similar delaying tactics, and so do roe deer. The does are mated in the autumn, but the fawn embryo stops developing at the segmentation stage (very early on) and only starts again the following spring.

Labor: First, Second, and Third Stages

Surprisingly, it is not known what causes labor to start. Inevitably and consequently there are many theories. They include:

1. Aging placenta.
2. Increasing movement of the growing uterus.
3. Increasing size of the fetus.
4. Increasing irritation by the cramped intestines.
5. Hormone secretions—estrogen tends to drop just before labor starts, oxytocin tends to rise.
6. Metabolic change—either mother or child may produce substances during metabolism that trigger labor.

Despite the ignorance about the actual trigger or combination of triggers, labor can be artificially induced if need be. The needs include death of the fetus; postmaturity—very old fetuses are not only larger, but also harder to mold through the birth canal; Rh-factor difficulties —blood transfusion may be necessary, and the sooner the better, within reason; poisoned pregnancies; premature rupture of the membranes. Labor is artificially induced only very rarely before the 35th week. Induction methods include oxytocin injection, rupturing of the fetal membranes, or dislodging these membranes from around the circumference of the cervix.

Normal labor, whatever its cause may be, is generally regarded as having three stages. (The following description by no means fits every case, but is an attempt to give a representative picture.)

The first stage starts with regular uterine contractions. These occur initially every 20 to 30 minutes, then increase until they occur every two to three minutes, with each contraction lasting perhaps up to one minute. Therefore, as the intervals between contractions are reduced, the contractions themselves are lengthened. The main function of this stage, which lasts 14 hours on average for first offspring (some say average is 16 hours, but all agree the time is shortened for subsequent births), is to open up the cervix, the neck of the uterus. Before labor starts, the pathway is emphatically blocked. By the end of the first stage the cervix is thinned. Its substance is molded to each side, the former "plug" diminishes, and a pathway appears possible. It is not known what initiates the uterine waves of contraction, or whether two waves start simultaneously on each side.

The second stage is the actual birth. The upper part of the uterus continues to contract and retract, with the lower part of the uterus more passively stretching to permit passage of the fetus. Deliberate stomach-wall and diaphragm exertion helps but is not vital; women in coma or with severed spinal cords can have normal labor. The membranes usually rupture early in this stage (or may have done so before the first stage began). The fetal head is gradually forced lower and lower until it meets the pelvic floor, the bones whose shape causes the head to rotate 45 degrees. The head is then born and rotates back again to its normal position in relation to the rest of the body. The shoulders are then born, following a similar encounter with the pelvic floor and a similar rotation. The head, which is now outside, is caused to rotate again as the shoulders are born, and the rest of the body then follows. The molding of the skull takes place during the second stage (made possible by softness of the bones and spaces between them).

The amount of pressure exerted by the uterus can be over 3 lb. per square inch, and it has been calculated that the total expulsive thrust on the fetus is about 24 lb. (An obstetrician once had a finger broken by a strong uterine contraction.) The duration of the second stage can vary enormously between minutes and hours, but the average for a first child is two hours; the length of time lessens with subsequent children.

The third stage is generally estimated to take twenty minutes. It begins after the expulsion of the baby and ends with the expulsion of everything else—the membranes, placenta, and remaining fluid. Even during the second stage the uterus shortens by some 6 in. After delivery it contracts upon the placenta, and its rhythms may cease temporarily. The placenta is then separated from the maternal tissues, a process lasting about eight minutes, but the membranes usually take longer to separate. More contractions follow, plus some exertion from the diaphragm or the abdominal wall, as the shrunken uterus rids itself of the unwanted tissues and fluid. Blood loss at this stage may be a pint, but this is still regarded as normal. Greater loss of blood is abnormal and is usually associated with the retention of the placenta, or part of it. Excessive bleeding—postpartum hemorrhage—occurs in 4 percent of deliveries, and about 20 women a year in Britain die from it, most of them at home where transfusion is less possible.

For the 96 percent who do not suffer from excessive bleeding, labor is over. The business of birth has finished. The puerperium has begun. The most dangerous journey in the world, to borrow one man's phrase, is the 4-in. trip down the birth canal. Now it is over and done with.

Labor is generally considered to be prolonged if it lasts more than 24 hours, although signs that it is slow or difficult can be seen long before that. The process is generally quicker in animals, save for some monkeys, who may take just as long. Cows and many other ruminants take two hours but sometimes up to 12 hours. Sheep take about fifteen minutes for each lamb. Sows, bitches, and cats take ten to thirty minutes for each member of the litter. With the mare everything is very rapid, usually five to fifteen minutes, and any difficulty often kills the foal. There is little quite like the prolonged and drawn-out sequence of events that precedes the safe delivery of each new human being. Also, whatever general practitioners may think or even stringently believe, most births do not take place at night. A huge survey in Pittsburgh, which examined 57,000 arrivals, discovered that 55 percent of them had the grace to appear between 6 A.M. and 6 P.M. Even so, birth is a nighttime business, for those happening during the day probably started at night, and those starting during the day probably reached their conclusion long after the sun had set.

Presentation

Babies are normally (95 percent) born headfirst (vertex presentation) and face downward. Very rarely (.4 to .8 percent) the face is born first, looking upward at the deliverer. The most common abnormality is breech delivery (i.e., buttock first—but may be occasionally knees first or one foot first). Breech deliveries of all kinds add up up 3.5 percent of births. They are unwelcome partly because they involve three deliveries, first the breech, second the shoulder, and third the head. (With normal presentations everything is relatively plain sailing after the head.) The mother is likely to fare just as well with breech and vertex births, and labor will be of similar duration (although breech delivery takes a little longer on average), but the baby is likely to fare less well (the breech-delivery mortality rate is three times higher than that of vertex delivery). A further presentation (.5 percent) is when the shoulder attempts to be born first. Worst presentation of all (and only prematures can actually be born this way) is the transverse, or cross-birth. It frequently results in the death of the baby, even if the obstetrician manages to correct the fetal position during labor.

It is "not properly understood" (this phrase is so beloved in the scientific literature) why most fetuses come to lie head downward shortly before birth (93 percent are head downward by the end of the 34th week). Certainly, the fetal head within the pelvic framework makes a neat fit, and this may be the only reason. Breech deliveries are more common, understandably, in premature than mature births and also, less understandably, more common with subsequent offspring than firstborn. Some women produce breech presentations every time; in fact, 14 percent of all breech deliveries are habitual. Breech presentations can be detected in late pregnancy, and efforts are made, often successfully, to change the position. They are not attempted too early (to give the fetus time to sort things out for itself) or too late (when enforced sorting out is impossible and the breech is too firmly entrenched in the pelvis). Efforts are usually made between the 34th and 36th week. Movement is effected manually, often without any need for anesthetic, and the fetus is coerced into the new position. Occasionally the fetus may counter all efforts by maneuvering itself (or being maneuvered by the uterus) back again into the original breech position. Breech deliveries almost always need a skillful attendant if the baby is not to be born dead, because the birth sticks at the head, the umbilical cord may stop pulsating, and the new life may then cease.

The birth of twins naturally complicates the conventional downward or vertex position within the uterus. Compromises have to be made. Even so, both are head down (double vertex) in 30 to 45 percent of cases. One vertex and one breech occurs in 35 to 40 percent of cases, with the vertex twin usually born first. Other arrangements such as double breech (8 to 12 percent) or one vertex and one transverse (4 to 12 percent) are much rarer. In both these cases, the horizontal twin is almost always born first. Rarest of all combinations is when both twins are transverse, lying across the uterus.

Labor for twinning generally starts early (by several weeks—average shortening is 25 days) and generally takes longer. Twinning pregnancies put the mother in greater danger, as maternal mortality is two to three times more severe. Twins themselves are also in greater danger than singletons, mainly because of prematurity and its consequences. When twins share one placenta (and therefore one blood circulation) the birth of the firstborn and the cutting of its cord can cause the second twin to bleed to death unless the firstborn's cord is clamped at the placental end as well as at the baby's end. Occasionally, Cesareans are necessary with twins, as when the fetuses become locked together in the narrow exit. Second twins are sometimes born after a long wait (even, very rarely, after a month), but the optimum time is short.

Uterine Crying

A fortunately very rare occurrence in childbirth is known as vagitus uterinus, or crying in the uterus. This still-imprisoned yelp must be alarming even to experienced obstetricians, let alone inexperienced mothers. Sometimes the cry is described as soft and whimpering, sometimes loud and gasping. At all times it must be the last sound anybody wants to hear. A case of it occurred recently in northern Scotland. The mother had had difficulties in the past (two abortions, one ectopic pregnancy, and one forceps delivery) and was five days overdue when this story began. The slight lateness, plus the earlier history, plus her present anxiety caused her physicians to decide that labor should be induced. They did so at 9:20 A.M. by rupturing the membranes, a customary method. More than a pint of liquid was withdrawn with a catheter, and there then came three loud cries from the fetus. They were heard by the two doctors, the three midwives, and the mother. Everyone was startled. First thoughts were that someone had wrongly brought some other baby into the room, but these first thoughts were quickly proved wrong. It was the fetus, and labor had not even begun. On several other occasions during that day it cried again, and labor finally began at 8:30 P.M., or eleven hours after that first awesome cry.

Fortunately everything else, such as the fetus itself and then the labor, was absolutely normal, and an 8 lb., 3 oz. boy was born at 4:10 A.M. the following morning. He cried immediately at birth, almost 19 hours after his first fetal call. Both mother and child were well. The event of vagitus uterinus is certainly rare (one man added up the reported cases until 1940 to find a total of 122), but one suspects that it would have to be far more common before anyone attendant upon such a birth could hope to forget the first shattering cry, however diminutive, from a fetus still locked within a uterus. The recommended procedure, provided the fetus is well, is to do nothing but wait for it to be born.

Birth

The History of Midwifery · The Chamberlen Family and
Forceps · Cesareans · Anesthesia · Home or Hospital? ·
How Long a Stay? · Maternal Death · Semmelweiss and
Puerperal Fever · Infant Mortality · Infanticide ·
The Sex Ratio · The Baby's Weight · Prematurity ·
The Puerperium · Paternal Labor · Ergot · Who Has Babies?

The business of delivering babies started well, but the deliverers then
deteriorated and so did their methods. The skilled became the unskilled,
and a modest knowledge of anatomy became an ignorance coupled with
uncleanliness and superstition. Midwifery and midwives reached their
nadir at the end of the Middle Ages. As the medical historian Dr. H. S.
Glasscheib puts it, the pregnant woman of those days "was completely
in the hands of ragged old harridans, who travelled from house to house
like tinkers with their old-fashioned labour chair, and filthy hooks hanging
from their belts." The chair, with only a horseshoe-shaped edge on
which to sit, followed the custom of sitting deliveries.

This labor chair, however unnatural it appears to us, was a reasonable
development of the time. The habit of lying deliveries upon a bed came
much later, roughly at the start of the eighteenth century. By no means
do all cultures conform. Two Germans described (in *Das Weib in der
Natur- und Völkerkunde,* first published in the nineteenth century)
40 different positions adopted during labor by women of different
areas. Most of the positions were more or less upright. A later analysis
of the birth customs of 76 countries outside Europe showed that
women in 62 of them favored upright positions, a classification that
included sitting, leaning, squatting, kneeling, and standing. The remaining 14 countries adopted positions that included lying prone, lying supine
(customary in Europe), and resting on all four limbs. The labor chair
would not be an anomaly in many countries today.

The midwives' hooks were in case of failure. "Child breaking" took place whenever a weak labor or a dead baby demanded it, and the off-spring were summarily hooked out, having been carved up in the process as much as was necessary. One major obstacle, not the fault of the midwives, was the prevailing prejudice against any form of exposure. Not only were men totally excluded (in 1521 a Hamburg doctor was burned for having disguised himself as a midwife), but the attending women had to grope in the dark beneath the skirts.

The Christian Church and its past attitudes did not help. The new life was more important than the mother's, for without baptism it was a lost soul. Either the unsuccessful midwives were dubbed as witches "who robbed innocent babes of the Holy Sacrament"—and such an indictment did nothing to raise the women's already miserable status —or great and diverting efforts were made to baptize the babe, come what may, birth or not. Curved syringes were fashioned that could eject holy water upon ailing fetuses still within a struggling uterus. A most unlikely reformer was Louis XIV of France, who did much to revolutionize obstetrics by watching his mistresses give birth. By taking an interest, the Sun King made such study respectable. Others followed suit, and gradually male midwives became fashionable, although not without considerable resentment from the well-established females.

The History of Midwifery

The progress of midwifery can be listed as a series of "firsts," most of which happened many, many years later than might be expected. The first book on the subject in English (*The Byrth of Mankynde*, prepared by Thomas Raynalde) was printed in 1540, a translation from a German work of 1513. The first original work in English is generally considered to have been William Harvey's *De Generatione Animalium,* published in 1651. Harvey had written it when in his seventies, long after his famous work on blood circulation. It was not until 1726 that the first professor of midwifery held office in any university: Joseph Gibson was given the post at Edinburgh, when that university was just about to have its flowering as the leading medical school. (Not one of the famous European medical colleges, such as Salerno, Paris, or Padua—where Harvey had been a student—then concerned itself with the subject.) But even Edinburgh did not have regular lectures on obstetrics until 1756, and a maternity hospital was not established there until 1793. In the same year France was the first country to pass decrees providing for the wel-fare and health of expectant mothers.

By the start of the nineteenth century there was no formal teaching of obstetrics in Britain, except at Edinburgh. The Medical Act of 1886 was the first to indicate that midwifery should be a necessary subject for medical qualification. In 1915 the first "antenatal clinic" was started, a particularly ill-chosen description, so dangerously close to antinatal. The first clinic was once again in Edinburgh, and by 1918 there were 120 of them throughout the country. (Marie Stopes's first antinatal, or birth-control, clinic only just missed coming first. It was established in London in 1922.) Today there are some 2,000 antenatal clinics in Britain.

The Chamberlen Family and Forceps

An interesting story, without much consideration for the Hippocratic code but with plenty for fame and fortune, concerns the development of forceps. Edmund Chapman was the first (in 1733) to illustrate and describe the "extractors," and before him William Giffard (in 1726) was the first to use them in a straightforward manner. But before both of them were the remarkable Chamberlens, a family of pioneers whose ethics did not match their inventiveness. Peter Chamberlen was born in Paris in 1560, but his Huguenot parents fled with him to England when he was nine. He later developed forceps, a device for clasping the baby's head and easing its passage in birth. Together with a brother-in-law, also called Peter, and the new instrument plus their own skill, the pair charged prodigious fees (always in advance) for attending at births. They traveled the country well armed, with the forceps locked in an elaborate chest. No one was allowed to assist them, and the delivery room was barred to every person and all eyes. Even the laboring women were blindfolded. Glasscheib says that, to confound the awe-struck and anxious relatives still further, the obstetricians rang bells, rattled chains, and banged with a hammer during the deliveries. Despite cloak, dagger, and bells, they were outstandingly successful.

The original Peter died (without issue) in 1626, and his brother-in-law and partner, Peter, inherited the instrument. On his death it went to his only son, who, unhelpfully, was also called Peter. This man used the instrument to good effect, having the queen of Charles II among his patients, and the midwifery fortunes of the family reached a zenith. The third Peter died in 1683, but before then a mixture of unwise political dabbling, plus a triumphant petitioning of Parliament by female midwives for their ancient rights, had caused the business to decline. Peter 3rd's son, Hugh, decided to sell the valuable device. (All the others had been called Peter Chamberlen, although one of them had been a brother-in-law, and the change of name seems to have partnered the change of luck.) He tried Paris first. Louis XIV's doctor, Mauriceau, provided Hugh with an awkward birth (a 38-year-old dwarf with a narrow pelvis having her first child) that Hugh should sensibly have declined. Hours later both mother and child were dead, and the deal was off.

Hugh returned to England, but then had to flee the country (the reason is obscure) for the Netherlands. There, Roger van Roonhuyze bought the instrument. Hugh vanished (to die in 1728) and the Dutchman received his ill-luck along with the forceps. At his first attempt, both mother and child died. A few more failures later, Van Roonhuyze sold the secret. Again there were failures, and another hasty sale. More and more failures and sales followed. Finally, the Amsterdam College of Medicine bought the forceps and showed just as little Hippocratic feeling by forbidding any doctor to practice midwifery unless he had bought the secret from the college. The price was 2,500 guilders plus an oath to reveal nothing. It was not until 1753, 20 years after forceps had been publicly described in England, that two Dutch doctors honorably bought the famous instrument and then honorably made it public property. But what they had paid for turned out to be a crude iron lever and certainly not the Chamberlen forceps.

Who had made the switch? Who had sold this iron bar in the first place and had kept the forceps? It is easy to suspect Hugh, the last of the Chamberlen medical line. On the other hand, his attempts at deliveries were outstandingly unsuccessful and had more of the touch of an iron bar about them than of nicely worked forceps. Could Peter 3rd, so long immured in the tradition of secrecy and in conduct generally unbecoming to the medical profession, have kept the secret even from his son and passed on to him that sinister bar? No one knows. It is still not known, even though in 1818, 90 years after Hugh's death and 135 years after Peter 3rd's, a cache of forceps was found at Woodham Mortimer Hall, near Maldon, Essex. Peter 3rd had once lived there.

The forceps practice did not quietly mature with the death of the inventive Chamberlens. It exploded vehemently. Perhaps the long years of secrecy, stretching from the sixteenth to the eighteenth century, so closely followed by the development and publication of many forms of helpful instruments, was too swift, and a reasonable use of forceps was as unlikely and improbable as reasonable behavior by a starving man suddenly confronted with food. Anyway, instruments had their heyday. Midwives reveled in them. William Hunter (elder brother of the John Hunter, who experimentally inoculated himself with venereal disease) was furious. Nature, he said, had apparently abandoned her work of propagation and left it to forceps. He himself carried a rusty pair, saying the better the midwife the thicker the rust. Eventually the craze died down, reaction set in, and nature was again left to her primeval self.

Midwives (and many of them were now men) were suddenly content to watch, to stand and stare. Sir Richard Croft did so for 52 hours while Charlotte, only child of the Prince Regent (later George IV), suffered before him. She died six hours after her stillborn child had been produced by nature, and Sir Richard then ended his own life with a bullet. (The failure of this royal birth had far-reaching consequences. The Regent's three elderly bachelor brothers promptly married to beget an heir to the throne. Within a creditably short time two daughters, one daughter, and one son respectively arrived for the three of them. The two daughters of the eldest brother died as children, and the mantle of inheritance fell upon the next daughter in line, Victoria.)

The forceps battle still flares from time to time. Thirty to forty years ago medical students in Britain were bombarded with exhortations to avoid the use of them at almost any cost. Dr. Grantly Dick-Read managed to write his famous *Childbirth Without Fear* without mentioning the word. Today forceps deliveries are frequent, but the whims of the obstetrician in charge tend to dominate. An American survey published in 1964 indicated that between one-quarter and one-third of U.S. births are assisted by forceps (the figures came from an analysis of all deliveries in 22 Naval hospitals). Although some of the hospitals used instruments on 60 percent and some on 10 percent of births, there were no differences in the death rates of the babies, either for the worse or the better.

Cesareans

The name "Cesarean section" indicates an antiquity far beyond that of forceps. Unfortunately, there is little evidence of the frequency of this drastic measure in the past, and no one even knows whether Julius Caesar was born in this way, as legend has it. (Probably not, as his mother lived long after his birth and the surgical simplicities two millennia ago were unlikely to have benefited both mother and child.) There is general agreement that Julius Caesar did not give his name to the operation, whether he suffered it or not. Some think the verb "caedere" (to cut out) is to blame, and others add that the father of Scipio Africanus called his son Caesar because he was cut out of the womb. Julius Caesar was a descendant of Scipio and therefore, according to this theory, he acquired both the reputation of being cut out plus the name from his forefather. Yet another theory holds that the term came from the Lex Regina, later called the Lex Caesarea, which forbade the burial of a dead pregnant woman until her baby had been removed.

Whereas no one knows the origin of the name there is even less certainty about the origin of the custom. The *Susruta Samhita,* the Indian textbook of medicine written between 800 B.C. and A.D. 400, recommended a cutting out of the baby should the mother die in labor. (The vagueness of the publication date cannot be helped, as disagreement abounds, but the textbook was a written statement of ancient oral tradition.) It is odd that, even though Dionysus and Aesculapius* are said —by some—to have been cut from their mothers' wombs, there is no mention of a Sectio Caesarea or anything like it in the Hippocratic writings.

There were and still are two sides to the Cesarean. On the one side the baby is cut from a dead mother; on the other the aim is to short-circuit a difficult birth and save two lives. Perhaps Caesar's mother, and many others, did survive the operation, but it is reasonable to imagine few successes. It is reported that Jacob Nufer, a Swiss butcher, operated successfully on his own wife in 1500. Not only did she live but also she bore him four more children afterward in the normal manner. Other distraught husbands, butchers, barbers, and surgeons, were frequently less successful in an age without either anesthetics or notions of antisepsis, and the practice of Cesarean section upon the living fell out of favor. It was not resuscitated until the end of the nineteenth century.

However, there was still great determination to extract babies from dead mothers, partly because the church was fervent in its demand for souls. Councils and synods urged on the operation, but midwives were reluctant either to state positively that a wretched mother had died or even more to cut her up. Remember that the morals of the times prevented them even from looking beneath the skirts, let alone below the abdominal wall. There were occasional successes. King Robert II of Scotland was allegedly cut from his mother, Marjorie Bruce, by a swift-acting hunter after the woman had broken her neck in a riding accident. King Edward VI, the son of Henry VIII and Jane Seymour, was also cut from a mother dying or dead.

Ashley Montagu writes that 2 percent of all deliveries in the United States are by Cesarean section. A Scottish hospital reported in 1964 that over 1,000 of its 18,102 deliveries (over 5.5 percent) had been Cesarean, with many mothers having four, six, or more. One woman

* Asklēpios, or Asclepius—anyway, the Greek God of Medicine, the person who may also have been a human around 1250 B.C.

has had twelve successful operations at this Glasgow hospital, and was "young enough to have a few more yet" (she was then 41). A Dublin woman apparently holds the existing record with thirteen. Whereas operations on the living are now notably successful, operations upon the dead are more complex. Is the mother really dead? What about attempts at resuscitation? What about the next of kin, and is the baby still alive?

An editorial in the *British Medical Journal* recently stated the problem. The child should be extracted as quickly as possible, and its chances are better if the mother has died suddenly rather than slowly. In any case, after five minutes the odds in favor of extracting a live infant become steadily worse, and after 25 minutes are virtually nil. Cases of longer survival have been heard of, and one child was successfully delivered recently after 45 minutes, while its dead mother was kept oxygenated by artificial respiration. The article recommended aseptic procedure just in case the mother decides to live after all.

Anesthesia

Coupled with the controversy over the interference of man or midwife with the natural process of childbirth, whether by forceps or other mechanical aid, was the storm over anesthesia. Once again, the church was loudly vocal. The idea that women might not suffer during childbirth was quite as painful to many men as the hardships normally suffered by the women. Certainly, the Bible reiterates the point. It supports the theme of inevitable and proper suffering. "I will greatly multiply thy sorrow and thy conception; in sorrow thou shalt bring forth children" (Gen. 3:16). A similar theme of anguish is found in Gal. 4:27, Isa. 66:7, Isa. 16:8, Isa. 21:3, Rev. 12:2, and Hos. 13:13. The thanksgiving ceremony called "The Churching of Women" is equally to the point: "the snares of death compassed me round about: and the pains of hell gat hold upon me. . . . We give thee humble thanks for that thou hast vouchsafed to deliver this woman thy servant from the great pain and peril of Childbirth." As soon as anesthesia was developed, there were assertions that no man had the right to rob God of the deep and earnest cries of women in labor.

Sir James Simpson, the introducer of chloroform, first used this anesthetic in 1847. His action brought the church down upon him, particularly when he used it to ease childbirth. The Scottish surgeon countered by quoting that God had caused "a deep sleep" to fall upon Adam during the process of extracting a rib to fashion Eve, thereby condoning anesthesia. (Presumably, there could have been counter-counter arguments in like vein, for were not all women punished with birth pain *after* Adam's deep sleep and Eve's misdemeanor?) *

Anyway, the anesthetists suddenly acquired a trump card when Queen Victoria gave it to them. She had frequently asserted that there were some displeasures in the repetitive and wearisome production of children, and on April 1, 1853, accepted chloroform. Dr. John Snow gave "one ounce" to her during the birth of Prince Leopold. This courageous act did not still the critics, and they exist today, but it was a body blow to the resistance movement. (Incidentally, this early story of chloroform is steeped in cross-references. Sir James Simpson, who had pioneered the use of chloroform in Britain six years beforehand, was to become a fierce antagonist of Joseph Lister, so soon to promote antisepsis. Dr. Snow, here acting as anesthetist, had already achieved immortality by removing the handle from a Soho water pump and dramatically reducing the local incidence of cholera, thereby proving it was waterborne. And poor Prince Leopold was the first sickly pointer to Queen Victoria's carrying of the hemophilia gene. It had probably arisen in her elderly father, although her child's illness was blamed initially by many upon the chloroform, either as a physical consequence of it or a spiritual punishment due to its use.)

Mimicking the history of the use and neglect of forceps for child delivery, which swung wildly from one extreme to the other, is the similarly erratic pendulum concerning the use of anesthetics in childbirth. The idea caught on. It had its promoters who used it to excess. Then came the detractors, those who said there was no pain whatever in childbirth, or there should not be and hence no need existed or should exist for pain-killing treatment. Grantly Dick-Read made his name famous as an advocate of this argument. He had written other books before 1942, but in that year *Childbirth Without Fear* was published. In the next 20 years it sold over 500,000 copies. Here are some quotations. "There is no physiological function in the body which gives rise to pain in the normal course of health. . . . The physiological perfection of the human body knows no greater paradox than pain in normal parturition (birth). . . . I am inclined to believe that babies are born entirely free from instinctive fears. . . . All fear therefore in a human being is acquired either by suggestion or by association. . . . From this it follows that faith eliminates fear." And, finally, a statement many may find particularly hard to swallow: "I am persuaded without a shadow of doubt that, with the exception of unforeseen accidents, the origin of every form of disease, both surgical and medical, whether hereditary or not, can be traced by

---

* Simpson also argued that "In *sorrow* thou shalt bring forth children . . ." was a mistranslation for "effort."

careful investigation to the influence of fear upon the human mechanism."

Many believe that in the past 20 or 30 years too much emphasis has been placed on relaxation and the exercise of the voluntary muscles. Sir John Peel, Surgeon-gynecologist to the Queen, is one of them. At a conference in Milan in 1965 he told 400 obstetricians that Dr. Dick-Read had been right for all the wrong reasons. The concept of painless labor was untrue, and the claim that women in primitive communities suffered no pain was less than a half-truth. Sir John did not like any form of indoctrination that led the patient to believe that "labor would be completely painless and all drugs harmful."

Pain-killing can be dangerous at childbirth (3 percent of all maternal deaths in Britain are due to anesthesia, according to *Perinatal Mortality**), and not only can drugs affect the baby as well as the mother, but anesthetizing a woman in labor is difficult. Professor J. Stallworthy, of Oxford, has called it "one of the most difficult tasks an anaesthetist has to perform." At the Milan conference Sir John summed up present knowledge by saying pethidine was the drug of his choice once labor had started. With regard to the second stage "what you do depends on the philosophy and the expectation of the patient, and the availability of anaesthetic and obstetric personnel."

Home or Hospital?

As experts are not always readily at the beck and call of every woman in labor, even in hospitals, more frequently at home, these facts are bandied about in yet another traditional argument concerning childbirth: should babies be delivered at home or in a hospital?

In England and Wales some 70 percent of all deliveries are in a maternity institution, whether a hospital or something smaller. In 1927 the figure was 15 percent; so the revolution has been outstandingly rapid. In the United States, Sweden, and Australia, the proportion is even higher. The principal argument put forward in favor of an institutional delivery is that countless forms of aid and assistance are at hand. Against this is all the familiarity of home, with the emotional comfort it possesses, and the friendly local doctor dropping in to add one more to a family already familiar to him.

Both points of view were expressed with candor at the 1965 congress of the Royal Society of Health. Sir Dugald Baird, professor of obstetrics and gynecology in Aberdeen, said bluntly that hospital delivery was safer. A birth caused too much upset in a small house. But Dr. Andrew

* This British survey, published in 1963 by N. R. Butler and D. G. Bonham, is an extremely important compilation of facts relating to death at birth.

Smith, of Durham, said hospitals paid inadequate regard to personal dignity and emotions. Maternity patients were no longer the humble poor; they were articulate women wanting the most out of the experience and were not just "walking wombs, and vehicles for foetuses." Supporting him, Dr. P. A. S. Lowden said the myth of hospital superiority must be destroyed. Seventy-two percent of hospital deliveries were done by midwives, 4.2 percent by consultants. The argument is eternal, but a delegate from Cardiff described a unit that provided some of the best of both worlds. In it mothers were delivered by their own doctors, and then packed off home, some within 100 minutes, all within 18 hours.

Statistics on the subject are bewildering. Some reports (such as *Perinatal Mortality*) conclude that home births should be virtually abandoned if deaths are to be much reduced. Others (such as "Domiciliary Midwifery," an article in *The Lancet* of December 5, 1964) conclude that if hospitals cannot show themselves better than homes, then home births should continue or increase. Certainly home births cost a country less money. With over 800,000 births in England and Wales every year, 500,000 of which are delivered in institutions, with a ten-day puerperium (or length of time after childbirth when a woman needs professional care) commonly recommended, some 5 million maternity-ward days are spent every year. On any one day, quite apart from those at home, there are 13,500 women lying in maternity institutions. In the United States, where an even greater proportion of deliveries takes place in institutions, and where there are nearly 4 million births a year, there must be over 100,000 women in the maternity wards on any single day.

How Long a Stay?

An important and frequently challenged point is the length of stay in hospital. Ideas on the subject have altered radically even within the last dozen years. In 1955, Britain's Central Midwives Board stated that "the lying-in period is not less than fourteen days nor more than twenty-eight days after the end of labour." Six years later the board said it "was not less than ten days nor more than twenty-eight." In 1959, a committee report on maternity services thought that "normal (not average) length of the puerperium should be ten days." This committee, bearing in mind a rising birth rate and a general bed shortage, had considerably eaten into those more leisurely two to four weeks. More nibbling was to follow. In a Yorkshire hospital, it was decided to send 30 percent of the mothers home after two days, provided that birth weight, home conditions, and fitness of mother and child were all suitable. This rapid dismissal of one-third brought down the average length of stay considerably. Since then other institutions have tended to reduce those arbitrary ten days. (According to one surgeon this committee report was responsible for ossifying the idea that there was something inherently valuable in care lasting ten days.) By 1962 the average length of stay in Britain was 9.5 days in nonteaching hospitals, 11.1 days in the London teaching hospitals, and 9.2 days in provincial teaching hospitals. By 1965, an average of three to four days had been lopped off even these times. Length of stay includes time before birth. Women do not, in general, produce their babies on passing through the hospital doors, but wait and labor awhile. Therefore, the average length of stay, whether for the right reasons (doctor and mother both wish it) or for the wrong reasons (the maternity wards are suddenly under pressure), is already notably less than ten days. The current feeling is for no fixed rules and more judgment about individual cases. Philip Rhodes, professor of gynecology at St. Thomas's Hospital in London, wrote in 1964 that "the length of the puerperium . . . should be assessed for each woman and her baby, and not preordained."

Maternal Death

A résumé of the history of obstetrics and the rise and fall of different theories is totally invalid without an account of the attitude toward puerperal fever. It was the scourge of childbirth, and a great dread. More specifically, it was often an invasion of the raw places of the new mother by streptococcus hemolyticus. These wounds were the lacerations of the birth canal and the huge area where the placenta had been. Given opportunity, the streptococci would multiply rapidly. The first symptoms of this "childbed fever" came on the second or third day after labor, but only when the bacteria moved into the nearby veins and lymph vessels did the symptoms become really severe, with much fever, shivering, prostration, a fast pulse, and abdominal pain. General inflammation was then gaining the upper hand, as so frequently occurred. When the bacteria reached the general circulation, they caused septicemia accompanied by a very high temperature, delirium, prostration, and death. Every midwife knew the list of symptoms only too well. Puerperal fever was all too common. It did not always kill, but it was always feared.

Like so many infections, it was rare in the days when humans lived more separate lives. It increased with the increase in town life, and it reached unparalleled peaks with the creation of large maternity hospitals in the eighteenth and nineteenth centuries. The bacteria would leap with ease, so to speak, from victim to victim, from an infected woman to another woman who would soon be equally infected, as the students, midwives, and doctors went from bed to bed. Maternal mortality figures were terrifying. Perhaps a hospital would be safe for a while, and then perhaps this would be broken by a death rate of one in four, or more. With such odds, it is little wonder that mothers gave thanks in the "Churching of Women" for their deliverance.

Semmelweiss and Puerperal Fever

Quite the most desperate tale in the research for safe childbirth and on puerperal fever is provided in the life and death of Ignaz Philipp Semmelweiss. From beginning to end it has all the ingredients of melodrama, the battle with authority, his downfall, the poignant manner of his going, and his eventual vindication. Essentially, Dr. Semmelweiss's contribution to obstetrics was an insistence on cleanliness, upon the washing of hands. He objected that students should go directly from the autopsy room into the delivery room. He believed they somehow carried the disease from the dead women they had been examining, or even dissecting, to the living women who next received their attention and who, in so many cases, were dead women a few days later. He ordered washbasins to be placed strategically between the two rooms and advocated washing. The students would have nothing of his plans, or of his soap and water. Academic freedom, they said, was at stake. Who did he think they were? Midwives? Semmelweiss, never a tactful man, was content to call them murderers. On the following day he was dismissed.

All this took place, not in the Middle Ages but during the last century. Semmelweiss was born in Budapest in 1818. He qualified in 1844, and was fired from the Vienna Hospital two years later. He was dismissed despite the fact that the casualty rate for mothers attended by students was far, far higher (often one in four died) than for those attended merely by midwives. Only the students examined the dead, and mothers implored to be left alone by them. Semmelweiss wandered sadly to Venice, and in 1847 he suddenly heard that his friend, the anatomist Jacob Kolletschka, had died, following an apparently insignificant scratch received during a dissection. At the postmortem (and Semmelweiss luckily was in Vienna that day) all the symptoms of puerperal fever were apparent in the dead man, all the swelling and inflammation.

Suddenly Semmelweiss saw the light. "Puerperal fever," he wrote to the Vienna Medical Society, "is a blood poisoning caused by the poisoning that forms in the corpse. . . . It is transmitted to the pregnant women by the examining doctor." On this occasion his ideas were listened to by at least two men who could help him. He was offered a maternity clinic to test the theories and therefore had to recruit some students for the testing to be exact. The midwives left, and the students entered. So too did death. Mortality jumped from 9 percent (even the cleaner midwives had much to answer for with one mother dying out of ten) to 27 percent. So far, in one sense, so good. All students who had examined the dead were then forced, with Semmelweiss always on the alert, to wash their hands in a chlorinated solution. Mortality promptly dropped to 12 percent. This was good, but no better than the midwives. A cancerous woman provided a final clue. Semmelweiss had examined her, and then five normal women in labor. All five promptly died. The distraught physician realized the agents of death must be present in all dead tissue. So, thenceforth, every student, whether from the mortuary or not, was forced to wash. Mortality at long last plummeted right down to less than one maternal death in 100.

Success? Yes, but not for Semmelweiss and not even for his system. Obstetricians came to look, but went away amazingly unconvinced. Handwashing can do no harm, said Germany's top man, but purging and bloodletting are preferable. (Bacteriologically, these were still the Dark Ages, although their days were numbered. Louis Pasteur was then 27 and Joseph Lister 22.) Semmelweiss, frantic and with the symptoms of schizophrenia descending upon him, never held himself back. "Murderer," according to one report, was the mildest expression he used. In 1849, just five years after qualifying, Semmelweiss was dismissed again, this time for good. Broken, dazed, apathetic, indifferent and poor, he returned to Budapest.

Hungary welcomed him and gave him a job. He married an 18-year-old girl, who was to produce five children for him, two of whom died in infancy. He was permitted to establish his washing routine, and he brought maternal mortality down to less than 1 percent, but his general well-being was increasingly at the mercy of his mental health. His writings, when he started them again in 1857, were generally rantings. (His most famous work, published in 1861, was poorly received at the time; but this treatise fetched more than $12,000 in November, 1965, at a Sotheby's auction.) He also took to posting placards on walls: "Fathers, when you summon a doctor or midwife, you are summoning death. . . ." At the great Congress of Gynecology held in Paris in 1858 its president, M. Dubois, mentioned Semmelweiss only to pooh-pooh his theories: "It is possible these were based upon some useful principles, but the correct execution of them entailed such difficulties that the highly problematical results did not warrant their exploitation."

Shortly afterward, while he was still in his forties, Semmelweiss's schizophrenia got the better of him, and he was sent back again to a Viennese clinic, this time as patient not doctor. Just two weeks after arriving, he suddenly succumbed. An infected wound, apparently the result of his last postmortem examination, caused septicemia. He died on August 13, 1865, from the same bacteria he had sought to conquer all his life.

The pathos is that he died young (he was only 47) at a turning point in the war against bacteria. On the very day before his death, Lister began to disinfect wounds experimentally in Glasgow, and in the same year a Parisian physician, Villemin, reported that TB was emphatically a contagious disease; he had succeeded in proving the tubercle's guilt. Bacteriology had begun. As Semmelweiss had known only too well, the reactionary groups would not give up easily. Fourteen years later, having isolated the streptococcus of puerperal fever, Louis Pasteur was still having a rough time in the Paris Academy. "It is not miasma," he shouted, "nor anything but the nursing and medical staffs who carry this microbe from an infected woman to a healthy one."

The tide, despite those who would not acknowledge this, had already turned. Semmelweiss could so easily have lived to see the day. He would have been 67 when Lister wrote: "Without Semmelweiss my achievements would be nothing. To this great son of Hungary surgery owes most."

Semmelweiss died, it should be reiterated, not in the mists of antiquity, but a century ago. And his death was by no means the end of puerperal fever. It was only the prelude to the beginning of the end. The fever as a major horror had many more years to run. For instance, in an obituary of Dr. Miles Phillips, who died in 1965 and who had started to specialize in midwifery after graduation in this century, it was written: "Puerperal sepsis, in his time, was the scourge of obstetrics." The scourge was therefore still rampant very recently. Nowadays it is laid low. Should it occur today, despite precautions, the sovereign remedies are penicillin and the sulphonamides. Semmelweiss's battle has finally been won.

About the most shaming aspect of the whole history of midwifery is that, on occasion, more mothers died than babies. Adult women ought to be able, one might suppose, to survive the trauma of childbirth better than their brand-new and diminutive offspring squeezed so abruptly into a separate existence. Yet puerperal fever, marching triumphantly up and down the wards, found the raw wounds of the mothers far more susceptible to attack than the mewling objects that had caused them.

A report from the Hôtel Dieu in 1664 (the words "hospital," "hotel," and "hostel" are all etymologically the same, and took time to settle into their present meanings) stated during one epidemic that 33 percent of their mothers had died either during or shortly after childbirth. Semmelweiss's Viennese hospital caused maternal mortality to be almost as high. National figures, not that such facts were collected, must have been lower, since home confinements were never so dangerous as hospitals could be. St. George's Hospital in London commented sadly in 1856, when its own maternal mortality rate was none too good, that "women delivered in their own habitations were often living in the greatest filth and poverty and very limited accommodation, and yet these women seemed to do infinitely better than those who are removed to spacious buildings where every attention can be devised." The same report stated that there were only ten deaths out of 2,800 home deliveries (or .35 percent). The hospitals could scarcely compete. In the same year, Sir James Simpson, in his *Obstetric Memories,* wrote that among maternal deaths "only a comparatively small proportion are the direct result of convulsions, hemorrhage, rupture of the uterus or other more immediate or primary complications and accidents connected to parturition: the great majority of these maternal deaths is produced by puerperal fever."

"Until about thirty years ago," Sir Dugald Baird has written, "the most urgent problem facing the obstetrician was maternal death." Only within thirty years has the baby been receiving something like the correct amount of attention as well. Whereas, the maternal mortality rate in England and Wales (including abortion) has dropped to .026 percent (or one mother in 4,000), the infant mortality rate (stillbirth and neonatal) is still over 100 times higher. The mother is doing well these days; the child is less likely to do so.

Before leaving the mother, that percentage maternal mortality rate should be translated into less impersonal terms. It means, with 850,000 births a year, the deaths of 212 mothers. In New York in 1962 it was calculated that 43 percent of all maternal deaths were from abortions —mostly illegal. Yet, abortions apart, that figure of 212 maternal deaths a year in England and Wales will surely come down. A report from Northern Ireland's Ministry of Health considered that deaths were "definitely unavoidable" among only 13 percent of the mothers who died between 1960 and 1963. All sorts of happenings were to blame: home confinements were permitted which should not have been; some women never told anyone they were pregnant; correct diagnosis of impending trouble was not made until too late; the emergency flying squad did not arrive—and over the four years, the errors pushed the total to 95 maternal deaths out of 132,104 births.

The future will inevitably reduce the death rate still further, but it cannot effect a reduction similar to that of recent years. The maternal mortality graphs indicate dramatically that many of us alive today were apparently born in a kind of Middle Ages of obstetrics. Take the figure for the United States as a whole. In 1915, not so long ago, the number of white mothers dying was six per 1,000 births (the number of Negro mothers dying was, and still is, at least double the white figure). By 1930 the figures were still the same. By 1940 the white figure was down to three per 1,000, the Negro eight per 1,000. By 1950—a big leap—it was .6 per 1,000 for whites, two per 1,000 for Negroes. By 1960 .25 for whites, one for Negroes. In other words, the proportion of women dying in childbirth had been divided by 25 for whites in thirty years, and by ten for Negroes. As Sir Dugald Baird put it, thirty years ago the problems were infection, hemorrhage, and obstructed labor; now antibiotics are used against the infections, transfusions against the hemorrhage, and Cesareans against obstructions. So the graph has come plummeting down.

Not every place is like the United States or Europe. In 1930, when the white U.S. figure was six deaths per 1,000, the figure in India was 23 per 1,000. Sir John Megaw, then director general of India's medical services, considered that 200,000 Indian mothers died every year in childbirth. He also calculated this meant that one-tenth of all Indian wives would die as a result of maternal labor. The modern blessings of antibiotics, blood transfusion, and quick surgery are still to come in India for most of her laboring women, for it is a country where most people are born, live, and die without a qualified doctor's single attendance.

Infant Mortality

Now to the offspring. Once again the Dark Ages have only just passed. At the time of the Spanish-American War, the present discrepancy between, say, India and Europe scarcely existed. In 1900 the Indian infant mortality rate was calculated at 232 per 1,000. In England and Wales it was then 154 per 1,000 and in the United States 122 per 1,000. By 1951 India was still in similar straits (116 per thousand) but the English figure was 30 per 1,000, and the American 29 per 1,000.

South Africa manages to maintain such a discrepancy even within a single country and at the same time. Recent infant mortality figures are 28 per 1,000 for whites, 65 per 1,000 for Asians, 127 per 1,000 for Coloreds (mixed), and 116, 250, and 397 per 1,000 for Pretoria,

Cape Town, and Port Elizabeth Africans. Would the South Africans agree with Sir George Newman, who wrote in 1916 that "the death rate of infants is the most sensitive index we possess of physical welfare and the effect of sanitary government?"

Infant-mortality figures for the genuine Dark Ages do not exist. They only begin to arise nationally in Britain after the registration of births, deaths, and marriages had become compulsory in 1837. By the middle of the nineteenth century infant mortality in towns was 200 per 1,000 (like town Africans in South Africa today). This means that at least one-fifth of all babies born alive never reached their first birthday.

In those days it was emphatically best to be breastfed. Near the city of Manchester in 1904, according to A. V. Neale, the death rate was 128 per 1,000 for breastfed babies, 263 per 1,000 for cows' milk babies, and 439 per 1,000 (or nearly one out of two) for babies fed on condensed and sugared milk. By the end of Edward VII's days, the British national rate was 116 babies dead after one year for every 1,000 born alive. By World War I, it was 108 per 1,000. By the time peace was declared it was near 90 per 1,000. By 1923 it was 72 per 1,000. By 1928 it was 60 per 1,000. By 1935—and the Depression could not have helped—it was 62 per 1,000. By 1940 it was 57 per 1,000. By 1945, despite, or because of, food rationing for all plus full employment, it was 45 per 1,000. By 1950, the time of the Korean War, it was 38 per 1,000. By 1955 it was 27 per 1,000. By 1966 it was 20 per 1,000 or a total of 17,000 babies dying in the year before reaching their first birthday. Some other European countries do better, notably Sweden with 15 per 1,000. Some do worse—such as Yugoslavia with 80 per 1,000. The United States, ranking 14th in infant mortality, has 24.3 infant deaths per 1,000 live births. In all countries there are regional differences. However much the infant-mortality figures may be successfully trimmed in the future, there is always likely to remain a hard core. Some of the congenital malformations will see to that. The determination of a hard core to withstand medical advance is already manifest in mortality tables, and it shows up in the first seven days of life. In 1910 there were 76 infant deaths (per 1,000) between the ages 4 weeks and 52 weeks, a number now slashed to 6. In the same year there were 15 deaths per 1,000 between a week and 4 weeks, a figure now cut to 2. But also, in that same year, there were 24 deaths per 1,000 in the first week, a figure now modestly pruned to 13. To sum up: more children in Britain die of natural causes during the first seven days than in the next 30 to 40 years.

Hand in hand with the declining death rate for infants has gone a reduction in the stillbirth rate, the number of babies born dead. In

1928 (and once again a recent decade appears deeply embedded in the
remote past) the proportion was 40 per 1,000 births. By 1939 it had
fallen to 38 per 1,000. Then came the war, and the most dramatic fall
in stillbirths on record: by 1945 it was 28 per 1,000. By 1955 it was
23 per 1,000 and by 1966 it was only 15 per 1,000. Even so, this means
14,000 stillbirths in England and Wales in a year. In the most recent
figure for the United States, there were more than 65,000 attended
fetal deaths in 1964.

All this improvement, one feels, should have narrowed the gap of
class inequality. It has done nothing of the kind. The social distinction
remains as open as ever. In 1943 Professor Richard Titmuss pointed
out that despite improvements, despite a reduction in infant mortality
and the stillborn dead, the range of social class inequality in 1931 was
as great as or greater than it was in 1911. More recently, James Kin-
caid has told the same story. Even though the National Health Service,
Britain's socialized medicine, was initiated in 1948, on the basis of
equal care for all, the class discrepancies have remained just as constant.
From Class I (professionals) right through to Class V (unskilled
laborers), the death rates increase in the same sort of ratio as always.
Stillbirths for Class I in Britain were 16 per 1,000 in 1949, and 13
per 1,000 in 1958; for Class V they dropped from 26 to 24 per 1,000.
Death rates for infants up to a month old fell from 16 per 1,000 for
Class I in the first fourteen years of the National Health Service down
to 12 per 1,000; with Class V they fell from 30 to 24 per 1,000. France
reports a similar constancy among the classes. Hungary, on the other
hand, does not. There, according to E. Szabady, the manual and non-
manual differentiation has narrowed.

Countless factors are to blame. One is that tall women have fewer
stillbirths than medium-sized women, who have fewer than small women,
whatever the class. The higher classes (or socioeconomic groups) have
more tall women. Another is that girls who grow up with many brothers
and sisters are more likely on average to produce stillbirths—and the
poorer classes have larger families. A third is that education helps to
cut down infant mortality and Class V is less well-educated. And many
more. Will it be one generation or two before the welfare state can
knock down a class structure which, without the black-and-white clarity
of the United States or South Africa, shows up inequality just as emphatically?

What of the future and that hard core of deaths? The World Health
Organization conducted its own mortality survey in 1962. Its conclusion was that in every country 20 percent of the mothers constituted
90 percent of the risks. Each country therefore should make doubly
certain that its 20 percent receives the necessary extra care. In Britain a

doctor with a list of 2,500 patients is likely to have, with the existing birth rate, 43 pregnant patients in a year. Two-thirds of them will probably go to a maternity unit, and he will deal with the remaining third, perhaps 15 a year, at their homes. Plainly those at home should include few or none of WHO's 20 percent with 90 percent of the risks.

Infanticide

Another hard core, nothing to do with natural causes (at least not in the strict sense), is infanticide, the killing of the baby. Only the mother can be charged with infanticide; anyone else involved may be charged with murder. Britain's Infanticide Act of 1938 provides that "Where a woman by any wilful act or omission causes the death of her child, being a child under the age of twelve months, but at the time of the act or omission the balance of her mind was disturbed by reason of her not having fully recovered from the effect of giving birth to the child, or by reason of the effect of lactation consequent upon the birth of the child, then, notwithstanding that the circumstances were such that but for this act the offence would have amounted to murder. . . ." she is guilty of the felony of infanticide. She may then be dealt with as if she had committed manslaughter. Some think the law too lax, permitting a mother to get rid of a child with minimum consequences. Certainly the felony of infanticide, according to C. J. Polson, is censured with great sympathy and understanding, for the child is assumed to have been born dead until the prosecution proves otherwise.

Certainly no judge has imprisoned a woman for such an offense recently, even though a life sentence is theoretically possible. Others think the law incredibly harsh, for it involves the wretched mother in perhaps two visits to the courts and the delays of legal procedures. More women are charged with the offense than are brought to trial, but those actually tried with all the pomp of an assize court were 17 in 1960, 13 in 1961, 17 in 1962, and 13 in 1963. These women, unless granted bail, were confined to prison hospitals while awaiting trial. At least the law is better than it used to be before the first Infanticide Act of 1922, which introduced the offense of infanticide. Until that time the killing of infants was always treated as murder. Between 1906 and 1921, 60 women were sentenced to be hanged for causing the death of newborn children, and for 59 of them the sentences were commuted. The exception was Mrs. Leslie James, a housekeeper of 39, who was convicted on July 24, 1907, for suffocating a newborn child she had agreed to adopt for about $17. She had adopted other children for money, and the jury in this case made no recommendation for mercy.

The basic reason for the existing leniency and the desire for greater relaxation is that postnatal depression is a very common result of birth. In some women it may reach uncontrollable heights. "The mother's temperature suddenly rises, she is restless and depressed, shortly she becomes intensely emotional and impulsive, she may be suicidal or infanticidal, or both," according to an obstetrical textbook.

The Sex Ratio

Back now to more natural happenings and the incomprehensible matter of sex ratio. Why should more boys be born than girls? Why are more boys born during and immediately after a war? Why is there such a waste of males before birth? Why is the ratio different in different areas?

In Britain 105.6 males are born alive for every 100 females (but the gap has recently been widening, and the trend is continuing). In the United States, the ratio is about the same for whites, but 102.6 males to 100 females for Negro births. Greece and Korea both have 113 males per 100 females, but in Cuba it is 101 males per 100 females. After birth, the ratios change because males die faster than females. Parity, or equality in numbers, in Britain, is reached by the age of 30. The United States puts the age of parity higher, in some areas as high as the age of 50. In both cases, as males continue to die faster, the ratio is eventually reversed with more women than men alive. By the age of 55 men are dying, quite suddenly, very much faster than women. By the age of 95 every man is outnumbered by four women. Women have started dying at a greater rate than men by the age of 75 merely for the reason that most of the population at that age is female. Men cannot then die in comparable numbers because so many men have already died.

The story is the same in the uterus. There are more males to start with, and more of them die during gestation until the ratio at birth is something more than 105 males to 100 females. At conception, 266 days beforehand, the ratio may well have been 150 males to 100 females. Some scientists put it as high as 170 to 100 (or nearly 2:1), while others put it as low as 120 to 100. No one knows. Certainly many more stillbirths are male than female, whether born at the correct time or miscarried many months earlier. A huge United States survey put the ratio at 134 males to 100 females for those stillbirths produced when due, 201 to 100 for those miscarried at the fourth month of pregnancy, and 431 to 100 for those produced two months earlier. Unfortunately, even though these figures (of Ciocco) are constantly quoted, the situation is less clear-cut than it used to be. Perhaps the midwives and doctors, it is now suggested, confused the sex. After all, the clitoris and penis, being the same lump of embryological tissue to start with, do look remarkably similar in the early stages of development. But, despite differences of opinion, no one has yet claimed that more females are conceived. It is still undeniably true that more males start life and die off earlier all along the line.

No one knows why the males are the weaker and less viable sex from start to finish. They are bigger and therefore more of a problem at birth, but what has birth to do with miscarriages? They carry a Y chromosome, and not two X's like the female, but what precise benefit— if any—do those X's give over the Y? No one knows.

Nor is it known what pushes the sex ratio at birth up and down. The Boer War to a small extent and the next two wars to a large extent saw an increase in the number of male births in Britain. Nature, it can be said, was merely repairing the ravages of war. (She also steps up male production in neutral countries at the same time, although not so much.) If one puts beneficent Nature kindly but firmly to one side, what else can cause the wartime changes?

Again no one knows for sure. Theories that hold some water, because they are backed up in part by some evidence in their favor, include an increase in young marriages, which can increase the male ratio; full employment, which means greater prosperity and fewer stillbirths— hence more males; an absence of husbands except for brief periods, and therefore more conceptions by the highly fertile who might produce more males as another of their attributes; and a relative lack of intercourse and therefore pregnancy, enabling the uterus to rest and be a better place for the weaker male fetus when it does come along. Different authors choose the theory they like best, and no doubt there are others.

Apart from the war story, and taking many other surveys into account, it has been found that the sex ratio is high (i.e., there are more males) among the offspring of mixed-race marriages (notably between Negro and white), of AB blood group mothers, of radiated fathers (as shown by the two bombs dropped on Japan in 1945), of very old mothers of 50 or more, of United States Air Force fathers who either fly transport aircraft or who do not fly, and amongst offspring that are the first-born or who are blood group O. (None of this means that, e.g., transport pilots will produce only boys; merely that they deviate slightly from the average proportion.) On the other hand, girls are slightly more frequent than normal among the offspring of high-performance-aircraft pilots, of mothers who smoke or were radiated, of older fathers, of unskilled laborers and manual workmen, and among illegitimate children or among offspring with older brothers and sisters. Professor A. S. Parkes, of Cambridge, summed up the heterogenous collection of differences by stating that wherever conditions are rough, as with illegitimates and un-skilled fathers, more boys will die, and therefore more girls will be in evidence. As a theory it fits—almost.

Fifty years ago everything was nicely balanced so that, with more boys dying and more born, the sexes were exactly equal in number between ages of 15 and 19. Obviously, said everyone, it is arranged that every Jack should find a Jill when both are at the right reproducing age. A country like India gives a different picture. Throughout the whole of the subcontinent's census history, Indian Jacks have not had enough Jills. In 1921 there were 940 women for every 1,000 men. In 1951 there were 947. More males are born there (as well as elsewhere) but the infant girls are treated with less enthusiasm, and are then rapidly subjected to years and years of remorseless childbearing.

One suspects that Indian conditions represent a truer historical pic-ture than twentieth-century Britain. Therefore, the sex ratio should, by this comparison, be reversed with more females born. Also, with the human method of reproduction, Nature is being wasteful by giving one wife (or nearly one wife in India) to every man. One man could (and kings like Rameses II, Louis XIV, or the musical King of Siam did) sire many children while his true wife is gestating only one. The animal kingdom does not help with an explanation, but merely indicates how deep-rooted is the relative weakness of the male sex and how basic the greater number of male conceptions. Cows produce 134 males to 100 females in stillbirths, and 105 to 100 for live births. Pigs are similar, as are rats, mice, and birds. Horses produce more male stillbirths, but more female live births. The general picture, therefore, is the same. Males die faster, with some likelihood of parity at the reproductive age, and yet with little likelihood that any female will remain unmated whether in the mousehole, the bovine herd, the Indian village, or the twentieth-century western world. The human female is even less likely to be un-mated in the future. We are heading, says Professor Parkes, "for a world shortage of marriageable females." The cause is the greater sur-vival of males.

We are also heading, willy-nilly, for a time when the sex ratio will be adjustable. Claims have been made (by L. B. Shettles in 1961, for instance) that male sperm can be distinguished from female sperm in bulk (it is the male who ordains the sex) or that they can be separated. Someday, both will be possible. Will there be a rush for male chil-dren? Certain countries today treat female offspring with something of the reverence they accord to yet another litter from the cat. Will they maintain that attitude when women are in short supply? One longs to know, but one's ignorance will do nothing to halt the arrival of an artificial sex-determining mechanism. The contraceptive pill will soon be either pink or blue, or both, with either boys or girls or neither temporarily in demand. There may even be a pill ensuring twins.

Humanity is most undecided about the laws of chance, particularly when a baby's sex is involved. On the one hand, great financial stakes will be placed at a racetrack on most slender odds; on the other, most families will consider themselves somehow odd if all the siblings are of one sex. An outsider's chances in a race, listed at 63 to 1, will cause many to stake hard cash. The thought of having either six boys or no boys at all from six pregnancies, each of which has a likelihood of 63 to 1 against, will strike most mothers as totally improbable.

In fact, again assuming six successful pregnancies and disregarding the slight inequality in the sex ratio, the chances for and against particular boy-and-girl combinations can readily be assessed. The chances are 1 in 64 (or 63 to 1 against) that all will be boys; 6 in 64 (or 29 to 3 against) that there will be 5 boys and 1 girl; 15 in 64 (or 49 to 15 against) that there will be 4 boys and 2 girls; 20 in 64 (or 11 to 5 against—almost 2 to 1) that there will be 3 of each; 15 in 64 (or 49 to 15 against) that there will be 2 boys and 4 girls; 6 in 64 (or 29 to 3 against) that there will be 1 boy and 5 girls; and 1 chance in 64 (or 63 to 1 against) that there will be no boys.

Putting this another way, the chance that all 6 will be of the same sex is 1 in 32 (or 31 to 1 against); that 5 will be of one sex are 6 in 32 (or 13 to 3 against); that 4 will be of one sex are 15 in 32 (or 17 to 15—almost even); and that both sexes will be equal are 10 in 32 (or 11 to 5—almost 2 to 1). Having three boys and three girls is therefore much less likely than having four of one and two of the other. Having five of one sex and only one of the other will cause many mothers to worry about themselves (or their mates). What, they ask, is causing this one-sex emphasis? The answer is, probably, nothing; or, at least, no more than the chance (6 in 32, or 13 to 3 against) of getting either five heads or five tails if you toss a coin six times.

The Baby's Weight

Weight and the fact that males are heavier has often been blamed for influencing the sex ratio. Bigger babies, assuming equal mothers, can plainly be more of a problem at birth, but the size difference can hardly be a problem in the early days of pregnancy, when males are also less viable. At the fetal age of 8 weeks, both male and female young weigh 5 gm.—⅙ oz.—and sex weight differences are scarcely detectable until a month or two before birth. At birth the average male is heavier by 3 to 5 oz., and he has spent, on average, a day less in the uterus than a girl. The weight at birth is important, partly because it can be correlated, so far as the population is concerned, with survival chances.

Today's enthusiasm for recording birth weights is intense. Fathers sending telegrams consider the offspring's poundage as exciting as its sex or general well-being. Such interest did not exist in the past. There appears to be no mention of birth weight in any ancient Greek, Roman, Arabic, or Hebrew writings. The first mention, according to one surveyor of this subject (Cone), was in a book by Mauriceau, the seventeenth-century French obstetrician who cleverly produced a laboring 38-year-old dwarf to confound Hugh Chamberlen (see page 144). Strangely, the Frenchman put average weight at "13 livres," or almost 15 British pounds. As if the subject were fishing, even this tall story was topped in 1747 by the English surgeon, Theophilus Lobb, who wrote that 16 lb., 7 oz. was "a representative baby." Quite suddenly, reason and better estimates prevailed. The German Röderer of Göttingen wrote in 1753 that past writers were "hallucinating" as he found weights to be 6 lb., 12 oz., for boys, and 6 lb., 5 oz., for girls. The first proper English study (in 1785) put both weights some 7 oz. heavier. And there, on average, give or take an ounce or two, they have remained.

As a temporary digression into the animal world for comparison, the human birth weight is neither particularly big nor small. Bats produce infants of a few grams. Marsupials, like the kangaroo, give birth to minute embryos ½ in. or so in length. The largest marsupial, 6 ft. tall, is the red kangaroo; its young are born when 2 cm. long, weighing less than a gram. At the other extreme, still within the range of mammals, is the blue whale, the largest animal that has ever existed. Its calf is 22 ft. long and weighs almost 10 tons. This huge thing is milkfed for half a year (and is sexually mature two and a half years later when it has grown to 75 ft.). A baby African elephant is the weight of an overweight man. A baby blue whale is the weight of a full-grown African elephant. A human mother, producing some ten young of 7½ lb. each in her lifetime, is giving birth therefore to about three-fifths of her own weight during her life. A mother mouse gives birth to a quarter of her own body weight in a single pregnancy, five times her body weight in her mouse lifetime.

The mean birth weight of boys and girls together in European communities is about 7 lb., 4 oz. Pygmies, the smallest human beings, produce babies averaging 5 lb., 11 oz., according to one Congolese survey. Birth weight is almost entirely under the mother's genetical influence, not the father's. Weights range from virtually nothing at all, in extreme prematurity when the chances of survival are nil, up to 11 lb. or so when chances are again less satisfactory. Weights of 5 to 10 lb. are often regarded as normal, despite their disparity. It is strange that this "normal" divergence is preserved in adult life. From women of 100 lb. to men of 200 lb. is the normal range that embraces most of mankind. Although countless babies that are either extremely underweight or equally overweight survive, the optimum weight accompanied by the greatest chance of survival is slightly higher than the mean weight. Mortality is then, according to one large survey (Karn and Penrose), less than 2 percent. Mortality increases as birth weight diverges from normal. Babies of either 6 lb. or 9 lb. have a mortality of 3 percent. If they are 5 lb. or 9¾ lb., the mortality has gone up to 5 percent. Mortality then leaps up as divergence increases. It is 10 percent for babies of 4½ lb. or 10½ lb. and far more severe for babies lighter or heavier.

The European groups produce heavier babies than other racial groups. A world average is nearer 6½ lb. than the European 7 lb., 4 oz. Particularly small are the Southern Indians and the Ceylonese, which are about 6 lb., and those African Pygmies, which are even smaller. Unfortunately, no one knows whether these differences can be attributed to ethnic origin (as with black skin) or poor maternal diet and physique or a wretched environment or a mixture of the lot. Studies on Europeans point up a few of the complexities. Birth weight rises with birth order. Second babies are heavier than the firstborn by about 3½ oz. Third babies are heavier still. Thereafter, the trend is less definite. Possibly the increasing age of the mother has a countereffect on weight. Other countereffects are smoking, maternal height, and a small pregnancy weight gain. Smoking mothers produce babies that average 5 to 7 oz. less. Short women also produce lighter babies, and so do light women. Finally, mothers who put on little weight during pregnancy produce slightly smaller babies than average. Much of this work was done at Aberdeen, Scotland, where the Medical Research Council had an excellent obstetric unit for many years.

Prematurity

The incidence of prematurity makes nonsense of traditional birth weights. Also modern methods of treating these smallest of all independent humans is making nonsense of earlier beliefs about their survival possibilities. Every year, the survival percentages for each weight range improves. Miniature babies less than 2 lb. are occasionally nursed into a normal existence. The current limit for survival seems to be about 1 lb., 10 oz., but survival is then unlikely. Such minute forms have only spent about

two-thirds of the traditional time in the uterus. They are more than half
the length of a normal baby and only a quarter of the weight.

Internationally (and even premature babies have to be defined), any
birth weighing less than 5½ lb. is called premature. Other definitions are
a length (crown to heel) of less than 18½ in. or a head circumference of
less than 13 in. or any delivery up to the 35th week after fertilization.
Apart from being small, light, and badly proportioned (compared with
an ordinary baby), a premature's wide-set eyes are usually shut, its cry
is weak, and its temperature regulation is bad. Also, its nails are short.
Its skin is without fat, being wrinkled like an old man's, and dull red
and transparent. Its body and upper face may have some hair that falls
out, and all its movements are without strength, causing a frequent difficulty in establishing breathing. At least 100 premature babies are born in
Britain every day, or one in 25 of all births. In the United States, it is
generally estimated that 6 to 7 percent of all births are premature, giving
something like 700 as the daily figure. (That definition of 5½ lb. or less
confuses the picture. Some 5½ lb. babies are merely light in weight for
their age and maturity. Others of the same weight, the true premature
infants, are not nearly so advanced.) By weight alone, 6.5 percent of all
English and 6.7 percent of all American babies are premature.

The youngest, smallest, and most delicate group of premature babies
with any chances of survival were probably conceived some 24 to 28
weeks before. At birth, which may frequently be a very abrupt business
compared with normal labor, they weigh less than a third of normal
birth weight, their length is slightly over half normal, and their head and
chest circumferences are again only slightly over half normal. The difference in proportion between these and a normal baby is roughly equivalent to the difference between a normal baby and a two-year-old. They
require much nursing, particularly to detect early signs of trouble. One
surgeon recommends four nurses in each premature unit for every nine
babies. The incubator has to be kept at 80°F. to 90°F. and a humidity of
60 to 70 percent. Food is usually given—in minute quantities—after 48
hours, and then through an instrument much resembling a fountain-pen
tube. (Earlier feeding is recommended by some, but vomiting can be a
problem; therefore intravenous feeding is sometimes given.) Weight falls
initially, as with normal babies, but the pickup time is slower. A baby
of 2 to 3 lb. will take six weeks to put on another 2 to 3 lb. Food is given
every three hours, night and day. When the baby is feeding properly and
can regulate its temperature and is no longer vomiting, it can leave the
incubator for the cot, but it must be a cot kept in hot (80°F.), moist
(50 percent humidity) air.

Gradually things improve and the premature infants attempt to catch
up physically and mentally with the other babies, born weeks or months

later but of the same conceptual age. It takes years for the smallest of them to reach the normal weight for their age. It used to be thought that, mentally, prematures had the dice loaded against them, partly because the abnormal number of severe defectives among the prematures (10 to 15 percent) lowered the average intelligence for the group as a whole. When these are discounted, the premature appears remarkably normal. D. J. Baird concluded a survey by saying there is "no clear indication that . . . premature expulsion from the uterus does the fetus any serious harm." (Some notable and historical prematures have been Napoleon, Isaac Newton, Charles Darwin, Victor Hugo, and Voltaire.)

What does occasionally do harm is to confuse a full-term but diminutive baby with one genuinely premature. Recently it has been asserted (e.g., at a symposium at the end of 1965 by Dr. Sydney Gellis, of Boston) that perhaps 30 percent of all alleged prematures are, in fact, dangerously underdeveloped full-term babies. It has long been customary to disregard maternal statements about the date of their last menstruation (and hence the onset of pregnancy) whenever fetal weight appears to belie those statements; after all some women can be gloriously vague on the subject. Now, say Dr. Gellis and others, mothers were often right and the doctors wrong. There are genuine prematures, and there are also poorly developed nine-month babies. Of the two, the prematures are to be preferred. A baby weighing 4 lb. when born after 34 weeks has, he said, a better chance of being normal than a baby weighing 4 lb. when born after 40 weeks.

Some causes of prematurity are known. They may already afflict the mother (such as high blood pressure or diabetes), or they may be linked to the pregnancy itself (such as an abnormal uterus), or they may be associated with the embryo (such as malformations). By no means does each cause always have the effect of producing prematurity. Also, by no means is every cause known. About 50 percent of prematures happen without any detectable cause, and some women just regularly produce premature babies. Whatever the cause, the lot of any baby cast out before its time from the snug, aquatic cocoon of the womb is being improved year by year. Babies of 26 oz. have survived. Will even such exceptional successes become the rule in the future? Will there even be a case for inducing them from women who resent the load of pregnancy and prefer the substitution of an artificial incubator for their own bulging bellies?

The Puerperium

As soon as the placenta has been delivered, the puerperium (or puerperal period) begins. It is the time of reversion, while everything more or less returns to normal, and it takes roughly six weeks.

The changes in the uterus are a dominant feature of this time. Before delivery it is 12 in. long. Immediately after delivery (as can easily be seen during a Cesarean) it shrinks to become a pallid and wrinkled thing 7 in. by 5 in. by 3½ in. This weighs 2 lb. or so. After a week it weighs half as much. After six weeks it weighs a mere 2 oz. In size it is then about 3 in. by 2 in. by 1 in. No one has yet adequately explained how so much uterine tissue both shrinks and disappears, but despite this impressive shrinkage, a uterus that has produced a baby is detectably different from one that has not. There may be afterpains after birth, perhaps for two or three days, occurring mainly in mothers not having their first child. The uterus, by continuing to contract and relax, causes the pains, often when the baby is put to the breast, thereby indicating a connection between the uterus and the mammary gland.

The vagina, hugely stretched in birth, takes a similar time to revert to normal, although the first birth always leaves it slightly wider. The hymen, never completely destroyed even in childbirth, remains as persistent fragments of tissue. The abdominal wall should return virtually to normal, although flabby people can become flabbier. Striae, or small strips of skin, can remain as permanent reminders of the enormous stretching of the abdominal wall for all those months of pregnancy. The breasts change, but more about them under lactation.

Menstruation comes back slowly, and the speed of its return differs depending upon whether the mother is producing milk, and whether it is her first child. On average, according to American sources, the first menstruation returns within six weeks for 25 percent of mothers, within twelve weeks for 61 percent, and within 24 weeks for 77 percent. In other words, over three-quarters of American women are back to menstruation, these days, in less than half a year. The proportion would be smaller if more women were breast-feeding. It is not true, despite widespread confidence, that the nursing mother cannot become pregnant. Instead it is true that, at least for the first few months, a lactating mother will not menstruate, and a pregnancy is unlikely in the absence of menstruation; but the golden rule of "milk, therefore no new baby" is by no means gilt-edged. When a new baby is conceived, milk from the old one often dries up fairly soon.

Other changes are that blood quantity (30 to 40 percent more than normal at the time of birth, i.e., three to four pints more) reverts to normal within a week. The bladder is unusually active after birth, with perhaps four or five pints emitted within 24 hours. Unfortunately, it sometimes fails, and retains rather than loses liquid, at this time. This demands the use of a catheter, and more frequently than is usual with ordinary nonemptying bladders because of the abnormal quantities of urine involved after birth. Pulse rate may slow and temperature may rise slightly in the puerperium. Too high a temperature or too rapid a pulse indicates fever. (It used to be thought there was such a thing as "milk fever," with lactation somehow causing the rise in temperature. This is now dismissed as untrue but probably, in the past, it was the first indication of bacteria-induced puerperal fever.) Bacteria always do reach the uterus within 48 to 72 hours (quicker if the labor has been long) but they tend to get washed out by the blood discharged from the shrinking uterus.

At birth, the mother's weight naturally drops as she is relieved of the baby, placenta, and fluid. Average weight loss caused by these is 13 lb. In the next few weeks, average extra weight loss is 5 lb. (These averages are more meaningless than most, as women can gain anything from 0 to 60 lb. during a normal pregnancy and therefore have more or less to lose.) Coupled with the increased activity of the bladder is the decreased activity of the colon. Defecation is likely to be delayed for a few days. Despite the flood from the bladder, the mother of a new baby is usually dehydrated, and so drinking is important. In general, provided everything is going satisfactorily, women feel physically well during the puerperium.

A word now about words. Keen students of awkward phrases will have been quick to observe examples here, exemplified by women "who are having a child not their first" or "any pregnancy that is not the first one." Medical literature uses instead some excellent and convenient words, which I have been careful to resist. They are undoubtedly handy terms but ponderous, or so I considered, for the uninitiated. All women having their first pregnancies are primigravidas. For their second and successive pregnancies they are multigravidas. Birth itself is parturition and the woman is parturient at birth. After birth she is a primipara, and her uterus, etc., can be called parous. After her second child she is a multipara, and a group of such women are multiparas. After each birth they and their organs are postpartum. The puerperium and puerperal fever have already been encountered. It was sentences like "The multigravid 38-year-old suffered postpartum hemorrhage, though when primiparous her puerperium had been . . ." that I did not wish others to encounter, however brief, accurate, and to the point.

Paternal Labor

The role of the father during labor is improving. Many hospitals now welcome his presence during birth, and he is no longer such a comedy butt. Husbands can get in the way, become distraught, urge the wrong action, faint, scream, and yet be the one person the laboring woman—if not the obstetrical staff—wishes to have nearby. There is even argument, and evidence, that he may suffer during his wife's pregnancy from symptoms resembling hers. A magazine article in January, 1965, quoted work suggesting that one father in nine suffered from minor ailments without any good physical cause during the time of his wife's pregnancies, more so than men whose wives were not pregnant.

Known as the Couvade syndrome, from the French verb meaning to brood or hatch, the idea of a father's suffering has a venerable history. It was spoken of in the sixteenth century, and there have been some very improbable events throughout the centuries, even to the extent of a man's abdomen swelling hugely and inexplicably to subside when he has seen his newborn child. Male lactation is also on record, with even a story about a man in a lifeboat who succeeded in producing milk for a baby also on board. Most paternal symptoms, according to Conlon and Trethowan, who made a recent investigation, reach their peak at the third month. It used to be thought, in some places, that witches or midwives could transfer labor pains from the woman to the husband. In others it was made more certain that the husband should feel pain by hanging him by his heels in the next room. Without doubt the present trend of having the husband in the same room to help more positively is on the increase.

Ergot

Ergonovine, often a useful drug today for the delivered uterus, deserves amplification. The history of this drug goes back into the past to a time when, somehow or other, its properties were accurately divined. (Many of the old remedies were undoubtedly nonsensical, but embedded among traditional folklore are gems of knowledge that make one wonder about the alleged nonsensicality of the rest.) No one knows how or when, but it was learned that ergot could be useful during the delivery of a child.

In 1808 a New York physician, John Stearns, wrote that he had been repeatedly importuned by a local midwife to find diseased heads of rye and administer them to laboring women. He did so and described the amazing results. Long before this old midwives' tale was thus reported and subsequently made use of by the medical profession, diseased rye and ergot had had a powerful history of their own. Ergot is a fungus that preys on grasses, particularly rye. If the small black spurs it causes are mixed with the flour and made into bread there can be, and have been, great epidemics. The disease of ergot is a painful gangrene of the extremities. Fingers, toes, and tips of ears rot away as the ergot disrupts the blood flow to those parts. There were major outbreaks of the disease, known as St. Anthony's fire (after the third-century Egyptian saint) in the Middle Ages, notably in France and Germany. A pilgrimage to St. Anthony's shrine did have the secondary advantage of moving the patient, probably, into an area of unaffected rye and St. Anthony would probably be granted credit for any cure. Ergotism reappeared in Russia in the last century, and it was even reported in this century in the English city of Manchester, in 1928, and in France, in 1951, although there is argument concerning the true nature of those outbreaks.

Anyway, back to 1808 and Dr. Stearns. The magic stuff was used to hasten labor and to prevent undue bleeding afterward, but it was abused as well and frequently brought death rather than birth. The dosage was often grossly wrong. As soon as chemical technology was sufficiently developed, ergot was subjected to intense scrutiny. One by one, its powerful alkaloid constituents were extracted—ergotoxine (1906), ergotamine (1918), ergonovine (1935). The first was later found to be a mixture, the second proved too slow in its effects, but the third, ergonovine—called ergometrine in Britain—is a powerful tool of the obstetrician. According to J. Chassar Moir, professor of obstetrics and gynecology at Oxford, who did the first crucial experiments with ergonovine, the drug probably provides the best single method of checking bleeding after birth and of curtailing the third stage of labor. The ancient black heads of rye have finally found their proper place.

Who Has Babies?

In Britain, some girls start before they have reached their teens, and some finish in their 50s. At the lower end, the age of 12 is usually the minimum. In London, for example, in 1963 two babies were born to 12-year-old mothers. Girls of 13 had 4 babies in the same year, girls of 14 had 19, girls of 15 had 93, and girls of 16 had 196. Marriage for girls in Britain is permitted after their 16th birthday, but only 6 percent of British babies are born to teen-agers (or those younger). In the ten years between reaching 20 and leaving 29, girls produce 62 percent of their babies. In the next ten years, 30 to 39, they produce 29 percent. In the years after 40 only 3 percent are born. The span is short. At 15 it is considered too early. At 45 it is almost always too late. With women living, on average, over 70 years, the fertile span is therefore less than half their lifetime. With allowances for custom, tradition, and fertility, the actual span is even shorter. In the fifteen years between the ages of 20 and 35, women produce over four-fifths of their babies.

Although only 3 percent of British babies have mothers over 40, and although women over 45 consider rightly that their fertile days are probably over, there have been some remarkable cases. Phyllis Keeble, a Welsh woman who was seven times a grandmother and whose oldest child was 31, became a mother for the eleventh time in October, 1965. She was then 53. Beating her into the position of oldest British mother is Winifred Wilson, of Cheshire, England. She was 55 in 1937, when she had her ninth child. (It is easier to have later children if pregnancies have been frequent, although Mrs. Keeble had not had a baby for 16 years when she almost broke the record.) The world record seems to be held by Ruth Kistler, of Portland, Oregon. She was 57 when she produced a baby in 1956. Men, on the other hand, can be, and have been, fertile well into their 80s or to the end of their days. No man seems, so far as I could discover, to hold the position of world's oldest father as a record-breaking consort for Mrs. Kistler of Oregon. The ancient inhabitants of Georgia in the Soviet Union make the boldest claims.

More than half of British babies (56 percent) are born to marriages of less than five years. And 84 percent are born in the first ten years of marriage. The rest are born later or—as 7 percent are born to no marriage at all—earlier. Despite the numbers of pregnant brides ("It was nice seeing the three of you coming down the aisle" is inevitably shouted by the inevitable drunk), about 60,000 illegitimate babies are born in England and Wales every year, and in 1965 it was estimated that the United States had 291,200. London has twice the national average. The peak birth period of the year for all babies is the second quarter, with conceptions in July, August, and September. The last quarter of the year sees fewest births, November having fewest of all. The annual birth graph, starting from the November minimum, rises steadily until March. It stays fairly constant until May or June and then declines again to November, with a minor rise in September (due to December conceptions).

British people conceive, therefore, somewhat in tune with the seasons, with more conceptions occurring at the warmer times of the year. But the warm times are also the holiday times and the days of least unemployment, most money, a greater quantity of rain, and anybody is entitled to choose his own particular reason why British people conceive more on average between July 1 and the start of their pheasant shooting season three months later. Certainly science has no answer as yet.

⊸§ 13 §⊷

Lactation

Human Milk · Breast-feeding · The Price of Milk ·
Advantages and Disadvantages · Polythelia ·
Keeping Abreast · Weaning

Human Milk

Human milk is usually bluish-white, tastes sweet, and weighs slightly more than water. Essentially, like all milks, it is an emulsion of fat globules (which make it white) in a fluid. The protein adds the bluish coloration. Milk production is usually greatest from those breasts that have increased most in size during pregnancy (although all rules are likely to be broken here as elsewhere) and large breasts that do not grow are generally not good milk producers. Breasts can fail to grow at all during pregnancy or each can increase in size by almost 50 cu. in. (a total volume increase of almost 3 pt.). Average increase for each breast is about 12 cu. in. Although there is usually rapid enlargement of breasts during the first two months of pregnancy, this is an increase in the size of blood vessels. After the third month the breast tissue itself begins to grow.

The content of human milk fluctuates from person to person, from birth to birth, and from the start to the finish of the feeding period, whether it is weeks, months, or years. Average composition is 1 to 2 percent protein, 3 to 5 percent fat, 6.5 to 8 percent carbohydrate, and .2 percent of salts. The rest is water. Cows' milk has double the protein (goats, ewes, and sows have even more), the same fat proportion (although different proportions for the different fats), and less carbohydrate (4.9 percent). Cows also have more thiamin, more riboflavin, four times more calcium, less iron, and less vitamin C. Human milk will also contain alcohol if drunk sufficiently by the mother.

[173]

Breast-feeding

Whether to breast-feed or not is extremely dependent upon custom and need. It varies from 1 to 2 percent (as in certain maternity units in the United States or Canada) to 99 percent or above (as in poor Bengali villages). The percentages can be reversed. In Calcutta 18 percent of well-to-do mothers fail to start lactation. In Minneapolis, after an intensive breast-feeding campaign, 96 percent of mothers were doing so at the end of the second month, 84 percent after six months. Maternal milk, although an admirable food initially, is not so for all time, even if the supply is maintained. Beyond nine months or so, the human child needs other foods to supplement it. (Many mammals are breast-fed for much longer: orangutan, three to four years; some chimpanzees, two years; macaque monkey, eighteen months; baboon, one year.) Malnutrition and prolonged breast-feeding in humans often go together (as does the idea that prolongation of breast-feeding will prevent another conception, another mouth to feed). In any case, a nursing mother needs another 1,000 calories herself per day.

Ample milk production does not begin the moment a child is born. Initially, the breasts produce only colostrum, a pale-yellow liquid that can be expressed from the nipples long before birth. It has a little protein, a little sugar, and quite a lot of fat. In some animals, such as the cow, horse, and goat, valuable antibodies that could not get through the placenta are contained in the colostrum. They help to immunize the newborn against disease. This boost to the colostrum is less important with humans as the placenta is less of a barrier.

Real milk production begins only after the hormones have had a chance to adjust to the postnatal situation, and proper flow usually starts on the third day. With women having their first baby everything tends to occur both later and less gently. A new baby fasts after birth, permitting the delayed milk production to be on time. In one study of babies who were given as much as they would take, the first day's consumption was a bit more than 1 fl. oz. for every 2 lb. of the birth weight, and even the second day's was only twice that. When 8 to 30 days old, they were taking eight times the first day's intake. The fasting inevitably leads to weight reduction, both by water loss and the breakdown of tissue. Weight loss for healthy babies is often one-tenth of the birth weight, or 11 oz. of the original 7 lb. The human baby is remarkable for its tolerance, and many animals would perish if not more squarely nourished during the first vital days (piglets start suckling before the last of the litter is born).

During pregnancy the nipples enlarge and become more supple. The dusky ring around each of them, the areola, becomes duskier (certainly during the first pregnancy) and larger, its diameter becoming one and a half times as wide as it had been.

Breast-feeding can either fail to start, be suppressed artificially (by the injection of estrogen), or continue for years. A. C. Haddon observed in 1908 that islanders of the Torres Straits, near Australia, sometimes continued a single lactation for three years, when presumably an offspring was perfectly capable of intelligent speech and of asking for it. Milk production itself can either be nil or overflowing in its abundance. In earlier times, when alternatives to human milk were scarce, dangerous, or even nonexistent, the wet nurse was much in demand when the mother's milk failed to run. Other members of the family often supplied the need. David Livingstone, the exploring missionary, observed grandmothers frequently fulfilling this role in Africa. Elsewhere, as with Maoris and American Indians, the grandmothers helped out because mothers were too busy on other tasks.

The Price of Milk

Today, when everything has its price, there can be money in milk. Ronald Illingworth, in *The Normal Child,* refers to two women in the United States, one of whom sold 30,000 oz. in two lactation periods for $3,717, and another who sold her excess after only one offspring for $2,020. The value of their milk was therefore about $1.75 a pint. It was reported from Stockholm in July, 1965, that a young Swedish woman named Loborn was receiving ten Swedish crowns for every quart or so of her excess milk. Mrs. Loborn's child consumed 1⅓ pt. a day, but there were more than 2 pt. a day extra for the Orebeo Maternity Hospital in Stockholm, meaning about $3 a day extra for the Loborn household. Yet another woman, who must surely hold one of the most useful of records, is said to have been able to keep seven babies happy on her supply. She could produce 10 pt. a day, or one-third of that of a fair cow.

Advantages and Disadvantages

Whether or not to breast-feed is not so much a perennial argument as the swing of local prejudices and convictions. Primitive places have no choice, and even if they had a choice, a feeding bottle in the tropics without hygienic discipline is a lethal weapon. In places with a choice, the authorities are, in general and in principle, in favor of breast-feeding.

However, ordering a woman to breast-feed is a different matter. She has her own views. A recent article in the *British Medical Journal* made a formidable list of maternal reasons put forward against breast-feeding. They were an inability to know how much the baby was getting; the fact that bottle-fed babies do just as well; the pointlessness of starting if failure was to follow; the embarrassment of either disliking it or liking it too much; the loss of figure; the nuisance, particularly with dribbling nipples; and the pain associated with bulging breasts, with uterine contractions, sore nipples, or even an abscess. As the article affirmed, it is a formidable array.

The main advantages and disadvantages can most suitably be listed. Generally accepted benefits are:

1. It is the right food in the right proportion.
2. It is cheap.
3. It is simple, readily available, and correctly warm.
4. It assists in the healthy regression of the uterus and recovery from childbirth.
5. It contains some antibodies (e.g., against the common cold) and helps to keep various illnesses at bay for longer.
6. It encourages (if all goes well) the bond between mother and child.
7. It is reasonably sterile and leads to far less gastroenteritis.
8. It will mean less soreness around the baby's bottom, even though feces are looser.

Disadvantages are:

1. It is often a struggle to establish. Bottles are temptingly near at hand.
2. The baby cannot be fed without the mother.
3. Some breasts just do not produce enough at the best of times.
4. Worry, etc., can stop even a good flow.
5. Breast and nipples can be painful.

Despite the benefits, despite the simplicity and naturalness of it, despite the gentle prodding of the medical profession in favor of it, breast-feeding in Europe is probably rarer than it has ever been before. In the United States two out of five women give their babies a chance to suckle. In Britain the proportion varies widely, and a recent attempt to sum up the situation said only that "it is still quite commonly practised." It is the minority rather than the majority who establish it. There have been huge follow-up surveys of breast and bottle-fed babies, but no lasting differences have been established. There is much talk about psychiatric benefits, both to mother and child, but they are hard to prove.

There is no comparison between the two methods in countries where hygiene is regarded casually. A milk bottle, unboiled and unwashed, can harbor pathogenic bacteria to a devastating degree. The milk itself may not be good even straight from the cow, or whatever animal is milked in that area. (Goat, ass, camel, llama, caribou, dog, horse, reindeer, sheep, water buffalo, and cow all contribute their milk to humanity—somewhere.) Human milk, although sterile by comparison with anything that has been standing in a bottle, is not completely so. One survey showed that 93 percent of babies were drinking in staphylococci with their milk. Differences in the nature of cow and human milk mean a different population of bacteria in the baby's colon. Breast-feeding leads mainly to Bacillus acidophilus, but cow's milk leads to Escherichia coli. Without any shadow of doubt, the second type of colon is more likely to suffer from gastroenteritis. Even in Britain at the turn of the century the mortality of bottle-fed babies was far, far higher. The reliability and cleanliness of cow's milk is quite a recent advance, and it took huge strides between the world wars.

With maternal milk a vital commodity in previous generations, the purveyors of notions for stepping up its production had their field day. Illingworth has amassed a few of the recommendations. They include eating powdered earthworms, dried goat udder, cuttlefish soup, shrimps' heads, boiled sea slugs, powdered silkworms in wine, and blowfly larvae garnished with wine from glutinous rice. A more physical recommendation was tickling trout, forcing expressed milk into the jaws, and then setting the fish free. Equally physical, but demanding less sleight of hand, was the practice of a husband's providing breast stimulation by sucking it himself. The so-called "witch's milk" has nothing to do with any of these vintage recipes. It is the secretion produced from infant breasts. Every fetus encounters many maternal hormones. Some of these stimulate breast growth, both in males and females because breasts are present in both, and at birth the small breasts may actually be secreting this witch's milk. The event is common.

Two final points about cow's milk concern allergy and ionizing radiation. For some reason or reasons, more children are intolerant of cow's milk. It has even been suggested that a few inexplicable infant deaths may have been caused by extreme sensitivity to some cow-milk protein. These days the problem of allergy to milk is usually circumnavigated by finding some suitable, synthetic milk substitute.

Getting around ionizing radiation is less easy. Fallout falls everywhere. Cows, by skimming off the grassy top layer of any field, are also skimming off much of the strontium 90 that has descended upon it. Strontium and calcium are similar chemicals. Consequently, as milk is rich in calcium, it is also rich in strontium 90 when nuclear fission has added it to the grass diet. The milk of cows, due to their grazing technique of food gathering, is several times more radioactive than human milk.

Polythelia

Quite a frequent abnormality is the possession of more than two breasts. They occur on what is known as the mammary line, and are said (by some) to affect 1 percent of the human population. This mammary line exists early in embryonic life. At seven weeks from conception it is clearly recognizable, but almost all of it then disappears leaving only a small spot of tissue on each side in the chest area. These spots become male and female breasts. Should other nipples develop, they occur somewhere along the old line. If superimposed on an adult human, the mammary line resembles the traditional shape of a vase. On each side, the lip of the vase is at the armpits. The lines then travel down through the conventional breast positions and nearly meet in the genital area. Extra or accessory nipples are somewhere along these lines, a condition known as polythelia. Should they develop into something more breastlike than mere rudiments, the condition is called polymastia. Frequent sites are within or near the armpit. An Egyptian doctor in Cairo reported recently that they were "common" there among Greek, Armenian, and Lebanese inhabitants, less among native Egyptians. He said that males had them more frequently, and the usual spot was 3½ in. below the normal nipples. They were generally single, slightly hairy, and only occasionally accompanied by a partner on the other side.

In a sense, bearing in mind the evolutionary complexity of human history and the wide assortment of mammary arrangements among other mammals, it is reasonable to expect the human species to have occasional variations. Most primates (monkeys, apes) have just one pair of milk glands, but an insectivore called centetes has eleven pairs. Usually the total is related to litter size, as with pigs, dogs, and cats. Animals with a small number of glands may have them in the chest area (humans, most other primates, bats, sea cows, elephants, sloths), at the other end, the inguinal area (whales, ungulates—the huge hoofed group, which includes cows, horses, hippos, giraffes, rhinos, etc.), at each end (rodents), or in a row joining both ends (cats, dogs, pigs).

There are plenty of oddities. Cats have four on each side, but they do not all necessarily function at the same time, with perhaps the front two active, the back two quiet. Bats, hanging upside down and with their single pair at the chest—or bottom end—have a pair of false teats at the other end (called pubic teats) from which the young can hang more conveniently. Whales have a single pair; each may be 6 ft. wide and a foot thick during lactation, but as with various rodents and the mole, the whale's nipples may be far from the glands.

All mammals have either nipples (as with humans) or teats (as with cows) except the monotremes (such as the duckbilled platypus). Their exuded milk merely flows onto the surface through scattered pores and has to be licked off the hairy body by the young. The coypu, the aquatic rodent that invaded the southeast of England so overwhelmingly, has a lateral system. The young travel on the mother's back as she swims, and the nipples are conveniently placed more toward each side of the normal ventral position. All in all, as mammals are one big related group, it seems not too unreasonable that the species man should every now and then produce something other than the traditional pair.

Keeping Abreast

The traditional pair has been of dominant interest to countless humans, notably in the twentieth century. Somewhere along the line, the importance of breasts as a source of natural food suddenly adopted second place to their importance as stimulants of sexual appetite. Babies have been denied the comfort of a breast for fear that the breast's shape may subsequently not be such a comfort to the mother. And some mammary girls have reached pinnacles of success solely on account of their own glandular gifts. Dr. Erwin O. Strassman, of Houston, Texas, concluded after a survey of 717 childless women that, as a rule, the bigger the breasts the smaller the IQ. All of this interest in one organ is not, of course, entirely arbitrary; nor was it chance that caused such a rumpus when creators of fashion thought that toplessness might catch on in 1964. And it was not guesswork when many predicted its failure. The breasts, wrote Dr. C. B. Goodhart, of Caius College, Cambridge, do form an important part of a woman's biological equipment for courtship. "It is a question not so much of morals as of tactics to consider at what stage in the proceedings they are to be deployed to the best advantage."

Innumerable societies other than our own use the woman's breasts both before and during intercourse, but few insist as we do in the western world upon their concealment. Where clothes of any form are worn, the genitals are always hidden. Not so the breasts. As C. S. Ford and F. A. Beach put it, "the bare bosom is usually not inconsistent with ideals of feminine modesty." These authors also amassed information on different preferences for the differing breast shapes. Whereas nine of the societies in their investigation just wanted large breasts, two wanted them to be upright and hemispherical, and two (both in East Africa) wanted them long and pendulous.

Science has no answer as yet for the visible prominence of areolae, the dark circular backgrounds to the nipples. Admittedly they contain glands (of Montgomery, named after a nineteenth-century Irish obstetrician) that, by secreting a fatty substance, protect the area against the trauma of suckling, but their signpost visibility in light-skinned people is without any explanation. One suggestion is that babies, fumbling their way through life and possessing only hazy sight, need all the assistance they can get to find that vital nipple. Certainly the areolae darken during pregnancy, but babies with black mothers and also white babies in the dark seem to find their way equally successfully.

Weaning

The process of weaning begins after a few days or after a year or two. Once again, the subject is full of controversy. Naturally the child should be weaned if the milk is drying up, but in any case by the time he weighs 16 lb., he is taking (at the normal rate of 2½ oz. a day per pound) some 40 oz. of milk in 24 hours. Mixed diet is then considered satisfactory. Weaning is often a time of intense mortality. In West Africa the children suddenly removed from reasonably sterile milk and fed with quite unreasonably pathogenic adult food get gastroenteritis and die in large numbers. Weaning is often upsetting to mothers, partly as the breasts may hurt, but also because the break can hurt emotionally. Babies can find the process upsetting if the previous regimen of warm milk flowing from the nipple was entirely satisfactory, and powerful methods have in the past been used to make them think again, particularly when weaning has been long delayed. Once again Illingworth has a list. Breast deterrents include bitter sap, wrapping nipples in hair or putting on tobacco, soot, aloes, garlic, ginger, and red pepper.

A final point is that no animal, despite the birth of singletons in so many species, has just one breast. For this the mothers of twins can be grateful. A satisfactory sight is of a well-organized arrangement in which a pair of twins, both with their heads supported by their mother's hands, with their bodies gripped by her elbows, and their legs sticking out behind, are contentedly sucking, one to each, at the pair of breasts before them.

✑ 14 ଛ

Twins and
Abnormalities

Occurrence of Twins · The Value of Twins ·
Multiple Births · Twin Diagnosis · Conjoined Twins ·
Proof of Separation · Why Twins at All? ·
Congenital Malformations · Registration of Malformations ·
The Principal Afflictions · German Measles ·
Thalidomide, Contergan, and Distaval ·
The Cause of Malformations · "Maternal Impressions"

Occurrence of Twins

Twins, identical and fraternal, occur in Britain about once in 87 births. Many other countries have more, e.g., Belgium has one in 56, and many have less, e.g., one in 125 or fewer still in some South American countries and among certain groups of Mongoloids. In the United States, Negroes produce twins more often than whites, and many African tribes have particularly high ratios. (The Yoruba of western Nigeria are said to produce twins in every 22 pregnancies.) Together, twins weigh more than a singleton, but not twice as much; the average British weight is 5¼ lb. each. The maximum live-born recorded weight for twins is 20 lb., 6 oz. The maximum stillborn twin weight is 35 lb., 8 oz. Fraternal twins are nearer in weight to each other at birth than identical twins, presumably because they have a placenta each instead of having to share one competitively. Twins in Britain are born earlier (on average 248 days after conception), triplets earlier still (233 days), and quadruplets even earlier (223 days). Britain has had no successful quints. Each triplet generally weighs less than each twin, but the total may be more. The maximum total recorded is 23 lb., while the British maximum is 21 lb., 13 oz. A royal bounty for triplets (£3) was introduced in Britain in 1849 but was abolished in 1957.

Twins face greater difficulties from the start, as they die more frequently, both as abortions and at or shortly after birth. Maternal mortality is also higher with multiple births. Twins have a higher incidence of mental subnormality and cerebral palsy. There is some evidence to suggest that the larger twin may be the more intelligent, and the second twin to be born is more likely to die at birth. With European groups, roughly 63 percent of all twins are of the same sex, 37 percent are one boy, one girl. Twins marry less. Fingerprints of identical twins are not completely identical, but have extreme similarity.

Mothers are more likely to bear fraternal twins as they get older; there are 4 per 1,000 births for women of 20, and 16 per 1,000 for women aged 40. The rate then falls off rapidly. Also women are more likely to have twins as they have more children—quite a distinct phenomenon from the age increase.* Contrary to fraternal twinning, the chance of identical twins hardly varies with maternal age. Identical twins have the same blood groups, and left-handedness is common among them. The difference in the twinning rate among different races and countries is almost entirely confined to fraternal twins. The identical-twin rate hardly varies throughout the world and fluctuates between one in 260 and one in 340 births. In Britain, with a fairly high total twinning rate, the proportion of identicals to fraternals is about one to three (25 percent). Conversely, in Japan, which has a low total rate, the proportion of identicals is far higher, better than one to one (60 percent).

Twins run in families. Identical twins do not, but fraternal twins do, although without any definite rules. There is evidence that it can come through the female line alone, or from both parents. A pair of fraternal twins born at the same time can have separate fathers, although this is extremely rare. The rate of fraternal twins in Britain has been rising, from one in 117 births between the wars to one in 110 between 1951 and 1956. It is thought that better food is responsible. Certainly, the fraternal-twin rate fell during World War II in occupied France, the Netherlands, and Norway, but not in Denmark, Britain, or Sweden, where there was no serious food restriction. Recent reports from Scandinavia suggest that illegitimate offspring are more likely to be twins than the offspring of married parents.

---

* Insurance companies offering cover against twins do, in general, mind about the age of the mother as well as a history of twins in the family. The premium is 2½ to 4½ percent of the sum insured for average cases.

There is much argument (e.g., D. Burlingham in 1952) that twins should be given a greater chance to go it alone in childhood and not be identically dressed, etc. If one identical twin is homosexual, his brother almost always is. If one fraternal twin is homosexual, his brother is also homosexual in about 50 percent of cases. Good dogs can distinguish between the scents of identical twins, although there is initial confusion. A bizarre rarity occurs when identical twins definitely from the same egg are born with a different sex. It is thought that faulty cell division has caused the male to be normal (XY) but the female to be immature (XO). The twins should both have been male.*

The first problem with twins is what to call them. Identical twins are also known as one-egg twins, monozygotic twins, monovular twins, uniovular twins, similar twins. Fraternal twins are also known as dissimilar twins, nonidentical twins, two-egg twins, dizygotic twins, binovular twins, diovular twins. I shall stick to identical and fraternal. As a complication, it should be remembered that identical twins are only similar and not the same. Even Siamese twins show marked differences.

Fraternal twins are undoubtedly caused by the ovulation and then the fertilization of two ova. There is much less certainty about identical twins. It used to be thought that all of them were caused when the egg divided into two cells, which then mistakenly separated to form two independent, single-celled embryos. These then divided, according to the old story, but their subsequent two-celled stages remained correctly united and eventually grew into one pair of identical twins. Recent work suggests instead that identical twins are formed much later. Dr. J. H. Edwards, of Birmingham, England, reported to a Genetical Society meeting in November, 1966, that only 30 percent of identical twins are formed before implantation (and that happens six days after fertilization); the remaining 70 percent are created after implantation.

He made his deductions after noting whether the chorion and amnion were in fact double or single for each pair of identical twins. A single-ton offspring has only one each of these fetal membranes, but identical twins were by no means as uniform in this respect. Dr. Edwards's report made it abundantly clear that the previous belief in just one type of identical twin was entirely false; so too was the conviction that identical twins were always the result of a divided cell that failed to remain united. For the time being, he has totally upset the subject and made it far more fascinating.

* The chapter on inheritance explains the sexual ramifications of X and Y.

The Value of Twins

Twins are a godsend and of prime importance to the biologist. They enable him to come to grips with the nature versus nurture arguments and those on whether a characteristic is born or made. With any laboratory animal an experiment can easily be planned to discover whether, for example, height is inherited, a matter of environment, or a complex product of the two. With humanity always breeding at random and living at random, there is no such simplicity. Is a man's final height due to inheritance or due to the way in which he was brought up? Richer people in Britain are taller. Is this because richer people give better food to their children or because taller people are more likely to have taller children—and are more likely, once rich, to make them richer too? Twins often provide an answer to this sort of question, and in two main ways.

Sometimes—and this is the prime benefit—identical twins are not brought up in identical fashion. They are separated at birth or very soon afterward and are brought up in different homes. In other words, their genetics are indisputably similar and their environments are not. A clear line has been drawn between the two. The second point, less of a godsend but also of importance, is that most fraternal twins are brought up together. In other words their genetics are different but their environment is the same. Both these situations are good substitutes for experimental breeding of humans. Countless statements about humanity would be impossible without the support of a twin study to provide the evidence. Sir Francis Galton (1822–1911; genius, polymath, cousin of Charles Darwin) was the first person to write about the possibilities of twins as a source of information; he published his first study in 1875. Literature and mythology had long been interested in twins, notably Castor and Pollux (fraternal, although each had another partner in his egg), Jacob and Esau (fraternal), Romulus and Remus (probably fraternal), Viola and Sebastian (fraternal). Yet it was up to Galton to point out the advantage of having twins to study. Neither literature nor mythology is as interested in identical as in fraternal twins.

Multiple Births

Once upon a time it was thought that a neat formula existed for calculating the chances of multiple twinning. Hellin, a German, said it was a matter of squaring (for triplets) and of cubing (for quads) the actual incidence of twins. He said, bearing in mind that European twins appear roughly once in every 80 births (in Germany then, the figure was 89), that triplets appear once in 80^2 (6,400) births and quadruplets once in 80^3 (512,000) births. There is, for Europe, some sort of validity for this "law," but it is only a rough guide. In 1957 there were born in Britain 9,273 twins, 95 triplets, and 3 quadruplets. Triplets were down and quadruplets were up by Hellin's law.

The United States always has the complexity and greater interest, biologically, of its two principal races. Negroes are definitely up for all forms of multiple birth. American Negro rates per million births (with the white rate in parentheses) are 13,423 twins (10,059), 141 triplets (85), and 1.8 quadruplets (1.0). Once again Hellin's law does not fit; triplets are down for both races, and quadruplets are down for whites but absolutely correct for Negroes. Some say his law is 82^2 and 82^3 for triplets and quadruplets, or even 87^2 and 87^3. These figures usually fit even less well. The best that can be said for the law and the reason for mentioning it is that it is a fair guide, a kind of reminder of multiple-birth frequency. Anyone wishing to lay a bet on anyone's chances of producing more than a singleton baby should bear Hellin in mind.

Multiple births above four are very rare indeed. The arrival of four, although a staggering confrontation for the average family, is rare, but does not set the world on fire. Britain has at least one quadruplet birth a year, and the United States has one new Negro set and three white sets. Other countries with similar medical abilities have similar figures. The arrival of quints, never yet successfully achieved in Britain, occurs once in 20 to 40 million births. The world can expect to see about two lots a year, but in many countries they fail to live. The most famous were the Canadian Dionne girls, who were all alike and who all came from the same egg. The Argentine quintuplets were, conversely, all different and from five eggs. The United States had a set of quints born in January, 1964, in Aberdeen, South Dakota. Their arrival did not just cause an upheaval in the family; it also created a complete change as jobs were given up, visitors were prepared for, money poured in, and earnest economists debated on television the overhaul this one multiple birth would inevitably mean to Aberdeen's commerce and financial state.

The stimulation of the ovaries, artificially and by the follicle-stimulating hormone (see Fertility), means many more multiple births and will presumably continue to do so until the dosage is corrected. Although most of these multiples have died, some have had happy outcomes and therefore form part of the record of successful multiplicity (although one can argue over their "successfulness" as a singleton was presumably intended).

Such a birth was the case for a 26-year-old New Zealander in 1965. She had been given hormone treatment, and by the 12th week of gestation her uterus was the size normally reached after 20 weeks. At the 18th week an attempt was made, with an electrocardiogram, to count the fetuses. Counting two fetal heartbeats, with their slightly different timing, is fairly easy. Counting more is far more difficult, and the instrument failed. So one X-ray picture was taken, which showed four fetuses and room for another. The following week the mother was admitted to a hospital. By the 26th week she had a waistline of 45 in., but that was a maximum. Labor began at the end of the 33rd week. It was short and uncomplicated. A 4-lb. male was born first headfirst, followed, after nine minutes, by a female, 3 lb., 3 oz., born bottom first. Then, after six more minutes, came another female, 4 lb., 3 oz., again headfirst. Five minutes later there was another female, 4 lb., 2 oz., bottom first. Finally, after four more minutes, there was a headfirst female of 3 lb., 7½ oz. In short, 19 lb. of humanity—all five dissimilar—had been born in less than half an hour. All were in good condition, save number three, who needed artificial respiration for ten minutes. Having failed to provide her solitary daughter with a sibling for six years, the mother had made up for lost time by arriving home, 15 days later, with five. It was only the fourth time anyone had ever done so (some say sixth, but I could find no firm evidence of the other two). There have also been successful sextuplets, one in western Brazil and one in Mexico.

Twin Diagnosis

Diagnosing twins has its own problems, particularly when the twins are small. Often it is the mother who first has suspicions. She may know of twins in her family. She may feel larger than normal—and most twins are born to women who have already had the experience of one child. She may complain of discomfort. If the woman is indeed large and is found to have a girth of 40 in. or over, suspicions can increase. They can increase even more if the developing form is felt to have more than a reasonable complement of limbs. A more positive method than this feeling (palpation) is listening to the heartbeat (auscultation). Normally, in a conventional pregnancy there is just one distinct heartbeat. With twins there are two. Either two men with two stethoscopes, or one man with one counting the heart rate in one area and then in another, should be able to state that there are two individuals within if such is the case. An X ray will be proof, but the current dislike for any extra radiation may weigh against it. Nevertheless, it would show up the two fetuses and would show if there were a third. Many a midwife delivering twins has been surprised to receive triplets. Even twins can confound the deliverer by being born at different times. In Texas, for example, Mrs. Rita Castro gave birth to a boy on December 9, 1966, and then to a girl on January 8, 1967.

As soon as the probability of twins has been established during the mother's pregnancy she deserves greater care. She also needs more rest. The birth of twins carries, on average, a greater risk than normal; in one out of 14 twin births at least one twin dies (figures from 1959 in England and Wales), and in one out of 75 twin births both die. The statistics for triplets that year show that all three survived in 75 out of 87 births. This means that at least one baby died in approximately one triplet birth out of seven.

Conjoined Twins

"But I am not me any more," said Santina Foglia in May, 1965, on recovering from the anesthetic. It was true. She had been separated from her Siamese twin sister, Giuseppina, and both were doing well. In 1959, the two Italian girls had been born joined together at the lower end of their spinal cord. For four years they had lived and played as one person. Then they had their first operation. Two anuses had to be created, conjoined parts had to be separated, and the final separation came when they were six. It was successful, and they became two people. Three weeks later, even though they had previously fully mastered a cumbersome technique of getting about on their four legs, they had learned again how to stand up. Within a month each took her first independent steps. They had joined a very small group of less than four score people who had been born as less than two score and who had been successfully separated.

The most famous Siamese twins of all, Chang and Eng, were not strictly Siamese, as they had Chinese parents, but they were born in Bangkok in 1811. (The Siamese called them the Chinese twins.) With a shared liver, joined together at the lower end of the chest bone, they were taken to the United States at the age of 18. Eng and Chang, meaning "left" and "right" in Thai, were exhibited by P. T. Barnum in his circus. The world flocked to see them, and the name Siamese twins has been indissolubly linked ever since with a conjoined birth (scientists refer instead to parabiotic twins).

Conjoined twins existed long before Barnum jumped on the bandwagon. In the year 1100, the Biddendon maids were born in England and lived for 34 years joined from their shoulders to their hips. James III of Scotland kept the "Scottish brothers" at his court. A pair of Hungarian girls, born in 1701, were joined back-to-back, sharing both anus and vagina. One pair of girls, called the Blažek twins and similarly joined, complicated matters still further when one became pregnant. Through the pregnancy the other girl continued to menstruate, but both of them produced milk when a healthy and normal boy was born. Long before Chang and Eng were born, attempts at separation surgery had been made, notably by a Basel doctor in 1689.

Not until this century, in Britain in 1912, was the world's first successful separation performed, and in the last 20 years there have been nine separations. With modern surgery, whatever Barnum might have said about the matter (and *Medical World News* recently suggested he would have sold tickets to the operation), Chang and Eng could probably have been divided successfully. As it was, they lived to be farmers in North Carolina, they married two daughters of a clergyman, and they had 22 (or 21) normal children. At the age of 69 (or 63), Chang died —of a clot on the brain, it is thought. Eng then died within a few hours of his brother. A postmortem showed no reason why he should have died, and a physician at the investigation wrote that the cause of Eng's death was probably "fright."

No one knows the extent of parabiotic twinning, or the cause. Some say that there are six such births recorded in any year (rarer than quadruplets, more common than quints), with a lot dying in neonatal days and a lot being quickly killed, as with many gross malformations. Others have assessed the incidence as high as once in 80,000 births. Some 70 pairs have been described in medical literature, and more of them are female than male. No conjoined pair has lived as long, either before or since, as Barnum's twins, the famous pair who gave their name to this rare consequence of a single fertilized ovum that divides to form twins, but never quite separates them.

Proof of Separation

Quite apart from the surgical separation of Siamese twins, ordinary twins have been inadvertently separated by hospitals. With babies everywhere, the mistake cannot be hard to make. When the error is discovered, perhaps years after, mothers are understandably reluctant to swap children merely to keep the books straight. A famous case of this kind occurred in Switzerland. One day, shortly after World War II, the father of a pair of twins was told about a boy called Eric (the journals stick to pseudonyms even in the original descriptions). The man's two 6-year-old sons, Victor and Pierre, were dissimilar, but Eric was said to be the double of Victor. And Eric had been born in the same hospital on the same day. A professor was informed, and he became convinced that Eric and Victor were identical twins, but Eric's mother refused to entertain any such notion and clung to the boy. Eric's father was dead. The doctors took blood samples and discovered that Pierre was definitely not the son of the mother he had been living with. Unfortunately, by blood group tests alone, it was not proved impossible for Eric to be the son of the mother clinging to him. Further tests had to be carried out to sort it out.

Sir Archibald McIndoe, well known by then for his wartime prowess with burned pilots and others desperately in need of plastic surgery, was called in to help. If Eric and Victor were indeed identical twins, they would accept grafts of skin from each other. By the same token, Pierre would reject them. Grafts between any two individuals will only take if those two people are identical twins. Sure enough, the grafts between Eric and Victor did take. Those between Pierre and Victor did not. Eric and Victor were therefore identical twins. Informed of the powerful evidence operating against her own affections, the foster mother of Eric relinquished him and took Pierre in his stead.

Hospitals must make the error of muddling babies from time to time. Only under very rare circumstances, as with the three Swiss boys, will the mistake manifest itself. The rest is silence.

Why Twins at All?

Twins complicate pregnancies. They die more frequently than single-tons. They cause their mothers to die more often than normal births do. On the other hand, why are there not more twins? Most animals produce more than one offspring at a time (called polytocous, as against monotocous).

The reason, if it can be put so bluntly and teleologically, is a compromise, a result of the forces of selection. The trouble with litters is that there tends to be intrauterine competition among their number, with the fastest grower being the strongest and the most active at securing a nipple. The smallest piglet may not even find a nipple at once; therefore he may not survive. The selective pressure on a litter is for speed of development, for survival first and foremost over one's brothers and sisters. Even the second human twin is more likely to die than the first, mainly because the placenta detaches itself too early. There is no similar struggle with a singleton, Either he makes it, or he does not. He never has to behave like a squealing piglet. He can relax. He can take his time over development, whether born weighing 5 lb. or 10 lb.

It is this relaxed and leisurely period of development that is important. Young mice are born after 19 days, having competed as embryos within the womb, to face further competition outside it. The human baby lingers on, comfortably. It is born at about the time when any further growth in size would be unmanageable within the confines of a human mother. Unlike many other singleton deliveries, such as so many of the ungulates, which have to run the day they are born, the human baby can continue its relaxed growth. Only at the age of 1 does it totter to its feet. Only at 2 is it running and roughly half its height. Only at 12 does puberty begin. Only at 20 is it fully grown. Such unhurried progress, so different from the subpanic anxiety of imminent shortage with which a piglet sees the world, is a boon to a more advanced developmental process, involving greater learning time and less reliance upon instinct. Being a singleton is a necessary precursor to this lengthy period of maturation.

The lengthened growing period is common to the higher primates. It happens both before birth and after birth. As Sir Peter Medawar has said, birth itself is a movable feast. Animals can be born soon and immature (as with mice), late and mature enough to run (as with ungulates), or late and physically mature enough to do nothing but suckle (as with man). The more advanced the primate, the longer the gestation period. Also the more advanced the primate, the lengthier the postnatal growth period. It is 2 to 3 years with lemurs, up to 7 years with monkeys, 11 years with the great apes, and 20 years with man. This is not because man is bigger than the monkeys. The apes, such as gorillas, are often far bigger than man.

Such elongation of time, growth, and learning could not have happened without the birth of singletons, and in practically all the Anthropoidea single birth is the rule. Twins are the exceptions to this rule. It is not known why they should happen, or for that matter, why they should not happen more. It is known that they are selected against—to use evolutionary language; they are less likely to survive; the dice are loaded against them, whatever the cause. As it happens these dice are even more heavily biased in many primitive communities. Twins are frequently killed as soon as they show themselves. The woman, it is often said, must have taken another man if she has produced a second child. Or the mother, distressed by the paired abnormality, is shamed into killing them herself. Both the natural pressures of decreased viability and the superstitions of human societies have been leveled against the twin. Both must have had their influence upon this minority group. Both have seen to it that 99 percent of all births, a fraction less here, a fraction more elsewhere, are of the favored and solitary form, namely singletons.

Congenital Malformations

Nine months is plenty of time for doubts to fester in most maternal minds about the normality of the infant they are incubating. Will all the fingers be there? And toes? And nails on those toes and those fingers?

The whole process of fetal development is so bewildering that any mind can be excused if it veers wildly from total confidence to an abject lack of it. Why shouldn't there be five toes on each foot? Why should there? The maternity authorities, books, people, and pamphlets, generally attempt to bolster the confidence either by skating around the problem or by making light of it. Consequently, only when the child has been born, and inspected, does an average mother become totally convinced of its normality.

Registration of Malformations

In the past, congenital malformations, defined as gross structural defects present at birth, were relatively unimportant. So many babies died from infection that the few who died from gross defects were statistically swamped. Nowadays, following the medical triumphs over infection, the numbers of babies suffering from malformations are more significant. They form a higher and higher proportion of infant deaths. Simultaneously, more and more of them are surviving. At the turn of the century only about one-thirtieth of infant deaths was attributed to malformations. By 1960, the proportion was certainly a fifth, perhaps a quarter, perhaps even more. As the causes of these malformations are largely unknown, the proportion is likely to increase still further as babies are steadily prevented from dying for other reasons. There is no immediate promise of any big drop in the numbers of deformed babies born. At present about two in every 100 are born with some blatant and severe malformation. Another two or so in every 100 are born with defects either less severe or less noticeable until some time has passed.

In all accounts detailing the extent of the malformation problem there is a vagueness about this extent. Surprisingly, a major cause of this uncertainty is the gross shortage of information. Only in July, 1960, in London, did the world hold its first international conference on congenital malformations. Only in 1964 did Britain initiate a system of notification of congenital abnormalities. Until then almost all British figures were extrapolations of facts collected in Birmingham and Scotland. Even now, the system does not include children of all ages, and many malformations do not manifest themselves for weeks, months, or even years after birth. In the United States there are some areas where not more than half the malformations are reported. Scandinavia, which has a good record of low infant mortality, has only recently set up malformation registries. In Finland, for example, reporting of all malformations in the newborn has been obligatory just since the beginning of 1963, and Finland is a pioneer in this field.

Apart from a lack of general registration there are plenty of other causes for lack of facts. In the past, no one cared too much about any physical defects in spontaneous abortions. (Recent work indicates that a quarter of these fetuses have detectable abnormalities.) Also in the past, no one cared too much about stillbirths and their defects. Autopsies on them are rare. Examination of their chromosomes, which could be highly relevant to the malformation problem, was hardly ever made, but it was common at the major centers. A consistent classification of the possible defects, plus their varying combinations, is still at a primitive level. Finally, with members of any one family having their babies up and down the country, it is exceptionally hard, if not impossible, for any researcher to discover familial links in any particular defect or set of defects. Lack of good and global information is certainly a dominant difficulty.

Nevertheless, despite the paucity of information, some general points have emerged. A higher standard of living does not reduce the number of malformed offspring. The world's races appear to be similarly afflicted, so far as total numbers are concerned, but each race has its own partiality for certain afflictions. Likewise, the sexes are equally affected, but certain afflictions beset one sex or the other more frequently (for example, males more often have harelips). Malformed babies have a poorer chance of surviving than ordinary babies. Normally, 95 percent of ordinary babies alive at the 28th week of pregnancy will still be alive five years later; if malformed, only 50 percent will be alive by then. With some malformations, such as anencephaly—or virtual absence of brain—none will be alive at the end of a week.

Only about half of malformations are detectable at birth, but signs are almost always apparent by the end of the first year. Some malformations are more likely to be detected at birth or shortly afterward if the birth is in a hospital. Mongoloids, for example, are less frequently reported in home deliveries, but some malformations do not manifest themselves to anyone—however expert—until very late in life. A few are genetically determined—i.e., inherited—but most congenital malformations are not. Congenital means manifest at birth; genetical means determined at conception. This clear-cut distinction of meaning is blurred by man's current inability to observe many congenital defects at the time of birth; but, nevertheless, there is a distinction between something that has been caused genetically and something that has not. German measles causes malformations on occasion, and such causation is not genetical. However, to blur the issue once again, one individual can, for genetical reasons, be prone to suffer from a totally nongenetical agent, such as German measles.

A final complexity is associated with bad information; different places and people have such different ideas about recording defects. Is a mongoloid child who has died of pneumonia dead because his mongolism made him more susceptible to the disease or not? Similarly, what is a malformation? How gross does this gross structural defect have to be? Plainly, the lack of a brain, of an anus, of a fused palate, or of a heart wall are all gross; but slightly webbed toes or the possession of a small sixth digit or just the merest fragment of that small sixth digit—are they gross? All biological activity resents being neatly pigeonholed, however enthusiastic the efforts of the biologists.

Yet certain defects, without any shadow of any doubt, are congenital malformations. They can be listed, together with their distinguishing characteristics; so can some of the suspected and infamous causes, notably German measles and thalidomide.

As a foreword to these lists it should be pointed out that practically everything can and does go wrong with human development. Take the eyes, for example. There can be no eyes, or just the development of a single median eye, or varying degrees of fusion of the two. The eyes can be much smaller than normal. Or there can be distortions of the retina, of the iris, of the cornea. Or the cornea may be opaque, in one eye or both. The opacity may be a ring or total. The pupils may be slit-shaped, and there even be more than one pupil per eye. There may be far too much pigment or next to none, as in albinism. The lens may be minute and spherical. There are also several kinds of congenital cataract and there are squints, glaucoma, a total absence of tears, and blocking of the tear ducts. And so on. There are countless ways in which some part of some development of the human system can, and does, go awry. Yet, there are far fewer ways in which development frequently goes wrong. Some errors are common. Some, happily, are extremely rare, possibly recorded once or twice. The body is just more prone to make certain errors or to have such errors inflicted upon it, during development. Of all these eye defects, only one is common, and that is congenital cataract.

A further relevant point is the length of time during which a certain area of development is susceptible. As with the manufacture of some engineering structure, each part has a critical time. Assume every builder on a job is drunk for a week. The parts of the job most severely affected will be those they are working on at the time. The parts already completed will be relatively immune from their alcoholic actions, as will the sections still to be begun. It is their handiwork of that particular week that would be most disastrous. So too with human development. Any malevolent influence will be most likely to affect organs in their crucial and critical developmental stage. For the brain it is from the 2nd to the 11th week.

For the eyes it is from the 3rd to the 8th week, the heart 2nd to 8th week, the fingers and toes 4th to 9th week, the teeth 6th to 11th, the ear 6th to 12th, the lips 4th to 6th, the palate 10th to 11th, the abdomen 10th to 12th. In pregnancy, the first 12 weeks after conception form the crucial developmental period. The subsequent six months are mainly devoted to growth. Hence, with the few causes of malformations that have been found, such as German measles and thalidomide, their influence has to occur during the first 12 weeks rather than the remaining 26 for it to be most destructive.

The Principal Afflictions

Thus a combination of organ susceptibility, of timing, of the powers of the causative agent, of the genetics involved, either directly or indirectly, of the resistance of the fetus and its mother—all such factors and many more must be influential in creating the list of congenital malformations that afflict man—or rather one in fifty or so of his children, or over 20,000 a year (60 a day) in the British Isles. Of the 876,566 births in England and Wales in 1965, 16,580 malformations "observable at the time of birth" were notified. Therefore, in that year such malformations affected 1.89 percent of all births, live or still.

The malformations not noticeable at the time of birth expand the total in the weeks, months, and years after birth.

In Britain, the central nervous system is the commonest site for major malformations. The three principal deformities are anencephaly, spina bifida, and hydrocephalus. One or other of them or a combination occurs once in every 150 births. Anencephaly mainly strikes female babies and it is always fatal, either before birth or very shortly after. It involves the major lack of brain tissue. From one in 500 to one in 2,000 babies are born with it in European communities.

The main malformation at the other end of the spinal column is spina bifida, where the skin often fails to cover the spinal cord completely. There are various forms, some invariably fatal, particularly when coupled with other maiformations. In Britain, its incidence, 2,500 babies a year, is more frequent than anencephaly. In the United States, it killed 1,186 babies in 1964.

Slightly less common but often found associated with spina bifida is hydrocephalus. Sometimes called "water on the brain," it is an excessive accumulation of liquid within the cranial cavity. An abnormally large head, either at birth or within the first few months of life, is the most obvious sign. It is nearly always fatal if in association with other nervous malformations.

All three of these most unpleasant malformations vary in incidence according to social class, age of mother, and geographical area. Information from Africa is slight, but good evidence from Uganda shows a total lack of anencephaly and spina bifida. Northwest Europe is particularly prone to these two malformations, but Northwest Europeans are less prone if they have emigrated elsewhere.

A totally different defect, but one with undeniable effects upon the central nervous system, is mongolism. In 1866 this unfortunate name was given to the one in 600 babies born who are often congenital idiots, and whose eyes bear a very superficial resemblance to Asian eyes. It was later discovered that a mongoloid's defects are linked to the possession of an extra chromosome. Asia in general has reasonably resented the name of mongolism, and continual effort is being made to replace the well-entrenched term by the more medical description of Down's syndrome.* Anyway, such babies are usually born small. They are recognizable either at or shortly after birth. They occur in all races. Their hands are stubby, their little fingers particularly. Their palm prints have unique characteristics. Many of their organs, apart from their brains, are poorly developed, and they are much more likely to be born to older mothers. Their eyes do slant, but for quite a different physical reason from the normal Asian slant: the distinction is particularly important for the offspring of marriages with some Asian blood in them. The raising of mongoloid children is beset with problems, but the happy nature of many of these children can provide considerable compensation. By no means do they all have extremely low IQ's—there is great variation in intelligence. Two-thirds of all mongoloid children are still alive at 5, but only a quarter if they have other defects as well. The incidence of mongolism rises with maternal age; if mothers are 20, the risk is one in 3,000, if over 40 the risk is one in 100, and may be even higher for mothers over 45. If mongoloids have children there is about a 50-50 chance (although evidence is scarce) that their children will also be mongoloid.

After the central nervous system, the circulatory system is the second most common site for major malformations in northern Europe and white America. In Britain about 4,000 babies a year are born with heart defects. Perhaps half of them are discovered at the time of birth. The remainder are generally discovered before their first birthdays, but some take years to manifest themselves.

Briefly, the defects can be holes between the heart's chambers, anomalies in the big blood vessels, or the failure of the fetal circulation of blood to change fully into the postnatal type, a change necessitated by

* Named after the nineteenth-century English physician Langdon Down, who described the condition a century ago.

oxygen coming from the lungs rather than the umbilical cord. Surgery is making great advances among the very young, but congenital heart defects still cause many deaths. In a recent 14-year survey, 37 percent of babies possessing such defects were dead in a week, 54 percent in a month. The causes of heart defects are about as little understood as brain and cord defects, but German measles is definitely to blame for 2 percent of them, although how and why is a different matter. Of babies born with congenital heart defects 25 percent will be alive five years later, but only 15 percent if there are other defects as well.

About two in 1,000 of all babies in Europe are born with one of the three types of cleft palate and lip. Harelip (called Group I) accounts for 20 percent of them; cleft palate (Group II) for 46 percent; and combined cleft palate, gum and lip (Group III), for 34 percent. Sometimes, the lip clefts are two-sided; but if one-sided, the left side is the more common. Fathers of all these children are older than average, and mothers are older than average for Group III. Birth weights of all groups are low, and about 20 percent of the victims have another kind of malformation as well. When a harelip or a cleft palate occurs in association with other malformations, death is the rule within a few months. If there is only a harelip or cleft palate, death is rare, and 87 percent are alive five years later. (This repetition of viability up to the age of five does not indicate that the fifth birthday is a turning point. It is just that five years is a traditional follow-up time for congenital malformations and for diseases like cancer.)

Cleft palates and harelips cry out for surgery, and there is a great deal that surgery can do. Group III is most difficult, and repair work is generally begun six to eight weeks after birth. As Group II infants can swallow normally, although they cannot suckle, there is less urgency. The cleft palate is usually repaired between the first and second birthdays. Group I babies can swallow and suckle, and therefore treatment need not start until they are fully weaned. Because speech is so important, and because poor speech can lead to poor reading, and because poor reading can mean poor progress at school, palate and lip repair is carried out, if possible, before speech begins. As one surgeon has put it, treatment should allow these infants to speak well, look well, and eat well, in that order. Most children will develop normal speech if palate repair is done in time. If the operation is not done until they are, say, 10, most will not develop normal speech, however much the speech therapist may try to get the right sounds out of a misshapen instrument (although orthodontic appliances can help). Good speech also requires good hearing, and many cleft-palate babies have poor hearing as well. The possibility of this double handicap should always be suspected.

Inheritance plays a part in harelips and cleft palates. If normal parents have one child with a harelip, the chance that the next baby will have one is 4 percent. If two of their children have them, the chance for the next baby goes up to 9 percent. If one of the parents has a harelip also, and one baby has one, the chance for the next goes up to 17 percent. With cleft palates, which afflict females more than males, the odds are different. With both parents normal and one cleft-palate baby, the chance for the next baby also having one is only 2 percent. If one parent and one child have cleft palates that chance goes up to 15 percent.

In European communities about four babies in 1,000 are born with some form of clubfoot or talipes (from Latin: *talus,* ankle, *pes,* foot). Correction of the defect is begun very early—in fact, almost immediately after birth. There are many methods, and the results are usually good. About a quarter of talipes babies, or one in 1,000 of all babies, have both talipes and some other malformation. There is, once again, a genetic link for this deformity. One deformed baby means a greater chance than normal that other offspring will be similarly deformed, and they are greater still if the parent was a victim.

About three babies in 1,000 in northwestern Europe are either born with pyloric stenosis, a blocked stomach exit, or more frequently develop a blockage in the first few weeks after birth. It is five times more common in boys than girls. It was often lethal before 1920, but nowadays surgery is nearly always effective. The alimentary canal can also, more rarely, be blocked elsewhere along its length. A fairly frequent condition is a blockage at the very end, called an imperforate anus. About 500 British babies a year are born with it, and skillful surgery is necessary.

Congenital dislocation of the hip affects one baby in 1,500, generally girls, by a ratio of 6:1. It is more common in breech births than head births (because of the lie and not of the birth) and among winter babies than summer babies. It is most common in northern Italy, among Lapps and red Indians (which suggests tight swaddling). It is usually diagnosed late, sometimes after several months, when walking starts, sometimes after two years, sometimes later still. Therefore, it is not strictly congenital, but is generally considered so.

So much for six groupings of congenital malformation. About 90 percent of all malformations come under these headings. The remaining 10 percent, either more or less for different areas, includes every other type of congenital defect, all those defects of the eye already mentioned, all known gross errors of development. Very briefly a few of these others are:

CONGENITAL DEAFNESS. Affects one in 3,000. Often caused by German measles.

ACHONDROPLASIA. Affects one in 40,000. Short, thickset, square-headed dwarfs. Intelligence and fitness good. Ability to breed poor. Cesareans imperative when they give birth.

POLYDACTYLY. Extra fingers. Affects one in 1,000 in Europe, more in Africa.

ACCESSORY AURICLES. Additions to the external ear. Easily removed surgically. Conversely, the external ear may be absent and can be added by plastic surgery.

ICTHYOSIS. Large group of anomalies characterized by scaly skin and dryness, with or without reduction or complete absence of hair follicles or sweat glands or both.

Various concluding generalizations are possible. Most races suffer similar numbers of malformations. Most common sites for malformations are the nervous and circulatory systems. Most malformations are readily detectable at birth or shortly afterward. Most hamper chances of life. Most causes are unknown. Inheritance is involved in many of them. Most common malformations can be classified under a few headings. Most other malformations are extremely rare. Many appear in association with other malformations. Such associations are most likely to be fatal. There is little or nothing that most mothers can do to offset malformations. There is much that surgery can do. Most babies that die at birth or very soon afterward are dying not because of malformations, but the proportion of malformation deaths is rising as other neonatal causes are attacked and controlled. Many of the congenital anomalies regularly fluctuate in their incidence according to the season.

German Measles

Now to the two most potent malformation stories of recent years. First rubella*, alias German measles. It was in the middle of World War II that a paper linking German measles with malformed babies was published in Australia by Dr. N. McA. Gregg (later Sir Norman). He was an eye specialist and so saw many children with congenital cataract. His brilliance lay in also realizing, after a German-measles epidemic, that many of their mothers had contracted German measles during their pregnancies. The startling figures were 78 cataract children

* A sort of translation, or rendering, of the original German term *röteln*, both words indicating redness. Confusingly, ordinary measles is called rubeola.

and 68 German-measles mothers. Once he had put two and two together, the rest of the world rapidly confirmed his opinion.

Catching German measles early in pregnancy somehow causes an offspring to possess malformations more frequently than normal. Apart from cataract, these are principally deafness and heart defects. The earlier the mother contracts measles during pregnancy the worse it is for the fetus within the womb. There have been countless surveys that emphasize this point. A recent one gave the malformation risk as 60 percent if rubella is contracted during the four weeks following the last menstrual period, 35 percent in the next four, and 7 percent in the next four. So the first three-month period, or trimester, is the crucial one, and the very first month the most crucial of all.

These loaded dice immediately raise ethical questions. Should abortions be permitted, or even compelled, for mothers who have a 60-percent chance of producing a malformed baby? As a complication, mothers have been uncertain if the sickness they had was German measles or merely a rash or fever. The disease is not very severe. It often does not even create a rash, but it is highly infectious and tends to come back in epidemics every 7 to 12 years. (It was such an outbreak that brought the minor spate of children with cataract to Dr. Gregg.) The severity of the epidemic, as judged by the affected mothers, does not seem to be partnered by any similar severity of effect upon the fetuses. Stranger still, one twin may be badly affected by the mother's catching of rubella, the other twin may be quite unharmed.

Fortunately, in 1962, and 21 years after that famous Australian report, the German-measles virus was successfully grown in a laboratory. And less than three years later a practicable one-day test was devised in the United States for confirming and accurately diagnosing German measles. This research only clarifies the ethical issue. Should the woman who has definitely had German measles during the first four weeks of pregnancy be permitted, or encouraged, to abort her probably malformed infant? Should young girls be deliberately infected with rubella in a kind of antibody finishing school? No vaccine has yet been generally distributed, but claims for an effective anti-rubella vaccine were made in mid-1966 by scientists from the U.S. National Institutes of Health. By early 1967, at least four rubella vaccines had been developed and were being given limited trials in man.

As if to hammer home some of the difficult factors involved, the United States was suddenly hit by a vast epidemic in 1964. There were nearly 2 million cases, including tens of thousands of pregnant

women. Although all the affected babies from this single epidemic were
born either that year or in 1965, it will be some time before its full
effects can be listed. Preliminary estimates say it caused at least
20,000 stillbirths, miscarriages, and birth defects. Total deafness is
easy to detect fairly swiftly in a child; partial deafness is far harder
and takes much longer, but already estimates have been made that
half the children whose mothers were affected are suffering from at
least a partial hearing loss. It is easy to equate this natural disaster with
the man-made tragedy of thalidomide.

Thalidomide, Contergan, and Distaval

The thalidomide disaster does have several fortunate aspects. It was
lucky, in a sense, that it produced a rare malformation. It was good
that a German doctor saw and promptly stopped the malevolent
connection between drug and defect. It was fortunate that certain countries, notably the United States, never even sold the drug. Now there is
even a hypothesis that the living victims of the drug might not even
have survived to be born had their mothers not swallowed thalidomide and thereby prevented their deformed fetuses from being aborted
naturally. A large proportion of natural abortions are malformed, and
no one knows how thalidomide has its effects. Until this is known
hypotheses will inevitably arise concerning the effects it does have,
particularly in this relatively unexplored world of cause and effect in
congenital malformations.

Germany synthesized the new nonbarbiturate hypnotic in 1956. It
was tested on animals, found to be satisfactory, and then given to human
beings. As a sleeping pill it was more than satisfactory. It was cheap,
it gave a good sleep, and it would not kill would-be-suicides. Above all,
it was effective in reducing the nausea of early pregnancy. In West
Germany, where it was first marketed as Contergan, the drug was very
popular; it could be bought over the counter without a prescription.
Such a profitable drug did not go unnoticed by other countries. Many
of them made thalidomide. Britain did so, called it Distaval and sold
it. Australia sold it. Other countries had other names—Softenon, Talimol.
The United States made it but, to the eternal credit of the Food and Drug
Administration, did not sell it. The land of Rachel Carson, of intensive
crop-spraying, of Los Angeles smog, of Nevada's atomic explosions, of the
people who eat 300 tons of barbiturate a day before going to bed, who
kill 50,000 a year on their roads, this same land considered that the
new drug had failed its safety tests. A few Americans swallowed
thalidomide, partly because one or two trials were conducted, partly

because it was available elsewhere, but they were very few. In that country, with nearly 4 million pregnancies a year and a highly active drug industry pushing a new, cheap, and popular hypnotic and anti-nauseant, the effects could have been catastrophic. As it was, West Germany suffered the most from its creation.

By 1959 cases of phocomelia were beginning to show up in German hospitals. This condition, in which small hands and feet are attached to the trunk by a single small bone, is usually extremely rare. It is one of a variety of limb defects, such as amelia (total absence of limbs) and micromelia (very short limbs). By 1960 such defects were appearing even more frequently, with phocomelia heading the list. By 1961 the frequency went up several times over. And the defects were appearing more often in other countries, in Britain, where Distaval had been available since 1958, in Japan, in Australia, and in the rest of Europe. During 1961, a mere five years after the drug's first synthesis, many German doctors were urgently trying to find a cause for the surge of phocomelia. Thalidomide, still unsuspected, had been put on the prescription list (meaning it could be sold only with a doctor's prescription) in April of that year for quite another reason: prolonged taking of the drug was being blamed for a form of neuritis and a wasting away of certain tissues.

Dr. Widikund Lenz, of Hamburg, was particularly active in asking young mothers what had happened to them during their pregnancy. Where had they been? What had they eaten? By November he suspected the drug Contergan. A noteworthy proportion of the women had mentioned it; so back he went to the others and found that a greater proportion had not even bothered to mention it, knowing its innocent reputation. At once he called a meeting and notified Contergan's manufacturers. On November 20, 1961, he reported to the Düsseldorf Pediatric Society. Similar detective work was being done in Australia by Dr. W. G. McBride, and he too notified the drug company. Suddenly, after five years of tranquillity, events moved fast for the new drug. Before November had ended, the drug had been withdrawn from the German market. McBride's suspicions gave rise to urgent cables between Australia and London. The German Ministry of Health advertised in newspapers and television that women should not take the drug. And in Britain, Distaval was quietly removed from the market on December 2 of that year. The sudden flurry then subsided into an uncanny quiet. The British people were almost totally unaware that anything untoward had been happening.

In the United States there was also silence. It was to be broken principally by a heart specialist, Dr. Helen Taussig. In January, 1962, she heard casually from a former German student of hers about the rash of phocomelia victims in his country. The next day she impulsively flew to have a look. On leaving Germany for London she felt 90 percent certain that thalidomide was to blame. On leaving Britain, having heard about Australia too, she was 99 percent certain and flew back to America determined to publicize her findings. This single personal mission was to break open the subject, once and for all. For some reason, about which the world's journalists should feel a certain disquiet, those German advertisements had never been noticed for the news story that lay so blatantly within and behind them. Dr. Taussig spoke at the American College of Physicians, and the press at last realized what had been happening.

The British public first read about and understood the horror of thalidomide in their newspapers in the summer of 1962. This was six months after the drug's quiet removal from the approved list. There had been intermediate newspaper references in the depths of the parliamentary columns. Only during the subsequent months did editors finally give thalidomide the space it merited and made certain that the difficult name of this six-year-old drug became a familiar household word. So, by the time the hue and cry began, the fox had already gone to ground. Nevertheless, pregnancy is nine months long. Mrs. Sherri Finkbine, an American who had swallowed the drug, kept its name in the headlines by her efforts, which were eventually successful, to have an abortion in Sweden, and so rid herself of a possibly malformed child. At that time there were many other women carrying fetuses within them that might have been deformed by pills taken in 1961. Time would tell how many.

In 1964, when time had told, Britain's Ministry of Health published *Deformities Caused by Thalidomide*. This survey was limited to live-born children. It showed that 349 malformed children were born in England and Wales between the beginning of 1960 and the end of August, 1962, to mothers who had certainly, or probably, taken thalidomide. In 1964, 267 of these children were alive. Bearing in mind the difficulty of collecting all the facts, the concluding estimate of this report was that between 200 and 250 children were living in England and Wales with thalidomide-induced deformities. There had originally been fears that the numbers would be far worse. In Germany they *were* far worse. In November, 1965, Dr. Lenz, who had delivered his report four years earlier, said that there were 7,000 thalidomide babies in the world; of these the majority were in West Germany. The original total of thalidomide children may well have been double Dr. Lenz's 1965 total. Two other German doctors attempted in 1964 to reexamine all the children they had seen between 1959 and 1962 who had had defects typical of thalidomide teratogeny. They could not examine 45 percent of their former 400 malformed patients; that 45 percent had died.

Science is still trying to explain how thalidomide has its teratogenic, or malforming, effects; but effort is also being made on direct behalf of the affected children. By now they are of school age. They need prosthetic limbs, they need surgery. They need special schools—Germany will have built 80 by 1969. They need psychological care.

Britain regularly kills 7,000 people a year on its roads, and in a thoroughly man-made manner, but there is something additionally tragic about the man-made malformations of the 7,000 living vicims of thalidomide.

The Cause of Malformations

Plainly, German measles and thalidomide are guilty. Ionizing radiation is also guilty. Hiroshima and Nagasaki made that abundantly clear when the pregnancies of August, 1945, were delivered. Diabetic women and women with prediabetic signs also produce more defective children than normal (diabetes is itself a defect caused by something else). Vitamins in excess, hormones, measles, high altitudes, lack of oxygen, cosmic rays, gas poisoning, syphilis, mumps, polio, chickenpox, any and every sort of virus infection, quinine, antibodies, food deficiencies—the list of suspects is huge, but medical science has not found guilt an easy thing to prove.

However, unlike the law, the present attitude is to consider everything guilty even if the evidence is lacking. Give a pregnant woman nothing, and give her even less in the first three months, sums up much of the current attitude toward medication for mothers-to-be. A warning note was inserted into the recent new edition of *Clinical Pharmacology,* which stated, "The medical profession clearly has a grave duty to refrain from all inessential prescribing of drugs with, say, less than ten to fifteen years widespread use behind them, for all women of childbearing age." It used to be thought that the womb, nature's own sacred womb, was somehow exempt from disaster. Rubella in 1941 and thalidomide in 1961 shook that complacency. Like two enemy agents suddenly discovered in the stronghold, they have made everyone else suspect for a time.

In the past there was simplicity. Malformations, it was said, were caused by "faulty germ plasm." Now there is no longer simplicity. There is solely a bewildering list of malformations, a huge array of suspects, and yet an exciting feeling that at last the subject has been opened up. Alas, but radiation, German measles, and thalidomide should get most of the credit for this awakening.

"Maternal Impressions"

A postscript to this subject is "maternal impressions," defined as effects on the fetus resulting from similar impressions on the mind or body of the mother. There have been some uncanny examples—or coincidences. The pregnant mother catches her arm in a folding chair; lo and behold, the baby is born without that very same arm. Coincidence? Or cause? A writer in the *Journal of the Tennessee Medical Association* recorded in 1910 that "Mrs. ——, twenty-three years old and about two months pregnant, was one day very badly frightened by her son, aged two, nearly cutting off his left thumb, the member hanging by but a thread. She was without anyone to assist her and dressed the injury as best she could. Her mind constantly dwelt on the accident and in due time she gave birth to a boy, who, to my great surprise, had his left thumb hanging from his hand by a thin pedicle of flesh." Such an incidence is called a photographic impression, owing to the similarity between the trauma and the defect. Scientists working in this sphere are prepared to accept that certain "impressions" upon the mind or body of the mother have led to consequences for the fetus, despite the fact that most pregnancies punctuated by shocks of all kinds lead to normal healthy babies. But current thinking excludes the idea that maternal shocks cause "similar" defects in the baby that resemble the original trauma. Coincidence is always possible, but nothing more: the photographic theory of maternal impressions cannot, these days, be upheld.

⊰ 15 ⊱

Inheritance

Background · Chromosomes · Coding · Mutations ·
Intersexes · Inherent Traits · Hemophilia · Tasters ·
The Hapsburg Lip · Albinism · Height · Color ·
Baldness · Color Blindness

Take care to get born well.
George Bernard Shaw

By way of introduction to this subject, here is a potted version of the mechanism of inheritance, more to outline the form the chapter will take, than to make immediate sense of human genetics.

In a sexual system all offspring acquire their inheritance from both parents. The sperm and ovum fuse to form a single cell, with all the inherited material being within this single cell. Therefore, because of this fusing, each parent must have a system for presenting only half a human cell's vital needs. The two halves then unite in fertilization to form a whole cell. That united cell must have a system for dividing to form more cells, each similar, each carrying the same quotient of inheritance, and each dividing equally. Within each divided cell there must be an arrangement for the storage of all this inheritance, so that its information exists throughout the developing body. And, of course, there must be a mechanism for converting all this store of information into reality, for acting upon it, for transforming the single cell into a multicellular adult of the correct and inherited kind. He becomes a man, and not a mouse.

Now some names. The system for forming half a cell is called meiosis. After fertilization the system of normal and equal division is mitosis. The storage of information is principally within the chromosomes of the nucleus, each consisting of long strands of deoxyribonucleic acid, here-inafter called—as is the custom—DNA. Within the DNA, and according to the arrangement of chemical bases on its structure, is a code that ordains which proteins are to be formed, when, and how. With the coordinated production of these proteins by the DNA, the development of an individual gradually unfolds. He becomes Homo sapiens, and not Mus musculus.

Therefore, chromosomes have to be described first, as their manner and form are crucial to meiosis and mitosis and to the storage of information. Next comes coding, and the very recent work in cracking the most condensed blueprint of all time. Then, having established the mechanism, come its faults. First, mutations, the irreversible changes. Second, the larger scale chromosomal errors when bits break off to cause intersexes and mongoloids and some cancers and inevitably much else besides. Finally, the end products of all this inheritance, whether correct or faulty: the inherent traits of man. Why do women pass on hemophilia and yet not suffer from it? Why do blue-eyed parents virtually always produce blue-eyed offspring? Why albinos? Why not more of them? Why any?

Background

Practically all the work on this subject is very new. The first correct count of human chromosomes was made only in 1956. DNA rose to fame only in the 1950s. Code cracking began only in the 1960s.

Nevertheless, ideas on breeding are older than historical man. Some unsung hero must have been the first to take certain hopeful-looking grasses, select the most promising, breed from them, and thus artificially develop cereals fit for man and his burgeoning agriculture. Much later and long before biologists had anything to say on the theory of breeding, practical genetics was highly skilled. The monoglot but multifarious world of the dog is a testament to this ingenuity. Compare also the natural and wild ponies or the early Przewalski's horse of central Asia (now seen mainly in zoos, but occasionally in Asia) with a Derby winner or a Shire stallion. The original British Soay sheep, now found only on St. Kilda, the westernmost island of Scotland's Outer Hebrides, produce a 1½-lb. fleece; modern fleeces are 28 lb. or so. A medieval farmer got 3 cwt. of wheat from each strip-shaped acre; modern yields are 30 cwt. Radishes of 28 lb. have been grown. Cows can produce 10 gal. of milk a day, not one gallon or less as formerly.

Part of all this improvement lies in better cultivation, better disease control, and better understanding, but better genetical methods are paramount. Robert Bakewell, a practical biologist who lived in the eighteenth century, before the word "biology" had even been coined, had much influence on the increasing dimensions of British livestock. The average weight of bullocks sold at London's Smithfield cattle market in

1710 was 370 lb. The average rose to 550 lb. in 1732 and 800 lb. in 1795—or more than double in less than a century.

However, this good practical work, founded on controlled mating, was not scientific genetics. That began in 1865 when Gregor Mendel, a teacher-priest of Moravia, sent an article on hybridization in plants to *The Proceedings of the Brünn Society for the Study of Natural Sciences.* It was not the obscurity of the journal that prevented this article from becoming famous, but a transient blindness among the appropriate scientists. Charles Darwin died in 1882 having never heard of Mendel, who died two years later. The article was the formal birth of genetics, but only at the turn of the century was this birth finally registered when three biologists from Germany, Austria, and the Netherlands rediscovered Mendel's work.

Briefly, Mendel had produced a theory that accurately predicted the nature of the hereditary mechanism. Before his work, again very briefly, inheritance was thought to be an alloy or amalgam or random blending of parental properties; after him it became an assortment of discrete inherited units, the genes of genetics. Mendel's brilliance was accompanied by an apparently complete foreknowledge of the results of his experiments even before conducting them. He seemed to comprehend the system entirely without knowing anything of the mechanics. It is even said that Mendel's gardener fixed the results according to Mendel's preconceptions. The actual hereditary mechanism, then still totally unknown, has unfolded with twentieth-century discoveries into a most positive vindication of the man who died, not as a revered scientist but as the revered abbot of the monastery of Brünn.

Chromosomes

Chromosomes have provided the framework for almost all of this twentieth-century activity in inheritance. They were discovered in the last century, but meant little to anyone. Chromosome means only "colored body," and each one showed up colorfully within the cell's nucleus when the material was suitably stained. Then, in 1903, they were stated to be the carriers of genetic information. It was not mankind's chromosomes that were studied in those early days of genetics, but primarily those of a minute insect often to be seen flying above trash cans and garbage. The fruit fly, Drosophila, was for many decades and still is a humble and willing servant of geneticists. Its eight large chromosomes are easy to see, and the members of this helpful species breed rapidly— like flies. Mankind's chromosomes were never so easy to detect in those early days, and for 30 years all books said we had 48.

Suddenly in 1956, better techniques were to shake the genetical world and make it blush. J. H. Tjio and Albert Levan reported from Sweden that they could count only 46. Inevitable disbelief followed, but so did many other counts of 46, and 46 it will always be. Strangely, all the great apes have 48, an inconsistency between man and his nearest evolutionary relatives that poses a problem. Other species, far less closely related, have widely differing chromosomal counts. Examples of species having more than man, apart from the apes, are the chicken (78) and some snails (54). Less than man, apart from Drosophila, are the hamster (22), the honeybee (16), the frog (26), the cat (38), and the mouse (40). There is a temptation to say the more advanced the animal the more the chromosomes, but the rule is soon trampled upon by the exceptions.

The new counting techniques were possible because of microscopy advances. Even before these were available, it had been known that chromosomes closely resembled entwined strands of wool. Shortly before a cell divides, the strands become very positive and are in fact doubled. Then, as if pulled by invisible threads from each side of the cell, each double strand is separated. The invisible threads continue to pull from their opposite poles and have soon amassed a group of chromosomes around them, with just as many in each group as there had been in the single group before it divided. Forty-six, in human cell division, have become 46 plus 46, and soon the cell itself divides to form two cells, each with the correct chromosomal complement. Such is mitosis (from the Greek for thread).

Reduction division, or meiosis (from the Greek for diminution), so necessary to give the sperm or the ova half the correct number of chromosomes, is a very similar process. The strands of wool become more positive, just as before, but are not doubled. Consequently, when the same polar attraction starts work upon those chromosomes to pull half each way, the 46 divide to become 23. Further divisions, to produce more sperm or more ova, then take place as in conventional mitosis, and 23 chromosomes regularly divide to produce fresh cells, each with 23 chromosomes in them. The number will change again only at fertilization when 23 meet 23 to produce 46, when the ova and the sperm meet to fuse into the fertilized egg. Half that fertilized egg's chromosomes have therefore come from each parent.

Not all the strands of chromosomes are equal, although the uninitiated eye finds them remarkably similar. Each chromosome is split down the middle, but is still attached at one point (called the centromere). The chromosomes are like short lengths of two-stranded wool that threaten to part, and the centromere is like a blob of glue holding them together.

As the strand lengths are different for different chromosomes and the blob is unevenly placed, some chromosomes are long, with long arms and long legs; some have short arms and long legs; some are short with short arms and legs; and some are medium-sized. There seems every variation on this theme, but each variation does in fact have a brother, a partner similar in appearance. There are 23 pairs of chromosomes in man, rather than 46 separate ones.

The glaring exception to this regular pairing occurs in males. Females are all right, their 23 being nicely matched with another 23. In males there are two that do not match. These are the sex chromosomes, which determine a person's sex. Whether someone is black, big, clever, or blue-eyed does not show up on his or her chromosomes, at least not with present-day techniques; but the fact of sex is blatant under the microscope. Both males and females have 22 similar pairs, but females also have a similar 23rd pair, both of which have been named X chromosomes. Males have a dissimilar 23rd pair, one X and one named Y. The Y is far smaller than the X. With females the division during meiosis of 23 pairs into 23 single chromosomes is straightforward. The female eggs are then, all 22 plus X, all alike. With males the division of 22 of the pairs is straightforward, but the XY 23rd pair is less so. The X goes one way, the Y the other. Hence, males produce during their meiosis two types of sperm, a 22 plus X type and a 22 plus Y.

It is for this reason that the male is the arbiter of an offspring's sex. During fertilization the female's 23 chromosomes (X plus 22 others) will meet a sperm bearing either X plus 22 others or Y plus 22 others. If X plus 22, the sperm's X will pair with the egg's X to form XX, i.e., a female. If Y plus 22, then Y will meet X to form XY, i.e., a male. The Y makes for maleness, its lack makes for femaleness; but why is for the future to say. Somehow the genes on that short Y chromosome cause those glands to develop which, in their turn, cause the male organs to develop. Within that Y are coded all the necessary instructions for determining maleness.(Plainly the time will come soon—when parents will be able to choose the sex of their future offspring. Dr. Augustus B. Kinzel, writing in the magazine *Science* in 1967, warned "we can expect sex predetermination by 1980.")

Coding

First, the size of the problem. A favorite spy-story device is the use of microdots for passing on information—a comma or an exclamation mark is the shrunken image of some document. When suitably enlarged this small image yields its secrets. This refined expertise is nothing compared with the minuscule scale of the genetic code. Human cells each contain about six-trillionths of a gram of DNA, and there are 28 gm. in an ounce. As there are 3 billion people now living on earth, and as each individual egg cell that initiated all these people contained no more DNA than those trillionths of a gram, this means that all the DNA information for all those people weighed .02 gm. (I am indebted to the geneticist Theodosius Dobzhansky for this arresting calculation.) Taking the arithmetic still further and bearing in mind the population growth of recent centuries, it could well be that the total inherited and informative DNA of every individual born since the time of Christ has weighed no more than a gram. The world of microdots is gargantuan by comparison.

The history of DNA has been short. Only during World War II was the idea first promoted that the substance responsible for hereditary messages was DNA. The structure of this extraordinarily complex molecule was determined only in the early 1950s, and the code started to crack only in the 1960s. The rapid progress in this science of molecular biology was achieved when scientists of various disciplines worked together to solve the biological problem. Of the two Nobel Prizes given in 1962 and shared by five men for work in this field, only one, J. D. Watson, was trained as a biologist. Two were physicists, F. H. C. Crick and M. H. F. Wilkins, and two were chemists, M. F. Perutz and J C. Kendrew. (Watson was also the only American in an otherwise British achievement.)

Long before the code began to be cracked there was a basic understanding of the mechanism involved in the progression from one cell to one adult, from the store of facts within DNA to the realization of all that information in the end product of a developed human being. Basically, the order of events was known. First make the proteins, which would then make the body, partly by forming its structures, partly by making the enzymes that control its chemical reactions. It was also known that only 20 different substances—called amino acids—were needed to make the proteins and thus the enzymes and thus the body. The amino acids are consequently called the building blocks of development. The order in which these blocks are picked up to make each protein ordains what kind of protein it is, what kind of enzyme and structure it makes, and thus what sort of development results. It had long been known that whatever controlled this order controlled the development, and it has been known since the war that DNA, somehow, did the controlling.

Having simplified this issue, it is now necessary to complicate it to give an indication of the scale of things. There are only those 20 kinds of amino acid, but an average protein may contain 150 different amino-acid molecules, all amassed in the right order. As amino acids are themselves fairly complex molecules, the proteins are even more so. Each protein molecule contains many thousands of atoms, whereas some simple molecule like sugar has 45, penicillin 40, and sulphuric acid 7.

Within each cell there are probably a few thousand different proteins at work, producing different enzymes, causing different chemical reactions. Taking the body as a whole, there must be many times that number of large protein molecules at work. And all of this is ordained by the information contained within those wispy threads, the long tenuous molecules of DNA. These DNA molecules possess somewhere between 100 thousand and 10 million atoms. As molecules they are big; but, even so, they are small in comparison with the chromosomes that contain them. Chromosomes are small enough, demanding good microscopes even to be seen, but the thinnest are 100 to 200 millimu across (a millimu is a millionth of a centimeter). A DNA molecule is only about two millimu across.

Now to the code. Although it is long and thin and gives rise to multitudinous activity, the DNA molecule is made up of only four types of chemical units. Just as proteins are made from the 20 building blocks of amino acid, so DNA is made from a repetition of just four chemicals. There are many tens of thousands of these in each molecule, but only four types—adenine, guanine, cytosine, and thymine. They are all chemical bases, and hereafter are called A, G, C, and T. Somehow their ordering along the DNA chain controls the order in which the right amino acids are picked up to make a protein. Plainly, the order in which just these four kinds are arranged would be inadequate for 20 different kinds of amino acid. If A meant one amino acid, G another, T a third, and C a fourth, there would be 16 left over that could not be called upon. The code was obviously more complex. It was then thought that the order of each pair of bases might be the controller of a single amino acid and could ordain which amino acid was to be taken from the pool. Unfortunately, there are only 16 possible pairings of A, G, C, and T (namely AA, AT, AG, AC, TA, TT, TG, TC, GA, GT, GG, GC, CA, CT, CG, and CC) and these are still fewer than the 20 amino acids. These 16 types of arrangements could not therefore provide a selection of 20 amino acids. So, it was inevitably wondered whether the magic number was three because two was plainly inadequate.

If A, G, C, and T are thought of as threesomes there are 64 different ways in which they can be arranged—AAA, AAG, AGA, GAA, AAC, and so on. Sixty-four is therefore ample for a selection of 20. In the 1960s it has been proved that this triplet arrangement does form the code. Some amino acids are chosen by more than one triplet, and some of the triplets act as punctuation to mark the end of the formation of a particular protein. The first amino acid to be correctly associated with a definite triplet was phenylalanine. This happened in 1961. As with the deciphering of any code, the first crack is the important one. Thereafter the secrecy falls apart. After 1961 it did so very rapidly, and by 1965 the code was broken. The controlling sequences of bases, whether one triplet or several, have all been identified with the 20 amino acids. Just what controls which has been unraveled.

The work went on so quickly that, within the same year, the code was actually being utilized. Such work poses many questions for the future. Will molecular biologists be able to tinker with DNA now that they know its secret? Will they be able to knock off an atom here, add one there, thereby changing inheritance? Will they be able to rid us of defects, or add advantages? Will they ever be allowed to? Sir Macfarlane Burnet, the Australian virologist, confessed in 1966 that he had been fascinated by molecular biology "since before some of the great molecular biologists of today were born. . . . But, as a man, as a doctor of medicine, it worries me intensely. At the human level, where is it leading us? What good can it do?"

Mutations

Nature has been knocking off atoms and adding them here and there ever since life began. The essence of life is stability, but the essence of evolution is the ability to change. Mutations are the main mechanisms for permitting change and are therefore desirable. They are also most undesirable, for they often kill and generally harm. Their changes are irreversible, and they are very rare.

It is not known how rare. It just happens that, from time to time, cells suffer hereditary alterations. For ordinary body cells the change means, provided they are still capable of division, that the cells stemming from them will thenceforth carry the new characteristic. The change may be for the good, for the bad, or inconsequential. Anyway, it dies out when the individual body dies. But this is not so if the change has been in his or her germ cells, the producers of sperm or ova. The future descendants will also carry this change. And this change will remain a permanent characteristic until it too is changed in some fashion by yet another mutation. And so on. Species will be replaced by quite different forms. And they in their turn will be replaced. Long before the science of genetics began, the poet Shelley wrote: "Man's yesterday may ne'er be like his morrow; naught may endure but mutability."* He was absolutely correct.

* As a coincidence Shelley drowned the very year that Gregor Mendel was born.

The delicacy implicit in the whole coding system makes it quite plain why any alterations are likely to be harmful. After all, mutations are random changes, and only the very smallest have the greatest likelihood of being acceptable. Hence, in a sense, their rarity. Were they frequent, no organisms could survive such a plethora of unwelcome change. Experimental evidence suggests that one germ cell in 100,000 or possibly only one in a million carries a recent mutation. Lots of effects can increase this rate. Radiation is one of them, a fact discovered in 1927. Many chemicals can induce mutations, but no way has yet been found to reduce them, and such a discovery would be welcome.

People talk about mutations as if everybody knew precisely what happens in any one of these changes. In fact, no one knows the course of a single mutation in forms of life higher than bacteria. Is the change that causes, for example, achondroplasia (the thickset, large-headed form of dwarfism) a single change in a single part of the DNA code or the picking up of one wrong amino acid, or of many? Or is this mutation a combination of mutations that manifest themselves only if they involve a minimum number of changes, a quorum of alteration?

The molecular biologists unraveling DNA will inevitably sort out a few mutation answers in time. Allowing for the traditionally rapid rate of discovery in this new branch of science, the time should not be very long.

Intersexes

Klinefelter's syndrome is the awkward name given to an unfortunate form of sexual development. The sufferers are male, they are always infertile, their testes are exceptionally small, they scarcely ever have to shave, their breasts may grow, and they are likely to be of poor intellect. Many examples of this abnormality had been recorded in the past, but no explanations. And several other forms of physical sexual abnormality like Klinefelter's syndrome were known. Some were called pseudo-hermaphrodites, some pseudomales, but all were unexplained. Suddenly in 1959, the whole area of intersexuality was burst wide open.

In that year Patricia Jacobs and John Strong, both working in Edinburgh, reported their examination of the cells of a Klinefelter man. It was only three years after the revolutionary Swedish work that had made chromosome study a more precise act and had fixed the human number at 46. The Klinefelter chromosomes were counted in Edinburgh, and they came to 47. One extra chromosome was responsible for the developmental mix-up of this form of intersex.

Mutations, whatever they are precisely, are changes that are microscopic by comparison. They somehow alter the hereditary units, but on a minute level compared with the relatively gross aberration of the addition of a whole chromosome to the standard complement of 46. The effect of this major alteration is sufficient, with Klinefelter sufferers, to prevent any likelihood of the abnormality being inherited.

Also in 1959, it was discovered that several mongoloids had an extra chromosome. It was different from Klinefelter's, and no mongoloid has since been found without this additional chromosomal fragment. Therefore, somehow, its presence must cause the poor intelligence, the inabilities, and the physical abnormalities of the mongoloid. As with Klinefelter's, the extra chromosome was found to exist in every body cell examined. Therefore, the chromosomal error must have been present at conception. As the parents of both types of abnormality are usually perfectly normal, the error must have been in the chosen sperm or egg.

The mongoloid chromosomal addition is an extra chromosome of the pair known as pair 21. The Klinefelter extra is another X chromosome, i.e., one of the 23rd pair. Normal females have two X's, and normal males have one X to partner their Y, but Klinefelter's have two X's and one Y. It becomes immediately apparent why their masculinity is both trampled upon and accompanied by female characteristics. XXY contains both the coding for male (XY) and for female (XX); hence the muddle; hence the intersex.

The 1959 disclosures opened the gates. Turner's syndrome,* long observed, like Klinefelter's, but with opposite effects, was found to be represented by only 45 chromosomes. In this case there was no Y, and just one X. As XX is the customary female condition, it is therefore thoroughly understandable that the Turner sufferers (called XO) are all immature females, each with a diminutive uterus, small genitalia, sometimes without an ovary at all. They are also very short people. Other wrong numbers found include XXX females, XXXX females, XXXY males, XXYY males, and even XXXXY males, with 49 chromosomes instead of 46. The medical journals regularly record details of this spate of discoveries, and caused one reader of the British journal *The Lancet* to complain in doggerel fashion: "Wouldn't it be nice, say, just once or twice, to open this journal and not find pictures of peculiar, hieroglyphic creatures which look like worms, but are called chromosomes?"

One of the latest to be discovered has been notably rare, namely XYY. As XY is the normal male, and Y makes for the maleness, it might therefore be construed that XYY's were doubly male. An investigation was made in a Scottish hospital for difficult criminals and rapidly

* Both Henry Herbert Turner and Harry F. Klinefelter were Americans, the first a gland specialist, the second a physician.

the rare XYY anomaly became almost common. A few XYY's had been previously described; then nine men were found in this one hospital, and most of them were taller than average. Since that first examination of a state prison-hospital some ordinary prisons have been examined. At Nottingham, for example, one-fifth of the men over 6 ft. were found to be XYY's. It was first thought that the extra Y would possibly cause, apart from tallness, more aggression, more sex crimes, more wild behavior. It now seems as if the association is with modest crime, with pilfering, with stupid stealing. Society does not mind about the height, but it locks the men up for their behavior. The extra Y, it seems, is the real villain. Therefore, should courts of law hear cytological evidence before locking up a man in the hope that mere punishment will rid him of the insidious influence of something as permanent as one more Y chromosome?

The sex chromosomes do not hold a monopoly for aberrance. There is that extra No. 21 for mongolism. An extra No. 17 or No. 18 has also been found—no one is certain which. And an addition has been noted to the chromosomes of the No. 13 to No. 15 type—again there is uncertainty. However, there is complete unanimity of opinion that all individuals affected have multiple defects and often die within a few years of life.

With 46 chromosomes controlling human development, it is scarcely surprising for the possession of 47 to cause such an upheaval that death follows. It is more surprising that the possession of 45, 47, 48, or even 49 in other cases has not caused more of an upheaval in development and viability. The two chromosomes principally in charge of sex determination seem to be modifiable with less disruption to the body as a whole than if the modifications were applied to the other 44. The sex is disrupted because intersexes of one sort or another are formed, but the individual frequently survives.

Sometimes, as a variant, there are what have been called "mosaics." Instead of every cell in the body being uniformly and distinctly deformed, some are and some are not. Or some are deformed one way, some another. Presumably, in mosaics, the deformity arose not before conception but shortly after the multiplication of the original cell had begun.

To sum up. Mutations are inheritable changes, either for the subsequent body cells or for subsequent offspring. They can, by radiation and chemicals, be made to occur faster but not slower. They can be lethal. If not, they are probably harmful. Chromosomal changes are much cruder, and the traditional number of 46 chromosomes can range from 45 to 49 with varying results, often lethal, often damaging, almost always associated with reduced fertility.

Attempts to summarize any aspect of human genetics inevitably lead
to oversimplification. Be warned that a work exists called *Humangenetik,*
described as *Ein kurzes Handbuch in fünf Bänden.* The idea of anything
short in five volumes is forbidding, and a reminder of that international
elephant story. It seems four teams of scientists, British, American,
French, and German, set out to study elephants. The British, Americans,
and French described the elephant's sport, size, and love life, respectively.
The German studies produced six volumes, entitled *Das Elefant, ein Vor-
wort.* Human genetics is also a huge subject.

Inherent Traits

The DNA carries the information. The chromosomes carry the DNA.
Mutations are changes in this information, and intersexes, mongoloids,
and so on are manifestations of changes in the chromosomes. The inherited information, whether mutilated or not by change, leads on to
the development of the individual's characteristics. The information received is different for each and every one of us. Men are most emphatically not born equal.

The most useful, overworked, and misused word in the subject of
genetics is "gene." There is a vagueness about it, a lack of precision that
is treacherous. It is defined as a factor of inheritance, a chromosomal
unit, the carrier of heredity. The genes are presumed to lie along the
chromosomes (and elsewhere), each one having a finite responsibility.
They are the agents of Mendel's "particulate inheritance," the separate-
ness he demonstrated, now the basis of genetics. Yet, for all that, there
is an imprecision about this concept of a gene. How many do we have,
for instance? In 1960 Professor Curt Stern, of the University of California, wrote that "the true figure is probably not less than 2,000 or
more than 50,000." He hazarded 10,000.

So, bearing the roundness of this figure very much in mind, and being
correctly suspicious of its validity, the number 10,000 is a convenient
assessment of the human genetic inventory. At once, that number should
be doubled and be considered as 10,000 pairs. Each individual, as is
well known, receives a nearly equal contribution of genes from each
parent. (The slight inequality is associated with those 23rd, or sex,
chromosomes.) The child gets 10,000, according to this current assumption, from his father and 10,000 from his mother. It is correct
to write of 10,000 pairs rather than 20,000 genes, for each of the 10,000
is coupled at fertilization with a similar partner from the other 10,000.
They are like two sides of a coin.

The coin analogy is helpful. Imagine having two sacks of coins. In each sack there are 10,000 different coins, and each coin has heads and tails, totaling 10,000 pairs. Each coin in each sack has its partner in the other sack. Now take one of the sacks, shake it up, and pour its contents on a table. Each of the 10,000 coins it contains will show heads or tails. This assortment can be considered as the chance contribution of a single sperm. Do the same with the other sack, and it represents the equally chance contribution of one ovum. Pair up each coin with its partner, and these 10,000 pairings form the genetic material for the offspring. With each coin from each side having two possibilities, the number of possible combinations is virtually infinite. Hence —quite apart from factors such as mutations—the uniqueness of the individual.

Now imagine one coin out of the 10,000 plus its partner. Each has a head and a tail, and so there are four possible combinations—head head, head tail, tail head, and tail tail. These four varieties give a clue to the mechanism of dominant and recessive genes. A characteristic is said to be dominant if it manifests itself whenever it can, even when it forms only half the final pair. Suppose that heads indicates dominance. Out of the four combinations, three include heads, and only one does not. Therefore, if a dominant gene is involved in the situation, its effect will be three times as common as those of its recessive partner.

Brown eyes and blue eyes are an example. The brown-eye gene is dominant, the blue recessive. Babies may have inherited from their parents either brown and brown, brown and blue, blue and brown, or blue and blue genes. In the first three cases the baby's eyes will be brown, and only in the last case will they be blue. If a blue-eyed person marries another blue-eyed person, all their children should be blue-eyed because they have inherited no brown-eyed (dominant) genes. The same is true for albinos. Albinism is similarly recessive. Pigmented skin and eyes are the dominant form. Most people inherit genes for pigment from both parents. Some of us, one out of 70, inherit a gene for pigment from only one parent, and nothing—or albinism—from the other. However, the pigment gene is dominant, and so normality results. Only if albinism is inherited from both parents, which occurs once in every 20,000 fertilizations, does an albino result, with the characteristic white hair, pink eyes, and general lack of pigment.

With dominant characteristics, the rarity of the gene is also important. Brown eyes are dominant over blue and are common. So brown-eyed people, although they may be carrying blue-eyed genes, are likely to marry brown-eyed people, and therefore extremely likely to produce brown-eyed children. Achondroplasia, the massive form of dwarfism, is a rare dominant character. If a dwarf marries a normal person, the chances of an achondroplasic child are only even. If the dwarf marries another dwarf the chances are still only three to one the child will be achondroplasic.

Unfortunately, clear-cut precision is exceptional. A single gene for a single characteristic is rare, not the rule. Even the blue-eye/brown-eye situation is more complex, with possibly three gene pairs involved, as two blue-eyed parents can (in about 2 percent of cases) produce brown-eyed children. Other characteristics are, like eye color, known to be caused by more than one gene, and some genes are associated with more than one characteristic. Qualities like intelligence (which is no one thing), height, build, and color are controlled by more than one gene. Intermarry a short, intelligent, thickset Negro with a tall, stupid, thin European and the offspring will be a bewilderment of variation.

Inheritance is a hodgepodge, as well it might be. The mutations that have permitted evolution, that have permitted man to be evolved differently from the monkeys, have happened in no set fashion. Consequently, our inheriting is no orderly system but a muddled assortment of interacting genetic factors that, somehow or other and through that coding system, have led to the development of distinct human beings. Knowledge about human genes is sparse both because of the impossibility of breeding human beings experimentally and because of the general lack of information from past generations. But, however knowledgeable humanity becomes, the arrangement of genes will always be seen as a hodgepodge. Take the eye, for example. Little enough is known now, save that a single gene for the eye will never be discovered. It is too big an organ and too complicated for such simplicity. Probably hundreds of genes are involved, each controlling, each playing its part or being dominated, each the result of all those years of evolution since the first light-sensitive areas developed into the direct ancestor of the human eye.

It is humanity's fringe characteristics, such as eye color and albinism, that are better understood genetically than its main properties. Dominant traits (with the recessive condition in parentheses) that have been well studied include:

Brown eyes (blue); pigmented skin (albinism); roman nose (straight nose); black skin (white skin); curly hair (straight hair); dark hair (fair hair); nonred hair (red hair); shortsightedness and farsightedness (normal vision); early baldness—males only (normal hair); free earlobes (attached earlobes); long eyelashes (short eyelashes); large eyes (small eyes); achondroplasia (normal stature); blood groups A, B, and AB (Group O); more than five fingers or toes (normal); webbing between fingers or toes (normal); very short fingers (normal).

This odd list gives little idea either of humanity or of human variation. Not every human characteristic is controlled conveniently (one pair of genes is most satisfactory) or is suitable for study. The manifestation of the characteristics must not be blurred by too many other genetic influences and must be obvious. Something like free or attached earlobes is ideal; something like the shape of a forehead is not. Another difficulty is the timing of the gene's action. Most effects, such as blood groups, are present when the child is born. Some, such as hair and eye color, are not definite until shortly after birth. Others, like early baldness, show up much later, and a few of the heritable diseases are later still. Glaucoma, which can cause blindness due to increasing pressure within the eyeball, is an example of a late manifestation.

Nevertheless, despite the great complexity involved when two individuals fashion at random another individual, despite the great blurring of most genetic effects, despite the unscientific manner of human breeding, despite the 25 years between one generation and the next, despite this and despite that, there are already some fascinating insights into human inheritance. Once again, they make an odd and apparently arbitrary list. From it I have made my own choice, the first of which is the disease of bleeders, most strangely called by its Latin name the "love-of-blood" disease.

Hemophilia

Wrongly considered to be caused by inbreeding, it has achieved notoriety in modern times mainly because it has plagued the royal families of Europe for three generations. Almost always the victim is a man. All men receive it from their mothers, the so-called "carriers." The few women who do actually suffer from the disease, instead of merely passing it on, have the ill-fortune not only to have a hemophiliac father but also a mother who is a hemophiliac "carrier." Since hemophilia is a rare disease anyway, such a double circumstance is extremely rare.

The more common and traditional pattern is for a woman who is carrying this defective gene to marry a normal man. She may not know she has this defect, but if she has children the defect will manifest itself over the years. Half of her sons will, on average, be bleeders. Half of her daughters will be carriers like herself, and half of their sons will be bleeders. None of the affected men can pass it on to their sons, but all of their daughters will be carriers. And, once again, in the subsequent generation there will be the same 50-50 chance for the boys to be bleeders and the girls to be carriers.

The picture in any family is therefore not clear for many years. With most families, the clinical details of any forebears are poorly recorded and generally forgotten, but not so with royalty. It was therefore of enormous importance when, on April 7, 1853, assisted by the new gas chloroform, Queen Victoria gave birth to her eighth child. The sickly Prince Leopold proved to be a bleeder. He was the first indication that Queen Victoria, whose descendants were to percolate throughout the royal houses of Europe, was herself a carrier of classical hemophilia.

The disease had been known for centuries. The excessive bleeding of the hemophiliacs had even resulted in special rules in the Talmud. The Jews had written in the second century A.D. that boys need not be circumcised if two older brothers had already died from blood loss following the operation. More significantly, they added that the sons of their sisters were also exempted. They knew that the disease came from the mother and was passed on through her daughters. Early in the nineteenth century, several decades before Prince Leopold was born, several men, notably Professor C. F. Nasse, of Bonn, described the pattern of hemophiliac inheritance. Queen Victoria's diaries do not indicate that she understood the pattern as expressed in "Nasse's Law," but the full understanding of this pattern did not come until the discovery of sex chromosomes in the twentieth century.

The defective gene, which is responsible for the defect in the blood's clotting mechanism, is carried by the X chromosome; it is what is known as a sex-linked characteristic. The sex chromosomes determine a person's sex, but they also possess genes that cause characteristics irrelevant to sex, such as color blindness, webbed toes, muscular dystrophy, and hemophilia. A man receives his X chromosome from his mother, never from his father. Hence he can get this defect of the X chromosome only from his mother, never from his father. And women do not suffer from the defect because they have two X chromosomes, only one of which is defective and one of which is normal; the normal one gives her an effective clotting mechanism. To each daughter and to each son she passes on one of her X chromosomes. It may or may not be the defective one. Hence the precisely 50-50 chance that her sons will be hemophiliacs and her daughters will be carriers.

Queen Victoria's case is an excellent example of hemophilia in action. She had nine children, and the faulty gene was passed on to one son and two or perhaps three of her daughters. Four out of nine is as near 50-50 as the unevenness of the number nine will permit. As Victoria's antecedents had not in any way been victimized by hemophilia, a recent mutation must have been present in one of her X chromosomes. Perhaps she had received the faulty X chromosome from her elderly and longtime bachelor father, who died the year after Victoria was born, his only legitimate child. (Various families claim that their ancestors are in fact illegitimate children of the duke's but none of them claim that these illegitimate ancestors were afflicted with hemophilia.) Or perhaps he was guiltless, and the mutation occurred within herself.

In any case, Leopold was the first indication of things to come. He bled from trivial injuries, and his baptism was postponed for three months. Leopold's childhood was beset with illness, and even when he was an adult of 26 Victoria refused to let him visit Australia. Either his health would suffer, she wrote, or hers would for worrying about him. Nevertheless she let him marry three years later. He had time to be the father of a girl and to make his wife pregnant with a boy before he died at the age of 31, as a result of a minor fall and a major hemorrhage.

Even before Leopold's death and before he passed on his affliction (inevitably making his wife a carrier, although his son was safe), Queen Victoria had had further indications that, as she wrote, "Our poor family seems persecuted by this awful disease." Her daughter Alice, born ten years before Leopold, married in 1862. Two of her daughters were themselves to be proven carriers, and one son was a hemophiliac who died from a hemorrhage after falling out of a window at the age of three, eleven years before the death of Leopold. Another of Victoria's daughters, Beatrice, married in 1885. Of Beatrice's four children (the Battenberg/Mountbatten family) one was a girl-carrier and two were boy-victims. Both boys died without issue—one after surgery and one in action. Victoria's daughter Victoria may or may not have been a carrier. She gave birth to the Kaiser of World War I, who certainly caused others to bleed for him, but was himself exempt. Two of his brothers died early, at 2 and 11, and hemophilia just may have been present.

So much for the first generation, with one sick son, two carrier daughters, one suspect daughter, two normal sons, and three normal daughters. King Edward VII was one of the normal sons. Thus the present royal family, descended from him, has no fear of the disease.

Not so the descendants of Victoria's carrier daughters and of Leopold's daughter. Various royal males have testified, since the Queen's death, to the persistence of this defective X chromosome. Prince Henry of Prussia, grandson of the carrier Alice, died in 1904 aged 4. The Russian Alexis, another of her grandsons, was sickly, and Rasputin was frequently summoned. However, the boy died of a bullet and not of his hemophilia, when, together with his sisters, the family was shot following the Russian Revolution. Gonzalo, a grandson of Victoria's daughter Beatrice, died at the age of 20 after a modest injury suffered in a car smash. Alfonso, an elder brother of his, was also hemophiliac. He died only four years later, after breaking his leg and suffering a few cuts in another car accident. Both victims were without issue.

Nevertheless, the mutant gene probably still exists, despite the lack of issue and despite the early deaths. According to Professor V. A. McKusick, of the Johns Hopkins University, who studied the royal tree

in detail, there remain three females each of whom has a 50-50 chance
of being a potent carrier. Two are the sisters of the unfortunate Alfonso
and Gonzalo. Both are married, and both have had sons and daughters.
The sons are apparently not afflicted, but the daughters may well be
quietly carrying this unwelcome feature of Victoria's inheritance. Time
will tell whether the unwelcome gene will crop up again, or whether,
aided by early death and childless victims, the gene is no longer around
to plague Queen Victoria's descendants. After all, whether Victoria's
father did give it to her or not, the defect has already been reigning for
a century and a half, and it has caused much misery in that time. But,
concludes Professor McKusick, the prospect that it will reappear among
some of Victoria's male descendants, notably among some of her great-
great-great-grandchildren, is a "real one."

Queen Victoria's family, so beset with hemophilia, gives a depress-
ingly false picture of the extent of the disease. Only about one in 20,000
of the population of Europe is afflicted by it. Nonetheless, the National
Hemophilia Foundation estimates that there are 100,000 hemophiliacs
in the United States. In Britain there are 2,000 males without the
globulin factor in their plasma that is necessary for the normal coagula-
tion of blood. As yet there is no sign of a cure for the hemophiliac disorders, but the missing factor can be infused. The effect of such an
infusion is short; half of it has gone in half a day. In the past, bleeding
episodes have often led to permanent disability, adding positive injury
to the insult of hemophilia. British nurseries are now designed with
special care for the hemophiliac child, with padding, low furniture, non-
skid floors, and a preference for soft toys, but it is also argued that over-
protection can be harmful. With no cure foreseeable at present (only
the supplementary therapy is available), it will obviously be a little time
before the world can rid itself of the hereditary disease that Queen
Victoria called "the worst she knew."

Tasters

There is a group of chemical compounds that has been of bizarre interest to geneticists since 1931. In that year it was discovered that some
people could taste them while others could not. The compounds included
substances such as phenylthiocarbamide. To possess an ability to taste
a remote and unimportant chemical like P.T.C., as phenylthiocarbamide
is called, is a curious characteristic, but it is most emphatically an inherited trait. When both parents are nontasters, all the children will be
nontasters. If one parent is a taster and one a nontaster, the children
will be either, but probably tasters. If both parents are tasters, the chil-

dren also will probably be tasters. The situation, which is of practical interest in paternity disputes, is similar to the blue-eyed/brown-eyed story. Blue eyes and nontasting are both recessives. Both are controlled by an inherited single pair of genes, but both can be slightly complicated by the modifying actions of other genes.

In Europe and hence in North America, about 70 percent of the whites can taste P.T.C. Both Arabs (63 percent) and aboriginal Australians (51 percent) are less able in general to taste the substance, while Chinese (over 90 percent), Negroes (95 percent), and American Indians (up to 98 percent) are more able to do so. Among animals, who should never be forgotten in any discussion of mankind, most primates seem to be tasters. The evidence is limited, but 20 out of 28 chimpanzees in British zoos showed, in unambiguous fashion, an ability to detect the bitter unpleasantness of P.T.C. Why this ability, and why its variation between species and races? The only clue so far is a link between it and certain forms of thyroid disease, or nodular goiter; those who get this disease are more likely to be nontasters.

A casual link between one disease and a curious ability to taste does not have the compelling power of the hemophilia story, but both are invaluable material for researchers into human genetics. Both are detectable, neither effect is too confused by too many other genes, and both are clearly inherited. These characteristics, and others, ranging from the Hapsburg lip to color blindness, have all added their quota to the general knowledge of genetics. They are all examples of straws at which geneticists have had to clutch. The stream of inheritance that flows every time a new life is created is too great, too complex by far for detailed study. Straws are clutched whenever possible, and the following are further examples of them.

The Hapsburg Lip

Any group of women around any baby carriage or stroller or papoose bundle will be identifying inherited characteristics. Out of the myriad nose, forehead, and jaw shapes in the world, it is remarkable how similar father and son can be, or even mother and son and father and daughter. The shapes are impossible to define, but easy to observe. Sherlock Holmes, when investigating the Baskerville family, was himself astounded by the similarity between an ancestor and a modern. After mentally stripping the whiskers off a family portrait, he was quick to unmask a living descendant of the family posing in another guise. A famous example of a dominant family characteristic is also preserved in the Hapsburg line, a family rich enough to have had their portraits painted through the centuries and wily enough to have stayed in power and prosperity.

The Hapsburg lip is probably the work of a single dominant gene. The protruding and ugly lower lip is accompanied by a narrow jaw and often by a slightly open mouth. Fortunately, painters and engravers did not belittle the deformity, and it is depicted with fair consistency up to modern times. Notable possessors of the lip were the Emperor Maximilian I (born in the fifteenth century), the Emperor Charles V (sixteenth century), Maria Theresa of Austria and Archduke Charles of Teschen (eighteenth century), and the Archduke Albrecht and Alfonso XII of Spain (nineteenth century). Whenever a rare variant keeps on turning up in a family and is passed on only by the affected members, it is probably the work of just one dominant gene. Whoever chances to inherit it—the chances are 50-50—will manifest it and have an even chance of passing it on to each of his descendants.

Most of us have nothing equivalent to a Hapsburg lip, but there is a general and curious ability associated with the tongue. Some people can curve their tongue into a "U," with both sides pointing upward; some cannot. The distinction is most positive. The genetics of this characteristic have not been thoroughly worked out, and the advantage of being able to maneuver the tongue in this manner, although the spittle can probably be fired farther, is even less clear.

Albinism

"She became pregnant and brought forth a child, the flesh of which was white as snow, and red as a rose; the hair of whose head was white, like wool and long; and whose eyes were beautiful." The baby in question was Noah, later to build the ark and survive the flood. The description of him is from the Book of Enoch, allegedly written 100 or so years before Christ. The details describe an albino. As Noah was subsequently to populate the planet, one might expect a greater abundance of albinism among us. It is caused by a recessive gene, and therefore, assuming no selective disadvantages, one-quarter of us should be albinos. As it is, the incidence is far smaller, but all races are afflicted. It can be called an affliction because the total absence of pigment results in weak and astigmatic eyes, an intolerance for the sun, and of course, a rare disfigurement. European albinos can walk with reasonable equanimity in a region speckled with blond and pale people; not so the albino Negroes, Japanese, or Red Indians.

The customary ratio quoted for Europe is one in 20,000, or approximately 2,500 in Britain and 9,000 in the United States. In darker communities albinism is commoner. Nigeria has one in 3,000 and they are easy to spot in any Nigerian town. Among the San Blas Indians in Panama, the ratio is one in 132. The recessive gene of albinism is possessed by one in seventy Europeans, but only shows up when such a person, or heterozygote, marries another heterozygote. When both parents are albino, all the children will be albinos. When only one parent is albino, the children are heterozygote and look normal; there is no way of knowing, except after the birth of an albino child, who is heterozygote. If one albino has already been produced in a family, the chance that a subsequent child will be albino is one in four.

Finally, albinos can be piebald, and the lack of melanin is probably due to the lack of the enzyme tyrosinase. This catalyzes the first stage of turning tyrosine to melanin. The pinkness of the eye is not a positive pigment coloration, but instead a lack of pigment that permits the blood and its red color to be seen. In bright light, an albino's eyes can become very inflamed, and dark glasses are sensible. No cure exists for those who, like the patriarch Noah, have flesh as white as snow.

Height

Unlike hemophilia, Hapsburg lips, blue eyes, and an albino's skin, the inheritance of height is different in two distinct ways. For one thing, it is polygenic; many genes are involved. And for another, the population is not either tall or short, like blue-eyed or brown, hemophiliac or not; instead there is a continuous variation from the shortest to the tallest. There are very few at either end and a bulge in the middle. The distribution pattern is what is called the "normal curve." It is bellshaped, the lip of the bell flattening off to take in the very short and the very tall. The dome of the bell incorporates everyone else, the 95 percent or so who are neither very short nor very tall but whose height is slightly more than or less than the average. As with intelligence, which follows a similar pattern, or coloration or weight or virtually any physical measurement, the normal curve indicates the distribution. Most people are very near average; just a few are extremely clever or extremely stupid, very heavy or very light. There are so many genes involved that, however distinct they are individually, the resulting effect is a blur or mixture of their activities. Mendel's "particulate inheritance" still exists, but it is far harder or impossible to detect. Too many genes are at work.

Nevertheless, the hereditary mechanism is still most positive. Like still produces likeness; tall produces tall and short produces short. However, assuming that both tall and short men marry average-size women, the sons of the tall men will be shorter than their fathers, and the sons of the short will be taller than their fathers. There is, assuming a constant affection for average women, always a regression to the mean. In fact, many tall men can be embarrassed by short women and would like to have a hearing aid lodged in their umbilicus with which to hear them better. Similarly, short men will not be readily partial to relatively gigantic women. Like marries like as well as begets like.

If a man of about average height, about 5 ft., 8 in., or 68 in., marries a woman of average height, about 5 ft., 2 in., or 62 in., they can expect average-size children, i.e., 68 in. if male, 62 in. if female. If both parents are 68 in. tall, the girl is exceptionally tall, and they could expect sons taller than the father, girls shorter than the mother. A 68-in. girl is equivalent in height to a 74-in. man because of the 6-in. average differential between the sexes. (Some say the equivalent male height of a woman is reached by adding one inch for every foot of her height.)

In many ways height prediction for offspring is a matter of arithmetic. For boys, add the father's height to the mother's height plus 6 in. and divide by two to get the boy's final height. Assume a 70-in. father and a 60-in. mother. The son is 70 plus 60 plus 6 divided by 2. The answer is 68 in. For girls, assuming the same parents, the 6-in. differential should be subtracted. Therefore the equation is 70 minus 6 plus 60 divided by 2. The answer is 62 in. In this family, the girls will (probably) be taller than their mother, the boys shorter than their father.

However, predictions are by no means the same as results. A coin has a 50-50 chance of being heads or tails, but its perverse behavior can confound all predictions. Just as it can produce ten heads in a row for no particular reason, so can a human family make nonsense of forecasts. However, taking the population as a whole, the predictions make more sense. Family sizes then behave as they should and conform to the average pattern, the normal curve, the traditional outline of inheritance. A coin may be heads ten times in a row. It will not be heads 1,000 times in a row, but will be quite near to 500 heads and 500 tails. Large population numbers are necessary for good predictions in polygenic inheritance.

Small family numbers can make nonsense out of forecasting. Further nonsense, particularly with regard to height, is associated with the environment. Poor health, bad food, or the wrong upbringing can make the final height less than it should be genetically. Similarly, because of environmental difficulties in their youth, parental height may be less than it should be, genetically speaking. An average-size couple who were short of food in their growing period may produce a series of taller children. Once again, the predictions will have been proved wrong.

Strangely, the final height of people these days is not markedly different from earlier times. Suits of armor in museums appear small, but skeletal remains indicate a remarkable constancy. Today's average male height in Britain is from 67 to 68 in., varying slightly from area to area. Old Stone Age man in western Europe was, on average, 69 in. New Stone Age, or Neolithic, man was 66 in., Bronze Age man 68 in., Iron Age Celts 66 in., Anglo-Saxons 67 in., medieval British 66 in. Perhaps those suits of armor, perched crustaceanlike up on their stands, are arranged more squatly than they should be.

What has changed notably in recent years is the speed of growth. The average height of 11-year-olds in London's schools has gone up by 4 in. since the start of this century. Both puberty and full adult height are being reached earlier. Consequently, soldiers, for example, are now theoretically taller than they used to be because their heights are measured on recruitment; boys of 18 are now much nearer their final height than they used to be. Improved environment has speeded things up, although the genetics have remained the same.

Just because a baby is long there is no reason to believe it will be tall. Neither the height nor the weight of a baby is markedly affected by its genetic constitution. There is a belief that a child has reached half its final height by its second birthday. This is not true, but it is true that a child of exactly 2 is about half the height of an adult. Work carried out at Aberdeen, Scotland, suggests that good predictions of adult height could be made at the third birthday. For boys exactly 3 years old, their final stature was likely to be 1.27 times present height (in inches) plus 21. For girls, it was likely to be 1.29 times present height (in inches) plus 16.1. Thus, a boy of 3 measuring 3 ft., 2 in., will be slightly over 5 ft., 9 in., while a girl of 3 of similar height will end up 5 ft., 5 in. tall. The trouble with average formulas of this type, which are good for working out the average height of the population, is that individuals will be capable of proving them wrong, and their final height may be 2 in. on either side of the prediction.

Color

Skin color is another example of many genes at work, and most of the work has been based on Negro-white matings. The situation is complicated by the fact that whites are not without pigmentation, and Negroes are not pitch black. Moreover, the skin color of Africans varies much more than that of whites. The actual skin colors can be assessed fairly accurately by matching them with spinning discs on which colors have been painted in certain proportions. If a disc is spun fast enough, all its painted colors merge into one shade. A particular "white" skin of a normal European was once matched by a disc painted 5 percent black, 34 percent red, 15 percent yellow, and 46 percent white. Similarly, an ordinary Negro's skin was matched by 75 percent black, 13 percent red, 2 percent yellow, and 10 percent white. The white man is even less white than the black man is black.

When black marries white the mulatto offspring are, as is well known, a colorful mixture, neither white nor black, but various shades between. When these hybrids intermarry, the second generation is predominantly a similar mixture, but there are then some offspring much resembling the original black and white grandparents. Also, for some reason, the first-generation mulattoes are, on average, slightly closer to the white than the black parents in their pigmentation. There is a popular belief that the marriage of a white to another white who, due to some earlier mixing, has a black gene or two in his or her system, may suddenly produce a very black child, or throwback. Neither the term nor the likelihood is particularly acceptable to geneticists. In general in such a marriage, no child should be darker than the off-white parent, the one with the tarbrush's touch in his or her genetical makeup. However, if the couple both possess dark genes, the offspring can sometimes be darker than either parent. Many investigations of alleged throwbacks uncover the wayward behavior of a parent, and consequent illegitimacy, rather than any wayward behavior of the genes.

Panmixis is a term for total interbreeding. Consequently, it describes the situation when all racial barriers come down, and mates of all colors are chosen at random. Within the United States emotional barriers are still up, but Professor Curt Stern, of the University of California at Berkeley, has calculated what will happen to the color of subsequent generations if the Negro genes flow freely throughout the population. He has assumed ten gene pairs to be involved in pigmentation, with pure whites having no black genes and pure Negroes having all ten black. Assuming panmixis and assuming Negroes to be a tenth of the population, the resultant coloring will be very largely white: 48.4 percent will have only white genes, 36.4 percent will have nine white genes out of ten, 12.3 percent will have eight, and 2.5 percent will have seven. This total of 99.4 percent is classifiable as "light types." The remaining .6 percent, the "dark types," will have four, five, six, seven, eight, nine, or ten of the black genes. In other words almost half the population would be just as white as the whites are today, over half would be slightly tanned by their one or two dark genes, and only half a percent would actually have half a Negro's dark complement of genes as inheritance. Such a panmixis would in fact lead to fewer really dark faces than exist today. Not one man in ten, but one man in 200 would then have the traditionally black face of the Negro. At long last, his migration would have been absorbed into the nation of immigrants.

Baldness

Baldness well exemplifies the difficulty in studying the inheritance of a particular human trait. At first sight it is simple. Do the parents show baldness? Do the offspring? At second sight it is far more complex. Baldness can start at the back, like a monk's tonsure. It can creep up the part. It can start when a man is in his 20's. It can start much, much later. It can become total over the top. It can cease merely as an extreme thinning. It is, in short, no one thing.

Nevertheless it is probably inherited. It occurs predominantly in men, but is not a sex-linked gene such as hemophilia or color blindness. It merely affects men more frequently than women—which is not the same as sex-linkage. A bald man will often transmit the characteristics to about half his sons, but exceptions abound. It appears that there are two main types of baldness, both genetically different. In one, the thinning starts before 30, and is extensive before 40; in the other it starts later.

"No boy ever gets bald, no woman and no castrated man," noted Aristotle. The link between the three is the male hormone. The genes for baldness do not act if the level of androgens is low. The alleged link between baldness and virility, sometimes claimed hopefully by the bald, is only true insofar as bald men are more virile than boys, women, and eunuchs. A final confusion, irrespective of gene inheritance, irrespective of male hormones, is that hair thins with age in both women and men. This thinning is distinct from baldness, although women can go bald, and so can eunuchs.

The initial simplicity of baldness is therefore confused by age of onset, type of recession, association with male hormones and link with old age, and with more than one pair of genes in its inheritance. Simplicity yields to confusion, and predictions about the hairiness of future offspring are rarely hazarded. However, early and pronounced baldness does act as if a dominant gene is involved. It is only dominant in the male, and so a victim of early fall-out will, on average, cause half his sons to be similarly affected and none of his daughters. In the next generations, half of those sons and half of those daughters will cause half of their sons to go bald with the same rapidity.

Color Blindness

This is another anomaly that is generally inherited. Total color blindness is rare, it is from a recessive gene, and it affects both sexes equally. Partial color blindness affects about one person in 30, is from sex-linked genes, and is much more common in men than women. Brushing aside all exceptions, there are certain basic rules. When a normal woman marries a color-blind man, their children will probably be normal. When a normal man marries a color-blind woman the sons will be color blind and the daughters will be normal. Taking the first case a generation further, the normal daughters of that marriage are carriers of their father's color blindness, although unaffected by it. Hence, half their sons will be color blind, half normal, and half the daughters will be carriers like their mothers. If carrier daughters marry color-blind men, the situation will be aggravated; half of their sons will be color blind (just as if the father were normal), and half the daughters will be carriers, but the remaining 50 percent of daughters will be color blind. Finally, if a color-blind woman marries a color-blind man, all their offspring will be color blind.

As with hemophilia, the explanation of these ramifications is the X chromosome. A boy can get his single X chromosome only from his mother. A girl has two X chromosomes and gets one from each parent. If a girl has a color-blind father, she will have inherited his X chromosome and hence his defect, but she will have inherited a normal X chromosome from her mother. One defective X and one good X result in good vision; but she is a carrier. Half of her sons will receive the good X, half the defective X; thus half will be color blind, half normal. Give or take a number of exceptions, this is the mechanism of color-blindness inheritance.

Color blindness varies in its incidence among races. Europeans have a lot, but aboriginal Australians and Eskimos, for example, have much less. It is assumed that natural selection is still discriminating against the color blind and making it harder for them to survive in the more natural and primitive communities. In Europe about 7 percent of males and .5 percent of females are either color blind or color weak. In communities with less color blindness as a whole, the proportion of affected women is an even smaller fraction.

As an addendum to this tale, it is not coincidental that both hemophilia and color blindness are linked with the X chromosome rather than the Y. Almost all of the sex-linked characteristics, such as these two, are associated with the X chromosome. The reason is straightforward. The X chromosome is quite large, with plenty of room for genes. The Y chromosome, the chromosome peculiar to males, is a relatively stunted thing. Only one characteristic is known to be linked with the Y chromosome apart from maleness, and that is "hairy ear rims." It is pleasing in a sense that the complex world of genes should be associated with an item so matter-of-fact as space and accommodation upon a chromosome.

As a subject, only the surface of the inheritance of human traits has been scratched. Just a few characteristics have been studied because only a few have been amenable to study. The majority of inheritance is poorly documented, to say the least, and most unamenable. What facts are there about the inheritance of liver size, of memory, of virility? Also, as Kenneth Mather put it in his book *Human Diversity,* the inborn and the early inculcated are often hard to disentangle. As parents know to their cost, children can blame the same people for their inheritance and upbringing. Are the children stupid because their parents led stupid lives or, like their children, had stupidity thrust upon them? How much influence did the genes have, and how much did the surroundings?

Once upon a time no one cared too much about the environment. Peasants were considered ignorant clods and incapable of improvement because they were sons of peasants and not because they were brought up in ignorant homes. R. L. Dugdale in 1875 studied a particularly ill-fated pedigree of a family called Jukes. Old Max Jukes, long dead, had given rise by then to 709 descendants. These included 76 convicts, 128 prostitutes, 18 brothel keepers, and 200 paupers. The theory was that a bad seed, rather than a slum existence, was at fault. Similarly, and at the same period, Oliver Twist's essentially inbred goodness shone brightly through the wickedness of his foster world. Literature is packed with examples of "good breeding" and of inborn villainy. Racists have followed suit, forgetting circumstances and assuming instead that lack of ambition, laziness, love of corruption, and poverty of mind are inherited. Nowadays, circumstances are achieving a more realistic consideration in the mechanism of inheritance. The genes exist, but they are nothing without an environment. Put at its most basic, an individual needs food for development, however packed he may be with the best of genes.

I shall give the geneticist Theodosius Dobzhansky the last word: "It has been said before, but it will bear repetition, that the genes do not determine 'characters,' such as proneness to criminality or smoking habits; the genes determine the reactions of the organism to its environment."

⋐ 16 ⋑

Inbreeding

The Churches' Attitudes · Cousin Marriages ·
Forbidden Matings · Effects of Inbreeding ·
Incest · Genetic Recessives

It seems that society in every age has had taboos to discourage inbreeding. Probably these laws, which prohibit incest ("sexual commerce of near kindred," is the definition of the *Oxford English Dictionary*), were primarily to promote favorable relations within the camp. Father-daughter and uncle-niece matings could cause great disunity. It is unlikely, or so most anthropologists think, that the harmful effects of consanguinity would have been as much a spur for the taboos, had they been noticed, as the immediate disharmony caused by close matings.

The Churches' Attitudes

The religions emphasize the disharmony point. Most of the forbidden marriages are not based upon sound genetics. Before the recent revisions the Church of England's *Book of Common Prayer* used to list 30 types of relatives forbidden as partners for each sex in its "Table of Kindred and Affinity." Of this number only ten made genetic sense, in that some inbreeding would then be taking place. The Koran, as will be seen, is similarly restricting and only partly concerned with the harmfulness of consanguinity.

In fact, there is current argument in many places that the old laws should be brought more into line with modern knowledge. Ought outbreeding and more distant mating, now so much easier, be actively encouraged? Should first cousins still be permitted to marry? Should modern science be allowed a say in the matter to try and reduce the toll of, for example, those congenital malformations more likely to be observed in the offspring of near relatives?

[232]

To set the scene, it should be remembered that every group is inbred to some degree. Just as there has been antagonism to incest there has also been antagonism to outbreeding. The girl next door has been the ideal. It is not just parents in the American South or in Johannesburg, or Jewish mamas, whose children are pressed to marry "one of us." Mating has rarely been far-ranging. Geography, social barriers, and custom have seen to that. But even if mating had been more venturesome, everyone has two parents and four grandparents, and two parents for each of them, and the time soon comes when there must be overlapping.

Six generations ago, about the time of the War of 1812, we each had 64 direct parents alive. Sixteen generations ago, at about the time of the founding of Jamestown, there were, in theory, 64,000 direct parents (or ascendants) for each one of us today. Obviously, there must have been considerable overlap, and the actual number was much smaller. (Even the offspring of first-cousin marriages have already "lost" some ancestors, as they have six, not eight, great-grandparents. The loss is caused by having some common ancestors.) Going back to the time of the battle of Agincourt, the theoretical situation is yet more ridiculous, with 4 million direct ascendants for each one of us today. For Britain, since the population was then considerably less than 4 million, it is not a question of "What did your father do in the war?" but "What did your entire army of fathers, every manjack of them, do at Agincourt?" Barring recent immigrants to Britain, barring those of Henry V's men who died without issue, and barring lineages that stopped, every single man at Agincourt was a great-great-and-so-on grandparent many times over of every single person in Britain today. As 1415 was only some 22 generations ago we British, it can be argued, are an inbred lot.

Cousin Marriages

In fact, the situation is much more severe. Marriages are local affairs. A study in northern Italy showed that a man used to find his mate at an average distance of 600 yards. Then, after the invention of the bicycle, the distance leaped up to 1,600 yards. In Britain, despite intermingling and the invention of the automobile, 6 out of 1,000 marriages are still between first cousins. In the United States, it is 6 out of 10,000. Urban Austria, urban Brazil, and urban Spain are all similar to Britain, but studies elsewhere have shown far more inbreeding. The number of first-cousin marriages per 100 are Spain, 4.6; Nagasaki, 5; rural Japan, 7; Swiss Alp village, 11; Parsees, in Bombay, 12.9; Brazilian village,

19.5; and Fiji Islands, 29.7. Hence, in Fiji the occurrence is 50 times more frequent than in Britain, 500 times more so than in the United States. Occasionally, high prevalence is influenced by choice and social preferences (as with Indian castes and Japanese families) but generally inbreeding results from force of circumstances, such as isolation.

Inbreeding has sometimes been actively promoted. Royalty in ancient Egypt and the Incas of Peru were prominent examples. Rameses II had at least 50 daughters and he married quite a few of them. The Zande of Africa encouraged their chiefs to mate with their own daughters. Generally, first-cousin marriages are the closest inbreeding society allows. The Egyptians at their most permissive time (as among the Ptolemies) and the Incas allowed brother-sister unions; but nowhere, according to C. S. Ford and F. A. Beach in their excellent *Patterns of Sexual Behaviour,* are such matings permitted to the general population.

Marrying relatives sets up genetic trouble because it increases the chances that harmful recessives will manifest themselves. (There is more about dominant and recessive genes in the previous chapter.) Every human being carries potentially harmful recessive genes, but they can manifest themselves only when both parents not only possess the same harmful genes, but also pass them on, and the harmful manifestation then occurs in their offspring. Just as a child can be blue-eyed only when both parents possess at least one blue-eyed gene (although this recessive character does the child no harm), so can a child suffer from phenylketonuria (which causes a rare form of mental disorder if not detected soon after birth), amaurotic idiocy (which starts with blindness), or alkaptonuria (a metabolic disorder), for example, only if both parents happen to possess the recessive genes for these complaints. Only recessive PLUS a recessive can show up. Recessive plus anything else does not. Each of us inherits an assortment of harmful recessives, but each is likely to inherit a different lot. Hence the chances are that when one person's assortment does not match another's, and when they marry there is no pairing of harmful recessives, no phenylketonuria and the like.

The applecart is upset when like mates with like. Brothers and sisters have, on average, half their genes in common. Fathers and daughters (also mothers and sons) *must* have half their genes in common. (Whether inheritance "must be" or is so "on average" is important, but the difference can be forgotten in discussing populations.) The fractions become smaller as the relationships grow more distant. Granddaughters must have one-quarter of the genes of each of their grandfathers, and a further quarter from each grandmother. Nieces have, on average, one-quarter of their uncle's genes; and nephews have one-quarter of their aunt's genes. For still more distant relationships, such as a cousin, the proportion is one eighth. A cousin is, say, a mother's brother's daughter, hence the proportion is ½ times ½ times ½, or one-eighth. A second cousin is, for example, a mother's mother's brother's son's son and the compound proportion here is ½ times ½ times ½ times ½ times ½, or 1/32. Considering the embargo that society of every kind places on father-daughter matings (where half the genes are shared) and usually places on uncle-niece matings (where one-quarter are shared) it is remarkably casual about cousin matings (where one-eighth are shared).

Forbidden Matings

Until Britain's Marriage Act of 1949, the state and the Church of England forbade marriage with 30 different kinds of relation. Of this number, ten made genetic sense in that there existed, necessarily or on average, shared genes. The new act struck off ten from the original list, none of which had shared genes. In 1949, these ten were called "statutory exceptions," and they permitted a man's marriage with the sister, aunt, or niece of his former dead wife, or with the widow of his brother, uncle, or nephew. In 1960, as a further change, came the Marriage (Enabling) Act. This was much the same as the 1949 act, but a man's wife need no longer be dead, only divorced, for him to be free to marry her sister, aunt, or niece. Similarly he can now marry the former (and divorced) wife of his brother, uncle, or nephew; there is no need for her to be a widow. Taking these new acts into consideration, as well as the genetic relationships, here is the amended Table of Kindred and Affinity.*

Other countries and other religions have different rulings. In the United States, some states permit uncle-niece and nephew-aunt marriages, and yet a third of the states prohibit first-cousin marriages. The Roman Catholic Church forbids both second- and first-cousin marriages without special dispensation. (The unfortunate Anne Mowbray, who died at the age of nine and whose coffin was unearthed accidentally in London in the spring of 1965, had been married in 1478, when five years old, to Richard, Duke of York, then four. This had necessitated a papal dispensation, but not because of their ages. Anne's great-grandmother and Richard's grandmother were sisters.) Jewish law permits uncle-niece marriages, but not aunt-nephew unions. However, Jewish law bows down on such matters to local law. Muslim law is surprisingly similar to that of the Church of England, considering that a Muslim is permitted to be polyga-

---

* The text of the *Book of Common Prayer* of 1662 is Crown copyright and extracts used herein are reproduced with permission.

KINDRED AND AFFINITY

A man may not marry his	Common name	Now permitted?	Common genes? (whether "must be" or "on average")	A woman may not marry her
1. Grandmother		No	¼ (must be)	Grandfather
2. Grandfather's wife		No	Nil	Grandmother's husband
3. Wife's grandmother		No	Nil	Husband's grandfather
4. Father's sister	aunt	No	¼ (average)	Father's brother
5. Mother's sister	aunt	No	¼ (average)	Mother's brother
6. Father's brother's wife	aunt	Yes	Nil	Father's sister's husband
7. Mother's brother's wife	aunt	Yes	Nil	Mother's sister's husband
8. Wife's father's sister	aunt	Yes	Nil	Husband's father's brother
9. Wife's mother's sister	aunt	Yes	Nil	Husband's mother's brother
10. Mother		No	½ (must be)	Father
11. Step-mother		No	Nil	Step-father
12. Wife's mother	mother-in-law	No	Nil	Husband's father
13. Daughter		No	½ (must be)	Son
14. Wife's daughter	step-daughter	No	Nil	Husband's son
15. Son's wife	daughter-in-law	No	Nil	Daughter's husband
16. Sister		No	½ (on average)	Brother
17. Wife's sister	sister-in-law	Yes	Nil	Husband's brother
18. Brother's wife	sister-in-law	Yes	Nil	Sister's husband
19. Son's daughter	grand-daughter	No	¼ (must be)	Son's son
20. Daughter's daughter	grand-daughter	No	¼ (must be)	Daughter's son
21. Son's son's wife		No	Nil	Son's daughter's husband
22. Daughter's son's wife		No	Nil	Daughter's daughter's husband
23. Wife's son's daughter		No	Nil	Husband's son's son
24. Wife's daughter's daughter		No	Nil	Husband's daughter's son
25. Brother's daughter	niece	No	¼ (average)	Brother's son
26. Sister's daughter	niece	No	¼ (average)	Sister's son
27. Brother's son's wife		Yes	Nil	Brother's daughter's husband
28. Sister's son's wife		Yes	Nil	Sister's daughter's husband
29. Wife's brother's daughter	niece	Yes	Nil	Husband's brother's son
30. Wife's sister's daughter	niece	Yes	Nil	Husband's sister's son

mous. "Forbidden to you are your mothers and your aunts both on the father's side, and your nieces on the brothers' and sisters' side, and your foster mothers' and your foster sisters' and your mothers of your wives and your stepdaughters who are your wards, born of your wives to whom ye have gone in: (but if ye have not gone into them, it shall be no sin to you to marry them); and the wives of your sons who proceed out of your loins; and ye may not have two sisters; except where it is already done. Verily, God is Indulgent, Merciful!"* The Muslim can, like the Jew, therefore marry his first cousin.

Before moving on to the harm done by marrying near relations, the convenient word "cousin" should be defined. Basically, of course, it means the son or daughter of someone's aunt or uncle. There are in fact ten different types of cousin—or cousinships—from this basic formula, depending on whether the cousins are boys or girls, or one of each, and their parents are sisters or brothers, or one of each. In some countries, this relative straightforwardness is thrown overboard. Perhaps a man's father's brother may marry the man's mother's mother, and therefore present him with young cousins who are also his half-aunts and half-uncles. Professor Curt Stern speaks of a Navaho Indian whose parents were simultaneously first cousins, third cousins, and first cousins once removed. Working out the likelihood of genetic similarity among their offspring requires great devotion. Professor J. B. S. Haldane did it after emigrating from England to the familial bewilderment of India. He listed, named, and calculated the degree of genetic relationship for hundreds of possible cousinships.

Effects of Inbreeding

Without doubt, the offspring of near relatives who marry have a rougher time in life than those from unrelated couples. The nearer the relationship, the worse the time, the greater the chance of premature death, and the more likely the presence of severe abnormalities. Some recent reports illustrate the situation. With first-cousin matings in the United States the percentage mortality among their offspring for the first ten years is 8.1 percent against 2.4 percent for unrelated marriages. In France the figures for neonates (less than one month) is 9.3 percent against 3.9 percent. In Japan, for children from a year old to 8, the figures are 4.6 percent against 1.5 percent. Similar work has been done on disease (TB) and defects (malformations) in both groups of children. The percentages of those affected, according to a Swedish report, are 16 percent against 4 percent for the offspring of unrelated parents. In the United

* J. M. Rodwell's translation of the Koran.

States comparable figures are 16.15 percent against 9.82 percent; in France 12.8 percent against 3.5 percent. (These reports cannot be compared precisely with one another as differences exist in the compilation of the facts, but they do all indicate the same unfortunate trends.)

Certain congenital malformations show up very badly in first-cousin offspring. They are phenylketonuria,* alkaptonuria, amaurotic idiocy, and others, possibly including albinism. (Definitely not on this list, despite widespread belief, is hemophilia.) Between 5 and 15 percent of phenyl-ketonuria cases have related parents. With alkaptonuria the proportion is 30 to 42 percent (according to different countries). The figures appear alarming, but are considerably less so when balanced against the actual incidence of the two diseases. Phenylketonuria affects one child in 40,000; alkaptonuria one in a million. In fact, the rarer a disease, the more alarming the incidence appears for first-cousin offspring. With alkaptonuria it so happens that one in 500 of the general population carries its recessive gene. If two cousins marry, one of whom has the gene, there is one chance in eight that his or her mate will also have the gene. If the affected cousin marries anyone else, there is one chance in 500 that the mate will possess the gene. Odds can also be calculated for the offspring of these marriages. In the cousin-cousin marriage, the probability that a child will be affected by the disease is one in 32. In the cousin/anyone else marriage, the odds lengthen to one in 2,000.

Playing this kind of genetic roulette with future offspring is obviously unsatisfactory. Unfortunately, no one knows all the genes he or she carries, and therefore no one has any idea whether the marriage is genetically sound. Both he and she, if cousins, can know only that a greater risk exists for their children. The very rare recessive diseases will be slightly less rare for them; the common ones will be slightly more common. In the *British Medical Journal* the anonymous expert once wrote in his weekly column: "My own practice with first cousin couples who plan to marry is to explain the additional risk and to tell them that, if they really want to marry, it is a very reasonable risk to take." If one of their children is then afflicted with an autosomal recessive disorder (meaning that both cousins had the bad luck to possess and pass on the same harmful and recessive gene) there is then one chance in four that their next child will be similarly affected. The odds do not vary, however many children they have.

Some notable cousin-cousin offspring have been Charles Darwin,

---

* It is phenylketonuria that is primarily responsible for the routine testing of new-born babies' diapers carried on in many areas, for example, in New York State. Testing the urine will determine whether the child is a victim and therefore whether it must have a diet very low in phenylalanine during the critical early months of life.

Edward Fitzgerald, Toulouse-Lautrec, and John Ruskin. Although this is a brilliant collection, most authorities say Darwin was also a hypochondriac, Fitzgerald a homosexual, Toulouse-Lautrec a cripple, and Ruskin impotent. However, Darwin (after lengthy correspondence in the medical journals of today) is now thought to have been suffering from Chagas' disease, picked up in South America; Toulouse-Lautrec's legs were probably the result of a dominant gene for osteogenesis imperfecta.* And no one knows why or if Ruskin was impotent or Fitzgerald homosexual. Certainly, none of their complaints can be laid at the door of the cousin marriage that created them. And neither, for that matter, can their brilliance.

Undoubtedly, there will be fewer cousin-cousin marriages in the future. America's mixed and mobile community (with only 6 cousin marriages per 10,000) is an indication of the modern trend. In Utah in 1870 such marriages used to be 1 percent of the total; by 1890 they were .25 percent, by 1910 .1 percent, and now they are next to nothing. In France (in the Loire-et-Cher department), there were 6 percent in 1918, 3 percent in 1932, and 1 percent in 1952. Nowadays not only are people getting out of their valleys, but also families are smaller. Fewer brothers and sisters in one generation mean fewer cousins in the next. (My own family is a good example of this point. My father was one of nine siblings—he had seven sisters and a brother—and hence there were 23 first cousins for me and my brothers. My mother was an only child: hence there was not a cousin in sight on her side.)

Incest

Everything said about cousin matings is multiplied for closer relationships. It has already been pointed out that cousins have, on average, one-eighth of their genes in common. Because of this fact cousin matings are more likely to result in faulty offspring. Uncles and nieces have one-quarter of their genes in common; therefore the percentage of malformed children is likely to be greater still. Fathers and daughters, mothers and sons, brothers and sisters have half their genes in common (the parental relationships are certain to be 50 percent; the siblings have 50 percent on average); consequently the mortality risk for children from these closest of all incestuous relationships is four times greater than for the children whose parents are first cousins. Detailed studies of the offspring of close incestuous unions are rare, but London's Institute of Child Health has been examining the case histories of 13 such children. Of this number only five are both physically and mentally normal.

Emile Zola said incest was "so stupendously vile that I cannot decently

* Several falls in his childhood did not help. His father had similar trouble.

contemplate it." The eighteenth chapter of Leviticus is also most adamant. Incest is still customarily vilified by most of the population, although not so categorically and with a twinge of curiosity about the relationship's causes. It is presumably less common than it once was, and is presumably influenced by the same reasons that are reducing cousin-cousin matings, but the number of cases known to the police in Britain is actually growing. Whether for reasons of increased police diligence or not, although the prewar average was fewer than 100 cases a year, the average has risen annually. By 1965 over 300 cases were known to the police. Plainly the real total must be considerably higher. The law in England states that males over 14 and females over 16 can be charged with incest, and the maximum penalty is seven years' imprisonment. If the man's partner in the incestuous relationship is younger than 13, he can be imprisoned for life. Both in the England of Oliver Cromwell and in Scotland until 1887 the maximum punishment for incest was death. Public opinion on punishment has changed much since those days. A Liberal member of the Swedish parliament even announced in January, 1967, that he would try to change the existing law so that brothers and sisters could marry. Previously, a Swedish court had ruled that a 34-year-old man and his younger half-sister (both had the same father) could continue to live as a married couple; they have a normal child of eight. Public opinion may be changing, but geneticists are likely to be inflexible about the hazards of excessive consanguinity.

Genetic Recessives

There is a final sting in the tale of inbreeding. The fact that inbred marriages are on the way out does not magically remove the problem of all those harmful and recessive genes lurking within every one of us. It merely postpones it. When two cousins do have the misfortune to beget a malformed child and that child dies, the two recessive genes it carried die with it. Nothing is passed on to the next generation. If cousin marriages stop, that kind of swift elimination also stops—for the time being. As the years and the generations go by, the lack of elimination means the accumulation of a larger and larger number of recessive genes among us. Hence the greater chance of unfortunate pairings from unrelated marriages. Exclusion of consanguinity in one generation, as Curt Stern, of Berkeley, puts it, merely transfers the load of affected individuals to later generations. Cousins who decide to marry now may take a little cold comfort from the fact that, by accepting the risks today, they are doing something for all our descendants, for posterity. The fact becomes truer, and the comfort colder still, should a recessive defect chance to kill one of their offspring.

~§ 17 §~

Blood Groups

Karl Landsteiner · Transfusions ·
Blood-group Distribution · Group Advantages ·
How Many Groups? · Rhesus · Paternity and the Courts

All human beings belong to one of four blood groups. These groups
are distinguished by the reaction between the red blood cells of one
individual and the serum (the blood's liquid) of another. Either the
blood cells are distributed evenly in the serum, or they club together
(known as nonagglutination and agglutination). Red blood corpuscles
are said to possess antigens called agglutinogens; there are two agglutinogens (A and B) and two agglutinins (anti-A and anti-B). Blood
corpuscles may contain either A, B, both, or neither. These form the
four blood groups. Blood serum may contain anti-A, anti-B, both, or
neither. Corpuscles containing A are agglutinated by serum containing
anti-A. B corpuscles are similarly treated by anti-B. People possessing,
for example, A corpuscles do not possess anti-A serum, but do possess
anti-B. O people have serum containing both anti-A and anti-B. AB
people have neither. Trouble following the wrong blood transfusions
(A blood for a B person or vice versa) is almost entirely caused by the
reaction of the recipient's agglutinins against the introduced corpuscles.
The agglutinins of the donor's blood generally do much less harm.

Karl Landsteiner

Just as Winston Churchill's actions seem to cover more than the life-span
of a single individual, so does the name of Karl Landsteiner occur relentlessly in the history of the development of blood-group knowledge. Landsteiner, who was born the son of an Austrian journalist in 1868, became
a physician in 1891. At the end of the nineteenth century he was working
in Vienna on the curious clumping qualities of blood from different

individuals. In 1900 he described three blood types. In 1902 he added a fourth, thereby completing the A, B, O, and then the AB blood classification of mankind. Even at that time Landsteiner foresaw the importance of the different blood groups, but it was not until World War I's spilling of blood—and the subsequent urgent need for transfusion—that the importance of his work received general recognition. In 1922 Landsteiner emigrated to the United States and became an American citizen as soon as he could.

Five years later, with Dr. Philip Levine, he discovered yet another blood grouping; they proclaimed all human beings to have M, N, or MN blood. This secondary classification is irrelevant to blood transfusion, but scientifically exciting and of extreme genetical relevance in cases of doubtful paternity. Accused and unhappy males can be found not guilty of fathering some child if blood is examined and compared; but more about that later.

In 1930 Karl Landsteiner, then 62, received the Nobel Prize. Seven years later he started investigations that led in 1940 to yet another discovery. Working this time with Dr. Alexander Weiner, he hit upon the famous rhesus factor. It may seem valueless to care, let alone announce, that if a rabbit is injected with some blood from the Macacus rhesus monkey, the rabbit makes an antibody that has a clumping effect on the red blood cells of 84 percent of New York's white people. Yet the work was crucial. Without this breakthrough the 16 percent of women who have Rh-negative blood, and who until then frequently produced jaundiced and dying babies, would not find their condition treated with such care in maternity units today; but more about this later also. Landsteiner died in 1943, when still in harness (he had a heart attack while at work in his laboratory). More than any other man, he had made blood transfusion possible.

Transfusions

These began, as can be imagined, erratically and, oddly, with the assistance of Sir Christopher Wren. In 1665, the year of London's great plague, he suggested to the Cornishman Dr. Richard Lower that blood might be passed from one animal to another; apparently the transfusion worked. Two years later Arthur Cogan, a Londoner, capped this tale by passing into himself blood from a pig, and legend claims success. It seems that Lower, who became court physician to Charles II, let things be, but one of Louis XIV's doctors, Jean Denys, gave a patient a transfusion of lamb's blood. There was, reasonably, a violent reaction; but, less reasonably, the patient lived. In 1668 another patient died after similar treatment from an animal. (The purpose of this transfusion —with calf's blood—had been to transfer gentle and bovine characteristics to a philandering husband.)

Thenceforth blood transfusions in France were forbidden. No one attempted a transfusion of human blood, until 1818, when Dr. James Blundell, of London, tried it. The patient died. One trouble, which had nothing to do with blood grouping, was the clotting of the blood. Many different techniques were tried to keep it fluid and were soon successful, but then came the brick wall of blood groups. Some transfusions were entirely successful. Some were equally disastrous, and the whole of the nineteenth century had to pass before Landsteiner solved the riddle.

Now, transfusions are a commonplace. Over 2 million Americans receive them in a year. Britain uses over one million bottles of blood plasma annually. Blood banks are everywhere. There are even banks of extremely rare blood, as at the Chelsea Naval Station in Massachusetts (where, for example, Rh null is kept, reported so far in only five people). Swimming against this tide are, among others, the Jehovah's Witnesses. Unlike Christian Scientists, who ignore medical healing but are not definitely forbidden to take blood, the Witnesses accept hospital treatment but not blood. They quote the Acts of the Apostles, chapter 15 (". . . that ye abstain from meats offered to idols, and from blood") and Gen. 9:4 ("But flesh with the life thereof, which is the blood thereof, shall ye not eat") as authority for their principle, and since 1945 they have ruled out transfusions. Members of the sect achieve worldwide publicity when the enforced lack of transfusion precedes a death. Walter Stevens, for example, of Adelaide, Australia, refused permission in June, 1965, for his wife to receive blood during a difficult delivery of twins. She died shortly afterward, and the newspapers were quick to pounce.

Blood-group Distribution

All mankind, whether New Yorker or aborigine, is O, A, B, or AB. The letters seem unnecessarily complex, and I, II, III, and IV would seem a much better and simpler method of classification. In fact, Roman numerals were used originally, but they gave way to letters because the letters are more meaningful. A and B refer to the two clotting factors (technically these are two mucopolysaccharides, both known as agglutinogens) that human blood contains. These factors cause all the trouble. Without them blood transfusions would be relatively plain sailing. Blood type A (42 percent of western Europeans) has one of them, blood type B (9 percent) has the other; type AB (3 percent) has both and blood type O (46 percent) has neither. Group O is often called the universal donor, and in World War II only group-O blood was sent to the front in many areas; but it is a misnomer. For various reasons, not all group-O blood can be pumped into A, B, or AB people. Some group-O donors are more universal than others. (It all depends upon the amount of anti-A or anti-B agglutinins in their serum. Some O's have a lot. Most do not.) Similarly, the AB people, the rare 3 percent, are not the "universal recipients" they are frequently said to be.

To offset this nuisance value in transfusion, the ABO groups are interesting geographically. All races of man have them, but differently. During World War II, for example, during blood collection in northern Wales, someone noticed that Welsh names (Jones, Evans, Williams) produced more O and B blood than English names. In fact, all Celts are now known to produce less A blood than the descendants of those Anglo-Saxons who drove them back. Southeast England produces much more A blood even from its intermixed inhabitants today.

In fact, a history of Europe, albeit a short one, could be written from blood groups alone. The A people—whoever they were, they had a high A-group percentage—seem to have occupied Europe with particular entrenchments in Scandinavia, Spain, and Turkey. The O people fared less well and either preferred or were forced into the corners, such as Ireland, Scotland, the Pyrenees, Iceland, Sardinia, Corsica, and the eastern Black Sea. Meanwhile, the B's, never so plentiful, are more common the farther they are from Europe, whether up into Russia or down into the Middle East. The B's seem a second invasion force (the Mongols?) who were unable to oust the A's.

Globally, the picture is more complex. South American Indians are 100 percent O. North American Indians are also rich in O but have more and more A toward the north. They have virtually no B. Maoris and Australian aborigines are, like the Eskimos, half A and half O. West African Negroes are mainly O (52 percent) but equally A and B (21 percent and 23 percent). The top B people are the Ainu of Japan (38 percent), the Asian Indians (37 percent), and the Tartars (33 percent). Top AB's are the Congo Pygmies (10 percent), the Japanese (11 percent), and the Egyptians (10 percent). The O group is the most persistent. Some people have no A, like the South American Indians; some have no B, like many of the Indian groups farther north; and some have no AB, like almost all the New World Indians; but no group anywhere has no O. Thirty percent is about the lowest figure for O's, possessed by some Pygmy, Chinese, Russian, and Tartar groups.

The blood-group distribution therefore seems an awful mix-up. Why do the Basques have ABO proportions like the Australian aborigines?

Or why do the Greenland Eskimos and the French? Why do the Mongols, who are supposed to have supplied the ancestors of the Red Indian, have blood rich in B, while the Indians have next to none of it? The short answer is that advantages must exist for certain blood groups under certain conditions.

Group Advantages

In recent years some hints of differing benefits have begun to show. Professor Ian Aird, the surgeon, found English people with blood type O were more likely to get duodenal ulcers. More people with blood type A get stomach cancer (about 20 percent), pernicious anemia (25 percent), and even diabetes mellitus than those with O and B. Such slender information, which by no means implies that the blood groups actually cause the diseases, is a long way from explaining, for example, why all the B's died out as the Asian groups, so rich in B blood, entered the New World via the Bering Straits—which they almost certainly did.

Extra facts about the ABO system:

The blood group of an individual is established irrevocably probably by the end of the second month of pregnancy. Which group it is (useful in paternity trouble) can be found out by the 12th week of pregnancy if the shed cells in the mother's amniotic fluid are examined.

The muscle tissue of 4,000-year-old mummies has been blood-grouped. Bones long buried soon will be. Fraternal twins are more often of the same group than mere chance would indicate.

O mothers married to A fathers produce more miscarriages (certainly in Japan, and probably elsewhere) than A mothers married to O fathers.

How Many Groups?

While the ABO groups are vital in transfusion, they are by no means the only groups. Second to be discovered was the M, N, MN system. Two genes control this. White Americans are, according to the Public Health Services Laboratory of Blood and Blood Products, 22 percent M, 28 percent N, and 50 percent MN, while English people are 32 percent M, 19 percent N, and 48 percent MN. For a child to be N, both parents cannot be M. To be M both parents cannot be N, and to be MN means that both parents cannot be exclusively M or N, all of which is crucial evidence for the paternity courts. Once again the geographical distribution is odd. Negroes, Pacific Islanders, and aboriginal Australians are rich in N and weak in M. Eskimos, Red Indians, the Welsh, Chinese, and Japanese are rich in M and weak in N. There is slightly more sense in the MN distribution than with the ABO's, but that Bering Straits migration is still awry. Asian Mongols have many N's among them, American Mongols hardly any.

Since Landsteiner started the blood-group avalanche, more and more have been found, such as the MNSs, the Rh-HR (the famous rhesus factor), the P groups, the Kell, the Lutheran, the Duffy, the Kidd, the Lewis, the Diego, the Hunter and Henshaw, the Sutter—most of these are named after the patients in whose blood they were first found. Therefore, a man is not just O or O and M, but—to quote the most common type of Englishman—O, MSNS, P_1, CDe/cde, Lu^bLu^b, kk, Le^bLe^b, Fy^aFy^b, Jk^aJk^b. London's Blood Group Research Unit estimates this lot occurs once in every 270 people, and there are 303,264 possible combinations of blood groups in Englishmen. Consequently, do not leave fingerprints or blood at the scene of the crime, particularly at some foreign scene. Any European's blood can be distinguished from a West African's 95 times out of 100, thus narrowing the field of suspicion abruptly.

It is reasonable to wonder where all these blood groups came from. Consequently, tests have been made on the higher animal species. Chemically, there are differences but many more similarities. Most monkeys are A or B, rarely both. The gorillas seem to be either A or B; chimpanzees are mainly A and sometimes O; orangutans and gibbons are A, B, or AB. It is strange that O, the most frequent group in man, is the rarest (except for 10 percent of the chimpanzees) in the apes and monkeys. The evidence is insufficient to provide any powerful pointers toward the origins of man. Perhaps the less well known groups, which perhaps have less evolutionary influence, will provide better clues when comparative work has been done.

Rhesus

If you are an Rh-negative girl (one-sixth of American and British girls are) marry a Basque or, better still, a Walser of Switzerland. But think twice about Pacific Islanders, Australian aborigines, and American Indians. You may be making life marginally easier for yourself and your obstetrician and considerably easier for your babies if you choose an Rh-negative mate. Thirty-six percent of the Basques are eligible, only 15 percent of white Americans and 16 percent of Englishmen, but no Red Indians, Papuans, or aboriginal Australians. Also hardly any Chinese or Japanese are Rh negative. If you do choose a Papuan, or even an Rh-positive Englishman, there is about a 72 percent chance that your baby will be Rh positive, like his father, unlike you. This could mean trouble, but such a marriage, with such a baby, is only troublesome in 2 to 5 percent of cases.

The reasons were at first poorly understood, but it is now known that fetal bleeding at birth, which causes the mother's blood to meet the fetus, is highly relevant to the fate of the next child. So are the ABO groups because, if the parents have different ABO groups, the new babies are less likely to suffer from Rh trouble. This stroke of good fortune is linked with the massive resentment between one ABO blood group and another, which blurs the minor resentment between the two Rh groups. Anyway, if you, an Rh-negative female, mate with an Rh-positive male, there will be fewer Rh-incompatible fetuses if you are O and he is A, B, or AB. Things are less good from the Rh point of view if you are A and he is O or A.

This trouble, this Rh incompatibility of the fetuses, has many names such as hemolytic disease of the newborn, erythroblastosis fetalis, kernicterus, and icterus gravis neonatorum. Whatever the name, it is basically a destruction of the baby's red blood cells. The mother (who has produced antibodies against her Rh-positive fetus) is doing the destroying. So the baby becomes anemic and jaundiced and, were it not for transfusions, would die 75 times out of 100, sometimes before birth. Present treatment is fairly straightforward. The sooner the baby is born the better (within reason), for the sooner it has left its mother's destructive (hemolytic) influence the better. Then its blood is exchanged to get rid of all those maternal antibodies and very recent work (since 1963) has even changed a baby's blood *before* birth.

Although antenatal transfusion is an extremely modern technique, it is likely to be outmoded almost at once by an even better system for protecting the victims of Rh incompatibility. Professors C. A. Clarke, P. M. Sheppard, and others at Liverpool University, after working with Rh-negative male volunteers, have devised a way of preventing Rh-negative mothers from producing antibodies against their Rh-positive offspring. By October, 1966, they had had success with 78 mothers (having used gamma globulin with what is known as a high titer of Anti-D). Other tests are now being conducted with differing quantities of gamma globulin. Everyone has high hopes for this new system, one of prevention rather than cure, and one in 200 of all British babies (roughly 4,000 a year) will both survive more frequently and have an easier time of it than at present. The period, therefore, between the first comprehension of Rh incompatibility and the discovery of an effective countermeasure has been less than three decades.

The clue that led to the unraveling of this story at the start of World War II was that virtually no first babies were affected, with one vital exception. If the Rh-negative mother had ever received a transfusion, the chances were (with 84 percent of us Rh positive) she had received Rh-positive blood; hence, she could have become sensitized, hence the preparation of Rh antibodies, hence her firstborn's blood would be cruelly attacked. Nowadays, no Rh-negative woman before her menopause is given Rh-positive blood. The situation is reasonably in hand.

But a fascinating upsetting of the situation came from Sweden in October, 1965. A girl, Rh negative, aged 24, had been a virgin when married in 1961. Consequently she had had no earlier children or abortions and no chance to get sensitized from Rh-positive blood. Also, she had never had a transfusion. But her first baby was born jaundiced, and she was full of Rh antibodies. Her second baby was similar. It was all a mystery until she admitted receiving blood at the age of nine during a girls' "brotherhood" ceremony. The amount transfused was presumably small, but Lund University doctors think it could have done the trick and sensitized her against her first child born a dozen years later. Anyway, they sought out and found her blood brother. Sure enough, she was Rh positive.

Although the ABO groups have been linked with disease in a few cases, the advantages of being Rh positive or negative are still totally obscure. As Sir Peter Medawar puts it (and he rarely misses the opportunity of a happy phrase), the Rh blood types are associated with nothing "except the unqualified incubus of transfusion accidents." It would seem better for the human race if all of us had similar Rh blood (and similar Kell blood too, for the same kind of story exists with that grouping). Why, therefore, the dissimilarity? There is still no explanation nearly 30 years after the Rh discovery. "It is not known," says Medawar. "It is merely being groped after."

Paternity and the Courts

Blood groups may be irksome in transfusions, but they are the breath of life in paternity cases. Many a male, harassed by accusations, has had cause to be grateful to his grouping, to hers, and to that of the child.

Can a man prove he is the father of a child? Can he prove that he is not? Briefly, the answers are "no" and "probably," respectively. The key is blood. There are three ABO-blood-group genes, and four ABO blood groups. No child can acquire a gene, and consequently a blood grouping, if it is not possessed by either parent. If the wife is group O, the husband group O, and the baby group A, that husband has no reason whatsoever to believe the baby is his. He can regard quizzically those of their friends who are A or AB. (The British courts accept blood-group evidence but do not have the power to order blood-group tests in paternity cases; this is possible in Scandinavia and in parts of the United States, including New York. The procedure starts to be really crucial when illegitimate children are to be given as much of the father's wealth as his legitimate offspring.)

If the mother is	*and the child is*	*the father can be*	*but not*
O	O	O, A, or B	AB (3% of European population)
O	A	A or AB	O or B (55%)
O	B	B or AB	O or A (88%)
A	O	O, A, or B	AB (3%)
A	A	Any group	
A	B	B or AB	O or A (88%)
A	AB	B or AB	O or A (88%)
B	O	O, A, or B	AB (3%)
B	B	Any group	
B	A	A or AB	O or B (55%)
B	AB	A or AB	O or B (55%)
AB	AB	A, B, or AB	O (46%)

The percentages are important. It is obviously easier to settle the paternity question if 88 percent of the population can be excluded rather than 3 percent or even 0 percent. (It's a wise mother who knows her lover's ABO blood group before she begins complicating the issue.) Taking the population as a whole, the probability of freeing a wrongfully accused man, using just the ABO groups, is only about 20 percent. So, other groups are used, such as the MN and Rh groups.

If the baby is MN	and the mother is M	the father cannot be M
" " " " MN	" " " " N	" " " " N
" " " " N	" " " " Any group	" " " " M
" " " " M	" " " " Any group	" " " " N

The MN test frees a man from responsibility in about 18 percent of cases. For the Rh test (if both parents are Rh positive, the child cannot be Rh negative; if both parents are negative, the child cannot be positive), the maximum chance of exclusion in western Europe is about 25 percent. If all three blood tests are used, any man has at least a 50 percent chance of disproving his paternity, and it could be more (75 percent) if further blood groups are tested. At present, 68 percent of men wrongfully accused of fathering children can prove their innocence by blood-group tests. In the world of fact—and the courts—fewer get off. Many women must therefore be telling the truth when they point the finger.

In Germany, 100 children and their correct fathers were once examined by an expert independent panel. (Paternity experts have a high status in Germany and Scandinavia. Not so in Britain.) Using customary methods (and merely looking at parents and offspring without any recourse to blood testing), the examiners had to decide whether it was probable, improbable, or not determinable that the children were correctly assigned. The results were emphatic. Ninety-three of the children were "probably" the sons of their fathers (varying from "more probable than not" right up to "probable to a degree bordering on certainty"); seven were not determinable; but none was said to be definitely not the son of his father. In other words, like produces likeness—an adage more correct, biologically, than "like produces like." The latter implies duplication, much like a printing press. In biology, certainly above the most primitive level, the offspring is only similar to its parents, not the same.

Apart from blood and resemblance, there are genetic extras such as eye and hair color. When both parents are blue-eyed, all their children ought to be blue-eyed, but occasionally an incomprehensible brown-eyed child creeps—legitimately—in. Two red-haired parents ought to have all red-haired children. And the same sort of thing goes for parents both tall, both with attached earlobes, both with straight hair, or both blond. They are more likely to have tall, straight-haired blond children with attached earlobes. Tall parents may produce short children, but on average they do so less frequently than short parents. Some characteristics obey definite rules, notably when only one pair of genes is involved (as with blue eyes). Some obey or follow probability, as when many genes are involved (like height and hair). Both types have a part to play in linking children with the parents who produced them.

In a blond, blue-eyed, tall, fair-haired community these particular characteristics are valueless in assessing paternity. The infrequent ones are more important. In Norway, a normal mother produced a brachyphalangic (short-fingered) child, a rare condition. The court asked the accused to hold up his hand. His fingers were short, and he therefore had to pay. Other men have been caught by the presence of hair on the middle digit of one of their fingers. This characteristic also cannot be passed on if it is not possessed. The courts can be wrong in coming to a yes or no answer, but it is possible to calculate—given all the facts about relative frequencies of certain characteristics—how probable or improbable a wrong decision may be (the postman of that Norwegian couple may also have been brachyphalangic, but this is unlikely). Curt Stern has called it "an exact numerical evaluation of the probability of correctness of a paternity judgement." The law already possesses a better phrase—beyond all reasonable doubt.

As a tailpiece to paternity, there is on record at least one case of doubled-sired twins. The mother (blood group O and M) produced fraternal twins, a boy (B, M) and a girl (A, MN). One man could have produced both, by being AB and MN; but no such man was in that mother's life. She had known, as the Bible uses the word, only two men, one being A and MN, the other B and M. The first could not have produced the boy, for where did the lad get his B from? The second could not have produced the girl, for where did she get her A or N from? Both men must have played their part.

The Growth of Babies

The Rate of Growth · Survival · Crib Deaths ·
Battered Babies · Developmental Progress ·
First Reflexes · Lungs · Brain · Sleep ·
Skeleton · Muscle · Fat · Heart · Kidneys and
Bladder · Spock · Swaddling · Child Law

From the child of five to myself is but a step, but from the new-born baby to the child of five is an appalling distance.

Leo Tolstoy

The human baby, already 266 days old at birth, is incapable of survival without help. Countless mammals who have spent less time in the uterus are able to stand and run within minutes of being born, whereas the human baby will stagger for the first time into a walk some 12 months after birth. Most mammal offspring find and feed from the life-supporting nipples with great competence; the human baby needs all the assistance it can get. By the time many other large mammals have grown up to rear their own families, the human infant is still slobbering around, falling down stairs, eating anything that comes its way, crying, getting lost, defecating at random, and generally behaving in a witless fashion. At what age, one wonders, would human infants be able to survive if removed from parental care and placed instead on some sumptuous island, rich in foods of every kind? At birth they would die virtually at once. At a year old, they would fare little better. At 2 they might get by, but apathy and precipices would ensnare them in the end. At 3 or 4, the mortality rate would still be tremendous, even assuming a disease-free island. Homo sapiens, the wise one, the pinnacle of evolution, certainly takes his time to achieve his wisdom.

The Rate of Growth

Nevertheless, the rate of growth is man's strength. His growth is slow. The whole pace is slow. The time before breeding is long. The days for acquiring and testing individual skills are seemingly endless. During the first 18 years of life a baby's stature, from top to toe, is multiplied less than four times, and although mothers may think otherwise, as nipples yield to bottles, and bottles yield to plate after plate of food, a child's gain in weight is pitifully slow by comparison with most other animals. A mere 5 lb. in the first three months, 14 lb. in the first year, 38 lb. in the first 6 years of life—such increments are most modest. (For comparison, a pig weighs 3 lb. at birth, and 200 lb. at 6 months; a Friesian calf weighs 100 lb. at birth, and can weigh 900 lb. ten months later.)

Even during the adolescent growth spurt, when boys (and to a lesser extent girls) eat hugely at meals and in between meals, when they gather food toward them much as magnets gather iron, the rate at which they put on flesh is small. A gain of 12 lb. in one year is a fair pubertal increment. The average height increase for boys at this time of most rapid growth is about 3½ in. a year, and 2½ in. for girls. Aunts and uncles express amazement at the weedlike change in stature, and rows of outgrown clothes give a more objective assessment; but, in fact, there is nothing biologically remarkable in 3½ in. a year, or less than a third of an inch a month. Mankind does take its time. A boy born 20 in. long and reaching 6 ft. after 18 years is growing less, on average, than 3 in. a year. From his first to his 18th birthday he is growing only about 2½ in. a year, and from the second to the 18th birthday only 2¼ in. a year. No other creature of similar bulk is quite so leisurely.

In a sense, growth has practically stopped by the time of birth. At the 12th week of pregnancy, the baby's increment per month is 600 percent. Four weeks later it is 220 percent, four weeks later still 120 percent, then 90 percent, then 50 percent, then 25 percent, then—in the last four weeks —20 percent. Most of the original growth power has gone by the time of birth; a small percentage remains to finish, in 18 years, the job that began so fervently nine months before. Growing up is—for humans—a slow business, particularly after birth, and is also a dangerous business.

Survival

The child is more prone than the adult to infection, and any country that achieves an improvement in its child-mortality figures generally does it by better control and treatment of infection. However, even in modern countries, many children still die. In Great Britain about 25,000 children up to the age of 14 die every year. Of this not negligible number, about 20,000 have failed to reach their first birthday. And of these short-lived infants, about 13,000 have not even survived for a month. In the United States in 1964, 99,783 infants died within their first year, 72,026 within the first month. That first month is made hazardous primarily by birth itself, by the trauma of the event, by actual birth injury, by the possibility of oxygen lack, by the problems of prematurity, and by unfitness for the sudden change. It is also the time when a large number of congenital malformations have a telling effect upon the statistics; severe deformities frequently lead to death in the first few hours of life.

In many poorer communities, even today, it is the exception rather than the rule for babies to survive into adulthood. Dysentery and the host of allied enteric disorders have probably been the greatest killers of all time for mankind; they are still formidable barriers to survival, notably at weaning time. Not so long ago in England more babies died than lived. In London, the births of 315,456 babies were registered between 1730 and 1749. Of this number 74.5 percent died before the age of five. By the end of that century, and in a similar 19-year period between 1790 and 1809, the births had risen to 386,393 while the deaths up to age five had fallen to 41.3 percent. To a very large extent this pair of facts alone explains the sudden surge in Britain's population. This percentage was even better than seventeenth-century mortality figures for the upper classes. Of the 32 royal children born between the reigns of James I and Anne only ten lived until they were 21.

Medicine in the eighteenth century was still archaic, towns were still foul, hygiene was still poorly attended to, poverty was extreme—and yet about twice as many babies struggled successfully through their first five years at the end of the century as at the beginning. By World War I 87 percent of babies were surviving until five, and today about 97 percent in advanced societies survive until their 14th birthday.

Control of infection in the community at large was primarily responsible for the improvement. Even since 1925 there has been huge change. In that year, there were 2,774 deaths in England and Wales from diphtheria, 988 from scarlet fever, 5,337 from measles, and 6,058 from whooping cough. The 1961 figures for these four diseases were 8, 3, 27, and 152 respectively, or 1.25 percent of the 1925 total. Some diseases and childhood ailments have proved more stubborn. Pneumonia and bronchitis dropped dramatically in the 1930s and 1940s, and have since remained steady, but congenital malformation deaths have stayed steady since the 1930s, thus forming a higher and higher proportion of child deaths. Deaths from birth injury, asphyxia, and prematurity dropped in the 1940s, but have since stayed fairly constant. Accident deaths have fallen slightly since the 1930s, with the rising number of actual accidents being just offset by the gradual improvements in surgery and nursing. Malignant disease in children has been slowly rising since the 1930s (although one immediately suspects that more accurate diagnosis has had much to do with the rise). The current order of severity for the causes of child death is birth injury (including asphyxia and prematurity), infection, congenital malformations, accident, malignancy, and then the various other relatively minor hazards. All in all, the first part of life is still the most perilous until the individual reaches middle age.

Which part of that early life is the most serious? In advanced countries the first month is definitely the most severe hurdle. In some primitive countries, the second year can be the worst. Their first year is relatively carefree, with a lot of breast milk (therefore reasonable nourishment, little contact with bacteria, and a close relationship with the mother's own immunity system), and not much opportunity for grubbing around and picking up infection. The second-year child is no longer carried so readily, nor fed so well, nor protected so happily from pathogenic bacteria. Infection and malnutrition then form a deadly alliance. The death rate in primitive countries for that lethal second year can be 50 times higher than in advanced countries.

It is the combination of poor food plus infection that is so disastrous. The same measles virus exists in the United States, Chile, Guatemala, and Ecuador. Its strength, or virulence, is roughly the same, but its killing power is totally different between the one advanced country and the other three. In the United States, children do not, in general, die from an attack of measles. In Chile, similar attacks kill 138 times more frequently, in Guatemala 189 times, and in Ecuador 418 times more frequently than in the United States (figures for 1959 from the Pan American Sanitary Bureau).

Diarrhea can be equally devastating, often killing—in Guatemala—within 24 to 48 hours after it has begun. Well-fed children do not, in general, die with such promptitude from similar infections. Attempts to discover which particular bacteria are killing Guatemalan children afflicted with post-weaning diarrhea have often proved unsuccessful; no known bacterial pathogen can be isolated. The conclusion is that many lethal diarrheas represent a reaction to bacteria that would not ordinarily be pathogenic to well-fed children. It is not just the bacteria, it is not the lack of good food; it is the crippling effect of the two together that still prevents so many millions of weaned children from reaching their second birthday.

Crib Deaths

Abrupt child death is not a feature only of poor countries. The crib deaths of advanced countries can be equally sudden. Their principal characteristics are that they are totally unexpected and generally inexplicable. United States estimates vary from 10,000 to 20,000 crib deaths a year. Some coroners prefer to blame a virus rather than unknown causes for these deaths; consequently, according to various pathologists, the U.S. figure may be as high as 30,000. British estimates are somewhat lower, but still large. Some say such deaths occur 14 times in every 10,000 babies; one town (Hartlepool) gave a rate of 35 per 10,000 babies. Even taking the lower figure this means that 1,100 babies are suddenly and strangely dead every year in England and Wales alone.

When put to bed the children are either well or have seemingly trivial symptoms; within a few hours they are either dying or dead. In Hartlepool there have been, in recent years, 20 to 30 infants dying every year between the ages of 2 weeks and 2 years. About half of these die at home, indicating a certain suddenness, and about 80 percent of these sudden home deaths come into the crib-death category. The remaining 20 percent are caused by entirely explicable accidents or disease. Of the 80 percent that are classed as crib deaths a definite cause of death is not found for most of them even after extensive postmortem. The highest death rate is between the second and fourth months of life, and most occur in winter at night.

Of course, there are plenty of theories about these sudden deaths. In the past, bedclothes and pillows were often blamed or the breathing in of vomit. More recently, particularly as child deaths from other causes are decreasing and raising the proportion of crib deaths, greater attention has been paid to this problem of the suddenly dead child and the possible causes are listed as allergy to some of the proteins in cow's milk, virus infection, the effect of abnormal parathyroid glands, the result of a maternal illness during pregnancy, and even cold. The wintry increase in the crib-death rate made people think of cold, although there seems to be no correlation between cold nights and crib-death incidence. An engineer recently took the trouble to write to the *British Medical Journal* with the idea that the babies might even be suffocating themselves with their own expired air. With a deep crib, and no side ventilation, he thought, the resulting accumulation of carbon dioxide could be silently fatal. Whatever the cause or causes, the thousands of abrupt crib deaths in the night are a reminder that a baby's existence is fraught with danger even in the well-nurtured, well-doctored western world.

Battered Babies

Quite apart from the modernity of crib death, or at least of it as a classification, there is another title equally new—the battered-baby syndrome. Some babies are literally battered to death by one or other of their parents, and many more suffer violent physical pummeling and mutilation. The British are kind to dogs but cruel to children, says the old maxim, and there is still much truth to it. Britain's National Society for the Prevention of Cruelty to Children investigates cases involving tens of thousands of children annually (39,000 cases in 1965 involving over 100,000 children). Roughly half the cases are of child neglect and roughly 10 percent of actual ill-treatment. In 1965, according to the Home Office, 275 men and 265 women were found guilty in magistrates' courts, and seven men and three women in higher courts, of willfully assaulting, ill-treating, or neglecting children in a manner likely to cause them unnecessary suffering or injury to health. And, for one reason or another, due to various forms of family breakdown, 11,213 children in England and Wales were received into care by local authorities during that year. Although cruelty is old, and the NSPCC itself is a Victorian foundation, the battered-baby name was coined only a decade ago.

An American radiologist, Dr. John Caffey, gave the classical description of the new syndrome in the *British Journal of Radiology* in 1957. The article and its subsequent publicity and discussion brought many more cases to light—a one-year survey of all U.S. hospitals revealed 749 cases. This is a frequent development following new descriptions, but the battered-baby accounts are complicated by the fact that all such pummeling is caused by other human beings. Therefore both ethics and the law are involved. It is not a matter of describing, say, a case of measles caused by a virus but one of positive ill-treatment caused by one particular person against a small child.

Eight years after Caffey's article describing the battered-baby syndrome had been published, the first conviction in England was brought against a man for murdering his children in this fashion. The jury could not accept the man's statements that the two children had received their injuries accidentally. This case's details well exemplify both the problem *and* the difficulties of detection.

In December, 1963, a four-month-old girl, Susan, was found dead in her crib, having been out of sorts for a few days. No doctor had attended her during this final illness, and her death was reported to the coroner. A pathologist discovered many bruises, a 4½-in. skull fracture, and a ruptured liver. The father mentioned that Susan had struck her head on the crib three days before her death, and he said the other injuries

were possibly due to his attempts at artificial respiration. An open verdict
was returned. Ten months later, there was another death in the same
family. Michael, who would have been Susan's younger brother had he
and she survived, died at the age of five weeks. (Michael must have been
conceived within a very few days of Susan's death.) Upon examination
the infant, Michael, was found to have 19 bruises and a ruptured liver.
This time, the father said his knee had accidentally caught the baby in
the stomach. After this death there was a trial. On January 19, 1965,
Laurence Michael Dean, aged 19, was convicted at the Old Bailey of
the murders of Susan and Michael.

Before and after this case, it had become clear that similar deaths
have obviously not been recognized in their true colors. With many
accidental deaths happening naturally, with victims too young or injured
to speak for themselves, and with parents only too happy to distort the
truth, Laurence Dean must have had many other quite undetected
predecessors. Professor Keith Simpson, the forensic scientist, writing after
the Dean case, said it was hoped that doctors will "sharpen their perception of the battered baby syndrome" for the crime is probably
widespread and can only too easily escape detection.

In the United States, where the problem is also serious, there is much
controversy over reporting such incidents. Should the doctor, a neighbor,
or a suspicious passerby tell the authorities? Some states, such as
California, insist upon the reporting of all injuries inflicted by violence.
Others do not, and keep mandatory laws only for violence from, for
example, guns. By August, 1966, 41 states had made it mandatory to
report child abuse, and just six months later only the District of Columbia
had no child-abuse law.

One final complexity is that some children can look for all the world
like battered babies, in that they are covered with scars and bruises,
but they can be victims of inherent weakness in their connective tissue.
The result is a skin that is easily cut and bruised, as well as the possibility
of a totally false diagnosis.

Developmental Progress

Assuming survival, a baby's physical development is a bewildering
assortment of achievements. Parents may consider each stage to be an
eternity in itself—an endless drooling, a perpetual repetition of "mama,"
a ceaseless and apparently hopeless determination to crawl, to stand, to
use a spoon without spilling everything at the very moment of putting it
to the mouth, to achieve the impossible, to grow up. Childhood is in-
terminable—and yet each stage is over in a flash. It is a time of continual

change—and yet lasts for 18 years. It is the development of a mature human being, with sexual maturity suddenly and strangely arriving some two-thirds of the way along the long route to adulthood.

At birth a baby is 7½ lb. of potentiality, but little ability. He (or she) can suck, he can swallow, he can salivate, he can cry, he can smell, taste, and hear. He can yawn, hiccup, sneeze, cough, and stretch. If on his face, he brings his knees under his stomach. If held by his feet, his head hangs down. He has a very long way to go, despite being over a quarter of his adult height. He is also a bundle of reflexes, some of which are extremely short-lived and pay temporary lip service to his evolutionary past.

First Reflexes

THE MORO REFLEX. A rapid change in position can initiate it. The arms suddenly fling outward, with the hands open, and then come together as in an embrace. The reflex is harder to elicit after two months.

GRASP REFLEX. Stimulation of the palm leads to a closing and gripping of the hand. For two months this grip can be strong enough for the whole weight of the baby to be lifted in this fashion. The same reflex exists for the foot, but the foot cannot grip. After about two months the foot grasp (always hard to elicit) disappears, and the toes then tend to turn upward and spread apart when the sole is stroked. This so-called "Babinski reflex" then disappears in normal children at about two years, and is replaced by a turning downward of the toes. (Should the Babinski reflex persist, it is an indication of some defect in the nervous system.)

ROOTING REFLEX. Touching of the cheek or corner of the mouth elicits head turning in that direction. Later on, the lips will also protrude when this is done. Initially, the lower lip is lowered and the tongue moves to the touched side.

BLINK REFLEX. Stimulation of the eyelashes causes blinking, whether awake or asleep.

SNEEZING. Irritation up the nose or even bright light can cause sneezing.

WALKING REFLEX. A baby can be made to walk by holding him vertically with his feet on the ground, and then moving him forward. The co-ordination and rhythm are good, but this reflex has gone by six weeks.

TONIC-NECK REFLEX. When lying down, the face will be turned sideways. If the head is then turned to look the other way, either voluntarily or if forced, the legs and arms will also change position. Those flexed will straighten, and those straight will flex. The reflex may not be present at birth, but goes after three to six months.

DOLLS-EYE REFLEX. Eye movement lags behind when the head is rapidly rotated. This is a very short-lived reflex, lasting only a few days.

CROSSED-EXTENSION REFLEX. If one leg is stretched and the sole of the foot stroked, the other leg bends and then stretches. Usually, this reflex has gone after a month.

GALANT'S REFLEX. Stimulation of the trunk between ribs and hip on one side causes a curving in of the trunk on that side. This reflex disappears after the second month, but reappears much later.

The development of a child follows a well-worn path, but every child takes a unique route of its own along that path. Read any book about child growth, with its generalizations of progress by each birthday, and they fit a particular child only in a very general way. Such activities as watching a dangling toy, squealing with pleasure, blowing bubbles, disliking certain foods, seeing a mirror image, placing one brick upon another, jettisoning the carriage's contents repeatedly, saying "why?" no less infrequently—all these and countless others are manifestations of progress, but their timing is highly variable. They are milestones along the way from being a pathetic, toothless, hand-flailing collection of reflexes, crying without tears and excreting without restraint, into the adult human form, a creature more of reason and sense than of reflex and instinct.

Such progress is by no means even. Thomas Carlyle is alleged to have said, as his very first words, "What ails thee, Jock?" to a fellow one-year-old suffering vehemently in the next crib. He then spoke only in sentences. Other children, who grow into adults of equal stature, are content to drool and speak meaningless absurdities until deep into their childhood. The milestones are indeed passed, but without too much concern for the calendar. The importance of human development lies in what takes place, rather than when it takes place.

Nevertheless, a punctual and triumphal procession through all the myriad stages of childhood does indicate normality, even though all normal children are relatively forward in some respects, relatively backward in others. If a baby lying on its stomach can lift its head momentarily at four weeks, readily at six weeks, recurrently at eight weeks, if it can bear weight on its forearms at 12 weeks, and raise itself at 16 weeks so that it can look directly forward, then average development is occurring. At 16 weeks, rattle-shaking begins, at 20 weeks the deliberate grasping of objects, at 24 weeks the bottle is grasped, at 28 weeks cookies—and much else—are soddenly sucked. At 32 weeks unsupported sitting is possible and supported standing. At 36 weeks nearby furniture is suitable support. At 40 weeks there is strength enough for the child to pull itself into a standing position. At 44 weeks one leg can be lifted, at 48 weeks a crablike shuffling is effected, and at one year a walk is possible, supported with one hand or even, however short-lived, with no exterior aid whatever.

All such activity and aptitude indicates a correct development of various organs, for balance, muscle, bone, brain, and vision are each involved. The outward and visible signs of progress are merely manifestations of all the organic changes taking place within. Nothing is possible without suitable development of the appropriate organ, or organic systems. They come first.

Lungs

Before birth a baby has no air in its lungs. The alveoli—the countless bulblike endings of the lungs—are mostly collapsed. The major airways of the bronchial tree and the nose and mouth are full of liquid, the amniotic fluid of the uterus. At the first vital breath the alveoli open up, and air reaches the lungs. Amniotic fluid is then absorbed through the alveoli, and by the third day all the alveoli have expanded. The first breath can make use of about half the potential lung space. By the third day, breathing at 30 to 80 times a minute and taking in about 20 cc. of air per breath, all available lung space is being used. Premature babies breathe faster and take in less air per breath.

Within a year the respiratory rate has gone down to 20 to 40 per minute and each intake up to 48 cc. In two years, the intake is 90 cc., in three years 125 cc., in ten years 320 cc., and in 20 years 500 cc. Breathing rate is then 15 to 20 times a minute.

Brain

The brain more than doubles its weight in the first year after birth— about 12 oz. to about 32 oz. Growth continues to be rapid, and by the age of three a child has already accomplished three-quarters of its postnatal brain growth. By the age of seven, the brain is almost completed (42 oz.) and by 10 it is virtually adult-sized (45½ oz.). Less is known about the actual development of the brain with regard to nervous pathways, etc., but certainly such pathways do develop, at least until the age of 4. Physical changes to account for intellectual development after this time have not yet been discovered.

The brain and nervous system form one-tenth of the total body weight at birth. By the age of 5 they are one-twentieth, and by adulthood one-fiftieth of the total. Naturally, no amount of teaching, coaxing, or practice will cause a baby or child to perform some skilled act until the necessary mechanisms in the nervous system are mature.

Sleep

Sleep, more closely associated with the brain than any other organ, is extremely variable from child to child. Dr. Arnold Gesell, the expert in preschool development, has said sleep can be one of the easiest aspects of child life to deal with or one of the most difficult. A difficulty lies in the amount considered—by the child—to be sufficient. A study of 783 Minnesota children aged 2½ showed their average sleep to be 12.9 hours, but they ranged from 8 to 17 hours. Many a child needs no more sleep than the average adult, and many children can bounce back into wakefulness in a totally nonadult fashion. From a dormant lump of flesh wracked with weariness they can leap up again 30 minutes later ready for hours more of play—if their former sparring partners are not incapable.

The newborn baby cannot help going to sleep. Within a year, the process can be inhibited by the child. Between the ages of 9 and 21 months, going to sleep is often partnered by some fearful head-banging and bed-shaking, or gentle rocking and finger-sucking. Waking up often sets two- and three-year-olds crying. Boys are more restless in sleep than girls.

Skeleton

At first, the skeleton is connective tissue, like the soft fontanels of a baby's skull; then it is cartilage, and finally it is bone. The process is not complete until the age of 25.

The skull bones are soft at birth. During birth, the head is often molded or distorted, but such effects usually disappear in a few days. However, the skull is still soft, and molding can continue caused just by the weight of the head as it rests on the bedclothes. Remarkably, the flattened skulls of three to four months sort themselves out and become symmetrical by the first birthday (except in those for whom genetics and family characteristics have ordained a flat-sided head).

There are, in fact, six fontanels (or fontanelles) at birth, the anterior fontanel the most noticeable and longest lasting. The posterior fontanel is also in the midline at the top of the skull, but 2 in. farther back. Two others are on either side, roughly where the temples are, and the final two are even lower down the sides of the skull and farther back. The anterior fontanel, which pulses visibly and makes any baby seem even more fragile and vulnerable, actually enlarges for the first two months after birth. It then shrinks, and finally closes. The actual time of its closing is notably variable; anywhere between 4 and 26 months (in one survey of 1,677 babies).

The proportions of the skeleton itself change markedly. At birth, the neck is short, the shoulders are high, and the chest is round. Later on, particularly between the ages of three and ten, the neck lengthens as the shoulders are lowered, and the chest broadens and flattens as the ribs slope increasingly downward. Children's arms look normal long before the legs do. E. E. Price has written that "a very casual observation of the posture of normal children will refute the suggestion that the legs should be straight." Bowlegs and knock-knees are common among three-year-olds. About a fifth of all normal children at the age of three are knock-kneed to the extent of having 2 in. or more between their ankles when they are standing upright with knees together, and many a bowleg does not straighten until the child is four or five. Flat-footedness is also a normal feature of infancy, and many children's feet toe in to an astonishing degree. As with flattened skulls, it is quite remarkable how seemingly deformed a normal child can be.

It should never be forgotten that the upright human is a recent occurrence. It is particularly relevant to remember this in connection with skeletal development. For geological epochs, man's direct ancestors were four-footed creatures with a horizontal spine. The change to bipedalism had, and still has, far-reaching mechanical consequences. "The erect posture that helped man master the animal world also makes him vulnerable to low back pain" states an advertisement that draws attention to this point. Just because the body is muscle, bone, and tissue does not nullify the engineering consequences of upending the structure.

Admittedly, the human body has changed many of its characteristics and proportions since that switch to two-leggedness, but its entire ancestry lies in a four-legged past. The changes since then have been amendments, not creations; they have been modifications of an existing form. There has never been anything equivalent to a scrapping of the old design plus the sudden initiation of a brand-new one. The skeleton has had to continue its supporting role without a break, during and after the upending process. From being horizontal to vertical, from being four-legged to two-legged and two-armed, it has had to adapt itself and make use of a structure primarily suited for another purpose in another age.

Muscle

At six months, the volume occupied by muscle is very small, by bone very large, relative to an adult. In the first three years of life, muscle grows faster than bone. X-ray pictures show muscle widths increasing at twice the speed of bone width. By the age of three or four, the two rates of growth are similar, and bone and muscle continue to grow equally. Then, at adolescence, there is a sudden leap forward in bone and muscle growth.

Generally speaking, the increase in a certain skill involving a muscle means that the part of the system in nervous control of that muscle has developed sufficiently for the skill to be achieved.

Fat

"Nothing is known," Professor J. M. Tanner has written, "of the physiology of the wave of fat which threatens to engulf the one-year old." This wave starts at about the 34th week of pregnancy. Subcutaneous fat is then laid down for the first time, and the process continues to produce the bicycle-tire one-year-old. (Of course some babies never swell in this fashion and are presentably slim throughout their lives.) The fat inflation customarily recedes after the first birthday and continues to decrease until the age of 7. It then increases again, although slowly. At adolescence, the increase may stop for boys, and the total fat may even diminish. It will not be replaced until adolescence is over and the boys are out of their teens. The traditional picture for girls is that there may be a very slight halting in the deposit of fat, but it is nothing like the masculine decrease. By the time their adolescence is over, girls have the correct feminine curves, which are formed and softened by the fat lying beneath their skin. If not beauty, then shape is more than skin-deep.

It is not known whether the balloonlike one-year-olds are more likely to grow into fat people. If they are still plumper than average at the age of three they will probably be consistently fatter than most throughout their lives. A child's abdomen can be, and often is, quite naturally, vast. Apparently distended beyond all hope of retreat, mainly by a disproportionately large liver within, the bulbous shape does in fact recede eventually. By his fourth year the child's outline is no longer a caricature.

Heart

The fetal heartbeat is 130 to 160 a minute. The pulse rate of a newborn baby is, like its breathing, very fast. An average is 140 heartbeats per minute, falling to 130 at one month (although it may actually rise in the first few weeks), to 115 for a one-year-old, to 110 at two years, to 95 at 8, to 85 at 12, and to 82 at 18. The heartbeat of girls is consistently higher, by about five beats a minute, throughout this slowing down. Conversely, blood pressure steadily rises. The systolic pressure may only be 70 (mm. of mercury) at birth, and less in prematures. By six months it is about 93—although blood pressures are notoriously unwilling to be associated with averages. By the age of six the pressure is about 100, by ten it is 110, and by 16 it is 120. In other words, blood pressure is doubled from infancy to maturity while the heart rate is almost halved. In the meantime the heart itself has grown twelvefold.

The newborn heart, despite its 140 beats a minute and its pressure of 70 mm./Hg., is very small. It weighs 24 gm., i.e., less than an ounce. By one year it is 1.6 oz. By the age of 6 it weighs 3½ oz., by 14 it is 5½ oz., and by maturity 10 oz. to 11 oz.

Kidneys and Bladder

At birth, the kidneys are, of course, small (the pair weigh less than an ounce) but in fact they are large in relation to adult proportions. They grow rapidly after birth, doubling their weight in six months, tripling it after a year. By five years old, the two kidneys weigh over 4 oz., by adulthood 11 oz. (i.e., the same as the heart).

The bladder may even contain urine when a baby is born, but the production of urine is initially modest. Some babies do not produce any for at least 24 hours. Such urine as is produced helps to create the postnatal weight loss. By the end of the first week, urine secretion is anywhere between 50 cc. and 300 cc. every 24 hours, but for the bulk of the first year the daily output is about 450 cc. (or 4/5 pt.). This is remarkably high, bearing in mind the total daily water loss of an adult, which, through lungs, evaporation, and excretion, is only about four times as much. By the age of five, the daily urine output is about 1.3 pt.

Bladder control, a subject that has generated fervor, remedies, and advice for centuries, does not become voluntary until, on average, the age of 15 to 18 months. (Once again an average is a guide, not a rule. Voluntary control can be much earlier, and very much later.) Control can be simulated beforehand by skillful maternal anticipation, but the first true stage of voluntary control is a child's awareness of passing urine at the moment of its passing. Later, the alarm is given seconds before the actuality, still giving no time for action by others. Finally, by the second birthday—or later, or earlier—mothers are given time, and then the child itself will gradually take over.

The agony of enuresis (or lack of control) can be prolonged if the ability to sleep is stronger than the ability to control. Child-care books offer help, but the problem is immense. A British medical journal article on the treatment of enuresis estimated that 15 percent of boys and 10 percent of girls aged five were afflicted by it, and still 5 percent of children by the age of nine. Buzzers that operate as soon as urination starts are the currently favored devices for treatment because they alert the child into a contraction of his sphincter; but they are not always successful. Some alarms wake everyone except the soundly sleeping bed-wetter who is failing to make the necessary excursions. Happily, for the child's and the problem's sake, the age-old remedies for enuresis, like applying stinging nettles to the penis, or hedgehog flesh, or goat's claws, are no longer considered valid. (Old wives who dreamed up tales never seemed short of blood-curdling curative recipes.)

Spock

If human growth were solely a matter of increasing body size, of improving kidney performance, of increased lung volume, and so on, it would be a matter primarily of measurements; but it is not. It is the development of a human being, a unique individual brought up in a unique fashion by young parents who have a mixture of love, sense, impulse, and tradition to guide them. Consequently, extra guidance is regularly sought after, particularly in societies where tradition is less powerful or not universally known and accepted. Why does this one cry so much? Why does this one not cry enough? Children never conform. This one loves its playpen; this one finds it hell. He loves company; he hates it. He loves toys, cribs; he hates toys, cribs. He likes the new baby, new people; he loathes them. He eats well; he will never eat. He sleeps. He wakes. He vomits. He defecates. He is loving. He is fat. He is spoiled. He sucks his thumb. Is your child a problem child? ask the advertisers—confidently. Is he sensitive? Are you doing the best for him?

The triumph of Dr. Benjamin McLane Spock occurred because his guidance proved more satisfactory than anyone else's ever had, and countless other authors have tried and are trying to be equally helpful. Dr Spock's *Baby and Child Care* has sold more than 17 million copies in 145 printings of one edition. No other book first published in the United States has done so well. It has also been the largest-selling paperback published in the world. The sociologists now talk of a Spock-reared generation, and since the book came out in 1946, Spock babies are already having Spock babies of their own. Some mothers have a Spock in every room "for instant readiness," a practice he has deplored.

In a recent interview, the author explained that "the book set out very deliberately to counteract some of the rigidities of paediatric tradition, particularly in infant feeding. . . . It emphasized the importance of the great differences between individual babies, of the need for flexibility, and of the lack of necessity to worry constantly about spoiling. . . . I didn't want to encourage permissiveness. I wanted to relax rigidity." Many have charged that in Spock they will find whatever guidance they are looking for, since he talks both of parental rights and of the baby's rights. Undoubtedly, more than any other author, he has relaxed the previously powerful rigidity, the sort that could not accept that some 2½-year-olds need 17 hours sleep, some only eight. His huge sales emphasize a general acceptance of the facts that babies are indeed different, that parents are different, and that nothing is simple about the complex development of each new human being.

Swaddling

Despite today's talk of freedom for the child and a general discarding of old traditions, babies are still cared for traditionally. It can also be argued that we constantly acquire new traditions. Take swaddling. Today's western mother would throw up her hands at the idea of the baby's not being able to throw up his. Yet, swaddling, used in the Bethlehem stable and by the Jews, Greeks, and Romans long before, was employed in Britain until the end of the eighteenth century, and there is a lot to be said for it. Many Russians, Yugoslavs, Mexicans, Lapps, Japanese, and North American Indians still do it. The promoters of tight and restrictive envelopment for the child have various theories about its values, but there is general agreement that the child is quieter, and not just because of *force majeure,* with all the blanketing. Swaddling does create less fretful infants. Very recently, E. L. Lipton and his colleagues put this ancient practice to scientific test. They examined total swaddling, partial swaddling (with arms free), and total freedom. With cardiotachometers, strain gauges, and thermistors to measure the infants' general activity, they concluded that swaddling does indeed reduce heartbeat, breathing rate, and crying and that it increases sleep. One can imagine many Russians, Yugoslavs, Mexicans, Lapps, and all the rest, and pre-eighteenth-century Britons, aghast as today's infants thrash themselves so regularly into a flailing, unfettered fury.

Child Law

Putting today's attitude to the rights of a child to one side, there are also legal rights for children. Primarily, no child in England younger than eight can be guilty of any offense. Keith Simpson in his book

Forensic Medicine refers to a two-year-old who deliberately suffocated a four-month-old brother with a pillow, but the law considers all under eight incapable of forming sufficient malice aforethought to be guilty of a criminal act. Between 8 and 14, to quote again from the same source, "there is the presumption of innocence which is rebuttable except in respect of certain sexual crimes." All people over the age of 14 are subject to the criminal law. (Hanging, when it used to be carried out in Britain, was only for those over 18.) American law varies from state to state, but some idea of an equivalent can be gathered from New York's new penal code. Anyone younger than 16 "is not criminally responsible for conduct," but those between 7 and 16 are subject to juvenile delinquency proceedings. A juvenile delinquent is defined as one "who does any act which if done by an adult would constitute a crime," but in his case the act is only a misdemeanor, not a felony. An anomaly of the old penal code has been pointed out in the jurists' commentary on the new. Formerly, a 15-year-old could be tried for the crime of murder. This presumed his capability for premeditation, a capability presumed beyond him in, for instance, automobile theft.

The problem of overlaying used to be much more serious in the days of worse overcrowding, and there are laws to protect the infant. It is a criminal offense if anyone over 16 who is drunk and who shares a bed with a child under three causes that child to die of suffocation. In 1911 there were 1,157 British cases of death caused by overlaying. There were 255 in 1937, but 517 after the war in 1947, a time of great housing shortage. The numbers have since decreased.

Finally, anthroposophists and others believe that each human spirit has some kind of choice in deciding which parents will be blessed with its birth. The spirits who choose poor parents are certainly the most masochistic because poverty will weigh the balance against them in almost every society; in the poorest, it can mean the difference between food and no food. In the rich countries, poverty is still chronic, and even in welfare Britain the poor have a greater familiarity with the hazards of life. They have more abortions, more stillbirths, more premature babies, a higher perinatal and infant mortality, more congenital malformations of the brain and nervous system, more deaths from respiratory and other diseases, more accidents, more bed-wetting, more speech disorders, more delinquency, and as a final testament to their poverty, the children become smaller adults.

"Why should the wives of unskilled labourers give birth to children, who are ten times more likely to die of malformations of the central nervous system than are the children of professional men?" asked Dr. John Apley in a lecture at Britain's Institute of Child Health. Is there one reason, or many? Has it to do with the father's job, or the house, or the air at the poor end of town, or what? How does poverty strike? "Man is a multiple amphibian," wrote Aldous Huxley, "living in many worlds at once. There is his heredity, and his environment; his family, his community and his society, and there are multiple causes for the multiplicity of effects in the development of a human being." "There is one condition," wrote Cicely Williams, "that affects or has affected every single member of the population, and which in some regions is associated with a mortality rate of over 50 percent. This condition is childhood."

For those who survive all the vicissitudes of the early years, who acquire scars and learning and phobias and skill, there is yet another and more specific condition to which all are subject. Coming long before adulthood, the phenomenon of puberty makes its premature addition to the complexities of growing up.

◄§ 19 §►

Puberty

Puberty is not adolescence. It occurs as part of adolescence and marks the changes to sexual competence. Adolescence, the time of growing up, lasts much longer and embraces the whole decade from childhood to adulthood. It is important to the human species that sexual maturity is achieved long before intellectual maturity. It is also achieved before physical adulthood. Growth continues, particularly with the male, long after the reproduction system has proved itself capable. Moreover, the age of puberty is gradually becoming younger, for girls and boys, and teachers in British elementary schools state that in the last ten years, for the first time, they have had to provide facilities for menstruating pupils.

Because girls experience the dramatic incident of the first menstrual loss, much more is known about female puberty dates than male. The average age of girls on this all-important day now varies between 13 years, 2 months, and 13 years, 4 months, in Britain, according to region. In the United States, the average is just below 13 years. In hotter countries, despite a widespread belief possibly engendered by the frequency of early marriages, the age of puberty is no younger, and there is some evidence that it occurs later. The actual range from which the British averages are taken extends from 9 to 17 years, with just as many girls experiencing their first menstruation on either side of the average age. This average age is certainly lessening. In 1890, it was about 18 months later, with 15 being the age of menarche, of that first menstruation. The minimum school-leaving age then was 12. In 1970, it may be raised from 15 to 16. In other words, 80 years ago puberty used to occur, on average, three years after most girls had left school. Soon it may be occurring, on average, three years before the minimum school-leaving age. Therefore what used to be a minority problem is no longer so.

[270]

There is an argument that the reduction in pubertal age may only be an apparent reduction. The removal, for example, of extremely delayed pubertal dates, caused perhaps by disease or extreme malnutrition, can lower the average date; hence an apparent shrinking of the average age at which girls experience menarche as soon as those reasons for delay have been eliminated by improved living conditions and medicine. Despite this argument, which is equally applicable in many other average findings, it is generally realized that the pubertal age is going down, and is still going down at just the same rate. An enthusiast of extrapolation once calculated, bearing in mind today's rate of change, that Juliet, for example, would not have experienced menarche until well into her 20's, a decade or so after her disastrous affair with Romeo. Obviously, the current rate of change is exceptional. It is even suggested that the present age recession is merely a restoration of the situation that existed before the appalling living conditions brought about by an industrial revolution and squalid urbanization. At present, there is no evidence that the trend toward earlier development has slowed down, let alone stopped. Nevertheless, as Professor J. M. Tanner put it, "commonsense dictates a stop in the foreseeable future."

Although menarche arrives on a definite date, there is no such clear-cut delineation with other changes of female puberty. Moreover, that first menstruation does not indicate a sudden fertility. It usually precedes the ability to rear offspring by a year or more. The earliest menstrual cycles occur without an egg's being shed from the ovary.

The first sign of impending female puberty is customarily the appearance of breast buds between the ages of 9 and 11. Yet the breasts will not reach maturity for another eight years or so. An average age for nipple pigmentation is 12 to 13. Pubic hair starts growing at about 11 and is well developed by 14, but it may start earlier and end later. Axillary, or armpit, hair comes a year or two later, probably starting between 12 and 14. The date of menarche, important as it is, is bounded on both sides by all the other manifestations of sexual maturity. Nevertheless, it almost always comes after the peak of the height spurt, the rapid growth in stature that is another feature of the age of puberty. Both puberty and the growth spurt occur earlier in girls than boys. Consequently, girls of 12 to 15 are often taller and heavier than boys of the same age. Boys not only have their growth spurt later, but carry on growing for a longer period. It is all over for girls by 20 or 21, but boys frequently go on getting taller until 23 to 25. (This point is often neglected by official organizations like the Army. A recruit's height at 17 or 18 is assumed to be his height for life.)

Boys are just as variable in their puberty dates as girls, if not more so.

In any normal group of 13- to 14-year-olds some boys are sexually mature and others are virtually immature. Such disparity provides a fertile field for feelings of inadequacy or abnormality. Penis development, for example, starts on average at 13 and lasts for about two years; but its development can start at 11 or 14½, and it can end at 13½ or 17. So, some are completed and mature before others begin. Usually, the first sign of male puberty is an acceleration in the growth rate of the testes. They start their period of rapid development at about 12 and end it at about 16, but some boys start it at 10 while others end it at 18. Pubic hair begins to grow between 10 and 15 and will have completed the bulk of its growth anywhere between 14 and 18. Generally, axillary hair begins a couple of years after pubic hair has started, but it can even reverse the situation by starting its growth first.

A girl of 18 has lost the childish voice she had before puberty, but the pubertal voice change is more marked with boys. The male larynx starts its growth spurt at about the time the penis is completing its period of accelerated development. Customarily, voice change is gradual and may extend over several years. Sometimes, during the time of laryngeal growth, boys may croak haphazardly in speech as their voices break. However ungainly the noise, nothing is in fact disintegrating; it is uncertainty in muscular control over the growing larynx that causes the hoarse warbling. Male breasts are not totally unaffected by puberty. The areola, that buttonlike background to the actual nipple, may enlarge and darken. In a third or so of boys, a lump of tissue may actually form beneath the areola, only to recede at some later time in adolescence.

Finally, much to the disgust of almost every adolescent, the period is one of extreme susceptibility to skin trouble. Acne is a form of skin eruption that is definitely linked with the sexual changes of the adolescent. Eunuchs do not suffer but will do so if given sex hormones; they lose their acquired acne when the hormone treatment is stopped. For some reason, the sweat glands become frequently plugged during adolescence and are then subject to secondary infection—hence the acne. The complaint is so common that it is said to be physiologic rather than pathologic, normality rather than disease.

Although male puberty demonstrably starts with an enlargement of the testes, and the age of this acceleration is about 12 but may be 10, mature sperm are not produced until the age of 14 to 16. Even so, as with the female, sexual maturity is reached long before physical and physiological maturity of the body as a whole. This single fact is of enormous importance and influence in human society.

✒ 20 ☙

Size

How long should a man's legs be?
They ought to be long enough to reach the ground.
Abraham Lincoln

Having started off as a single united cell, each human being grows until he or she consists of 50 trillion cells. That first cell is larger than any of its subsequent offspring—until the manufacture of further ova. Ordinary cell size varies from 200 to 1,750 cubic micra—a micron is one-thousandth of a millimeter—but each human egg is about 1.4 million cubic micra. Most mammal eggs are about the same size, but there is a wide range in adult mammal size. The smallest is the shrew and the largest is the blue whale. Isaac Asimov, who calculates such things, has estimated that a man is 45,000 times as massive as a shrew, while a blue whale is 1,300 times as massive as a man. Whereas the largest whale weighs 130 tons, the largest land animal alive today is the seven-ton African elephant.

It is highly relevant to the size of any land creature that weight increases proportionately to the cube of the length, breadth, and height. If one land animal has twice the dimensions of another, it does not have twice the weight, or even four times the weight, but eight times the weight. Human beings exemplify this law of volume. A child of two is approximately half the length of an adult and has approximately half his chest and hip girth, and yet he weighs about one-eighth as much. (On his second birthday I measured my son. His height, chest, waist, neck, foot, hand, and arm-girth measurements were all almost exactly half mine, but his weight was less than 28 lb. At the time, with my chest 42 in. against his 20 in., my foot 11½ in. against his 5¾ in., I weighed 210 lb.) Martin Wells once took this problem of weight, gravity, and mass a little further by comparing possible planetary life. The bigger the planet, the smaller the animal. Earth visitors to Mercury should carry a grenade or two, he pointed out, and to Jupiter a fly swatter. In any case the science-fictional giant spiders on spindly legs just could not exist.

[273]

The law of volume to length also applies in the normal adult population. Discounting dwarfs and giants, almost all the human population can be included within a two-foot range. Virtually everyone has a stature between 4 ft., 7 in. and 6 ft., 7 in. Therefore, the tallest are less than 1½ times as tall as the shortest. No such similarity exists for weight. It frequently occurs that a normal man is considerably more than twice the weight of a normal girl. Men are, of course, customarily heavier than women, but the difference is small between men and women of equal height. American women 5 ft. tall are, on average, only 5 lb. lighter than 5-ft. men. The average difference is only 3 lb. if both are 5 ft., 4 in., only 4 lb. if both are 5 ft., 8 in., and only 6 lb. if both are 6 ft. Consequently, most of the traditional weight disparity between men and women is due not to broad shoulders and muscles, but to the height differential.

The average European and American male is about 5 ft., 8 in., and weights 168 lb. The average female is 5 ft., 3 in. and weighs 142 lb. But in one American survey (of 6,672 people) it was found that, although the averages held good, the weight of 90 percent of the males ranged between 126 and 217 lb., and 90 percent of the women ranged between 104 and 199 lb. Therefore, although the word "normal" customarily applies to the characteristics of 95 percent of a population, the normal weights—of 90 percent—of these people varied between 104 and 217 lb.

Men reach a maximum average weight of 172 lb. when middle-aged (between 35 and 54). By the age of 75, the average weight is 150 lb., presumably because many fat men have already died. Women reach a maximum average of 152 lb. when even deeper into middle age (between 55 and 64). By 75, this average has dropped to 138 lb.

Dwarfs and giants are almost always the result of some malfunction of the pituitary gland. This diminutive egg-shaped organ, a mere ½ in. long and attached by a stalk to the base of the brain, is primarily responsible for the abnormal lengths of the very short and the very tall. Oversecretion or undersecretion of this gland's growth both lead to spectacular results. In fact, these hormones are probably the most spectacular of all human hormones in their effects when excessive or inadequate.

There are two main types of pituitary dwarf. In one of them, the Lorain type, the hormone deficiency results in just a very small human being, well proportioned—although with the measurements more of a child than of an adult. He may or may not be sexually competent, he is probably intelligent and certainly not ugly. In the second type, called

Fröhlich's, the results of pituitary abnormality are very different. This fully grown dwarf is fat, sexually underdeveloped, often stupid, lethargic and sleepy, and less physically attractive than the Lorain type. Other forms of dwarfism are caused by thyroid inadequacy (which also leads to cretinism), certain forms of diabetes, and other abnormalities, including, of course, the lack of food of the right quantity or quality. Early rickets, causing a high forehead and great warping of the leg bones, can cause adult dwarfs. The United States estimates it has 7,000 midgets. The Little People of America is a society with members all under 4 ft., 10 in., and every year there is a midgets' meeting to further their interests. The most hopeful line of research is the prevention of pituitary dwarfism by administering growth hormones as soon as their lack has been detected.

Conversely, there are all the forms of giantism (or gigantism). Principally, these indicate an overproduction by the pituitary gland, but there is a great difference if this hypersecretion occurs before or after the normal growth time has ceased. If produced before the end of adolescence, the extra-growth hormones will cause extra growth, and the resulting giant may be up to 2 ft. taller than a normally tall man. Their proportions are normal, and they hardly ever seem to get taller than 8 ft., 6 in. If the pituitary overproduction occurs after adolescence, the hormone does not succeed in increasing stature but causes acromegaly (Greek for large extremities). The ungainly appearance of this disease is the result of the extra-growth hormone acting upon those parts of the skeleton still insufficiently mineralized and still capable of further growth. The main growth areas are the hands, feet, and jaw.

Both these forms of giantism draw attention to the big unknown associated with growth. Why is it that a human being stops growing? He or she is still continuing to produce the growth hormone, and yet something happens to inhibit its effects at a certain time. Sex hormones, arising in abundance a few years before the end of growth, do have an inhibiting effect, but castrated animals with a grossly depleted supply of sex hormones stop growing just as surely, although the stoppage may occur slightly later. Even though animals vary in size from shrews to the giant blue whale and even though their proportions vary throughout this size range, some having huge feet and small tails or vice versa, there is a steady consistency throughout the animal groups: the size of the pituitary gland almost always bears a direct arithmetical relationship to the size of the animal. The bigger the gland, the bigger the animal. This is interesting, but it still does not explain why a certain quantity of pituitary gland leads to a certain size of animal, particularly when added to the extra dilemma that growth stops even though growth hormone is still being produced.

❧ 21 ❧

Physical Ability

Fitness · Athletics · Somatotyping ·
Man vs. Woman · The Future

"The preservation of health is a duty."
Herbert Spencer

"Attention to health is the greatest hindrance to life."
Plato

"Early to rise and early to bed makes a man healthy, and wealthy, and dead."
James Thurber

"Keep fit," shouts the sergeant. *"Yes, fit to drop,"* mutter his men.

Fitness

"Fitness," according to Sir Adolphe Abrahams, Olympic medalist, then Olympic medical adviser, "means a satisfactory adjustment to one's environment." It therefore means being able to run away from predators. It also means being able to sit at an office desk for eight hours without running anywhere, or wanting to. And it means getting wet through or thoroughly exhausted without succumbing to the first infection that hits at a weakened body. There is evidence that poliomyelitis invasions leading to paralysis often follow periods of strenuous activity. The magnificent physiques, with muscles arching and flowing over a broad frame, do not win the longest races. Marathon men are short and thin. Weight lifters have short legs and short arms. World record-holders of track events often have awkward, gangling, and even misshapen bodies. Michelangelo's broad-shouldered, long-legged, and well-muscled David would not have had a hope in any race longer than a medium sprint. The quarter-mile would probably have been his running event.

[276]

Mankind's athletic abilities are a great complex of abilities. In each of them, he is completely outclassed by at least some members of the animal kingdom. Man can run, briefly, at 23 mph on a smooth surface. Practically every mammal as large or larger, including heavyweights like the rhino and hippo, can outrun him, rough surface or smooth. Man can run a mile at 15 mph. Most mammals of similar size or larger could do far better. Man can just get over a 7-ft. bar. A bush baby the size of his fist could easily beat him. And so could countless ungulates and kangaroos. Man can jump 27 ft. into a sandpit. Animals do not jump into sandpits, nor do they jump once and then fall over; but, if somehow persuaded, jumpers like the impala and the springbok could plainly do better. Man's great weakness is the possession of only two legs, for most of the time neither leg is exerting any thrust. A four-legged system is almost always faster. Man has sacrificed two legs to have arms instead. Parallel-bars gymnasts and trapezists can do wonders with them, but think of a brachiating gibbon hurtling through the treetops or watch a monkey do wonders with just one arm.

Man instead is the great all-arounder. He can swim a bit, climb a bit, run a bit, jump a bit. He can also exert himself for reasons of his own, without either chasing or being chased as a necessary stimulus. It has been claimed that a man can outwalk a horse. George Littlewood, for example, walked 531 miles in six days in 1882. Man is not much of a swimmer, in that sharks, whales, seals, and penguins must consider his top speed of 3½ knots virtually stationary. Nevertheless, he has plodded on to swim the English Channel both ways. He cannot fly, but he is trying to; the enthusiasts are pedaling their man-powered flying machines ever faster and higher.

Athletics

Athletic competitions do not in general test mankind's all-aroundness; they test individual skills. There are pentathlons and even decathlons, but most events do not set out to discover "athletic man." Such an athlete would make more sense, were he to compete in every event, as a physical test for mankind. Today's specialization demands a special type. The shortest 400-m. runner in the Olympics is taller, by and large, than the tallest marathon runner. The heaviest marathon runner is 10 lb. lighter than the lightest 400-m. runner. Men who jump high, put the shot, or throw the discus almost have to be taller than 6 ft. to win. The longer the race over 400 m., the shorter the man who, on average, wins it.

All of these human abilities are being improved all the while. The shot-put record has gone from 51 to 70 ft. since 1909, a 30-percent increase in slightly over half a century. The 17-ft. pole-vault height, the 7-ft. high jump, and the four-minute mile, all previously considered obstacles near the human limit, have all been overcome. Ten years after Roger Bannister had run his world-famous mile in 6/10 of a second less than four minutes, 44 other athletes had run it in less than those 240 seconds. In 60 years, the mile record has been changed 20 times. Without doubt, it will be changed again and again in the future. Long-range forecasters are predicting that 3 minutes, 30 seconds, is the ultimate time for mankind to run a mile, and 3 minutes, 41 seconds, will be achieved by the year 2000.

Why the steady improvement? First, the number of athletes is far greater. The 285 participants in the 1896 Olympics were drawn from 50,000 athletes in training. The 10,000 participants at Tokyo in 1964 were representing about 100 million possible competitors. And the games of 1988, so the forecasters say, will have the representatives of at least double that number. Much of this increased representation is an invasion of talent from the world's less developed continents. Almost all the athletes sent to the games now from Australasia, the New World, the Soviet Union, or western Europe are of European stock. Africans and Asians have been poorly represented.

In athletics, the races are not born equal; neither are they brought up in equal fashion, nor in equal climates or altitudes. The differing potentialities of black and brown will have much influence upon future records. Even now, the American Negroes do three times better in collecting Olympic medals than their proportion of the United States population would indicate (although the Negro desire to achieve eminence in at least the fields open to him is probably influential).

One wonders avidly what will happen when the Watusi of Africa enter the arena. With an average male height of 6 ft., 5 in., some close to 7 ft., and a national fondness for jumping, they should sweep the field. Jumps of 7 ft., 4 in., have been recorded under circumstances far from ideal. They do not use a carefully balanced bar, but a firm rope between two trees. The Masai, also of Africa, are phenomenal walkers. An American team recently visited Masailand with a fiendish "treadmill," whose moving platform increased its slope by one degree every minute. Two of the Africans immediately beat the record of an American champion who had trained on the device for six months. The Masai pulse rates had gone up, but not their respiratory rates. Professor Ernst Jokl, who ran for Germany and now teaches at the University of Kentucky, has written of the superior athletic abilities of the Negro and quotes work assessing the order of "athletic efficiency"—Negroes first, Asians second, Europeans third. Only now are the black and brown countries entering the competitive territory formerly reigned over so casually by the whites.

Better training methods and longer periods of training must also have improved abilities. For an example of lengthy training, there is Ron Hill, a British athlete, who ran 4,324 miles in 1963. Nearly all the top Australian and American swimmers have started their hard training by the age of 12 or so. Although instructors have plenty of theories concerning the production of an athlete's top performance on a certain day, there is a scarcity of fact about the physiological and anatomical changes that take place during the training. When muscles get bigger, are the muscle fibers becoming larger? Do the blood capillaries multiply in the training of a muscle? And do changes happen in the nervous control of muscular contraction? It is thought that the capillaries increase and the muscle fibers just get larger; but most training methods are empirical, based on experience and not on physiology.

At present, record-breaking occurs relentlessly, but the sprint records are already harder to beat than those of the longer races, partly because training cannot do much to improve the "oxygen debt." All the oxygen used up during a 100-yd. sprint is replaced after the race is over. Some sprinters do not even bother to breathe during their ten-second dash; some gasp only once. A mile runner has to breathe in half his oxygen needs for the race during the actual four minutes of the race. Consequently training can do more to improve the replacement. This partly accounts for the improvement of 15 seconds on the mile record since 1921. In that year, Charlie Paddock ran the 100 m. in 10.2 seconds; since then only .2 of a second has been knocked off his time. The limit of mankind's sprinting ability is obviously very near. (One wonders if tenths of a second will be sufficiently discriminating in the years to come, and whether hundredths will become the rule.)

The first scientific attempt on a reasonable scale to find out about athletic man was carried out during the Rome Olympics of 1960. Some measurements of stature had been made at earlier meetings, but only sketchily. Dr. J. M. Tanner's survey at Rome was the first comprehensive study of the physique of the Olympic athletes. He and his team measured, X-rayed, photographed, and classified all the male athletes they could get hold of, and then drew their conclusions. They also somatotyped them.

Somatotyping

Somatotyping is one system of identifying physique; it considers shape alone, not size. It is based upon the work of William Sheldon in 1940. He tried sorting out the photographs of 4,000 American college students, and finally surfaced with the opinion that there were three extremes of body shape. The three were then awkwardly called endomorphy, mesomorphy, and ectomorphy. The endomorph is essentially rounded, with a round head, a bulbous stomach, a heavy build, and a lot of fat; but he is not necessarily a fat man. When short of food, he does not shrink to become a mesomorph, let alone an ectomorph; he just becomes a starved endomorph. The mesomorph is the sculptor's model, with a large head, broad shoulders, a lot of muscle and bone, not much fat, relatively narrow hips. When fattened up, he does not become an endomorph; he is then a fat mesomorph, for these three characteristic shapes are basically quite distinct. The ectomorph is the thin one, all sharpness and angle, with spindly legs and spindly arms, narrow shoulders and still narrower hips, without much muscle or fat, but with a large skin area relative to his diminutive bulk. Even when fattened up, he is still the ectomorph.

Each one of us, according to Sheldon, has a bit of all three in his frame. Even the three extremes, the spherical man, the Hercules, and the thin one, are all assumed to have a small fraction of one another's characteristics. Sheldon judged the amount of each characteristic possessed by each of his 4,000 pictures, and he rated these amounts from 1 to 7. The three extremes, the round, the Hercules, and the thin, were called 7-1-1, 1-7-1, and 1-1-7. The 7 measured the predominant quality. The figure 1 measured a token possession of the other two qualities. A medium man, with an equal amount of all three, was labeled 4-4-4. A man with some shoulders (of the mesomorph) and some roundness (of the endomorph), but with much more of the narrow angularity of the ectomorph, was pronounced 3-3-5 or perhaps 2-2-6. Despite the apparent difficulty of this type of subjective assessment, different assessors do in fact produce nearly identical classifications of a group of men. Judgment is much assisted by the use of standard photographs of all the different somatotype ratings.

If these assessments are then plotted upon a triangular graph, with the three extremes at the three corners, the picture is soon dotted all over like the target of an erratic rifleman. College students, who are chosen for their brains and not for their shapes, produce just such a random picture. However, students at a military academy, who are chosen mainly for brains and partly for shape, produce a modified arrangement of dots, like a bad rifleman with a consistent fault. The academy does not accept either the extreme endomorphs or those with too much endomorphy about them. The Olympic athletes produce an even more compact picture. Of the 137 men measured by Dr. Tanner, all were in one-half of the graph. No one at Rome scored more than four out of seven for endomorphy. The men were either ectomorphs or mesomorphs, or combinations predominantly of these shapes.

In other words, however determined, the 5-4-1's, the 4-3-3's, the 3-2-6's of this world, and many more still plumper and rounder, are not to be encountered at an athletic meeting. They should forget the whole idea of being an Olympic star. Schoolboys and soldiers, told hoarsely that it is just "guts" or "drive" that wins races, should examine their shapes seriously, and then yield if they are blatantly on the wrong side of the somatotype graph for the event. They just were not born for it. All the shot-put men, for example, are found to have their ratings clustered together in a bunch near the 4-6-2 area. The 50-km. walkers are similarly grouped, but in the 2-4-4 area. These are thinner men, less powerful and even less endomorphic. The 2-4-4's do not lift weights, or put the shot, or throw the discus, javelin, or hammer. They run races and would run circles around any 4-6-2 who dared to compete with them.

Moving from shape to stature, it is equally wrong to be ambitious for the wrong event. No shot-putter measured at Rome was under 6 ft., 1 in. Their arms were long, while those of the discus men were longer still. The high jumpers were all over 6 ft. Part of the answer is straightforward mechanics; a shot will travel farther if put from a greater height, and a discus will be given more momentum if whirled around a wider circle. Another point is that runners shorten as the race lengthens. The average heights (to the nearest inch) for the 400 m., the 800-1,500 m., the 5,000-10,000 m. and the marathon were 6 ft., 1 in., 5 ft., 11 in., 5 ft., 8 in., and 5 ft., 7 in. The tallest marathon runner and the shortest 400-m. runner measured at Rome were both 5 ft., 10 in. The 100-m. race does not fit into this gradation. Its runners were, on average, 5 ft., 10 in.

Weight mimics height precisely. The longer the race, the lighter the runner, with the 100-m. race the exception. The 400-m. average weight was 169 lb., and the marathon average was 134 lb., with the heaviest marathon man 11 lb. lighter than the lightest 400-m. man. The 100-m. average was 161 lb. Weight was also an important distinguishing feature among those competing in the running and jumping events and the throwing events. Every runner, hurdler, jumper, and walker measured at Rome was lighter than the lightest discus, javelin, shot, or hammer man. Discounting one particularly lightweight javelin thrower, the lightest throwers were 29 lb. heavier than the heaviest of the running, jumping, and walking men. Men using their arms to win are thus in a quite different weight class from those who use their legs to win, who have to carry their bodies with them. The heaviest man of all was a shot-putter of 256 lb., who was 6 ft., 4 in., tall. The lightest man was a marathon runner of 116 lb. who was 5 ft., 5 in. With one 2.2 times the weight of the other and nearly a foot taller, they might almost be considered different species. As it is, they help to exemplify the physical specialization of the Olympic Games and to illustrate the impossibility of determining an optimum physique or "athletic man."

A notable exception to all this is the remarkable Peter Snell, of New Zealand. His physique would pigeonhole him in the 400-m. class. He would not even look out of place in the 100-m. lineup. However, he was successfully trained to run farther, to use his sprint shape to run longer races very rapidly. At Tokyo, he won both the 800 m. and the 1,500 m. He has also broken the world records for the 800 m., 880 yd., 1,000 m., and the mile. He is not just an exception, but an outstanding exception.

Age is extremely relevant. A generality is the longer the race, the older the men running it. The average age of the 100-m. runner at Rome was 23. By 400 m. it was 24. At 1,500 m. it was 25; at 5,000 m. 26; at 10,000 m. 27, 20-km. walk 28, marathon 30, and 50-km. walk nearly 31. The youngest marathon competitor (25½) was less than a year younger than the oldest 100-m. competitor. All track-and-field athletes are, reasonably enough, young men; the oldest was 36 (a 50-km. walker) and the youngest was 19 (a high jumper). In the games as a whole, taking into account all the events including those the ancient Greeks never thought of, the age distribution spans many decades. At Helsinki in 1952, the youngest competitor was 13 (a swimmer) and the oldest (a clay-pigeon shooter) was 66. The youngest winners are invariably among the swimmers.

Normally, altitude is considered of little consequence. Most large cities, and therefore the sites of most Olympic Games, are only marginally above sea level. The International Olympic Committee decided to hold the 1968 games 7,400 ft. above sea level, at Mexico City. "Foolish, astonishing, absurd," wrote Roger Bannister. Many current athletes also protested, mainly because lengthy acclimatization is considered necessary. At such a height, the sprinters have a good chance of beating existing world records. The long-distance runners have not a hope of it. The sprinter has all his oxygen requirement within his system before the race, and will therefore be able to benefit in speed from the 23-percent difference in the air density. It will be easier running through the thinner air. For races over 800 m. this benefit will be outweighed by the extra and disadvantageous task of getting oxygen.

In 1965 Dr. L. G. C. E. Pugh, a Himalayan mountaineer and medical physiologist, made an exploratory foray to Mexico's high-altitude stadium. On his return he stated flatly that athletes would not be permanently injured by the experience, but performance in all endurance events would inevitably be reduced. Others have calculated from his figures that times will deteriorate roughly in accordance with the logarithm of the distance. For the 800 m., this suggests 2.6 percent longer, for the 10,000 m. 15 percent longer. The British athletes who went with Dr. Pugh were about 6 percent slower over three miles, even after four weeks of acclimatization, but they had been 8 percent slower on arrival. When compared with sea-level races, such running would put them way behind the rest of the field. Any runner with a superior technique for acclimatization and with a good ability to mimic sea-level performance in a higher altitude will clearly romp home at Mexico City. Conversely, any future sprinter trying to win records at sea level will have difficulty emulating those achieved in Mexico's upper air.

The Pan American Games of 1955, also held at Mexico City, give a positive indication of the bad times to be expected in the 1968 Olympic Games. If the swimming times of 1955 are compared with the speeds of the Pan American Games four years later at Chicago, the differences are extremely conspicuous. The 100-m. free-style race for men was 1.4 seconds faster at the lower level of Chicago, the 400-m. race was 19.9 seconds faster, and the 1,500-m. race was 2 minutes, 10.8 seconds faster. The difference for women was greater still: 3.9 seconds in the 100-m. race and 36.5 seconds faster for the 400-m. race. (The women did not swim 1,500 m.)

Man vs. Woman

Women will never equal men in athletics. A sport like swimming makes for good comparisons. In those Pan American Games, the men's times at 7,400 ft. were still better than the women's times at sea level, but women are improving their times at a faster rate than men, and some of today's records for women are better than men's records for the year 1900. Although men are physically more proficient generally, women athletes are certainly more proficient than countless men. Mary Rand long-jumped over 22 ft. at Tokyo. The male record is over 27 ft., but how many normal males could hope to beat Mary Rand's leap, which was the length of four average-size men, lying head to toe?

Women have a lighter and weaker build than men. On average, their bodies have a smaller percentage weight of muscle and more fat. Their legs are shorter and less muscular. Their bones are lighter and smaller. Their total strength and their individual muscle strength is less. Their shoulders are narrower and they have a lower center of gravity, good for standing firm in the shot put, bad for jumping. They have a lower general metabolism, with the male-female ratio 141 to 100. They have a smaller heart in proportion to body size, and smaller lungs.

Many societies do not enter female competitors in the Olympic Games. Some societies enter them only in some of the events. The United States favors women in swimming, less in running. This unwritten taboo does not include the American Negro, and the U.S. Negro women excel in the track events. Every possible argument seems to have been lodged at some time against women athletes—they will look like men, bulge with muscle, fail to marry, fail to have children, overstrain themselves, die young. The Olympics authorities, who plainly think otherwise, stirred up many of these arguments when they recently reintroduced the 800-m. event for women. The Venus de Milo may have been the Greek ideal of womanhood, but undeniably, with or without arms, she would have fared badly on the track. Athletic women do not look like her. A French delegate to a recent sports medicine congress said, "Although the predominance of male characteristics in female athletes is not rare, sports are not the contributing cause. It is rather these inherent anatomical attributes of the female that enable her to excel in sports." She too, like the male, has to be the right shape and size to win.

The inherent attributes of sporting women have recently been questioned. At the European Athletics Championships, held at Budapest in 1966, certain female competitors were asked to submit to examination to prove their femininity. Although no one seems to have said so outright, they were being asked to prove that they were neither male nor some form of hermaphrodite, an intersex combining femininity with masculinity (see the chapter on inheritance). Not everyone is emphatically either man or woman, and certain forms of intersex combine a theoretically feminine sex with many virile characteristics. If these characteristics help them to beat less virile females, they have an unnatural advantage, and the Budapest examinations were conducted to rule out intersexual unfairness. Significantly, some competitors withdrew from the Budapest games rather than suffer the questions and tests.

The Future

What of the future? Presumably, the athletic population will grow until all of humanity has a chance of competing. By then, the actual numbers of humanity will also have grown. Drugs may or may not be able to step up performance. Jokl says bluntly that "medical science does not know of any substance whereby a well-trained athlete's performance can be improved pharmacologically." The British Association of Sport and Medicine, in issuing a ten-clause policy statement denouncing the doping of athletes, also mentioned that in its view there is no known chemical agent that will safely and effectively improve performance in healthy subjects. Perhaps the future will witness some positive eugenics in the world of sports. At present, mankind breeds locally, at random, and without much genetic regard for the next generation. No expert in animal husbandry would think of employing such a casual system. Maybe the future will be less casual.

The difference between a Kentucky Derby winner and a run-of-the-mill, random-bred horse is considerable. The casual horse is completely outclassed. So, perhaps the athletes of today will be outclassed by the thoroughbreds of tomorrow. Height, for example, is good for high jumping. Systematic breeding of tall men and tall women would guarantee exceptionally tall offspring in a generation or two. After all, the bullocks sold at Smithfield market doubled their weight in the eighteenth century alone, when fenced enclosures permitted controlled mating. What size could man become? What weight and height? And what then would be the distance that he could put the shot or throw a discus?

Today, he is like a medieval cow, with no selective breeding except the natural sort. Tomorrow, the methods of the breeder, developed by man for meatier cattle and faster horses, may even be applied by man to make himself more meaty (for weight lifting), or faster (for races), or more agile than today.

◄§ 22 ≈►

Old Age

What Is Senescence? · How Long Is Life? ·
Record Old Age · Animal Comparisons ·
Changes in the Old · Causes

Others merely live; I vegetate.
Palinurus, *The Unquiet Grave*

*The old . . . are positive about nothing; in all things they err by an
extreme moderation.*

Aristotle

*Men of age object too much, consult too long, adventure too little,
repent too soon and seldom drive business home to the full period, but
content themselves with a mediocrity of success.*

Francis Bacon

*It is a man's own fault, it is from want of use, if his mind grows torpid
in old age.*

Samuel Johnson

Everybody wishes to live a long time. Nobody wishes to be old.
Sir Adolphe Abrahams

*There's a certain moment in life when you realize you're born with a
deadly disease which is life.*

Jeanne Moreau

Every child is suddenly confronted one day with the disturbing fact
that he or she will eventually die. It is so worrying a realization and so
distasteful to accept before being even full grown that the confrontation
is often linked with a determination to be the first exception. Later on,
having progressed through childhood, having left adolescence for adulthood, and having met the first positive deteriorations associated with
senescence, the determination not to die becomes more confused and
confusing. At what age should one not die? At Peter Pan's? As Chekhov's

[286]

perpetual student? Or with the worries and wisdom of a John of Gaunt ("old Gaunt indeed, and gaunt in being old," as Shakespeare put it, died at 59)? Plainly, being too old is too late, for King Lear hated anyone "that would upon the rack of this tough world stretch him out longer." Like Tithonus, who asked for and got immortality but carelessly forgot to ask for eternal youth as well, the actual prospect of a perpetual existence is as forbidding as death, unless its gift were partnered by innumerable other assets.

In fact, the prospect is as remote as ever. Despite our morbid interest in the subject, next to nothing is known about the mechanism of the aging process, and medical science has done next to nothing to achieve any prolongation of the traditional life-span. (It has merely enabled more humans to experience more of this life-span.) Certainly no one knows whether or how we may be able to control our rate of aging. Put at its crudest, the advances of medicine are enabling more and more of us to achieve senility. The man who dies naturally today at a grand old age is experiencing a most unnatural form of death. Such an end out in the wild is highly improbable, because predators and the other hazards of existence tend to kill off creatures long before they have lived sufficiently to attain even a moderate degree of senility. Small birds can live for 20 to 30 years; but, since at least half of each small-bird population is killed off every year, the avian individuals who achieve anything approaching longevity must be very rare indeed.

What Is Senescence?

Senescence has various paradoxical definitions. First, it begins at birth. (Think of wound-healing. This process is most efficient at birth and declines thereafter.) Second, as Charles Minot was the first to point out, aging is faster in younger than in older animals. Third, as Sir Peter Medawar defined it, senescence merely "renders the individual progressively more likely to die from accidental causes of random incidence." Finally, even that word "accidental" can be disputed because all deaths are really accidental. No one dies solely from the burden of his years; no one dies from old age.

On this last point, a clinical pathologist once tried to recall from his experience any patient for whom the burden of years had become excessively burdensome and who had died solely for this reason. The nearest person to suit these requirements was a man of 94 whose life had seemed just to fade away. Unfortunately it had done nothing of the kind. At the autopsy, a lobar pneumonia of four days' standing was discovered. The pneumonia, not just those 94 years, had killed the old man.

More commonly, the cause of death in the very old is an assortment

of causes. One actual cause may have been the coup de grace, but there
were several others waiting in the wings with their own rapiers if the
first coup failed to kill. One case quoted is that of a woman of 83 who
died of hemorrhage due to a duodenal ulcer. She also had trouble with
her esophagus, a hiatus hernia, gallstones, a faulty colon and duodenum,
diseased lungs, a fatty heart, calcified valves, an atheromatous aorta,
an ovarian cyst, a tumor of the uterus, a soft spleen, arthritis of the
knees, and two clots on the brain. Her doctor knew of many of these
deficiencies, but had been presented with no evidence of the others.
In any case, he would have been hard put to predict the one lethal
ailment of her unfortunate assortment; but it was certainly not her
four score years and three that killed her by themselves.

However, there is one quality of mere years that does great damage
entirely on its own. Modern society, although permitting its politicians
and its judges to care for our well-being until they are steeped in old
age, likes to evict most of its citizens from their customary employment
at 60 or 65. Quite suddenly, men and women are discarded. They may
well have lost initiative, and be finding their work rather more arduous
than formerly; but on one day, a birthday, they suddenly lose high
office, or at least medium office, and find themselves with no office at all.
The daily rate of retirement in Britain is 1,000 persons. The daily rate
in the United States, on the evidence of new Social Security awards
made in the fiscal year ending June 30, 1967, is 2,255. (Of course, a
minority have had to stop work before retirement age. Of those who
are in the civil service at the age of 25, one-quarter will have retired or
died before reaching 60.) Among the mass of people, wrote V. S.
Pritchett, "retirement is often a fatal assault on the ego, and calls for
an unusual gift of courageous adjustment in the person concerned."
To be cast out in this fashion just because of a birthday, without reference to actual deterioration, can be both a physical as well as a mental
assault. Removed from routine, the change can be physically disastrous
—although once again, there is always a specific cause of death. No
death certificate can give "He had to retire" as a fatal cause any more
than it can give "Anno Domini"; but a sudden banishment from useful
activity can accelerate a person's decline with outstanding haste.

How Long Is Life?

One of the most remarkable biological statements in the Bible is that
the days of our years shall be three score years and ten. In those disease-
ridden days, with so much Biblical talk of plagues and afflictions,
leprosy and sores, pestilence and hunger, the life-span of man was

reckoned to be 70 years. Now, in these days of welfare and Medicare, with talk of antibiotics and injections, of surgery and immunization, the average life-span is still 70 years. In the United States, it was 70.2 years in 1961, and 69.9 years in 1964. Both averages are as near the classical three score and ten as to make no difference.

Whereas the newborn Hebrew delivered in Judea had a slim chance of attaining his rightful old age, the newborn American has a chance better than 50-50. The Biblical span indicates man's potentiality; today's span indicates man's actual and average lifetime. Modern chances are better than 50-50 because so many infants die; one death at the age of one brings the average span rocketing down.

Recent figures for England and Wales show the life expectancy for a boy at birth to be 68 years, for a girl to be 73.9 years. Recent United States figures are more complicated (and more revealing) by splitting the races as well as the sexes. It is particularly interesting that the advantage of being white is, from the longevity point of view, about the same as the advantage of being female. White males have a life-span similar to nonwhite females, but the difference in expected span at birth between white females and nonwhite males is 13½ years.

Age	White males	White females	Nonwhite males	Nonwhite females
Birth	67.5	74.4	60.9	66.5
20	50.1	56.4	45.1	50.0
48	24.7	30.0	22.1	25.7
65	12.8	16.0	12.2	15.0

In one sense, it might appear from such a chart that mankind is immortal. The American white male, for example, can expect to exist for 67.5 years at birth. By 20 he can expect a total of 70.1 years. By 48, he can hope for 72.7 years, and by 65 for 77.8 years. By 77.8 years, he can perhaps expect, on average, to reach 80, and by 80 he can expect another couple of years. It is like the argument that the hare never catches the tortoise, because the tortoise has always advanced slightly during the time taken by the hare to reach the tortoise's last position. However, despite the average prospect of new life at each new birthday, the process is not infinite. All men will die in time. The hare will always reach the tortoise. The system has never been known to fail.

Although the Bible may speak of those 70 rightful years, and the modern statistician now speaks of them as the 70 average years, it took a long time for the average to creep up to the Biblical right. It has been reckoned (although with slender evidence) that life expectancy in Britain back in the Iron Age was 18. Later estimates, of increasing validity, indicate expectancies of 22 (2,000 years ago), 33 (the Middle Ages), 33.5 (1687–91), 35.5 (1789), 40.9 (1836–54), 49.2 (1900–02), and 66.8 (1947). Nowadays, people in large areas of countries like India have a better life expectancy than people in Britain had 100 years ago.

The poorer countries are still pushing up their average age of death, but the richer countries have already met a kind of limit. According to the Metropolitan Life Insurance Company, an American male of 65 in 1950 could have hoped for 12.8 more years. By 1962, a man of 65 could hope for 12.9 more years, marking a mere five-week improvement in longevity in a dozen years. American women, on the other hand, have gone marching on. In 1950, the U.S. female of 65 could have hoped for 15 more years, in 1962 she could expect 16 years. In those dozen years she had gained a dozen months of life.

The steady pushing back of the time for dying means a steady rise in the numbers of old people. There are 6.4 million people over the age of 65 in Britain, a sizable number not much less than the population of Chicago. By 1967, there were 18 million in the United States—equal to the populations of the New York and Los Angeles areas combined. By 1981 there will be 7.5 million old people in England and Wales, or 13 percent of the population, or 87,000 more each year. Should the medical profession reach its goal, said Sir George Pickering in 1966, "those with senile brains and senile behaviour will form an ever-increasing fraction of the inhabitants of the Earth"; he thought it a "terrifying prospect." Dr. Alex Comfort, the gerontologist, admits an increasing preponderance of old people and does not expect any radical change in the immediate future. "The best we can hope for from medicine and hygiene *alone* is that the average life-span will increasingly become 75–80 years"; the future will of course bring "palliative possibilities . . . but there is no graft, hormone or other preparation known at present which is capable of producing more than a limited reversal of a very few senile changes in human beings."

Today, even though there are relatively fewer old people than there will be, the problem of the aged is enormous. Of the 6.4 million British people over 65 at least half depend wholly or primarily on cash and other benefits from the government. Four percent, or 300,000, live in institutions; and severe incapacities, such as bad feet, the need for delivered meals, bad eyesight, bad living conditions, or even a totally bedridden condition, affect hundreds of thousands of others. The old are not only retiring earlier and living longer, but they have fewer children and a smaller chance of unmarried daughters to care for them.

Should the old be integrated or segregated in society? Peter Townsend, professor of sociology at Essex, says that "no industrial society has yet tackled imaginatively or consistently the problems produced by a growing number of old people." Both gerontology (the study of age) and geriatrics (care of the elderly) are in need of greater support. Dr. Patricia Lindop disclosed in 1964 that only 20 people in Britain were engaged in full-time research on aging, and there was only one professional chair on the subject.

Record Old Age

Record old age is a subject for extreme fantasy. Stories come out of Russia, for example, with tall tales about longevity. Georgia, with its minute population, has been alleged to include 2,000 centenarians now living. More than one grain of salt is necessary in assessing extravagant claims, particularly as most long lives have their infantile origins back in an illiterate and unrecorded past. In 1966, the Russians reported the death of Shirali Mislimov, allegedly aged 160, said to have been the oldest resident of the Soviet Union and to have fathered children until 1936; but one wonders about the recording of his peasant birth back in czarist Russia of 1806.

It is more likely that 115 is the authentic limit for mankind, and at least two people are generally considered to have reached this age. Ages beyond 110 are likewise extremely rare, but centenarians are almost common. Buckingham Palace sends telegrams on significantly ancient birthdays, notably the 100th, if reliably informed of the event. Nearly 300 such telegrams were dispatched in 1958, over 300 in 1959, 399 in 1960. However, the telegrams do not just record the 100th birthday, and they have to rely upon individual informants; therefore the numbers are not too reliable.

The figures of Britain's Registrar-General show that about 20 men die every year who are over 100, and about 100 women. Women traditionally survive longer than men, but the ancient stories from Georgia in the U.S.S.R. reverse the situation; it is the Georgian men who thrive deep into a second century, while their women scarcely reach their first. The better survival of men used to be the feature also of primitive communities. Presumably, the hazards of obstetrics were greater than the hazards of war, despite the additional and overall male weakness. The chances of anyone's putting 100 candles on a cake is about 12,500:1 against for men and 2,500:1 against for women.

Incidentally, it was during World War II that the claims of oldest inhabitants quietly became verifiable. Birth certification in Britain started in 1837. There had been parish registers for centuries before (back to 1538), but in 1943 the first woman died who was not only a centenarian (she was 106) but the possessor of a birth certificate.

In 1945, the first such man died—at 105. Apart from a lapse in 1948 when a woman died—at 115, having allegedly been born four years before certificates were introduced—current claims for longevity are now made in Britain in association with birth certificates.

Animal Comparisons

Mankind may not think so, as old age and death hurtle along with cometlike rapidity, but the human species is nearly the oldest-living species in the entire animal kingdom. Man certainly lives longer than any other mammal. Alex Comfort, and S. S. Flower before him, have sifted through zoological records, scientific literature, and countless claims to select the most ancient creatures. Among mammals, the Indian elephant may reach a 60th or 70th birthday, but otherwise only an occasional horse, hippopotamus, rhinoceros, and ass either pass or nudge up toward a 50th birthday. The authentic bird record is held by an eagle owl of 68, but some extravagant claims of greater antiquity have been made for cockatoos, vultures, geese, and parrots.

Certain reptiles undoubtedly beat mankind, notably many tortoises. Some are known to have reached 100 and still be going strong. One or two have reached 150. Crocodiles do less well, 50 being very old for them. Snakes may also live long, but they do less well in zoos and barely reach 30 years. The amphibia have a reputation for longevity, with some toads living to 36 and even frogs well into their teens; but no amphibian reaches man's age. Fish have an even greater reputation, and long legends are told about carp. Without doubt, some sturgeons have reached 70 and 80, and a 10-ft. halibut was once landed at Grimsby whose age—as shown by scale examination—was over 60. The carp stories may well be true, but no fish has yet been convincing, following scientific scrutiny, that it has lived longer than a long-lived human. No invertebrates, despite some languid mollusks, have yet proved a life of more than two or three decades; although, once again, age assessment is difficult.

The conclusion, whatever men may think, is that man is a very long-lived animal, beaten into first place emphatically by the tortoises and possibly by a few other contenders. Womankind does even better than mankind, although even she cannot compete with the tortoises.

Changes in the Old

"Fear old age for it does not come alone," said Plato. It certainly does not. Old people are a plethora of change. They have lost an inch of stature. Their hair has thinned from their heads, yet it may sprout thickly from nose and ears. Exposed skin, dry and wrinkled, may be blotchily pigmented. There are often dark flat warts on the body, and more frequently there are small, red spots on the abdomen. Limbs may shake. The jaw or head may also quiver, and walking may change from a stride into a shuffle. Hands and feet, in particular, may get cold.

Internally, the brain becomes lighter as it atrophies, while the grooves of its sulci become deeper and wider. Less oxygen is used by the brain. The ability to feel heat, cold, and pain may all lessen. Body temperature cools, and a thermometer in the mouth of very old men may read 2°F. less than normal. (Therefore, normal temperatures may indicate fever.) Certainly the sense of smell deteriorates as the olfactory fibers diminish; even the pungency of coal gas is undetectable by many of the old. The lungs shrink, the joints stiffen, the reflexes decrease, the pupils become lazy, the liver lessens its bulk, and the basal metabolic rate gradually falls—to about 12 percent of normal. Teeth are lost, and both jaws shrink, although the chin tends to jut out. Hearing suffers, characteristically for the higher tones, and so does vision. For females, the uterus and ovary may atrophy into minute fragments of tissue, while for males, the prostate may enlarge from chestnut-size to apple-size. Bodily composition varies between the young and the old. Between the 25th and the 70th birthdays, water content goes down from 61 to 53 percent, cell solids down from 19 to 12 percent, bone mineral from 6 to 5 percent, but fat goes up from 14 to 30 percent. Consequently, an old man, priding himself upon no weight increase during his middle-aged years, may merely have exchanged his youthful muscle for elderly fat.

Incontinence of the bladder is frequent, but incontinence of the feces is rare although constipation is a common complaint, possibly because the intake of food and drink by the old is much reduced. Cramp is common. The pulse rate normally decreases with age, but can rise again with the extremely old; the range of some pensioners in London was found to vary from 44 to 108 times a minute. Hearts can shrink or enlarge with age, and some hearts of people over 80 can be almost three times the weight of others. Blood pressure rises with age. The speech of an old person becomes not only tremulous but metallic. And, of course, there are all the chronic mental disorders, like senile dementia. Trevor Howell, in *A Student's Guide to Geriatrics* (1963), gives a disturbing list of ten questions to check a patient's degree of orientation and intellectual impairment. The disturbing point is their simplicity, for they include: where are you now, what year is it, what is your birthday and how old are you. Finally, to quote Marjory Warren, "Existence to the old often becomes a pathetic attempt to kill time, before time at last kills them."

Causes

What indeed causes aging? Whatever does happen is happening right from the start of birth, and it never fails to happen. As a system or mechanism or occurrence, it is perfection—it always succeeds. No one has ever failed to die. Progeria, the condition of premature aging, may first show its severe symptoms when children are starting school, and the victims die on average at 16, often from coronary thrombosis. The opposite condition, that of Dorian Gray or Rip Van Winkle, does not arise. Those who die very old look very old and are physiologically very old. The process of aging is unfailingly effective. It is not difficult to assess a person's age, possibly to within a year or two, certainly to within a decade; the passing of time produces too many clues for us to work on.

There are three main theories about the controlling factors of our rate of aging. The first concerns loss, the loss of too many cells or the loss of irreplaceable parts. Brain cells, for example, undoubtedly die off in their hundreds of thousands and they cannot be manufactured again after a very infantile stage in each human life. Some get killed, as by natural radiation, and some just die, but none is ever replaced. Unfortunately for this theory, although large parts of the brain or other organs can either be heavily damaged or partly lost, there is no effect on the rate of aging. It neither speeds up nor slows down in consequence. Moreover, animals have totally different aging rates but suffer cell destruction at similar speeds. Mere cell destruction cannot be the sole determinant.

The second theory concerns mutations. A dividing cell does not always divide correctly and provide two cells quite as satisfactory in every way as their single predecessor. All sorts of errors can creep in, aided and abetted by natural radiation. There is a long list of agents that have been blamed for causing cancer, for causing the berserk behavior of excessive proliferation; and there is just as long a list, or longer, of agents that could cause faulty replication of cells in cell division.*

This mutational theory does demand a fearful number of mutations for them to be so powerfully effective throughout a person's life. Perhaps the changes do not just put cells out of commission, but make the mutated cells harmful. Or perhaps the small loss of mutated cells has a more powerful effect with certain types of cell, such as the

---

* Alex Comfort has pointed out that any theory linked to cancer research is a sure grant-winner and therefore has something to be said for it. This is a reminder of two other faintly sick scientific aphorisms: "Cancer is God's gift to biologists" and "There are more people living off cancer than dying from it."

endocrine glands or some of the constituents of blood. It does not seem
—at present—as if mere changes of this kind are sufficient to be the sole
determinant of the aging process. Nevertheless, there was an interesting
announcement recently that 10 percent of the cells of very old women
had lost an X chromosome. The second theory may well prove to be the
correct theory, but only when the world's increasing number of gerontolo-
gists come up with some equally enlightening information as that 10-per-
cent loss of a whole chromosome.

A third theory, now falling swiftly out of favor, is concerned with
the accumulation of unwanted chemicals. It could perhaps be that
some vital substances can be replaced only at cell division, and a
general decline in the rate of cell division could lead either to a lack
of needed substances or to an excess of unwanted ones. The theory is
gaining less support these days partly because it assumes too static
a state of affairs in the living cell, whereas cells are dynamic systems.
Another point against this is that aging occurs also in animals that
continue growth and a generalized cell division throughout life. Mankind stops growing, but fish, for instance, grow and grow—until death.
In the meantime, they too have aged.

Spare parts and the storage of human tissue do not really influence
our aging. Some of us are uneven, in that one part needs replacement
prematurely; but aging is an increase both in the number and variety
of faults. Like an old car, the human body always has another part waiting to fail.

I shall give the conclusion to Alex Comfort. "To the question 'Can the
effective human life-span be prolonged artificially?' the most probable
answer . . . would appear to be 'yes.' To the further question 'By what
factor?' no meaningful answer can be given until we know more of the
nature of the predominant processes which determine human senescence."

⤳ *2 3* ⤳

Death

When Is Death? · The Signs of Death · Causes · Secrecy

> *Qu'est ce que la vie? La vie, c'est la mort.*
> Claude Bernard

> *Who dies and, dying, does not protest his death, he has known a true old age.*
> Lao-tzu

> *The death which a man suffers by one sudden means or another is usually infinitely more comfortable for him than his birth was for his mother.*
> William Joyce (Lord Haw-Haw, who was shot in 1946
by a firing squad in the Tower of London)

> *Die, my dear doctor; that's the last thing I shall do.*
> Lord Palmerston, on his deathbed

> *Lazy beggar would never work when he was alive. He can do summat now he's dead.*
> A Lancashire widow (quoted by J. B. Priestley)
who had put her husband's ashes in an eggtimer

Once again, there is paradox. Everyone knows he or she will die; but the medical profession does not believe that most people are aware of the fact when they are actually dying. Similarly, the more proficient mankind becomes at controlling death and prolonging life, the harder it is for anyone to state when death has definitely occurred.

For centuries there was no problem. Death occurred when movement ceased, when breathing stopped, and when no heartbeat could be detected for two to three minutes. Balancing a glass of water on the chest or holding a mirror or a feather over the lips were immemorial aids. Nowadays, there is no such simplicity. For one thing, it is now known there are various forms of suspended animation, caused perhaps by electrocution, by drowning, or by drugs. The signs of life can be absent,

[296]

but they can then reappear. It is not without precedent for a mortuary attendant to observe that one of his charges has plainly arrived prematurely.

When Is Death?

However, the old-fashioned simplicity is rendered problematic by today's inability to define death. Respiration and circulation can be maintained mechanically, and they frequently are during operations; but this is different from the mechanical maintenance of lifeless lives, those for whom no hope exists, those which are merely technical prolongations of the biological process. As one American neurosurgeon put it, "the look of life is maintained in the face of death." But asked another neurologist, "when do you pull the plug out, and make the expensive equipment available to someone who might live?"

Although it was the departure of the human spirit that doctors have been habitually checking by listening for signs of heartbeat, it is only recently that attention has been paid to the brain at death. Since the brain is more the spirit's home than the heart, the absence of life within the brain has recently been regarded as a surer sign of death. An electro-encephalogram, or EEG, can record the constant electrical flickering of a living brain; it can also record the absence of any such activity. When the EEG has produced a flat tracing for quite a time, when the patient has no reflexes, no heartbeat, no respiration of his own—only the pumping of the machine—then is the time, by today's rulings, for the machine to be stopped, for the plug to be pulled out, for death.

Nevertheless, there is still dispute about the length of time for that flat tracing. It is possible, after some forms of poisoning or extreme cold, for a victim to have a flat EEG showing no impulses for some hours and then for full recovery to follow. A full day with a flat EEG tracing is generally reckoned as a sure sign of death, although different cases require differing assessments.

In May, 1966, the French took a positive lead in establishing this point. The National Academy of Medicine in Paris decided that a man may be ruled dead if it can be proved, despite the artificial beating of his heart, that his brain will never again be able to resume control of his vital functions. The principal objects of the French recommendation were partly to clarify the situation and partly to permit organ transplantation to be carried out more effectively. Such organs can save other men's lives; but they cannot do so if they have been permitted to deteriorate grossly during the prolonged death of their original possessor. A failing circulation will cause a failing oxygen supply to those organs; hence their deterioration. This need not be the case if the body is pronounced dead, due to the lack of EEG readings, and then maintained under conditions of artificial survival as a storehouse of living organs; but for how long should the brain and the EEG be quiet? For 48 hours or less, said Professor de Gaudart d'Allaines, head of the commission presenting the report that was later adopted by the French Academy.

France is the first country to have faced death in this fashion, and to have regarded the situation squarely by taking action at a national level.

The Signs of Death

The skin becomes pale and loses its elasticity. There are changes in the eye, such as the lack of circulation in the blood vessels of the retina. (Some ophthalmic experts say they can see the red cells roll to a stop.) Muscles lose their tone, and the body permanently flattens in those areas that are taking the weight. Breathing stops, although it can confusingly start again after a lengthy pause. The pulse is undetectable and must be so for at least five minutes, although survival after longer pulseless periods is not uncommon. (Film characters, who rush up with their own pulses beating wildly and, after feeling a second or two beneath the coat of some alleged victim, pronounce him definitely dead, are being outstandingly hasty and brilliant in their assessment.)

Later changes are yet more definite. The body cools, and at a reasonably constant rate, i.e., about 2.5° F. per hour for the first six hours, if clothed and under temperate conditions. Later cooling is slower, perhaps 1.5° F. per hour after six hours. After 12 hours, the body will feel cold, and after another 12 it will—probably—have reached ambient temperature. A naked body will cool about 1½ times as fast as a clothed one, and a body immersed in water will cool about twice as fast. Due to lack of blood circulation there will be pale areas where the body has been resting, and ruddy areas all around them, into which the blood has drained.

Rigor mortis is caused by a stiffening of muscle fibers. Its time of arrival is highly variable, but it can be seen first in the face some four to seven hours after death. A few hours later, it has affected all parts of the body. Then, having lasted for perhaps half a day, it retreats very gradually, leaving the body flaccid once again. Within 36 hours this cycle of stiffness is probably completed, although rigor mortis is casual about its timing. For instance, what is called a cadaveric spasm, certainly a kind of stiffness, can occur at the very moment of death.

Decomposition, the final and most positive sign of death, causes a green tinge on the abdominal skin after about 48 hours in a mild climate. The bacteria responsible for putrefaction come mostly from the intestines. As newborn infants are relatively sterile, having no large bacterial population within their digestive system, they frequently mummify rather than putrefy. Dry hot air can do the same for children and adults. Putrefaction is also prevented to a large extent in those individuals whose bodies have been immersed in peat bogs after death. Corpses many centuries old discovered in Denmark, Germany, and the Netherlands have been preserved in a remarkably lifelike fashion. Apart from such exceptions as embalming* and incineration, the putrefying bacteria do their work with a distasteful and effective greed, though their effectiveness is hindered by burial or immersion in water. They achieve their biological entropy most surely between 70° F. and 100° F. Below 50° F., putrefaction is markedly slow or nonexistent, and above 100° F. some form of drying or mummification is likely.

Causes

In Britain, by law, a physician does not have to see a body after death, and only about two-thirds of all the dying are seen after their deaths by a doctor. Nevertheless, a death certificate has to be completed promptly by the physician who has been in attendance upon the dead man, stating the cause of death. The Registrar-General has certain rulings about the completion of these certificates, and about likely causes. No doctor can merely write: "He got sick and died."† By no means are death certificates always accurate about the cause of death. Recent surveys of presumed causes before and after necropsy have indicated great fallibility. Death certificates "are not worth the paper they are written on" according to one British professor, and yet great faith is pinned on them whenever they are consulted for mortality statistics. Perhaps necropsies should be more common, as in Scandinavia. Whenever British deaths are violent, suspicious, or unexplained, the problem of investigation is handed over to the coroner (whose other remaining tasks concern deaths in prison, treasure trove, and the removal of corpses from Britain).

The British are publicly ambivalent about causes. Everyone asks, but the facts are rarely printed. Newspapers occasionally mention the

---

* For an excellent account of the three methods of Egyptian embalming see the report by Herodotus in Jurgen Thorwald's *Science and Secrets of Early Medicine.*
† The *Nebraska State Medical Journal* recently reprinted some causes of death from earlier days: "Went to bed feeling well, but woke up dead." "Don't know. Died without the aid of a physician." "Had never been fatally ill before."

cause in their obituaries, but neither the *British Medical Journal* nor *The Lancet* does so. American newspapers are more forthright. *Time* magazine makes a point of stating the cause of death. However, the American ballyhoo of what to do about the corpse* is certainly not mirrored in the British Isles, where the subject is more hurriedly and less expensively hidden. Many in Britain today achieve their own ends without having seen the dead body of a single other human being. The British are also making certain that corpses are more speedily disposed of. By 1966, the cremation figure was 47 percent of the total, and increasing by 2 percent a year. Orthodox Jews still do not cremate, but the Roman Catholic Church has recently been relaxing its objections, and probably half of the total British dead are now cremated.

For every 1,000 people alive in Britain at the start of a year these days, 10 to 12 will die during that year. The figures for England and Wales indicate some 560,000 deaths a year, or 1,570 deaths a day. The latest published figure of the National Center for Health Statistics in the United States is 1,798,051 deaths in 1964. Despite infant mortality, accidents, and all human ailments, over half these deaths are caused by heart disease, cancer, or stroke.

Figures for the extreme past are notoriously unreliable; everyone seemed to die from the ague, flux, fever, or the vapors. However, it is only necessary to go back to 1900, and well within the history of reliable records, to find a totally different pattern in the causes of deaths. There is a distressing simplicity about the change. Practically every form of dying has become less common than the three modern and triumphant horsemen—cancer, heart disease, and stroke. In 1900 cancer killed 4 percent, and sixty years later 18 percent; heart disease then killed 12.8 percent and the figure rose to 16.9 percent; vascular lesions affecting the central nervous system—strokes—rose from 7 to 14.1 percent. As compensation there have been equally dramatic slumps. Tuberculosis fell from 10.4 percent in 1900 to .6 percent in 1960, and infant mortality fell from 23.5 to 1.9 percent. Accidents, suicides, ulcers, and many others have remained reasonably constant. Stillbirths and the deaths of infants less than a year old have been falling, but their percentages of the total deaths may have actually risen on occasion due to a rising birth rate.

Lung cancer also has its own tale to tell, as practically all the overall cancer increase for males in recent years can be accounted for by the increase in deaths from lung cancer. Of males who are killed by cancer, 39 percent in 1966 were killed by cancer of the lung; of females killed

---

* *The American Way of Death,* by Jessica Mitford, which drew attention to the rates of the funeral industry, made $112,000 for its author within two years. She also had a cheap kind of coffin named after her.

by cancer, the percentage from lung cancer was 9 percent. Britain's ban on television cigarette advertising became effective August 1, 1965, and the United States ordered all cigarette cartons to be labeled with a warning a few months later. It appears that cigarette smoking is too deeply ingrained a habit to be unduly influenced by such measures, and the authorities proclaim but do not prevent—despite harrowing announcements. American consumption of cigarettes was 217 packs for every person over 16 during 1963. It fell to 209 in 1964, following the report of the Surgeon General linking lung cancer with smoking. It rose to 213 in 1965, and despite the labeled caution, to 215 in 1966. Britain has been similarly casual, although the number of adult (over 16) non-smokers rose from 43 percent in 1961 to 46 percent in 1965. "It is possible to prevent about nine-tenths of the cancer of the lung which will otherwise occur among our younger generations if we can persuade them not to smoke cigarettes" said the chief medical officer of Britain's Ministry of Health in October, 1965.

A remarkable feature of our changing mode of dying, or rather of succumbing to various diseases, is the near totality of defeat for the ancient diseases. Dreaded names, still with great power to them, can no longer wield their fearful authority. In 1964, for example, there were no deaths from diphtheria in England and Wales, only 73 deaths from measles, none from anthrax, 17 from dysentery, 4 from poliomyelitis, none from smallpox, 44 from whooping cough, 2,484 from tuberculosis* (but only 41 among people under 25), none from cholera, none from plague. All the deaths from this frightening collection of names do not add up to the current number dying from Britain's traffic accidents, the 7,000 yearly deaths—or 1.3 percent of the total—that succumb to the internal-combustion engine. Nevertheless, as we have to die from something, quelling the ancient diseases merely opens up possibilities for the modern ones. And in the future, when medical science has triumphed over today's fatal assortment, there will always be—to use Dr. Comfort's expression—the next layer of the onion.

Yet, there is one sure sign of progress. Although we will die just as surely, the chances are that in the future physicians will be able to identify accurately more and more of the ailments assaulting us. In those days of agues and humors, the medical men were frequently at a loss for a description, let alone a cure. Even in Britain today about 1.3 percent of the population dies from "unknown causes." This percentage will surely drop. It is substantially higher in many other parts of the world, such as Greece (18 percent), Yugoslavia (25.1 percent), Ceylon (22.4 percent), and El Salvador (28.3 percent). The South African situation

* Even this figure fell to an average of 2,049 in the next two years.

reflects something of the schism of that country. Whereas the deaths of 4.8 percent of the whites have an unknown cause, the deaths of 21 percent of the urban Negroes are unknown. The figures are higher still for the Bantu living in the country.

Secrecy

Should anyone, such as a physician or relative, inform a dying person of his condition? Should he or she be told that a "terminal stage" in the disease has been reached? The most famous and frequently quoted pair of facts relating to the question serve merely to underscore the problem. Apparently 69 to 90 percent of British physicians questioned in various studies favored keeping the patient in ignorance, but 77 to 89 percent of the patients wished to know. The physicians hold the whip hand, in that they are the experts, they have watched the disease's course. Over 50 percent of American and British deaths occur in hospitals, while the patient—inexpert and sick—is obviously less aware of the actual situation, unless clearly informed. One patient reported to the inquirers: "I don't want to be denied the experience of realizing that I am dying." And at a symposium on the subject in the Soviet Union an American psychiatrist said, "We do not even permit the dying person to say good-bye to us."

The most famous personal case of this kind in recent years was that of J. B. S. Haldane. Here was a true scientist, alert and constantly fascinated by new information. He was no desultory dowager, ignorant of medicine and unwilling to understand. He was undeniably capable of absorbing facts, had he been told them. At the age of 71, he was operated on for cancer of the rectum. This he knew, and he even had a poem published by the *New Statesman* called "Cancer can be fun." However, he was not told the whole story, neither was his wife or other relatives. Eventually, after he had initiated several new investigations involving colleagues, he did learn his prognosis and that he had secondaries. "Now I shall have no time to rest before I die," he wrote to a friend. As soon as he had died (in December, 1964) Naomi Mitchison, his sister, wrote to the *British Medical Journal* deploring the secrecy and asking why the surgeon had withheld the vital information. The ensuing correspondence was extremely forthright, notably from John Maynard Smith, who attacked the custom of keeping quiet. He added that he believed he could accept "bad news with fortitude" but not "a continuing fear that the truth was being withheld."

In May, 1966, under the title "Timor mortis conturbat me" ("The Fear of Death Unsettles Me"), the British journal *The Lancet* had an article on the duty of physicians to dying patients. "A positive, courageous, and realistic approach to death and dying has been common, at least as an ideal, through much of history, but we seem to have lost it. . . . Could we not now usefully persuade ourselves to take a new look at death and dying?" President Lyndon B. Johnson echoed mankind's current inability to regard death as death when he cabled to the very old, very sick, dying and unconscious Winston Churchill: "Whole world prays for your speedy recovery."

Finally, at least in England, you do not legally own your body after you are dead. You may give instructions for its disposal during your life, but it is up to your next of kin to decide whether your wishes should be carried out. Should you wish to bequeath your body to medical research, it is necessary to notify the Inspector of Anatomy at the Ministry of Health. The government will respond, as on so many earlier instances in life, by sending the appropriate form—for death.

⊷ 24 ⊱

Suicide

Society's Attitudes · Suicide History · Who Commits Suicide? ·

International Rates · Students · Children · Methods ·

Suicide and Murder

The thought of suicide is a great consolation: with the help of it one has got through many a bad night.

Nietzsche

Sufferings and hardships do not, as a rule, abate the love of life; they seem, on the contrary, usually to give it a keener zest.

William James

Each advancing age period of life shows a steady and consistent rise in suicide frequency.

Louis I. Dublin

To my friends: My work is done. Why wait?
George Eastman, shortly before he shot himself, aged 77

Society's Attitudes

Before mentioning facts about the where, when, who, and how of suicides and attempted suicides, it should be pointed out that such facts are notoriously unreliable. Different countries, religions, and people have disparate attitudes toward self-inflicted injury, and their differing codes color the statistics. Is it likely, one wonders, that figures from Manhattan, Dublin, Rome, Lagos, and Tokyo are comparable? Furthermore, a society's attitude and its actual laws have frequently reached a high level of contradiction. Throughout this century, the conviction has been growing that suicidal acts are a form of sickness; yet in England and Wales until 1961 both suicide and attempted suicide were criminal acts, although rarely treated even as a misdemeanor, and until 1962

[304]

churchyard burials of suicides were carried out without any form of burial service.

At least, that was the theory. In practice, both burial services and consecrated ground were often used, depending upon the coroner's verdict and upon the bishop's feelings. Prayers were summarily altered if they were inappropriate. Coroners, pulled both ways by the ludicrous situation, constantly recorded verdicts of "suicide while of unsound mind," thus absolving the victim. British law did not like the custom because actual evidence of unsoundness of mind—apart from the wish for self-destruction—was often totally lacking. It was tantamount, wrote John Roy, "to making a psychiatric diagnosis without having met the patient." Before 1961, therefore, those who succeeded in killing themselves were judged insane, while those who failed in the act were charged as criminals. Before 1962, the Church of England's dictates were equally confusing.

Suicide History

The history of society's attitude toward suicide has of course helped to cause the muddle in which today's statistics are hidden and from which today's society wishes to extricate itself. Suicide is definitely not an entirely modern disease; some primitive peoples knew of it, others have laughed at the idea when questioned about it. Shame has always been a common cause of self-destruction, and another has been the need to accompany someone already dead, as in the practice of suttee in the East—mainly for widows. The Romans and Greeks did not, in general, regard suicide as a sin, except that the loss of a soldier was always to be deplored. Even the early Christians accepted the traditional attitude, frequently killing themselves. The Apostles did not condemn suicide, and the Old Testament makes no direct statement against the act, although it is possible to construe various indirect indictments of it. There were four important Old Testament suicides:* Samson, more of a kamikaze than a hara-kiri; Saul, whose armor-bearer then followed suit; Abimelech, for shame that he had been wounded by a woman; and Ahithophel, who made more of the classical suicide's preparations before hanging himself. The most famous historical case of Jewish suicide occurred when some 960 people killed themselves in the besieged fortress of Masada in A.D. 73 rather than suffer under the Romans.

St. Augustine was the first Christian to denounce suicide, even though several earlier victims of their own hands had already been canonized.

* I am indebted to Dr. Louis I. Dublin for this fact and many other equally arresting points about suicide's history.

Within a few centuries suicide was considered a crime as well as a sin. Jewish law had started to denounce suicide much earlier, and traditionally, despite high rates at times of extreme persecution, Jewish suicide numbers have been low. The Koran emphatically forbids self-destruction, saying in one place that suicide is a graver crime than homicide. Thomas Aquinas said much the same thing for the Christians; whereas murder kills a body, self-murder kills both a body and a soul. The Middle Ages, not famous for its tolerance of deviants, dragged suicides through the streets, removed hearts, drove stakes through them, and either failed to bury the corpse or interred it in some unholy place. If buried near a church, a later practice, suicides were grouped with stillbirths, criminals, the excommunicated, and all other outcasts. Eventually, in England in 1823, a month after a London suicide named Griffiths had been buried at the junction of Eaton Street, Grosvenor Place, and Kings Road, the custom of burying suicides beneath the highway was banned by Parliament. Not until the Convocation of the Church of England in October, 1962, was it agreed that a modified form of burial service could be used for suicides.

Legally, therefore, England had statutes against the suicide for ten centuries, for it was first called an infamous crime, a species of felony, in the tenth century. In 1961, the Suicide Act was passed, and no longer is suicide or attempted suicide a criminal act, although complicity in the suicide of another is still a felony. In the United States, despite an inheritance of so much English law, suicide has never been a crime, but attempted suicide is a crime in six states and Arkansas holds that a person aiding and abetting a suicide is guilty of murder.

Who Commits Suicide?

In Britain about 6,000 a year do so, or 16 a day. The figure is about equal to the road toll.* In the United States the straight suicide figure is about 22,000 a year, or less than half the road toll, or one every 20 minutes. At once, it should be reiterated that the official figures are almost certainly understatements, some say by 30 percent, with the actual totals for Britain and the United States probably nearer to 10,000 and 30,000 respectively. A self-killing is still frequently hushed up. WHO world figures indicate 365,000 suicides a year, and 3 million attempts. No suicide facts are published by China or the Soviet Union.

Despite imperfections in the statistics many generalizations are pos-

---

* It has often been asserted that mechanical failures causing car accidents are murder attempts. One wonders how many other failures of machines are really suicide attempts. Americans have coined a word for them—autocides.

sible. Males kill themselves more frequently than females. Attempted suicide is probably ten times as common as successful suicide, therefore indicating some 60,000 a year in Britain and 200,000 a year in the United States. Suicide attempts vary from harmless (the gas is turned on only when footsteps reach the house) to almost successful (only something unforeseeable prevents death). Most attempts involve some danger to life (although a British psychiatrist has said many self-poisoners are trying "to alter their life situation, not to die"). Among American whites, the suicide rate is five times the homicide rate; among nonwhites, it is the other way around. More women than men attempt suicide in most countries. Successful suicide figures increase with age; unsuccessful attempts reach a peak for both sexes at about 30. During the last 60 years, the number of male suicides has increased slightly in England and Wales—by 31 percent; the number of female suicides has risen sharply—by 171 percent; but the present ratio of male to female (for 1957 to 1961) is 1.47 to 1. Both rises may be influenced by the decreasing pressures not to disclose suicide as a cause of death, but this does not explain the changing male-female ratio unless it had previously been considered even more shameful for a woman, the bearer of children, to kill herself.

Peak periods for suicides are times of high unemployment, peacetime, spring or summer, and afternoon rather than morning. The world wars lowered the suicide rates a year or two after the fighting began. The Australian figures do not mimic too well the peak springtime levels of the northern hemisphere, for they are more erratic. Urban areas have more suicides than rural areas. America's worst is San Francisco. Professional and managerial people kill themselves more frequently than the semiskilled and unskilled.

Suicide is rare among children, a possible hazard of adolescence, a disproportionate problem at universities, and an increasing factor with increase in age. For Americans it is the tenth leading cause of death, and for teen-agers it ranks fourth. The Negro American is much less likely to kill himself than the white American. The American figure of 10 suicides per year per 100,000 people has remained remarkably constant since 1900. The current annual British figure is about 11 per 100,000. Marital status is important; from married to single to widowed to divorced the proportion of suicide victims goes upward. Roughly one male physician in 50 kills himself, and each British family doctor has on his list between 10 and 20 patients who, sometime in their lives, will attempt to kill themselves. According to Dr. Norman L. Farberow, co-director of the Suicide Prevention Center in Los Angeles, the doctor is "in a unique position to be the most effective agent in suicide prevention

. . . as 50 percent of all suicide victims visit a doctor during the last month of their lives."

International Rates

Michael Frayn once wrote in *The Observer* that Swedes are believed to have "the highest rates in the world for divorce, alcoholism, delinquency, illegitimacy, abortion, pacifism, road deaths, suicide . . . and sin. Only a tiny minority of cranks, such as sociologists and Swedes, would care to dispute these deeply held convictions." He is quite right. The proportion of Swedes who kill themselves does not exceed that of all other countries. According to World Health Organization figures (for 1961), the Swedish annual rate is 16.9 suicide deaths per 100,000 people. More suicidal countries are Switzerland (18.2); West Germany (18.7), with West Berlin (37); Japan (19.6); Finland (20.6); and Austria (21.9). The high figure for West Berlin probably reflects the age of its inhabitants because young people tend to leave the city; all towns with an elderly population tend to have high suicide rates in consequence. Countries with consistently low rates are the Netherlands (6.6), Spain (5.5), Ireland (3.2), and Egypt (.2). Practically every underdeveloped or developing country with a modest gross national product has a modest suicide rate. Nevertheless, to repeat the point a third time, all suicide statistics should be viewed with suitable cynicism, such as that Muslim Egyptian figure. Whereas the figures for England and Wales have been 10.2, 11.3, 11.5, and 11.3 in four recent and postwar years, the equivalent figures for Scotland have been 5.4, 7.7, 8.5, and 7.9 and for Northern Ireland 4.1, 3.3, 4.1, and 5. No one really believes that the Scot and the Ulsterman are so dramatically different from the Englishman and the Welshman; it is much easier to accept that the registration procedures for suicides are different in these different sections of the United Kingdom.

Students

Suicides by students are unhappily common. A recent survey of undergraduate deaths at Cambridge University listed 103 fatalities; of which 41 were due to accident, 27 to disease, and 35 to suicide. In 1951, it was estimated at Oxford University that the suicide rate among the students was 11 times higher than that of a similar age group among the general population. Oxford and Cambridge are particularly prone to suicide. In an investigation by Sir Alan Rook in 1959, he disclosed that 11 other universities had rates considerably lower than Oxford and

Cambridge, but even so these other universities had rates twice as high as the average figures for young men. The figures for University College, London, fall between the rates for the two old and all the younger universities in England and Wales. Female undergraduates very rarely kill themselves.

Apart from students, the incidence of suicide among adolescents and very young adults is low. In the United States, it is 3.9 per 100,000 for the 15-to-19 age group. The rate is then doubled for the 20-to-24 group, and it continues to rise with age until it reaches a maximum of 27.9 per 100,000 for the 75-to-84 group. Although women never kill themselves in such numbers, their suicide rate rises with age too, but reaches a maximum in the 55-to-64 age group.

Children

The fact that there should be any suicides at all below the age of 14 is so disturbing that their relatively small number provides little comfort. Only one in 400 of all American suicides is by a child under 14, but this means 50 a year. Most of these are at the older end of this age group, but about two a year are in the 5-to-9 group. Once again, the male-female ratio is still dominant; three-quarters of the children who kill themselves are boys. In the United States, the most frequently used method of infantile self-destruction is the firearm, with hanging or strangulation coming second, and the swallowing of a corrosive substance third. The ratio of unsuccessful to successful attempts at suicide is always very high in the very young.

Methods

The American affection for firearms is reflected in the suicide statistics. During the five-year period ending in 1959, for example, the methods used were firearms and explosives 47.1 percent, poisons and gases 20.8 percent, hanging and strangulation 20.5 percent, drowning 3.7 percent, jumping from high places 3.5 percent, cutting or piercing instruments 2.6 percent, all other means 1.9 percent. There is not too much difference in proportion in the methods used by the American child and the American adult.

The British, with firearms less readily at hand and with a larger proportion of houses piped with poisonous gas, choose gas for self-destruction more frequently than any other method. In a survey carried out over 33 years in the city of Leeds, the methods used were coal gas poisoning 49.5 percent, drowning 14 percent, poisoning other than carbon monoxide 12 percent, hanging 11 percent, cut throats 6.3 percent, all other methods—including firearms—7.1 percent. These figures from Leeds were published in 1962. Since then, the proportion of suicide methods has altered in Britain due to the sudden rise in barbiturate poisoning, notably among women. In 1962, for example, 20 percent of suicide deaths in England and Wales were caused by barbiturates.

There are some classic features of self-inflicted injuries. Fatal cuts, for example, are frequently preceded by very many tentative incisions before the final fatal wound. The drowned man will often have placed his accessory clothes, such as hat and gloves, in a neat pile before. The firearm victim has almost always chosen the right temple (or left, if he is left-handed), the center of his brow, the roof of his mouth, or the area over his heart for the fatal shot, having characteristically bared his chest beforehand. The gas victim will often have sealed the room and will have made himself or herself comfortable with cushions. The hanged man scarcely ever breaks his neck. A judicial hanging used to require a drop of 6½ to 7½ ft., according to the subject's weight, and the neck was broken in the middle of the cervical vertebrae. Most hanged victims have caused their deaths by asphyxiation, but some have killed themselves merely by blocking the neck's blood vessels. According to C. J. Polson, the jugular veins are closed by a rope tension of only 4.4 lb., the carotid arteries by a tension of 11 lb., and the actual windpipe, or trachea, by a tension of 33 lb. Thus, as the majority of hanging victims choose sites that enable them to die with both feet off the ground, they succeed in closing their tracheas because their weight always exceeds 33 lb.; but successfully fatal hangings have been carried out from doorknobs and even by people lying in bed. The human body is, to say the least, vulnerable to its own attempts upon its life.

Traditionally, suicide is thought of as the single act that causes death. Today, bearing in mind the maltreatment meted out by some to their bodies, by heavy drinkers who drink heavily until their premature death, by coronary victims who do not mend their ways, there is talk of "submeditated suicide." There is no reason why suicide should be instantaneous, or nearly so.

Suicide and Murder

Suicide and murder are common partners. One survey a few years ago showed that a third of the murders in England and Wales, or 50 a year, were followed by suicide. The partnership is less conspicuous in the United States, which has a similar suicide rate per unit of population but a homicide rate 15 times greater. Suicide and the highest buildings are also partners, although not so emphatically as the inevitable publicity would have us believe. The Eiffel Tower in Paris was the means to the end of 341 men and women in its first three-quarters of a century of existence (two survived the fall); but this average of five a year is eclipsed by the 500 or so suicides committed annually in the Paris region. The Golden Gate Bridge in San Francisco was the jumping-off place for 278 people in its first 28 years, but 10 deaths a year are soon swamped by the figures for California as a whole. London used to have many deliberate falls from the Monument in the City until wire mesh made this impossible, but there was a suicide from the new Post Office Tower even before it was completed and made suicide-resistant.

Finally, voluntary societies are growing whose aim is to help those tempted to commit suicide. In Britain, for example, the Samaritans is an organization started in 1953 by the Rev. Chad Varah. It makes good use of the telephone, and many towns have a number manned 24 hours a day. The Samaritans have found that fewer than one in 250 of their clients do commit suicide. At long last the medieval custom of driving a stake through the heart of any *felo de se* is being replaced by compassion and friendship.

⋙ 25 ⋘

The Brain

Animal and Human · Anatomy · The Cerebrum
and Its Lobes · Left-side Dominance · Sinistrals ·
Intelligence · The EEG · Brains Without Bodies ·
Palsy · Concussion · Memory · Nerves, Cranial and
Spinal · Transmission

Animal and Human

The human brain is neither the largest in the animal kingdom nor the
largest by comparison with body size. An elephant's brain is about four
times heavier than a man's, and many monkeys have a body-brain ratio
of 20 to 1, while the human ratio is nearer 50 to 1. Nevertheless, even
though mankind has been judge and jury in dubbing himself sapiens,
in referring to himself as the pinnacle of evolution, in distinguishing
between man and the animals, there is nothing quite like the human
brain.

As ever, there are innumerable conundrums. Brain bulk is undoubtedly related to brain ability. The evolutionary ancestors of animals and
mankind bear out this generalization; but, within the species man, brain
bulk seems strangely unimportant. One brain may be twice the size of
another without showing any apparent difference in ability. The largest
human brains, twice average size, are those of idiots. Machines can be
made to operate far faster than any brain and mathematical problems
of mind-boggling proportions are mechanically calculated before a brain
can absorb them, let alone provide an answer; but no machine has a
memory with a capacity in the same class as the human brain. Many
humans say that they never forget a face, one more configuration of the
same old theme of two eyes, a nose, and a mouth, and yet the memory

of one new telephone number spoken by that face is instantly elusive. Surely a face is more complex than a small finite series of figures? Louis Pasteur suffered a cerebral hemorrhage that caused moderate one-sided paralysis but did not prevent him from doing some of his best work. At the postmortem, years later, the injury was found to be so extensive that he was said to have been living on half a brain. The brain is undoubtedly sensitive to wrong cuts by the surgeon's knife, and gloved fists cause at least a dozen deaths a year in the boxing ring, but Phineas Gage achieved fame when he had a 13¼-lb. tamping iron blasted into his skull and his brain. He lost consciousness briefly, walked to the surgeon's office, and recovered physically. Admittedly, he became a drunkard and lost jobs thereafter, but he still had the wit to sell his skeleton, cash in advance, to several different medical schools, and the pushing of an iron bar with the diameter of about a half-dollar through his brain, the delicate and sensitive brain, demonstrated remarkable cerebral resilience.

Wars and surgery have, since Mr. Gage's accident 100 years ago, amply demonstrated man's ability to lose substantial portions of the brain without undue suffering. In 1935, a London conference was informed of the stabilizing effect upon a chimpanzee caused by the surgical severing of much of its frontal lobes. In 1936, a Paris conference was yet more fascinated to hear of a similar operation upon a human being. Since then, thousands of the mentally unbalanced have suffered the deliberate severance of the foremost part of each cerebral hemisphere, and many have benefited psychologically from this deliberate destruction.

Finally, although the brain is anatomically symmetrical and although many of its functions are entirely bilateral, some others are quite one-sided. One half is called dominant, and its loss is the greater loss. Had Pasteur suffered his hemorrhage on the other side, there would have been no question of good work; either death or a pathetic existence would have followed. For those parts of the brain that are bilateral and unaffected by dominance an extra complexity is caused by the fact that each half tends to organize the opposite half of the body. Neither dominance nor this crossing over simplifies comprehension of man's fantastic neurological anatomy.

Anatomy

The human brain is a soft lump of 14 billion cells, it weighs slightly more than 3 lb., and is so full of water that it tends to slump like Jell-O if placed without support on a firm surface. Predominantly, its structure is the huge pair of cerebral hemispheres that sit on top of the 10 to 15 percent of remaining tissue. This smaller fraction is much more varied, being composed of several entirely different portions of brain tissue, and fits into such space as exists in the cranium between the top end of the spinal cord and the huge convoluted growth of the two cerebral hemispheres. The complexity has been accentuated by man's upright stance. From a tetrapod creature whose spine and head were both horizontal, man has become a bipedal creature whose spine is vertical and whose head continues to look horizontally, and the central nervous system of spinal cord and brain has had to suffer this 90-degree flexure. Small wonder there is confusion at the point where the spinal column joins the brain.

Everything is simpler in fish. In even less advanced creatures, the central nervous system is merely a tube running the length of the body that swells modestly at the front end, where sense organs are predominantly situated and where sensory impressions are predominantly received. By the developmental stage of fish, the brain is in three parts, three separate swellings each linked to a sense organ. The front swelling receives impulses from the olfactory organs, the middle from the eyes, and the back from the organ of balance, later to be the ear as well. These three, forebrain, midbrain, and hindbrain, persist with their three roles in more advanced forms, but the expanding forebrain takes over all coordination from the other two.

It may be an oversimplification to say so, but if one part of the brain is to be expanded, it had better be the front part. To enlarge elsewhere is plainly a greater problem. Simplification or not, this is what happened. The paired lump of forebrain became increasingly important as the center of sensory correlation. To react suitably is not to react according to stimuli from one sense organ, but to sift through all available information from the exterior in one central control. By the time of the mammals, the forebrain was dominant in this regard, and the importance of the mammalian sense of smell was intimately bound up with the swelling olfactory lobes. When the primates were evolved, smell was less important, but the forebrain was by then firmly established as the center for interpretation and correlation. Therefore, again to simplify, but with good reason, if greater correlation and association are both required and advantageous, the forebrain needs to be expanded still further. Besides, unlike the midbrain and hindbrain, its expansion continues as before to present less of a space problem anatomically.

During evolution, the brain tissue doing all this correlating moved increasingly toward the outer surface of the forebrain. Called the pallium, cloak, or cortex, this correlating tissue made up the most advanced portion of the brain. Its area expanded when fissures and grooves were formed, as in a walnut, and a brain should be judged for its level of advancement more on the area of its cortex than on the body of brain tissue. In human beings, the cloak of cortex is only about ⅛ in. thick or less, but its area, enlarged by all the folds, convolutions, gyri, and sulci, is 400 sq. in. Beneath that cortex lies the maze of fibers and pathways that lead to and from the thin crucial skin of cortical tissue.

The human brain is the most exaggerated form of this development. The original forebrain, now so heavily grooved and with four paired and major lobes of its own, is over five-sixths of the human brain. Known as the cerebrum, its two halves forming the cerebral hemispheres, it performs all the higher and highest roles of human activity, the correlation of sensory impulses, of memory, of thought. The remainder of the human brain is tucked underneath the huge mushroom of cerebrum, and it also consists of four parts:

MIDBRAIN. Short and narrow. Still linked with vision in that it receives impulses from the retina and still acts as a center for visual reflexes, but it mainly consists of fibers going from elsewhere to elsewhere.

PONS. Just below the midbrain. Dominantly tracts of fibers.

MEDULLA OBLONGATA. The continuation of the spinal cord, where it first begins to broaden. Mainly tracts. Contains much of the crossing over of fibers, causing the left cerebral hemisphere's association with the body's right-hand side, and vice versa.

CEREBELLUM. Lies behind midbrain, pons, and medulla, below rear regions of cerebral hemispheres. It is also in the form of two hemispheres and, like the archaic hindbrain, is associated with the inner ear. Main cerebellar activity is to assist muscular coordination. Victims of a poor cerebellum move jerkily and without accuracy.

The Cerebrum and Its Lobes

Forgetting these four other parts and returning again to the cerebral hemispheres, a further division into four is necessary because the four lobes of each hemisphere have distinct roles, far more distinct than the lobes themselves.

FRONTAL LOBE. Also called the "motor lobe," it is at the front of the head. The precise motor area, which controls muscular movement, is only a narrow band of cortex at the back of this lobe. The band moves from the side of each lobe up to the top and down into the central fissure between each hemisphere. Each region of the body is linked with a part of this band. Stimulation of any portion of the band will always cause a muscle, even a particular muscle, to twitch in response in the appropriate bodily region. Progressing along the band from each side of the brain to the center, the bodily areas involved are the mouth (including speech, but more about speech later, under left-sided dominance), the face, eye, neck, thumb, fingers, hand, wrist, elbow, shoulder, trunk, hip, knee, ankle, and toes—in that order. The amount of band involved is certainly not proportional to the size of the body controlled by it: the hands and fingers use as much of the band as the remainder of the arms plus the legs and trunk. Digital skill is correspondingly more advanced.

In front of this motor band lies the premotor area. Its stimulation does not ever lead to the twitching of a single muscle, but to a more coordinated movement of a whole area. Presumably, this area affords general control, whereas the motor band affords greater precision. The remainder of the frontal cortex is not only far larger but far more mysterious. Called the silent zone, great quantities of it have sometimes been cut away or severed, as in tumor operations, to leave the patient remarkably unimpaired. A small nick in the motor cortex and there is immediate partial paralysis; a huge carving up of the silent cortex and, although personality is involved, notably mood, criticism, drive, and concentration, functional ability is scarcely modified.

PARIETAL LOBE. This lobe, which is separated by a deep fissure from the frontal lobe, also possesses a band but at its front border adjacent to the frontal motor band. This is sensory and it receives sensations of warmth, cold, touch and general movement from the body. The order along the band is virtually the same as the order for the motor band: the mouth, including taste, is low down on each side and the toes are in the central fissure.

TEMPORAL LOBE. The lobe nearest to the ears is reasonably linked with hearing, and the lobe on each side receives impulses from both ears. The area actually linked with hearing, as with most lobe areas positively linked with any function, is quite small. There is believed to be an association between memory and this lobe.

OCCIPITAL LOBE. The lobe nearest to the back of the head. Linked with vision. A small wound at the back of the head has often caused no harm other than total blindness. If only the visual cortex of the left lobe is destroyed, vision will still remain good for the right half of each eye's retina, and vice versa.

Whereas so much of the brain's volume is functionally vague, allied to intelligence but with no precision, there are portions of the cerebrum apart from these already mentioned that are quite the reverse. Below the cortex, or gray matter, the bulk of the tissue is white matter—the pathways of fibers. Nevertheless, at the base of it all, completely overshadowed in bulk by the great mass of the cerebral hemispheres, there exists some more gray matter.

Part of this tissue is the hypothalamus, a minute portion of the total brain—about 1/300—which seems to have a disproportionate share of duties. "Is there any pie in the vertebrate organization into which the hypothalamus does not dip its finger?" asked the writer of a medical journal article recently. This fraction of brain tissue is involved in the body's water metabolism, in temperature regulation (and therefore in perspiration and shivering), in appetite, in thirst, in the levels of sugar in the blood, in growth, in sleeping and waking, in emotions such as anger and pleasure, and in the cycles of the reproductive system; it is also the main center of the autonomic nervous system. Probably it will be found to be invested with yet more bodily authority when research workers have probed further into its vital lump of gray matter but, considering that it is smaller than a finger joint, the list is already impressive. Naturally, in so small but all-important an organ, minor damage —even the overcrowding presence of a tumor nearby—causes drastic alteration to the body's self-regulatory abilities. Similarly, with so many complex duties, less than a tumor can make a hypothalamus go wrong. Compulsive eating, the tendency to eat too often or too long, may merely be the fault of a hypothalamus whose appetite-control center is inadequately strict or faulty in its assessment of need.

Left-side Dominance

The fact that the cerebrum is completely divided by the superior longitudinal fissure to form the two separate cerebral hemispheres is highly relevant to bodily control. In effect, this division causes two regions, each capable of administration. Having two such regions of cerebral cortex incurs the possibility of a disunited command. Messages from one half of the brain can reach the other half, but the human brain obviates the need for this constant cross-reference by having one cerebral hemisphere dominant. The damage to Pasteur's brain, already mentioned, was to his nondominant half. He could not have suffered such damage to the left-hand and dominant side of his brain. Should a child receive damage to its left hemisphere before it is too late, some say before six months, it is possible for the right hemisphere to take its place. Later on, the chain of command is too firmly embedded, and the dominant hemisphere cannot have its higher and more authoritative role taken over by the inferior half.

Almost always, the left hemisphere is the dominant one. It possesses the speech center as well as wielding unspoken power over the right hemisphere. Why the left should be so dictatorial in this fashion is quite unknown. Allied to this ignorance, often unhelpfully so, is the problem of right- and left-handedness. Since the left hemisphere controls the right half of the body, and since the left hemisphere is nearly always dominant, it might seem easy to explain the overwhelming majority of right-handers; but, alas for the presumption, left-handed people frequently have a dominant left hemisphere. Roughly 5 percent of the world's population (all areas, rich or poor, black or white, are equal) are left-handed to a greater or lesser degree, and yet the proportion of people whose brains have been discovered after disease or surgery to be right-sided is much smaller. Similarly, it is a great rarity for speech to be controlled from the right-hand side, but again this is information encountered only by chance, and there is plenty of disagreement over the occurrence of left-handers with right speech, right-handers with right speech, and so forth.

Sinistrals

The Economist once had a buoyant article on the Declaration of Human Lefts. Why, it asked, are those of the left camp gauche and sinister, whereas right-handers are not only right but dextrous and righteous? Whence this prejudice, which also stamps radical politics as left of conservatism? The sinistrals, as left-handers call themselves, have reason also to resent the design of things that favor right-handers, as well as the traditional association of left with wrong. One ardent sinistral even totted up Biblical references to rightness; he discovered 1,600, most of which were hostile to the left. Although animals, such as the higher apes, tend to favor one hand or the other and are not markedly ambidextrous (another loaded word, meaning right on both sides), they do not show a particular preference for their right side.

Man has been prejudiced ever since he has been able to record the fact. Most hand imprints on cave walls are of the left hand, indicating an Aurignacian preference for working with the right. Military burials after early battles consist of bones more grievously injured on their left side, indicating right-handed attackers. Castle bastions and keeps possess staircases that spiral upward in a clockwise fashion; right-handed swordsmen find them easier to defend. Scripts used to make use of the ox-turn system, ranging back and forth alternately, but most now favor right-handers as they run from left to right. Hebrew and Arabic are exceptions, and for thousands of years China was impartial by being vertical. Chinese custom has now been overturned, and the new cultural rule is to go from left to right. Most countries drive on the right, and most people walk on the right of the pavement irrespective of the driving laws in their country. Presumably, both are linked with the preference for keeping the right arm in the clear.

The pressure to conform, a strong and insidious force on its own, used to be abetted in the classroom by a reluctance to entertain left-handed writing. There is some evidence that such compulsion often went hand in hand with stammering, but there is also more recent evidence that it does not. Perhaps there are changes in the definition of left-handedness that have influenced the evidence and made it contradictory. Left-handers make use of their right hands more frequently than right-handers make use of their left, and plainly some people are only a little left-handed. Jack the Ripper, whoever he was, worked with his left hand. So did George VI, who also stammered. So did Admiral Nelson, although unwillingly, for his lost right arm had been his major arm. And so do an estimated 200 million in the world today, a huge minority group that suffers from the effects, as Thomas Carlyle put it after he lost the use of his right hand, of "probably the very oldest institution that exists."

Clockwise, the way the sun goes in the northern hemisphere, may have had its influence in the preference for the right. Counterclockwise and sitting on the left have always been inferior, often devilish, and generally sinister.

Intelligence

Man's cunning is lodged in his cerebrum, but there is no center for intelligence. This depends upon the cortex as a whole. Previous theories that the frontal cortex, as the most forward bulge of the central nervous system, was the foremost spot for intelligence have not been supported by the frequent surgical excision of large portions of its substance. Besides, even though the measurement of intelligence quotients, and whether someone is above or below the average of 100, gives an aura of unity to intelligence, it is no one thing. Therefore, it is unfair to expect it to have one location on the cortex, as if it were control of the little toe.

Dr. George Stoddard, in *The Meaning of Intelligence,* listed its multiplicity. He said it is "the ability to undertake activities that are characterized by 1. difficulty, 2. complexity, 3. abstractedness, 4. economy, 5. adaptiveness to a goal, 6. social value and 7. the emergency of originals, and to maintain such activities under conditions that demand a concentration of energy and a resistance to emotional forces." Similarly, Theodosius Dobzhansky said, "What is measured by the I.Q. is not necessarily the same as what is referred to in everyday language as intelligence, cleverness, aptitude or wit. Still less does the I.Q. give an estimate of the value or worth of the person." It has also been said that a chimpanzee will start scoring well on intelligence tests only when another chimpanzee has set them.

On learning, Alfred North Whitehead wrote: "It is a profoundly erroneous truism, repeated by all copy books, and by eminent people when they are making speeches, that we should cultivate the habit of thinking what we are doing. The precise opposite is the case. Civilization advances by extending the number of important operations which we can perform without thinking about them." Sir Peter Medawar, in *The Uniqueness of the Individual,* took Whitehead's statement a stage further to produce its converse truth. "Learning is two-fold: we learn to make the processes of deliberate thought instinctive and automatic, and we learn to make automatic and instinctive processes the subject of discriminating thought."

The intellectual abilities of others are equally hard to comprehend at both ends of the scale. In one issue, *Penguin Science Survey* had articles exemplifying the abnormally incapable and the abnormally skillful. One was dedicated to the several thousand spastic children born each year whose brain damage makes it difficult for them to draw a diamond. Normally, a child can copy a circle at the age of three, a square at five, a diamond at seven. Two years of development, therefore, separate each achievement, all three of them seeming equally elementary to the adult and yet major milestones to the struggling child. And one of them is an unattainable milestone for the average spastic. At the other end of the scale, when normal problems shrink to nothing, is Professor A. C. Aitken, of Edinburgh University. He was asked to turn 4/47 into a decimal. After four seconds he answered, giving one digit every three-quarters of a second: "Point 0851063829787234042553I9I4." He stopped there—after 24 seconds, discussed the matter for a minute, and then started up again. "Yes, 191489. I can get that." Five-second pause. "361702127-659574468. Now that's the repeating point. It starts again at 085. So, if that's 46 places, I'm right."

The EEG

Appreciation of the mechanics of intelligence should take a step forward when current obscurity is diminished about the origin of electroencephalogram waves. It is nearly 40 years since these waves were discovered. Toward the end of the nineteenth century, various men had shown that the brains, notably of dogs, possessed changing electric potentials, but it was up to Dr. Hans Berger, of Jena University, to open up the subject.

For five years, he applied electrodes to the human skull, and he studied the fluctuating patterns of the potentials his delicate galvanometers succeeded in recording. This psychiatrist then recorded his results in *Über das Elektrenkephalogram des Menschen*. For the next five years, while the world disregarded his claims, he continued to work, to record his results, and to use the same title in writing them up in the German journals. He was particularly suspect for his repeated contention that he could distinguish between different wave patterns. Recording the waves at all was improbable; differentiating their patterns was even more so.

Suddenly he was vindicated. Professor Adrian (later Lord Adrian) also recorded waves; Britain's Physiological Society saw them; the "Berger rhythm" was applauded, and electroencephalography—electric brain writing—has never looked back.

Sometime after a child's eighth birthday the dominant rhythm, called by Berger the alpha rhythm, changes from its childish speed of 4 to 7 cycles a second and starts increasing to its adult frequency of 10 cycles a second. Basically, it is an idling rhythm, for it is most manifest when eyes are closed and minds are empty. Its casual tremor is abolished the moment anything happens, whether the eyes actually open to see something interesting or visual images are merely imagined, so that the brain records greater excitement.

With the arrival of sleep, different wave patterns appear, and an EEG —the advanced form of Berger's equipment—can indicate when someone is asleep, dreaming, unconscious, anesthetized, or waking up. This synchronization of waves is of course a problem. Brain cells might be expected to discharge at random, but instead there is unison. Are there pacemakers in the brain regimenting the discharges? Of what use is the rhythm? And why are different wave patterns associated with an epileptic fit? The complexity of the rhythms involved, so cleverly detected by the assiduous Dr. Berger, are still just as complex, and the job of deciphering the patterns created by varying stimuli is being handed over to computers. Therefore, although the human brain is far more cunning and compact than any computer and although computers were devised by human brains, it may be computers that can inform the brain what makes it tick so cyclically, and why. Fantastically, a U.S. Air Force scientist has taught himself to alter his alpha rhythms, switching them on and off at will. He can therefore speak his mind without moving a muscle.

Brains Without Bodies

Modern brain research is also profiting from a newfound ability to keep isolated brains alive. The so-called donor dies, but his brain is maintained independently. In 1963, this could be done for a few hours with monkeys. By 1965, it could be done for 24 hours, and a system had been developed that used the blood supply from a larger monkey to flow through the disembodied brain. Similarly, some Japanese scientists have succeeded in freezing a cat's brain for six months, thawing it and demonstrating once again the normal EEG rhythms even though the original cat was long since dead. Such work is highly relevant, not just to brain surgery but to heart surgery, when the normal pumping is interrupted. The brain, accustomed to a blood flow of a pint a minute and consuming—at rest—about one-fifth the body's oxygen supply, is customarily damaged if without blood for longer than 3 to 5 minutes. (Strangely, some accident victims have suffered longer periods without an efficient blood flow to their heads without subsequent brain injury, but normally the brain is highly intolerant of blood neglect.) A living brain suspended upon a laboratory bench, nourished, and kept alive on its own, is a triumph of physiological technology; it is also worrisome. The brain is the organ of consciousness, of sensitivity, of feeling. What happens when it alone survives?

Palsy

Although the adult brain savagely resents oxygen lack, the brains of a fetus and of a newborn child are strangely permissive. This boon to childbirth (an adaptive feature?) allows more time than would otherwise be possible for the changeover from umbilical respiration to lung respiration. The infant's blood may become temporarily deoxygenated, but at least the brain is resistant to the short-term lack of rich blood. Nevertheless, birth can cause brain damage. Breathing must be established soon after birth if persistent damage is not to be caused, but any damage to the brain may be a feature either of the time before birth or of the time after it. It may be genetic and (these days, at least) inevitable if the damage is caused early in fetal life. It can be genetic and preventable, as in phenylketonuria, generally when any damage is caused after birth. It can be an occurrence of pregnancy, of birth, or of some cerebral insult after birth; and it all adds up to a total of .2 percent of the general liveborn population who suffer from cerebral palsy.

Palsy is another word for paralysis. Brain damage in the motor areas associated with movement causes paralysis of one sort or another. A spastic is one sort of palsy. His cerebral cortex is involved, and he is weak and stiff in various parts of the body to varying degrees. An athetoid has damage to his basal ganglia, making movement wild and uncoordinated. An ataxic has cerebellar damage, and all movements are consequently unsteady.

Of the three, spastics are most common, but damage causing trouble with bodily movement is only one aspect of cerebral impairment. There are also the intellectual and sensory spheres, and severe mental retardation is more common than the physical retardation of the victim of palsy. Some 3 percent of the population has an IQ lower than 70; roughly .5 percent is lower than 50 and therefore classified as morons or imbeciles. More frequently, damage to the brain is slight, and the effects less dramatic. Dr. Richmond S. Paine, professor of pediatric neurology, Washington, said, "It seems a reasonable estimate that 5 percent to 8 percent of the entire population may have some reflection or suggestion of cerebral damage."

Concussion

Picture the scene. (Most film directors have.) The victim walks into the room and glances about him. The villain, whose earlier glancing had supplied him with a vase, poker, or paperweight, knocks out the victim with one crucial blow. The victim slumps, stays unconscious awhile, then comes to, shakes his head, takes in the situation, and rushes out of the room. It's all easy. It is bogus.

The causing of unconsciousness is genuine enough; it is the instant recovery that is improbable and misleading. Concussion is most likely to be caused if the head is rapidly accelerated—a threshold speed of 28 feet per second is sometimes given. The speed of the blow is therefore important, whatever the size of the blunt instrument. It so happens that a rabbit punch on the neck and a straight left to the jaw are both good at producing acceleration, but a short neck with thick muscles is more able to resist efforts to accelerate its head. Any subsequent unconsciousness may be so fleeting that the victim is scarcely aware of it; it may last less than 30 seconds, as with most boxing knockouts, or it may last for days and weeks, as in many car accidents.

Generally speaking, the unpleasantness of the return to consciousness and the extent of amnesia surrounding the events are proportional to the degree of unconsciousness. Nausea, headache, unsteadiness, and amnesia are probable if the concussion has been at all prolonged. The instant recovery and awareness of the screen victim are both highly improbable and give the impression that such a mishap is annoying but trivial. Dr. Macdonald Critchley, a specialist in the effects of brain mistreatment, has said no unconsciousness can ever be regarded as trivial, that blood clots could form and enlarge as a result of the injury, that evidence exists of association between tumors and severe concussion, and that blows that do not even cause knockouts can cause damage to brain cells.

Boxers still die regularly. So do participants in virtually all other sports; but, unlike most other sports, the aim of boxing is calculated violence. In 1965, when Sonny Banks died of a blood clot on the brain at the age of 24, three days after he had been knocked out by Leotis Martin, he was the 64th American boxer in five years to die of ring injuries. Dr. Milton Helpern, New York City's chief medical examiner, has performed autopsies on dead boxers. *Medical World News* quoted him after he had conducted studies on four knockout victims: "When burr holes were made in the heads of the unconscious boxers, brain tissue oozed out like toothpaste from a tube." The four men had survived unconscious from 55 hours to 9 days after their knockouts. Two of them had hit their heads on the mat when they fell, two had just slumped to the ground.

Memory

"If we remembered everything, we should be as ill as if we remembered nothing," said William James, and for a long time that just about summed up mankind's ability at comprehending mankind's memory, or indeed the memory of any creature. R. W. Gerard lamented in 1949 that current understanding of the mind "would remain as valid and useful if, for all we knew, the cranium was stuffed with cotton wadding." B. D. Burns, reviewing the whole subject of memory theory eight years later, concluded that no hypothesis had proved "a wild success." Finally, the worm slowly began to turn. "It may well be that we are at last on the way to solving . . . how memories are stored in the brain," said Lord Adrian in 1965.

It was the planarian flatworms whose habits and abilities made such a striking contribution. Not only can they be taught things, but they can be cut in half to grow each end anew and they can eat one another. They have not much in the way of a brain, but they do have memory. For instance, the worms curl up from the effects of an electric shock; in an experiment the shining of a bright light preceded the electric shock, and worms already subjected to this treatment started curling up the moment the light came on. This memory of theirs is somehow stored within the body as a whole. If a worm is cut in half, both the head half and the tail half will remember the electric shock treatment after they have each grown a new tail and head respectively. More impressive, worms ignorant of the light-and-shock procedure that eat other, already conditioned worms will learn more rapidly when it is their turn to be trained. Human cannibal lore has frequently asserted that strength, intelligence, or power is acquired by consuming the strong, clever, or powerful; worms bear this out—at least for worms. (This whole worm story is either praised or denigrated in turn, mainly because many other scientists have not been able to repeat the experiment.)

So what was it that the worms had been eating? What is edible knowledge? At about this time, in the late 1950s and early 1960s, scientists in other fields were investigating ribonucleic acid, or RNA. RNA had already been closely examined for its messenger role in the procedure of turning inherited genetic information into the physical actuality of a new creature. The task of RNA is to act as a copy of the genes and pass on this impressed blueprint for the correct construction of bodily protein. In theory, therefore, the ability of RNA to handle information seemed to make it a suitable agent for the handling of memory. So the worm-cannibalization experiment was made again. This time half the worms were subjected to a chemical that selectively destroys RNA, and, sure enough, a link was established between the presence of RNA and the inheritance of memory.

An animal like a planarian worm can eat a huge molecule like RNA without breaking it down into its component parts during digestion. Higher animals break down all their food before building it up again. Therefore, the worm experiment was performed with rats by extracting RNA from certain sections of their brains and then injecting this RNA —thus bypassing the destruction of digestion—into the veins of other rats. The donors had previously been taught a task; the recipients had never encountered it before, and yet they learned it quicker than other rats who had not been blessed with an RNA injection. So, perhaps ribonucleic acid will soon be universally acknowledged as the chemical basis of memory. Or perhaps the whole timorous house of cards will come tumbling down when additional evidence refutes everything gained so painfully thus far. It is interesting that the drug magnesium pemoline has benefited some ailing memories, and the same drug steps up the activity of an enzyme that facilitates production of RNA. It adds one more card to the house.

Finding the chemical basis is only half the story (or less). Memory has three ingredients—the three R's of registration, retention, and recall. Everyone registers more than he can retain, retains more than he can recall. If RNA is the chemical that, by having its molecular pattern altered during registration, is the card-index basis of memory, this fact does not explain how the card index is either maintained (retention) or used (recall). What is the system that does either or both?

Similarly, there is short-term memory—looking up a number, dialing it and forgetting it—and there is long-term memory. Are these different or merely two aspects of the same phenomenon? It is relevant that memory difficulties of the aged have been demonstrated to be dominantly difficulties of recall; short-term retention is scarcely influenced by advancing years.

For some reason, human beings have traditionally accepted their individual levels of intelligence as something immutable and the luck of the genetic draw. They have been far less reconciled to the apparent waxing and waning of their memory and regard forgetfulness as a personal fault, unlike the preordained attribute of intelligence. Countless courses proclaiming memory improvement testify to this belief. Judging by the rate at which memory research has suddenly accelerated, it may well be that humanity's suspicions are correct—memory may be boosted long before anyone can boost his intelligence as a whole.

Nerves, Cranial and Spinal

"On old Olympus' topmost top, a fat-eared German viewed a hop." So runs one of the nonobscene jingles for remembering the brain's cranial nerves. Obviously, the central nervous system does not exist in isolation; it must be connected to every part of the body. In all there are 43 pairs of nerves joining the central nervous system with everything else. Of this number, 12 pairs go to and from the brain itself, and 31 pairs go to and from the spinal cord. The nerves may be either entirely sensory—passing information only inward and toward the brain—or, more frequently, they may be a mixture of incoming and outgoing fibers. Each of the 43 has specific functions; hence the necessity for knowing which does what; hence the jingle for the 12 names: olfactory, optic, oculomotor, trochlear, trigeminal, abducens, facial, auditory (ear), glossopharyngeal, vagus, accessory, and hypoglossal.

Once again, everything makes much more immediate sense in the more primitive forms of animal life. Fish, for example, have both cranial and spinal nerves (although only 10 cranial nerves and a varying number of spinal nerves), but everything is simpler. The brain and spinal cord lie in a straight line, the nerves branch off along the length of this central nervous system much like rungs on a ladder, and they tend to be associated with an organ lying nearby. The first one receives impulses from the nose, the second from the eye, and so forth down to the tail. The human being acquired this same system, but only after it had been evolved for the differing shapes of the amphibians, the reptiles, the mammals, and the primates. The result is that number one cranial nerve still receives impulses from the nose, number two from the eye, and so on, but neither nose nor eye nor brain nor any other organ is situated in the same manner as in the earliest fish. Consequently, the regular runglike simplicity has gone. Instead, the cranial nerves run much more awkward courses in their atavistic efforts to join the same organ to the same bit of brain even though both brain and organ have radically altered proportions, sizes, shapes, and locations.

The spinal nerves are also much more complex in the human being than in fish. The ladderlike regularity exists to a certain extent, but the human spinal cord does not even run the entire length of the human backbone. It starts where it joins the brain and then continues downward for only 18 in. After the small of the back and for the last 10 in. of the spinal column, there is no spinal cord, only a horse's tail of fibers and tracts and occasional nervous complexes. Fibers leading from this spinal cord are always both sensory and motor. Even though the cord is quite long and is connected to 31 pairs of spinal nerves, as against 12 pairs of cranial nerves for the brain, and even though it is so important a trunk route for impulses, the spinal cord is far, far less bulky than the brain. It is about ½ in. wide and weighs only an ounce, one-fiftieth of the brain's great weight.

Transmission

Messages travel along nerves as electrical impulses. The original energy to cause these stimuli may have been mechanical or chemical or thermal or osmotic or electromagnetic or electric, but the energy of nerve transmission is always electrical. An impulse is a change in potential. Consequently, it is tempting to think in terms of electrical wiring, of current that flows rapidly along conducting wires from A to B, but the parallel breaks down at innumerable points. An ordinary electric current, for example, flowing along a copper wire does not travel at quite the speed of light, 186,000 miles a second, but it goes almost as fast. The impulse traveling along a nerve achieves at best about 350 ft. a second for the long fibers, much slower for the short ones. Instead of being comparable with the speed of light, its fastest speeds are a mere 250 miles per *hour,* and its slowest speeds are more like those of a walking man. A working rule is the larger the fiber the greater the speed. Man does not possess very large fibers, unlike many more primitive animals, such as the squid, and therefore human nerve transmission speeds are beaten by the nerves of many animals, let alone by electrical wires.

Other parallels are equally unsatisfactory. A copper wire is well insulated so that little current leaks out en route. The membrane lining a nerve axon is said to be a million times leakier. Also, the conduction of copper wire is so good that most of the electrical energy is satisfactorily delivered to the other end. The conduction of an axon is so bad that, were conduction the only means for getting the impulse to the other end, as in copper wires, the impulse would die out almost the moment it started the journey. Instead, the axon's system is self-propagating; the electrical charge is amplified all the way along the axon, and it arrives at the other end as good as new. In general, nerves cannot transmit feeble messages. Either the original impulse is strong enough to trigger the nerve's firing, or it is not. The system is all or none.

The axons, despite all differences, can nevertheless be called the nervous wiring of the body. Each axon is part of a neuron, a nerve cell, and the axon is one finely stretched extension of that neuron. It is so fine that it is often only 1/250 in. in diameter, and yet its length may be several feet. Its thinness partly indicates the number of axons that must be present in the body's nerves, such as the sciatic nerve in the thigh, which has the thickness of a pencil. As a rule, no one acquires any new neurons during life. His complement at birth or shortly afterward is his complement for his remaining years.

When a neuron dies, it cannot be replaced. The nerve cells are so specialized that they have lost the ability to make new cells, and neurons are being lost all the time. Should an axon be cut sufficiently far away from its mother cell, the peripheral part of the axon will slowly wither and die. The neuron itself will not necessarily die, although part of the axon on its side of the cut may perish. Sometimes the remaining axon will grow afresh from the region of the cut toward the peripheral area that it used to serve. Growth may be slow, but some higher animals have demonstrated an ability to grow new axon at the rate of 3 to 4 mm. a day. This rate of about an inch a week means that quite a time may elapse after the axon's severing before it arrives again at its destination and establishes a functional connection once more. Should the nerve be severed within the central nervous system of brain and spinal cord, the connection is broken for all time; but this does not always create such a severance as this seems to imply. Often, the body can find a way around such a problem. Other pathways are made use of and developed with use.

The all-or-none transmission of a stimulus along a nerve fiber means a system even simpler than the Morse code. There are not even dots and dashes, just dots. The dots are all equal dots, none louder than the rest. Therefore, the only way to vary the intensity of such a stimulus is to alter the frequency, the number of dots per second. Even though a nerve amplifies a stimulus as it travels along the fiber, the whole system is back to normal very rapidly, so much so that several hundred impulses can be impelled along a given fiber every second. Frequencies higher than 1,000 impulses per second have been experimentally measured in some mammal fibers, but human fibers usually conduct at frequencies lower than 100 per second.

Incidentally, the many billions of neurons within the nervous system of each human being give some idea of his or her potential and excellence compared with the modest neurological equipment of an insect. The bee and the ant, apart from being objects of veneration for wisdom and diligence, lead complex social lives and construct cunning homes for themselves. The bee has about 900 nerve cells, the ant 250. Mankind, not always wise or diligent, has many million times more neurons at his command, whether he uses them skillfully or not.

⋙ 2 6 ⋘

Sleep

It appears to be a rule that the bigger and more important a subject the deeper human ignorance is on that subject. What initiates birth? What makes the brain more capable as the childish years pass by? What causes old age? And what happens in sleep? Why is it necessary, bearing in mind the hazard of closed eyes in a hostile environment, and why can the brain not work without partially shutting some of itself down for a third of life?

Another generalization about big, important subjects is that the few crucial facts known have been discovered only recently. The first detection of the brain's electrical rhythms, the minute flickerings that change so radically when a person goes to sleep, was made only in the 1920s; Dr. Hans Berger published his findings in 1929. It was only in the 1950s that the two principal kinds of sleep, orthodox and paradoxical, or nondreaming and dreaming, were first worked out; Dr. Nathaniel Kleitman published his important paper on the subject in 1953. Only since then has it been discovered that both kinds of sleep are crucial to anyone's well-being; to be deprived of dreaming is as bad or possibly worse than deprivation of orthodox sleep; Dr. W. C. Dement did his striking experiments on dream curtailment in 1960. Finally, even though the interpretation of dreams is as old as the hills, modern thinking is largely based upon a book that appeared with this century; Sigmund Freud published his *Interpretations of Dreams* in November, 1899, to earn immortality, ridicule, fame, and $115 in royalties.

Like all major subjects, sleep is afflicted with misconceptions. Recent work indicates that no one, however tired, sleeps like a log; that everyone dreams, whether his powers of recall are good or not; that dreamless sleep cannot be called the best kind, because times of dreaming should always punctuate sleep; that dreams are lengthy affairs, possibly totaling two hours a night (they are not over in some sort of cerebral flash); that old people do not lose any desire for sleep as they grow older; and that conventional talk about deep sleep, or that one hour before midnight is better than two hours after, does not fit in with modern notions concerning the rhythms of a normal night's sleep.

Some elemental facts about sleep:

Its average length (according to a large French survey) is 7 hours, 20 minutes.

This duration is remarkably constant from age 30 to 80.

It is not strongly influenced by sex, intellectual ability (except for very low IQ's, who usually sleep longer), or cultural background.

Exercise during the day does not cause longer or shorter sleep.

Sedentary workers are 10 times more likely to take drugs than highly active people.

Women take sleeping drugs more than men.

About ten days is the record for staying awake by a normal person.

The body is relatively unmoved for at least the first few days of wakefulness—weight, heart rate, blood pressure, reflexes, stay normal, and the bodily temperature has its ups and downs equivalent to the traditional rise and fall of day and night routine. It is the brain that is so drastically affected by sleeplessness.

In the United States, there have been some notable "wakeathons" (long bouts without sleep). The traditional picture is of slightly deranged behavior by the third day, such as unreasonable laughing or irrational irritability. The normal cyclical rhythm is not forgotten, despite its interruption, because the desire to sleep during the second night is greater than during the following day. After the third day, derangement becomes more exaggerated. There are wilder imaginings, a belief that others are destroying the experiment, that the floor is heaving, that food is poisoned; all such delusions and hallucinations suddenly come to an end after 200 hours or more with the permitted arrival of sleep. In one famous wakeathon, Peter Tripp, a disc jockey, kept awake off Times Square for 201 hours, 13 minutes, and then fell into a normal sleep lasting 13 hours and 13 minutes.

Quite the most significant discovery so far is the recent realization that sleep has a cycle. A person going to sleep first falls into orthodox sleep. An EEG measuring the minute voltage differentials playing about his brain detects the changes that inevitably occur as a person slowly sinks from wakefulness into sleep. Some 90 minutes later, the brain's electrical rhythms revert to the sort of pattern indicated by the EEG when the person had been in the act of falling asleep. At the same time, the eyes

start moving about behind the closed lids. It is tempting to call this time
a period of light sleep, but the description is unworthy because, despite
the activity recorded on the EEG and by the eyes, there is also great
depth to this kind of sleep; muscles, for example, are then even more
relaxed than during the initial and orthodox sleep. Both types of sleep
are vital, both occur alternately, and neither depth nor lightness is a
valid term in this regard. During a typical night's sleep, a person will
oscillate from orthodox sleep to the rapid-eye-movement kind some
five times. Orthodox sleep is always longer and may consume 80 percent of the night. The remaining 20 percent, indicated by the quite different pattern on the EEG and by eye movement, is known as paradoxical sleep. It arises after intervals of 90 minutes. Each burst of this
paradoxical sleep lasts only 10 to 30 minutes at the beginning of the
night, but may last for an hour by the end of it.

Once again, the remarkableness of a discovery lies in its simplicity.
In the late 1930s, E. Jacobson drew attention to the association between
dreams and eye movement. Later, Nathaniel Kleitman, Bill Dement,
Eugene Aserinsky, and others working in Chicago experimented with
this idea. Sure enough, those awakened at the time of eye flickering
could in general speak of dreams; those awakened during orthodox
sleep could scarcely ever recall them. If anything is recalled from this
time, it tends to be simple cogitation of the day's events, not the spicy,
glamorous, fraught, inconsequential, hostile, and abject sequences typical
of the dreamworld. Considering the number of hours mankind has
spent watching either womankind or any sleeping person, it is remarkable that no earlier scientific notice was taken of these jerky eye movements, still less of their association with dreams.

An experiment then took place in 1960 to discover the importance
of dreaming. As soon as the EEG moved away from orthodox sleep and
as soon as the eyeballs started their blind activity, the volunteers were
awakened. Soon, they were allowed to sleep again, but they then slept
in orthodox and not dream sleep. They were awakened whenever dream
sleep began to manifest itself, and for several nights the regimen of no
sleep with dreams was rigidly applied. Then, for five blissful nights, the
men were allowed undisturbed sleep. There were three findings. First,
there had to be more awakenings as time went on; on the first night
the men had to be awakened from a dream state only five times, but
on the fifth night the numbers of necessary wakenings were twenty to
thirty. Second, during the five uninterrupted nights, the EEG and eyeballs recorded double the normal dreamtime, suggesting that a backlog
was being made up. Third, despite the awakenings, each man got seven
hours' sleep a night; but during daytime, for all that, they behaved irri-

tably, tensely, and with many of the characteristics of men deprived of the greater part of their sleep requirements.

In other words, mankind has to dream, or at least to have the kind of sleep generally accompanied by dreams. When Peter Tripp finally slept for 13 hours, having waited over eight days to do so, he dreamed for 3 hours, 46 minutes (or 28 percent), of his total sleep time. When still awake and suffering hallucinations, they had come roughly every 90 minutes, as if they were the attempts of a befuddled brain to follow its traditional, cyclical pattern of sleep. Customarily, those deprived of sleep take more orthodox sleep than normal at their first sleep; but, if pep pills or similar stimulants have been the cause of their prolonged wakefulness, they will take more dream sleep than normal when sleep is eventually permitted to catch up with them.

Babies and infants sleep, as is well known, for a large part of their neonatal day; but babies and infants, as is less commonly appreciated, have quite different ideas over the amount of sleep they require. An average requirement is 16 hours, not 22 as is printed in some of the literature distributed at British maternity centers. One study, which involved close observation of babies to determine whether they were really asleep or merely quiet, discovered a remarkable sleep range among infants in the first three days of life. They were awake from 1 to 13½ hours out of the 24. Some of them were therefore sleeping more than twice as long as others. Similarly, although the average length of the maximum sleep period throughout the 24 hours was 4.4 hours, some of the infants could sleep for 10 hours without waking while others never achieved more than 2 hours, 6 minutes. Mothers and maternity homes may have invented neat rules for the offspring; but the offspring have had nine months to themselves in which to fashion quite distinctive personal attributes and behavior patterns.

A newborn baby, sleeping his 16 hours a day, or a lot more, or a lot less, spends about half of it in the dream kind of sleep, half in the orthodox kind. For a young child the dreamtime drops to 30 to 40 percent of the total, and it further falls to 20 percent by adulthood. As premature infants are thought to spend an even greater proportion of their sleep in the dream state, it is presumed that the fetus sleeps longer than the newborn child and dreams proportionately more. As it is hard to visualize, and impossible to prove, that a child in the uterus is dreaming, it is perhaps better to say it is experiencing a type of sleep that will later be accompanied by dreams.

Most certainly, a fetus has established a rhythm of sleeping and waking before it is born. As an adult sleeps once a day for a third of that day, and as a child sleeps twice a day for a total of half that day, and as a newborn infant sleeps half a dozen times a day for a total of two-thirds of each day, it is assumed that the elderly fetus sleeps for a longer proportion of each 24 hours and has bouts of wakefulness even more intermittently than a newborn baby.

Mankind tends to regard sleep as the abnormal and wakefulness as the normal state. (There is not even an easy English noun for the state of wakefulness.) It is now generally considered, having taken note of the premature infant's addiction to sleep and its occasional lapses into a more wakeful state, that sleep is the prime condition invaded later on by increasingly lengthy periods of wakefulness. The distinction also becomes important in theoretical evaluations of the subject—can there be a sleep center in the brain that sends a man to sleep, or an awakening center that irritates him out of his normal, passive, and sleeping condition?

Animals do not, at least not yet, help to unravel the sleep problem. Undoubtedly, many go to sleep, notably mammals and birds, and there is also some justification for saying that fish lying on the tank's bottom at night are asleep. Only mammals seem to exhibit the two kinds of sleep, dream and orthodox. Animals do to some extent explain the apparent vulnerability of sleep by proving themselves remarkably adept at waking instantly. Dr. H. Hediger, of the Zurich and Basel zoos, used to glide on tiptoe toward his elephants, but they always heard him coming. Only in the disturbance and din of a circus was he able to catch some elephants sleeping and to assess their sleep periods as 2¼ hours a night. Man, living in his own manmade circus of noise and battered sense organs and having to claw his way back from sleep into something approaching consciousness as the alarm galvanizes him into activity, has plainly lost 99 percent of his jungle sensitivity. It is even harder for him to imagine a central nervous system so finely balanced, as in the animals, between sleep and instant readiness.

This knife edge between the two forms of consciousness does not simplify the comprehension of sleep. Just what do animals gain from the short period when they appear to relax, but with a hair trigger attached to every sense organ? And why does a sheep sleep in the dream state for only 2 percent of the total time, while a cat is in that state for 20 to 60 percent of the sleeptime? Why does an infant need more sleep than an adult; are both brains equally taxed and equally in need of whatever sleep provides? And why does an adult in his thinking prime need no more and no less sleep than some hapless dotard shuffling wearily through yet another forgotten day?

Current bafflement has not stopped investigation. Recently, for example, Dr. Ian Oswald and others at Edinburgh University, suspecting that biochemical imbalance might underline the need for sleep, decided to introduce such an imbalance. Tryptophan is a vital amino acid, an essential ingredient in the human diet. Volunteers were given an extra and abnormal dose of it just before going to sleep, and it was discovered that some of them began their dream part of sleep exceptionally early in consequence. The work is exciting because it may lead to an understanding of the biochemical control of sleep, and such an understanding may even lead to a comprehension of the reason for the vulnerable third of each day spent in the cyclical depths of sleep.

Some random sleep facts:

A person loses 1 to 1½ oz. in weight per hour of sleep (or 11 oz. per night).

Body temperature falls during normal sleeptime, whether the person sleeps or not.

Less urine is produced per hour of sleep.

People move some 40 times a night (certainly no logs), with roughly 30 seconds of movement per hour.

Babies are only six times more active when awake than when asleep.

Girls sleep more soundly than boys.

Almost everyone can remember dreams when awakened at times of rapid eye movement.

Almost no one can remember them if awakened ten minutes after the eye movements have ceased.

Eye movements do not happen with those blind from birth, and most of their dream images are auditory.

Times of rapid eye movement are regularly associated with penile erections.

Some highly abnormal people have not slept for years.

Learning during sleep is impractical and probably impossible.*

Those who say they feel worse after sleep are right, because tasks involving dexterity are better done toward the evening.

The architect R. Buckminster Fuller once trained himself to have a half-hour's sleep every three hours, totaling four hours in every 24, for a year.

Computers may be made to "dream" in order to review and reject redundant material.

Narcolepsy is a rare condition that gives rise to irresistible and unwelcome attacks of falling asleep.

One of a pair of Siamese twins can fall asleep without the other.

* Twenty boys were once admonished 16,200 times in 54 nights at a summer camp not to bite their nails; allegedly, there were only 12 nail-biters at the end of the season.

Men have been acquitted of somnambulistic homicide, or killing when they were asleep.

The yawn, halfway between a reflex and an expressive movement, has defied attempts at explanation. It lasts a few seconds, it is sometimes partnered by stretching, it happens before sleep and after sleep, it accompanies weariness and boredom, it occurs in many mammals, notably the apes and monkeys, and one must be conscious to yawn. It is said to be contagious, but probably conditions that promote yawning in one person also promote yawning in those nearby. The act of yawning is often accompanied by increased tears, either because of direct pressure on the tear gland due to the yawn's facial contortions or because of nervous impulses partnering those that trigger this bizarre, openmouthed, and vaguely vocal form of behavior. The act, which is linked with a slight and fleeting increase in heartbeat and some constriction of capillaries, may be a physiological attempt to get more blood to lungs and brain; but blood flow is frequently boosted on many other occasions without the bewildering grimace of a jaw-cracking, ear-popping yawn.

The business of going to sleep is accompanied by other quaint traits. The eyes glaze over, for instance. This is thought to be merely the slowing down of the customarily swift jerks of the eye, as it leaps from subject to subject—or just leaps. Similarly, there may be a wavering of the eyes when they eventually do focus on their object. When the eyes are finally covered over by the lids, the floating feeling of going to sleep may be followed by the horrific, heart-stopping drama of apparently total spasm. Known in the books as a start (and feeling more like a convulsive stop to everything), the muscular contractions may occur in an arm or a leg or the whole body. They are more common in adults than children and, despite their brutal interruption of sleep, do not usually interfere with it during the rest of the night.

Snoring does not interfere with the snorer's sleep, unless acts of retribution are taken by others. It is described as "sounds made by vibrations in the soft palate and posterior faucal pillars during sleep." When children snore, which is not common, it is often due to swollen tonsils or adenoids. When adults snore, which they tend to do increasingly with age, it is frequently caused by a loss of tone in the palate muscles. This loss of tone has been blamed upon obesity, fatigue, smoking, overwork, ill-health, or just old age. Both sexes snore, and they tend to do so lying on the back with mouth open. There is evidence that snoring decreases during the dream periods of sleep, which can therefore give temporary respite to others. Snoring is harmless to the sleeper, despite the thunderous treatment of the tissues nearby, but surgery has often been attempted in an effort to reduce the noise. Other *ad hoc* remedies include hairbrushes or stones to keep a person off his back, pillows to keep his head more vertical, splints and pegs for keeping his mouth closed, and a wealth of inventions.

In summary, therefore, sleep is a vital need but its reasons are quite unknown. Dream sleep is equally vital, equally incomprehensible. Without sleep, a normal man will die quicker than without food. Since such ignorance over the main issue of sleep exists, it seems only fair that the ancillary factors like yawning keep us equally in the dark about their reasons.

Speech

Language most showeth a man; speak that I may see thee.
Ben Jonson

At birth a child knows nothing of speech, and until that moment has not made a sound. At the age of one it will say a few words. At two its words will be sentences—of a sort. At three it will talk incessantly. At four, given good hearing, sound intelligence, no speech impediments, and a normal willingness to learn and communicate, the child will have very nearly mastered the entire complex and abstract structure of language. As Professor David McNeill of Michigan put it: "In slightly more than two years children acquire full knowledge of the grammatical system of their native tongue." It is a matter of arriving, suddenly, abruptly, in a world of sounds, of imitating these sounds, making sense of them, and then making use of them. At birth a child not only knows no speech, but also, unlike an adult arriving in Peking or Ulan-Bator without a phrase book, has no concept of speech, no preconceived notions whatever, let alone refinements such as the difference between "bite dog" and "dog bite." It is a stunning intellectual achievement, unthinkable by most adults; yet it is carried out by every child even before reaching school.

The age for the various aspects of this achievement is extremely variable. Single words generally come at the first birthday, when children are also tottering into a walk, but the first-word range is at least from 8 months to 2½ years. Phrases begin at 18 months, but the normal range is certainly from 10 months to 3½ years. At two a child may have few words, or over 2,000. Some children complicate the issue further by speaking intelligibly, or intelligibly enough for friends and relations, and then relapsing into unintelligibility for a year or two for no apparent reason. An experiment by L. C. Strayer seems to indicate that speech training is effective but pointless. A pair of twins 19½ months old were just about to talk. One was given training, and his word power was boosted from one word to 35 in 5 weeks. His twin was then still wordless, but was immediately given training and he learned faster than the first. The experiment was stopped when he had reached 30 words. Soon, the children were equally adept once again, and each took his own time to acquire a vocabulary. Speech comes, in other words, when the child is ready to speak.

Some generalizations:

Speech comes later for twins than singletons.

Girls speak before boys.

"Dada" is usually said before "mama," owing to a preference for "d," not necessarily for the father.

Babies use far more vowels than consonants (adults use a vowel to every 1.4 consonants).

A baby's first vowels are those that adults form in the front of the mouth.

A baby's first consonants are formed at the back of its mouth.

Children learn to speak at different speeds according to their environment.

G. A. Miller said the most precocious child orator was a blind girl, the only daughter of wealthy parents. The slowest speaker is a hard-of-hearing twin born into a large family with poor parents who speak two or three languages.

Whereas 100 percent of a child's jargon is meaningless even to a parent (and to the child too?), although a general sense may be conveyed, quite a high proportion remains unintelligible even when speech has begun. D. McCarthy reckoned that only 26 percent of an 18-month-old child's talk was comprehensible, 67 percent at 2, 89 percent at 2½, 93 percent at 3 and 99 percent at 3½.

An infant deaf in both ears does not learn to speak without special training. An infant partly deaf in both ears may learn the sounds he can see being made—b, f, w—but not g, l, r.

No one knows how man's speech began. Of course, other animals convey a lot of information in sounds, but no other form of communication is comparable to mankind's talk. (The dolphin's chatter is still not understood.) There is a theory that holds that a better valve was developed in the human windpipe to lock air more completely within the chest cavity, thereby providing a firmer base for the arms. There is another theory that holds that mankind's first words were based upon the grunts, puffs, and groans that are the inevitable accompaniments to physical labor, each type of grunt being descriptive of a type of action. Be that as it may, man now has an effective larynx at the top of his windpipe. All air to and from the lungs goes through the larynx, but normally the laryngeal muscles are relaxed to leave a wedge-shaped opening, .7 in. long in men, .5 in. or less in women. Making two sides of this wedge are the vocal cords.

The vocal cords are not cords. They are membranes, more like reeds than any possible kind of cord, and a sound is made after the two of them have been brought together to close that wedge-shaped opening. If air is then blown through the larynx, preferably from the lungs—although noises are possible, particularly for the ventriloquist, when air is drawn toward the lungs—a sound will be made because the valve of the vocal membranes is constantly forced apart by the pressure behind it. Each forcing apart causes the escape of a puff of air and then the coming together again of the two folds. The vibration, which happens many times a second, occurs on more than one frequency at once. The basic tone of the human voice, despite the fact that there are other frequencies, is about 125 cycles a second.

Making a sound is not making speech; no one can talk through an oboe. It is necessary to articulate, to join together, before the basic note or notes are transformed into talk. The mobile articulators are the lower lip and jaw, the parts of the tongue, and the vocal cords; they have to move toward something. The fixed articulators are the upper lip, upper teeth, the ridge of gum supporting the teeth, the hard palate at the front, the soft palate at the back, and the sides of the larynx. Say any word and feel the inevitability of the articulation involved. Say "pop" without the lips touching, say "that" without pressing the tongue's tip to the upper teeth, say "she" with the tongue in either cheek.

There are five types of articulation:

1. Plosives, stops. Breath has to be stopped to make them, as in pie.
2. Fricatives, spirants. Breath is forced through some narrow groove, as in fine, thin, yes, she.
3. Laterals. Breath has to avoid the mouth's center and come around the sides, as in lip, low.
4. Trills. Vibration of one of the articulators, such as the tongue. No trills in English, but Scotsmen roll the "r."
5. Vowels. Whole air passage is more open than in first four, which are all consonants.

These different types of articulation, plus the different positions of each type (fine, thin, yes, she—all use different positions), permit a number of different sound elements to be made. These verbal elements are the basis of any language. English can be written phonetically, not as the 21 consonants and 5 vowels of the alphabet, but as 40 elements or phonemes. Some 14 or 15 are vowels, the remainder consonants. Of the 40, some are rarely used, some frequently, and only 9 are used in half of what we say, namely the consonants *n, t, r, s, d, l,* and *th* (as in then), the vowels *i* as in it and *e* as in river. However, the phonemes are insufficient to make a language by themselves. It is the pattern of their use rather than the sounds alone that enable us to communicate.

The 3 billion people in the world speak roughly 2,000 languages (this assumed total fluctuates wildly, for there is eternal disagreement over the extent of barriers caused by mere dialects) or 1.5 million people per language. English is a strong contender for the role of world language, and only about 2,000 words are necessary to speak it quite well. G. A. Miller has pointed out that, although the 50 most common words make up 60 percent of those we say and 45 percent of those we write, the limited vocabulary of Basic English does lead to inevitable losses— "blood, sweat, and tears" becomes "blood, body water, and eye water." Normal English uses several times the number as Basic English, and the extra words are important. In 1930, some telephone conversations were recorded and analyzed. The result was a total usage of 2,240 different lexical units (give, gave, and given are one lexical unit) and possibly 5,000 different words. A good fiction vocabulary is said to be 10,000 words, and a medical student reputedly adds 10,000 words to his vocabulary at medical school. James Joyce used 29,899 words in *Ulysses,* and the *Oxford English Dictionary* records 500,000 lexical units.

There are three properties of any sound, and human speech is also associated with these three—loudness, pitch, and quality. In the English language, changes in loudness and quality are more important than changes in pitch.

Loudness depends on the energy with which the cords vibrate, and this depends on the pressure with which the air is impelled past them. Fairly loud singing means the passage of as much as 200 cc. of air per second over the cords. A trained singer can be more economical with his reserves of air; he can get the same loudness from a fifth as much air. The power of speech can be measured in watts just as any other power source. A whisper is .001 microwatt, faint talk .1 microwatt, very loud talk 100 microwatts. All vowels radiate more power than any consonant; consequently, loud shouts for help stress the vowels, not the consonants. (The English "help" is not so effective as the Italian "aiuto" —eye-oo-toe.)

Pitch is determined mainly by the length and tightness of the cords. To some extent, pitch can be altered, and trained singers can move happily from one octave to another, but human growth causes conspicuous changes in pitch. Both boys and girls are born with cords about .23 in. long, and these grow in length much as the body itself grows. By two they are .31 in. long; by six they are .4 in.; by ten they are .46 in., and the boy's cords are then showing signs of growing longer even though the height of girls at this age may actually be greater than the height of boys. At 14, on average, a girl's cords are .46 in. long, a boy's .5 in. At 20, a boy's are .92 in., and a girl's are only .6 in. At 30, a man's cords are 1.2 in. (a fivefold increase since birth) and a woman's are .8 in. (slightly over a threefold increase). The change in pitch is not something that happens once in adolescence; it is changing throughout the first three decades, and it changes again at the end of life, when cords shorten and voices become higher. Sometimes, as with eunuchoids, the voice of an adolescent remains strangely unbroken; but this can usually be remedied rapidly by suitable treatment, and a normal male voice soon results. A true eunuch's voice does not break, provided castration is performed before puberty.

Quality, or timbre, depends upon the form and size of the various resonating chambers, the throat, the chest, and the mouth and its cavities. The differences among the vowels are made by alterations to these chambers, without much recourse to the articulation devices. A whisper is possible solely by adjusting articulation and cavities; the vocal cords are not made to vibrate. Consequently there is difficulty in guessing the sex of a whisper because the major clue of cord length and fundamental frequency is lacking.

Henry Luce, Somerset Maugham, Demosthenes, King George VI, Porky Pig, and roughly one in 100 of the general population are in the same speech category; their voices have all been subject to a stammer. To stammer or to stutter is the same, with the British prone to stammer, Americans to stutter. There have been efforts to distinguish the two —stammer being the hesitation, stutter the repetition—but the words are generally considered synonymous.

Two types of stammer are customarily recognized. The first affects two- to four-year-olds during normal learning of speech, as the child stumbles along in his efforts to be coherent and when the breathless urgency of the message is infrequently matched by the skill to impart its information. The second, the persistent stammer, first affects the four- to seven-year-olds, and just occasionally the first type merges into the second. Persistent stammer hits boys far more often than girls, it frequently disappears in the young of its own accord, it occurs more often with late speakers and in children of low intelligence, and it sometimes runs in families even when mimicry can be ruled out. The traditional belief in an association between stammering and left-handedness, notably when right-handedness is made compulsory, is not borne out by recent studies (see the earlier chapter on the brain). The several theories that stammering is purely psychological in origin are not assisted by the overwhelming frequency with which boys are afflicted, but a review on the subject by the *British Medical Journal* suggested that stammering is probably best treated by a combination of speech therapy and psychotherapy. There are few cases of completely successful cures, although stammerers can be made to lose their stammers in the presence of suitable noise, a noise that tends to make normal people stammer. Some stammerers can be helped by having miniature metronomes beating out the time for them.

Although earlier generations were entirely familiar with stammering and with the deaf-mute, there is a form of muteness that is entirely modern. Total laryngectomy, performed upon discovery of a malignancy in the larynx, is an operation that removes the voice along with the cancer. There are about 30,000 people in the United States without a larynx, and being suddenly unable to make a sound has been a bewildering shock for many of them. However, the majority of laryngectomized people can regain voice of a sort, even though they have to breathe through a hole in their necks and have no vocal cords.

Finally, as leaven, speech can lie, but can lies be detected? In 1965, a subcommittee of the House of Representatives Committee on Government Operations reported that the government owned at least 512 lie-detection devices for which it had paid $428,066. (The "at least" is because the Central Intelligence Agency was secretive about its methods of extracting secrets.) Joined to the average price of $836 for the machines were the more costly salaries of their attendants, and yet, according to the committee, "there is no 'lie-detector,' neither machine nor human. People have been deceived by a myth that a metal box in the hands of an investigator can detect truth or falsehood."

⋖ 28 ⋗

Temperature

Normal · Why Are Bodies Warm? · Chilling · Heat ·
Hibernation · Hypothermia

The heat of a body is the balance between heat gained and heat lost.
It is gained primarily by metabolism, secondarily from the environment
(normally cooler than the body), and then by shivering (involuntary
activity of skeletal muscles) and by the consumption of hot food. The
basic metabolism of a person at rest produces about 1,700 calories of
heat per day for men, 1,500 for women. This is sufficient heat (assuming
there is no loss) to raise the temperature by nearly 2°F. per hour.
Moderate activity may produce 3,000 calories, extreme activity 6,000
calories, or enough to raise the temperature by over 6°F. per hour.
Without heat loss, a fatal heatstroke would therefore occur within a
few hours.

Heat is lost primarily by radiation, convection, and conduction,
these three totaling perhaps 72 percent, but ambient temperature and
the amount of clothing worn will affect the percentages; secondarily by
evaporation from the skin, which is 15 percent under normal conditions;
and lastly by evaporation from the lungs (7 percent), by warming the
air taken into the lungs (3 percent), and by the expulsion of urine and
feces (3 percent). The normal daily temperate-zone sweat loss varies
between one and two pints, indicating 300 to 530 calories of heat
lost (the latent heat of the evaporation of sweat is .59 calories). The
maximum sweat rate may reach 3 pints an hour, but with a maximum of
about 21 pints in 24 hours, indicating a loss of over 7,000 calories—
four times the basal metabolic rate. Metabolism produces heat because
chemical changes frequently liberate as much energy as heat. During
muscular activity, only 25 percent of the energy produced is converted
into work; the remaining 75 percent is heat. Temperature regulation,

the achievement of the balance between heat lost and heat gained, is under the control of the hypothalamus in the brain. It is less efficient in the very young and the old.

Normal

The word "normal," as applied to human body temperature, is splendidly misleading. The little arrow on the clinical thermometer, doggedly directed at 98.6°F., gives the idea extra support, and the preciseness of that .6 backs it up even more. The awkward figure is the fault of the German physicist Gabriel Daniel Fahrenheit. Isaac Newton, a duo-decimal enthusiast, had wanted 12 units between water's freezing and boiling. Fahrenheit's new thermometer could do better than that, per-mitting more units. He liked the idea of putting the lowest temperature (made with salt and ice) at 0, letting water freeze at 32, giving the body 96, setting water's boiling point at 212, all of them nice mathematical numbers. Greater accuracy subsequently, and a determination to keep freezing and boiling 180 degrees apart (another nice number), meant that something had to give—and it was body temperature.

Normally, the majority of us do not have a "normal" temperature. Infants have a higher temperature; older people have a lower. Ordinary adults wake up with temperatures below normal and go to sleep above normal. Women are 1°F. hotter after ovulation. The armpit (or axilla) is 1°F. cooler than the mouth and the groin, and is cooler still in thin people. The rectum is almost a degree higher. While "normal" in the United States is 98.6°F., it is 98.4°F. in Britain. In Europe, it is 37°C.

The story of temperature-taking really began only 100 years ago with Carl Wunderlich (1815–77), a German physician in Leipzig. Although clinical thermometers were a foot long and took 20 minutes to register a man's temperature, he—more than anyone else—initiated the regular practice of recording a patient's thermal fluctuations. There is current argument that he did his work too well and that nurses now spend far too much time routinely recording temperatures; but it is also said of him that he found fever a disease and left it a symptom (which some-day, presumably, will be said of some man or men about cancer).

As many warm-blooded (homoiothermic) creatures go, man is cool. Among domestic animals (according to H. Dukes) temperatures are 99.7°F. for a stallion; mare, 100°F.; steer, 101°F.; cow, 101.5°F.; cat, 101.5°F.; dog, 102°F.; sheep, 102.3°F.; pig, 102.5°F.; rabbit, 103.1°F.; goat, 103.8°F.; chicken, 107.1°F. (varying from 105° to 109°). Human beings would be near to death or dead if kept at chicken heat. Mammals and birds are all warm-blooded, but some are better at regulation

Monotremes (like the duckbill platypus), marsupials (like the kangaroo and koala bear), and bats are relatively inexpert. The lower vertebrates (fishes, amphibians, and reptiles) are all considered cold-blooded, or poikilothermic. In fact, as Professor A. S. Romer, of Harvard University, says, there is some sort of regulation even among these forms, notably reptiles. Not only do they seek out hot or cold places, light or shade, but there are also "internal mechanisms of which we know little." The old fishermen's story that tuna often feel warm has recently been proved by marine biologists; the fish can maintain a temperature 25°F. warmer than the water they swim in.

Why Are Bodies Warm?

Why do we keep warm? Why at 98.6°F. or thereabouts? It is a compromise. On the one hand, chemical reactions are speeded up (roughly two or three times every 20°F.) with heat; on the other, enzymes, the catalysts vital to the body's chemical reactions, can be destroyed by too much heat. But it is no good living like a torpid lizard on a cold day. Similarly, it is unsatisfactory to cook one's enzymes (like the white of an egg being irreversibly cooked by heat). It so happens that most enzymes are inactive at freezing point, and they have been inactivated —quite a different thing—by boiling point. Animal enzymes work best at 100°F., or slightly more and slightly hotter than the human "normal." It has even been argued that humans do better when marginally more feverish. Certainly, athletes perform better in the latter half of the day when they are warmer. However, there is a limit, and an emphatic one, to the desirability of increased heat. By 111°F. or so, the destructive effects of heat (on the enzymes and other proteins) are equal to or greater than the ability of the body to repair them. The rate of destruction is then increasing perhaps 40 times for every degree rise in temperature, and so death becomes inevitable.

Human beings start life much hotter than they end it. Babies are poor at regulation at first. Cast out so finally from their cozy uterine incubator and rarely able to shiver, they drop 3°F. in the first hour (according to one survey) despite a room temperature of 80°F. to 85°F. A maximum drop of 4.6°F. was recorded at the third hour. The return to "normal" is always a slower business, but a spate of crying (increasing metabolism by 180 percent) can speed things up. With premature babies, heat regulation is even less perfect. Environmental temperature of 84°F. to 90°F., with a humidity of 65 percent (somewhat like midday at a hot Mediterranean resort), is best, according to E. H. Watson and G. H. Lowry. As the baby grows into an infant and then into a child, the average temperature first rises, then drops. Rectal readings under basal conditions have been recorded as:

3	months	99.4°F.
6	"	99.5°F.
1	year	99.7°F.
3	years	99.0°F.
5	"	98.6°F.
7	"	98.3°F.
9	"	98.1°F.
11	"	98.0°F.
13	"	97.8°F.

Girls tend to stabilize at 14, boys at 18.

To confound the picture of "normality" still further, there is a daily cycle. Babies acquire it quickly, and then follow the traditional pattern of a peak in the evening and a trough at dawn. An average between maximum and minimum is 2°F., but individuals can go up and down by 3°F. or more. Menstruation is a further complexity; during menstruation, the temperature is low. It increases slightly, with a small but pronounced rise (perhaps as much as a degree), during ovulation, when the ovary releases an egg. A hot bath, reasonably enough, sends the bather's temperature up to 100°F. or so. Exercise does even better. After three miles, a runner can read 105°F. rectally, but less than normal on his skin due to all the sweating. A long cool drink reduces mouth temperature by 3°F. and so may a blocked-up nose, with cooling air keeping oral temperature down. Infants can induce fever temperatures by quite mild bouts of rage, or drop 7°F. in a cold bath. A hot climate pushes the entire range of temperatures up by about 1°F., but natives (certainly in India) are neither hotter nor cooler than acclimatized visitors.

Chilling

Only very recently was the entire medical profession made forcibly aware of the perils of hypothermia in the elderly—or the fact that countless people in temperate places quietly freeze to death every winter. A special report published during November, 1964, in the *British Medical Journal* stressed that the condition, although unspectacular, had a "very high mortality rate, very much higher than is commonly supposed." One British physician even estimated 20,000 to 100,000 deaths each winter. The *British Medical Journal* said in 1966 it was still a major cause of death each British winter. Doctors who carry only the conventional clinical thermometers, which record temperatures above 95°F. (up to 110°F.), can be unaware of the actual and far lower temperature of their old patient. Dr. Geoffrey Taylor reported that the temperature of all old people falls below 95°F., often below 90°F., if the temperature of their rooms is less than freezing.

One trouble is the insidious nature of the chilling process. H. Duguid recognized three phases. From 98°F. to 90°F., there is a feeling of cold and shivering occurs. From 90°F. to 75°F., the subject is depressed and usually does not complain of feeling cold. His pulse slows down, blood pressure falls, and all shivering has stopped by 85°F. There is a downward path below 75°F., with survival rare. The temperature-regulating center ceases to function, and the body progressively cools until it reaches the level of the atmosphere. Circulation fails at about 70°F. To make matters worse, consciousness becomes clouded at about 86°F., and clothes may be taken off rather than put on. Another feature is torpidity and a desire to sleep. Those who can still walk, despite increasingly stiff muscles, may be giddy and suffer from impaired vision and look for all the world like wandering drunks, but anyone below 90°F. requires immediate treatment. (Considering the fact that many old people do die of cold, it is worrying to read frequently in books that "most deaths by freezing occur in abandoned infants and alcoholics." One wonders how many of those "alcoholics" are really victims of cold, suffering from impaired vision and balance.)

The *British Medical Journal*'s anonymous expert recommended (in October, 1965) slow warming. A rise of one degree an hour was sufficient and could be achieved by keeping the patient well covered in a room kept at 70°F. to 80°F., and by monitoring his return to a more warm-blooded and healthier state. For younger people, like sailors or mountaineers who are rescued in a cold state, the warming up should be as rapid as possible. They have tougher constitutions than the elderly, and therefore a bath at 111°F. will heat them with a minimum loss of time. Naturally, anyone falling overboard should be retrieved with even greater alacrity. According to Britain's Institute of Aviation Medicine, five minutes' immersion in water at 40°F., a fairly common ocean temperature, causes a body to become rigid and incapable of making the effort to keep the head above water. Death comes perhaps after two hours, perhaps after 30 minutes.

Obviously, a thermometer recording the conventional range of 95°F. to 110°F. is unsatisfactory. The *British Medical Journal* report recommended that 75°F. to 105°F. was necessary for general use. A range of 75°F. to 110°F. has also been suggested, in order to cope with the heatstroke as well. One English doctor in the winter of 1964–65 (not a very cold one), equipped with a low-range thermometer, took mouth temperatures of old people who were not ill. He found the average was 94°F., the lowest 89°F. The lowest temperature ever recorded in a person who suffered accidental hypothermia and survived was 64.4°F. A young Negro woman in the United States was pulled out of a snowdrift; she lost some of her extremities from frostbite but did live. (Russians frequently report such incidents, but omit details.) That woman had gone halfway to the freezing point from "normal" and back again. Particularly chilly comfort is the fact that no one immersed in water can actually freeze. Sea water freezes at 28.5°F., a temperature lower than fresh water's freezing, but body tissue freezes at about 27.5°F.

Frostbite is basically a blockage of the blood vessels; they constrict so much that blood cells cannot pass through them. At the same time, the vessels suffer injury, and consequently, when the limb is thawed out, the blood vessels leak and there may be clotting. Even at temperatures above freezing, the same kind of damage can be done, although far less speedily. It is then given such names as immersion foot, immersion hand, or trench foot.

Heat

Trouble from too much heat is more complex, partly because the body is more sensitive to increases than decreases in temperature, and partly because there are so many types of heat disorder. The book *Exploration Medicine* (in a chapter by C. S. Leithead) lists them. Briefly they are:

1. Heat syncope. Generally giddiness and fatigue. Sometimes fainting. Rest (not alcohol) will cure it.
2. Heat edema. Swelling of the extremities. "Deck ankles." Unimportant.
3. Water-depletion heat exhaustion. Sweating output not balanced by water intake; hence thirst, fatigue, giddiness, fever, then delirium. Death likely when water debt reaches 20 percent of total body water (20 percent of average total equals 22 pints).
4. Salt-depletion heat exhaustion. Salt loss in sweating not balanced by intake. Hence fatigue, giddiness, nausea, vomiting, cramp. Generally occurs only in unacclimatized. Seldom fatal. Normal daily diet contains .33 oz. of salt. Sweat may initially contain some .14 oz. of salt in each quart. As sweating may rise to a quart an hour, obviously depletion can occur. But body acclimatizes itself in a few days. Less salt appears in urine and sweat, and normal daily salt diet can be as before.

5. Heat cramps. Not necessary to visit tropics to get heat cramps, as stokers, miners, firemen, and athletes know. Disorder extremely painful (with knotted muscles) but never fatal. It is a very rapid form of salt depletion.
6. Prickly heat (miliaria). An irritating, inconvenient, and common rash occurring on skin wet with sweat. Not a hazard, but rashes can become infected.
7. Anhidrotic heat exhaustion. No sweating in affected areas, but blisters instead. Little understood and rare.
8. Heatstroke. Heat regulation may suddenly go haywire, sweating stops, and temperature goes up (above 105°F.), and delirium, convulsions, and coma occur. Rare but very dangerous. (*Exploration Medicine*'s recommended treatment makes startling reading: "Ideally, the patient is stripped, placed in a good stream of cold, dry air, and sprayed with water at 50°F. . . . or in a bath filled with ice chips and water. . . . Convulsions or shivering should not be allowed to delay the treatment. . . . Cooling should be stopped when temperature has fallen to 102°F. . . . chances of survival seldom better than 65 percent.")

As might be expected, the old and the very young are most severely affected by heat. Weak hearts in the old and vulnerability to dehydration in the very young are mainly to blame. Taking heat and cold together, the human body has a comfortable temperature range under normal conditions of some 3°F. This can be stepped up to 15°F., at most, without considerable alarm. Below 90°F. (if not before), there is urgent need for treatment. Above 105°F. (if not before), there is an even more urgent need. The range is small. Yet it has been extended from 64.4°F., with that frozen Negro woman, to a maximum of 111°F. or so under extreme conditions of heatstroke, a range of 46°F. (or the difference between the day for skating on a lake and floating in it).

The Negro woman, cold as she was, still had the temperature of a warm room. She was hot by comparison with a hibernating animal. Men cannot hibernate, but great efforts are being made to induce an artificially cool state. Cryosurgery, or crymotherapy, or—more facetiously—cold-blooded surgery, hinges upon the fact that cold tissue requires less oxygen; but first a word about natural hibernation.

Hibernation

The hedgehog in summer has a normal temperature of 92°F. to 95.5°F. (some four or five degrees lower than humans). The creature becomes comatose, with its own temperature fluctuating between 86°F. and 60°F., when the outside temperature falls below 62°F. This intermediate stage becomes true hibernation when the outside temperature drops below 57°F. The animal then remains about a degree above the outside temperature and, save for that one degree, is apparently cooling off like a block of wood or something similarly inert. However, unlike wood, its temperature never falls (except in death) below 43°F. The world may continue to freeze, but the hedgehog stays at 43°F. and can even wake up. According to Nathaniel Kleitman, the American expert on sleep, the hedgehog may be said to be cold-blooded when it can economize fuel by being so, but not when its life is endangered. Heart rate always falls with the falling temperature. In the squirrel it can go from 300 to 2 beats per minute, in the hamster from 500 to 4 beats per minute and in the marmot it can beat only 23 times per hour.

None of this is possible with human beings. The regulation system goes rapidly awry. It certainly cannot keep a watchful eye on the situation or prevent undue cooling as with the hedgehog. The human heart starts to fibrillate (or suffer tremor) at 64°F., and the nervous system stops transmitting impulses at 50°F. Man is definitely not a hibernating creature.

At least, he is never so under natural conditions. Since World War II, progress has been abundant in unnatural imitation of the cold state. In *The Conquest of Pain* Ronald Woolmer describes an operation using deep hypothermia: "The patient was a woman in her late thirties. Her face had the paleness of death. Her skin had the coldness of death—and more. Her eyes were glazed, and her pupils widely dilated. There was no hint of respiration. The heart was not beating, and the pressure in the blood vessels could not be measured. This state of affairs persisted for forty minutes, and during that time by all the usual tests the patient was dead."

Two hours later, she was chatting away in bed. Obviously there are great surgical benefits in not having a vibrant heart and in not having tissue urgently demanding oxygen. The maximum permissible time for stopping circulation at the body's normal temperature is three to five minutes. With a general cooling of 14°F. (and down to 84°F.), the time of stoppage can be ten minutes. Nowadays, cooling a body to 60°F. and stopping circulation for an hour is a standard procedure. Plainly, lower temperatures and longer times will gradually occur. A textbook now refers to 48°F. as the minimum tolerated "without apparent alteration in neurological or intellectual functions." And a major announcement was made in London in the summer of 1964, when a patient had successfully survived over two hours "in a state of suspended animation."

The procedure is either a matter of cooling the blood or cooling the body. Extracting blood, cooling it, and pumping it back again can cool a patient from 98°F. to 60°F. in less than an hour. Packing ice around a patient, as if he were champagne in happier circumstances, takes longer. One hour would bring the temperature to 86°F. Selective cooling, as against whole body treatment, can be simpler. Ice can be packed around the heart; or the brain, that most demanding tissue of all for oxygen, can have its own circulation blocked.

At a Copenhagen conference in 1965, a Japanese neurosurgeon, Dr. Tatsuyuki Kudo, described the cooling of brains to an unprecedented 43°F. His patients were first surface cooled with ice to 90°F. Then, by suitable exposure of arteries and veins, he drained the brain of blood and perfused that organ instead with a cold blood-substitute. Within 25 minutes, the temperature of the brain was down to 43°F. and the rest of the body remained at 90°F. The surgeon then started work on the cold, white, and bloodless brain. Subsequent warming up was also, according to Dr. Kudo, a relatively fast business. Some 3 to 5 pt. of new blood had to be used and, if surface warming of the whole body accompanied this transfusion, "revitalization" of the brain took about an hour. There were, he concluded, neither cardiac complications nor any other major side effects in the six patients who had experienced this particular trial procedure.

Hypothermia

Is human hibernation or prolonged hypothermia possible? At a symposium held in Toronto, "On Natural Mammalian Hibernation," in 1965, Dr. A. W. Dawe, of the United States Office of Naval Research, said it "might" be achieved in the "foreseeable" future. Much impetus behind such work is associated with the space program. Flights in space, at least beyond our immediate planetary neighbors, will be long and tedious affairs. Suspended animation could not only relieve the tedium but could also ensure, for lengthier trips, that old age did not kill off the crew before landfall.

Apart from space advantages and earth surgery, the science of hypothermia will inevitably have more to offer. Cold can kill tissue, and can kill it selectively. Undesired nerves (which die after five minutes at 5°F.) can be put out of action by cold-tipped probes. These devices have already been used in localized tissue destruction and have helped with Parkinson's disease (by causing brain damage in just the right place), breast cancer (by destroying the associated pituitary gland), and with operations on the eye. Plunging new babies into iced water instead of warm blankets is a bizarre aspect of hypothermia, but it was recommended in a 1964 American report on newborn infants who do not begin to breathe as they should. The theory is that, since such infants often suffer afterward from irreversible brain damage and cerebral palsy due to temporary oxygen lack, it is sensible to cut down their brain's stringent demand for oxygen during the respiratory difficulties following birth. The report claimed remarkable success with over 150 babies.

Yet another report, this time from St. Bartholomew's Hospital in London, described how a small girl on the point of death from meningitis recovered after ice packs had kept her five degrees cooler for a whole week. Normally, the swellings of meningitis restrict the brain's blood flow and therefore its supply of oxygen. The suggestion in this case is that the reduced demand for oxygen (caused by the cooling) meant that the brain could survive until the meningitis swellings had subsided. Without doubt, induced hypothermia, with its countless uses, will force many of us to spend many more hours on the chilly side of "normal" in future years.

Traditional temperature-taking, now over a century old, may also change. The mouth, the armpit, and the rectum, time-honored sites for ordinary thermometers, may yield their importance. Not only are other sites constantly recommended, such as the navel and even the ear, but thermography is gaining ground. There are several techniques for recording the whole pattern of a person's temperature, rather than the heat at one point. Patterns can be more informative. They can show regions of abnormality, such as cancers and arterial disease. Carl Wunderlich's regime of temperature-taking may yet prove to be indispensable, but the new heat cameras are all-embracing. They have much to say that no temperature chart, however conscientiously kept, could ever indicate.

Cryosurgery, crymotherapy, induced hypothermia, and thermography are all fairly novel, but cryoburial is quite, quite new. Dr. James H. Bedford, of California, paid $4,000 before his death in January, 1967, for permanent freezing of his body. He also left $200,000 for cryobiological research. Although the money will soon be consumed, his body will remain forever inside its metal container at liquid nitrogen's temperature of $-196°C$. In theory, he will be revived as soon as science is capable of such resurrection. In practice, according to present-day science, the freezing will have caused ice crystals to play havoc with his cellular structure. Revival of so shattered a body is likely to be impossible even for tomorrow's resurrectionists.

⤳ 29 ⤶

The Senses

Background to Vision · The Eye · Folds, Lashes,
Brows, and Tears · Blinking, Reading, and Accommodation ·
Color Blindness · Focusing Errors · Blindness · Hearing and
Balance · Deafness · Smelling and Smells · Tasting and
Tastes · Touch, Pain, and Itch · The Sixth Sense

Background to Vision

It is all very well to accept the general principles of natural selection
and that the pressure of this selection favors certain characteristics. It
is harder to accept the advantages of many of these characteristics when
they are being developed. To have a slightly longer neck, a slight ability
to fly, or a slightly stronger skin, each is plainly a modest advantage
right from the start; but to have the primitive rudiment of an eye is
less immediately beneficial. Originally, it must have been an area of
skin faintly sensitive to light. It could just have discerned, one assumes,
a difference between bright sunlight and everything else. Was this ability
so beneficial that natural selection could act upon it? Even the later
stages, the development of lens and orbit, are not nearly so straightforward as the giraffe's steadily lengthening neck, the cheetah's gathering speed. The world of botany, entirely dependent upon light, has
formed no eyes; in the world of zoology, animals must have originally
used their eyes much as a plant uses phototropism to maneuver either
toward or away from light, and yet eyes are now paramount. Nearly
every vertebrate has a pair, and there are innumerable forms of eye in
the invertebrates right down to the "light spots" of many single-celled
organisms.

Mankind has the typical pair of vertebrate eyes, although they have
moved around to the front. The majority of vertebrates have lateral eyes;

so does man in the first instance, when the embryonic eyes grow as two lateral stalks and bulbs from the brain. This fishlike appearance persists for many weeks, but the final result is two eyes at the front capable of binocular vision to a large degree. Both eyes can see the same object at the same time in most of the visual field; hence, an improved ability to determine distance and assess speed.

Useful as a third eye could have been to the vertebrates in general and to those wishing to see upward in particular, it never materialized in any proficient form. The lampreys (and others in this cyclostome group) possess a third eye, and it contains some retinal material; but it is not nearly so definite an organ as the lamprey's two other eyes. The cyclostomes are primitive fish, and in more advanced forms the third eye ceases to be an eye at all; instead the organ develops into a gland. Reptiles developed after fish, but certain reptiles, including the archaic Sphenodon of New Zealand, which has somehow survived out of its time, also possess a kind of third eye. However, it is as a gland, although of uncertain function, that the extra eye persists in animals of later evolution.

Probably, the eye began as a pair of eyes, and evidence from the fossil forms of the world's earliest fish suggests that this was so. Also, although the third eye is customarily spoken of as if it is single and in the midline, it is developed from one or both of two distinct outgrowths of the brain. They are the parietal and pineal organs. In man, the pineal outgrowth is a small, flat, oval portion of tissue attached to the brain by a short stalk. This fragment from the past is the most positive human remnant of the vertebrate attempt to possess more than two eyes. George Orwell's creatures of his *Animal Farm* originally recommended four legs, but later settled for two; the animal kingdom did likewise as two primeval pairs of eyes, dorsal and lateral, were dropped in favor of a single lateral pair, which, to a varying degree, moved around to the front. The pineal body was left for René Descartes and others to call the seat of the soul.

The Eye

Each human eyeball weighs ¼ oz. and has a diameter of slightly less than an inch. A male eye is bigger—by about 1/50 in.—than the female eye, and an adult eye is less round than the newborn eye. At birth, the eye is much nearer adult proportions even than the brain; whereas the body increases its volume 20 times or more after birth, the brain increases 3.75 times and the eye only 3.25 times. Of a baby's weight 1/400 is eye; of an adult's it is 1/4000. The human eye is not a close fit within its orbital cavity: eye volume is 6.5 cc. but orbital volume is 29 cc. Fish have large eyes, amphibians and reptiles have relatively small ones, but those of the birds are large. An eagle's eye is larger than a man's, and the owl's eyes occupy one-third of its head.

The sixteenth-century inventor of the camera obscura had to defy current opinion and state that the eye was always a receiver, never a transmitter of rays. Ever since, the science of optics and understanding of the eye have run parallel. Light waves entering the human eye first pass through the thick, transparent, and bloodless cornea, then through the anterior chamber, then through the pupil gap between the iris diaphragm, then through the lens, then through the large posterior chamber (both chambers are filled with fluid) until it eventually lands on the sensitive retina.

It is the iris that gives color to the eye. The iris, named after the Greek for rainbow, tends to be without much pigment at birth and appears blue (except in the dark races when it is brown even at birth). At the other end of life, the pigment changes, and some time after death all European eyes look a greenish-brown. Although blue eyes may seem to possess more color than brown, the effect is an illusion; brown eyes have more pigment. Irises can be piebald, or different colors, for each eye. The patterns on an iris, of rays, rings, and spots, are highly individual and have been suggested as an alternative to fingerprints for identification.

The circular opening slightly to the nose side of the iris is called the pupil (after the Latin *pupilla,* allegedly because the minute image of an observer within someone else's pupil looks like a little girl). In humans, the pupil is circular when dilated and contracted, and it is customarily circular in animals when dilated. In the contracted state, animals show much pupil variation, changing the dilated circle into a slit or even a dumbbell form. Many animals, such as the lower mammals and birds, can contract and dilate one eye at a time. In man, both behave equally even if one lid is closed. Normally the human pupil is between .1 and .15 in. in diameter; but extreme and abnormal dimensions of .06 in. and .3 in. have been measured. Pupils are affected primarily by light intensity and the distance of the object; but fear, interest, and numerous emotions can dilate the pupil. A pretty girl has been shown to open up a man's pupils by some 30 percent; conversely, men have unwittingly preferred female photographs in which the pupils have been touched up to look larger. But then nothing is new. Belladonna ("beautiful lady") was traditionally used to give this effect.

The lens is flatter at the front than the back, it is slightly yellow, and it is soft. With age it grows flatter, yellower, and harder. There is no blood in the lens, and it is sustained by the liquid on both sides of it. Cataract is the principal disease of the lens, and its first symptom is the appearance of stationary motes. Normally, all motes seen by the healthy eye float and jerk their spasmodic way in a person's vision.

The retina, at the back of the eye, is the destination of light waves. By then, they should have been correctly focused mainly by the cornea and partly by the lens, and the resulting image is upside down and smaller. Two 6-ft. men standing 10 ft. from each other are shrunk down to inverted images only .4 in. high in each other's retinas. The 20/20 vision of Americans or the 6/6 vision of the British (essentially the same, since one is expressed in feet, the other in meters) refers to letters on a card twenty feet or six meters from the observer. The letters in question are .35 in. or 8.75 mm. high. Such letters subtend an angle of five minutes, or one-twelfth of a degree, from the observer's point of view, and such a letter is shrunk down to an image only 1/1000 in. or .025 mm. high. It is this size of letter image that the retina and the brain have to decipher if the observer is to be adjudged visually competent.

The light-sensitive layer of the retina responsible for this competence consists of a multitude of cells called rods and cones. In the human eye there are approximately 125 million rods and 7 million cones, but information from these millions of receptor cells has to pass to the brain through the optic nerve, a relatively modest bundle of 800,000 nerve fibers. (Some say there are a lot more, but no one gives a number approaching that of the rods and cones.) Essentially, the retina is just an extension of the brain carried on this thin nervous stalk. The exit of the optic nerve causes the blind spot, an area devoid of receptors. The phenomenon, first discovered in 1668, can be detected by anyone with patience, two dots 3 to 4 in. apart and one eye closed. The precise working of rods and cones is still largely unsolved; but, briefly, rods are for night vision and can detect only shades of gray, while cones are for day vision and sort out colors. Birds active in daytime have a greater proportion of cones, and night birds have more rods. Nocturnal mammals, such as the bat and the rat, also have more rods but so, confusingly, does daytime man.

The fact that the eyes of many animals shine in the dark is due to the nature of the tapetum, part of the pigmented layer of the retina. There is no creation of light, as was formerly supposed, only an ability to reflect visible light. Human eyes will also shine if the observer is sufficiently near to the beam of light being shone at them; it is best to look directly along the beam, preferably by using a pinhole in the center of a reflecting mirror aiming the beam. I do not know the reasoning or facts behind the experiment, but in 1704 it was observed that a cat's eyes no longer shine if the animal is immersed in water: abolition of the customary refraction from the cornea was responsible for the change.

Folds, Lashes, Brows, and Tears

There are ancillary anatomical features associated with the human eye. The epicanthic fold is a fold of skin on the upper lid that gives Mongols their characteristic appearance. Other races possess this fold in fetal life but it disappears afterward. Eyebrows are frequently alleged to keep forehead sweat from the eyes, but it is probable they are primarily associated with expression. Some monkeys have white eyebrows arched in the human manner but surrounded by black hair—the effect upon sweat must be small but that upon the appearance is startling. Cilia, or eyelashes, are longer and more plentiful on the upper lid; they are continually falling out and each one of the total complement of about 200 per eye lasts from 3 to 5 months. They are usually as dark as the hair or darker, and they do not whiten with age. The human eye does not possess a nictitating membrane, or third eyelid. This extra, well developed in most mammals and other vertebrates and extremely apparent in the blinking of birds, could have been a protective asset; instead it is only a vestigial and immobile fragment of tissue in man.

Tears are essential to bathe the eye, and they are sterile. Each human tear gland is in the upper and outer part of each eye, and it produces tears continuously. Even though the eye is warm, constantly exposed to air throughout at least 16 hours of the day, blinked over, and generally susceptible to evaporation, it has been calculated that tear production is only from .017 to .023 oz. a day. Laughing, yawning, coughing, vomiting, cold wind, foreign objects, certain chemicals, and crying all step up tear production, and the traditional "good cry" will certainly produce in excess of .017 oz. All vertebrates living in air produce tears, and all humans over a few weeks old do. No animal other than man has yet produced convincing evidence that it can weep in response to emotional stress.

Epiphora, as scientific man has named this unique attribute (as well as a disease of excessive tears), is responsible not only for a considerable rise in lachrymal production but a considerable drop in the bactericidal property of tears. It was Alexander Fleming who investigated the property. Soon, lysozyme was isolated, the bactericidal agent that is present to a large degree in tears, and to a lesser degree in saliva and nasal mucus. Without some killing agent like lysozyme, the eyes, nose, and mouth would be unguarded entrances for the steady infiltration of unwelcome bacteria. The molecular structure of this natural antiseptic was worked out in 1965 by a team at the Royal Institution in London, the first enzyme ever to have been so described, thereby providing an excellent opportunity for further understanding of the little understood and all-powerful enzyme world. Unfortunately, although Fleming squeezed lemon juice into the eyes of his students, and collected the lysozyme that then rolled down their cheeks, it proved a poor remedy against disease. Generally speaking, the diseases we do catch know how to get around lysozyme.

Blinking, Reading, and Accommodation

No invertebrates blink, but most vertebrates do. Exceptions are some reptiles and animals living in water. According to Sir W. Stewart Duke-Elder, the ophthalmologist, true blinking does not begin in human infants until they are six months old. While rodents and cats blink slowly, primates are much quicker. A human blink lasts .3 to .4 second and occurs once every two to ten seconds. As the eye is actually closed for .15 second of each blink, an average man, assuming a six-second frequency between blinking, has his eyes definitely shut for nearly half an hour of each day spent awake. The blinking reflex can be halted for a time with conscious effort, and for still longer underwater, but few people can resist blinking even for as long as a minute. In water, the interval may be extended to five minutes.

The eyes themselves are never stationary. Not only is the head always moving slightly, causing ceaseless adjustment by the eyes, but the eyes themselves both jerk about and have a restless vibration. Only a very few seconds of arc are involved, but the constant activity enforces a constantly changing pattern of light upon the retina. Were it possible to fix the eye and clamp it in one position, vision would probably cease altogether. Each fragment of retina would then be receiving an identical and fatiguing stimulation.

Reading is also a jerky business, with the fixation pauses lasting from one-fifth to one-third of a second before the eye hurries on to the next stopping point. Nothing can be read during the periods of movement as the speed is too rapid. A person reading out loud has his eyes ahead of his voice, and usually he can continue for some five more words if the light goes out.

Accommodation is the ability to turn the eyes inward, an ability that deteriorates with age. A child can bring both eyes to bear upon objects less than 3 in. from his eyes; anything nearer is seen as a double image. Duke-Elder says that accommodation is about 5½ in. for someone in his or her mid-30's and there may be rapid periods of deterioration in the early 40's and again when the person has really encountered old age.

Vision is subject to many defects. Night blindness (nyctalopia) can be caused by disease, inheritance, lack of food, overexposure to light, or a deficiency of vitamin A. Day blindness (hemeralopia) can be caused by disease or inheritance. Night blindness is a marked inability to adapt to conditions of modest light; a normal eye can increase its sensitivity to light about 75,000 times within an hour of being placed in darkness. Day blindness is an ability to see normally when light is modest, but poorly when light is good. There are other failings, but the big three weaknesses in vision are color blindness, focusing errors, and blindness itself.

Color Blindness

Essentially there are six types of defective color vision, four of them common. Many forms of classification exist, and they are all based on the fact that normal color vision is a function of three variables (red, green, and blue) and these three enable a normal person to distinguish 150 to 200 colors in the spectrum. A color-blind person is either distinctly weak on one of the three variables (trichromatic), or he has to make do with only two of the variables (dichromatic), or he sees every color as a confusion of only one variable (monochromatic). Within each group, again bearing in mind that there are three possible types of failing, there are three subgroups: a color-blind person is weak on one of the three variables, or lacking in one of the three variables, or has to make do with no variables at all. Hence, the classification, and the words coined to describe the deficiencies. It may seem a moot point to distinguish between someone who cannot tell yellow from orange and someone who cannot tell orange from yellow, but the differences between them are real and valid.

Men everywhere are more color blind than women, and primitive or recently primitive people are less color blind than urbanized people. The sex difference is due to the fact that most color blindness is inherited in association with the X chromosome; since males possess only one X chromosome, any genetic defect upon it is likely to manifest itself. Females have two X chromosomes, and a defect in one can be masked by the normality of the other. (See the chapter on inheritance for a fuller explanation.)

Common name Colors confused   Frequency

TRICHROMATIC (3 variables)

(a) Protanomalous	Red-weak	Yellow and orange	Fairly common
(b) Deuteranomalous	Green-weak	Yellow and orange	Fairly common
(c) Tritanomalous	Blue-weak	Blue and green	Rarest (possibly nonexistent)

DICHROMATIC (2 variables)

(a) Protanopic	Red-blind	Red, yellow, and green	Fairly common
(b) Deuteranopic	Green-blind	Red, yellow, and green	Commonest
(c) Tritanopic	Blue-blind	Blue and green	Very rare

MONOCHROMATIC (All one color)	Total color blindness	All colors	Very rare

The difference between primitive and other people may have been brought about by the relaxation of natural selection previously working against color blindness. Whatever the cause, the frequency of this defect among Europeans and North American whites is greater than among Asians. Its frequency among Asians is greater than among Negroes, American Indians, and Australian aborigines. Eskimos have the lowest incidence in the world. In England, the frequency is greatest in the south and east; in France it is greatest near the sea; in India it is greater among Brahmins than lower-caste stocks. Perhaps all these high-incidence groups are furthest removed in time from direct food-gathering and from the disadvantages of color blindness. Finally, for some unknown reason, there is a link between color blindness and alcoholism; more alcoholics are found to be color blind than similar but nonalcoholic people.

European and white American frequency of color blindness is about 8 percent. A large survey in Norway and Switzerland reported that males afflicted with red-blind vision formed 1 percent of the male population, with red-weak vision also 1 percent, with green-blind vision 5 percent and with green-weak 1.5 percent. The total frequency among European women is .5 percent. Among Asiatic males it is about 5 percent, among Negro and American Indian males about 3 percent, and among Eskimo men about 1 percent.

To be color blind is not always a disadvantage; camouflage of any kind is easier to detect, whether military or natural, and the color-blind entomologist can often succeed in finding some concealed insect where others have failed. Everyone is color blind when light is weak. In the evening, an ability to discriminate red is the first to go, and the other end of the spectrum is the last to go. Blue is the first color to become perceptible in the morning.

Color vision in animals is thought to be poorly developed. It is hard devising tests to assess color discrimination as against luminosity differences, but it is thought that fish and amphibians cannot appreciate color, although they often prefer an area lighted with a particular hue. Some birds can perceive some colors, and many insects undoubtedly can. Mammals are generally poor at discrimination; dogs may have a slight sense, but sheep, mice, and rabbits have all proved themselves uninterested in color. Wave a green cape at a bull, and he will still behave in the traditional fashion. Wave a green cape at a monkey, and he will know it from a red one. The higher primates seem to be the only animals with a color appreciation that approaches or equals mankind's.

Focusing Errors

The three main troubles are:

HYPERMETROPIA. Too short an eye or too weak a lens. Focusing is therefore behind the retina. Called farsightedness or longsightedness.
MYOPIA. Too long an eye or too powerful a lens. Focusing is in front of the retina. Called shortsightedness or nearsightedness.
ASTIGMATISM. Unevenness. The focus point for horizontal rays is not the same as for vertical rays. Usually caused by a warped cornea.

Nero is said to have looked through an emerald to magnify objects, but eyeglasses in the modern sense do not appear in pictures until the fourteenth century, having allegedly been invented by a monk of Pisa in 1299. Ever since, victims of the three principal errors of focusing have had a chance to see more clearly. Nevertheless, these never help to preserve vision, as is often believed. In fact, notably in longsighted people, they may commit the patient to an increasing reliance upon them.

Myopia is named after two Greek words meaning to close the eye because shortsighted people have a habit of half-closing their eyes; this causes a smaller opening available to the light waves, thus better vision. Contact lenses, which do away with all of the external attachment of eyeglasses, leaving only the vital refractive material, have by no means proved as popular an alternative to eyeglasses as might have been supposed when they were new. Much more recently, the idea has been put into practice of changing the focusing power of the cornea by grinding away some of its substance. Particularly for shortsighted people whose corneas are too greatly curved, causing too great a bending of the light waves, the corneas have been effectively changed; they have been flattened to some degree and normal vision has resulted. For longsighted people, traditionally found among the elderly, such an operation is more complex; it necessitates increasing the curvature of the cornea. However much the cornea may be changed it is a static change; although the cornea does 60 percent of the focusing, it is the lens that has to adjust itself to alter the combined focusing power of both cornea and lens.

Sunglasses are predominantly a feature of the twentieth century. Practically no one needs them in ordinary conditions, but sales are phenomenal. In the United States, enough sunglasses are sold to give everyone a new pair every other year. Presumably, most pairs are bought without any intention of protecting the eyes, but of enlarging or concealing the ego. For those who wear very dark glasses—some are far darker than others—and who wear them steadily, whether at night or indoors, the eyes could well become too sensitive to ordinary light. But in that case, the wearer will have provided himself with one of the few valid reasons for wearing dark glasses.

Blindness

In Britain, a blind person is legally defined as someone "unable to perform any work for which eyesight is essential." In England and Wales the blind population, according to this definition, is 99,000, or one person in every 460. The United States definition generally accepted is more complex. It involves distant vision poorer than 20/200 in the better eye with best correction, or better vision where the widest diameter of the field of vision subtends an angle less than 20°. The estimated U.S. figure for 1966 was 421,250. Over half the England and Wales number has some degree of useful vision; the actual number of people without any useful vision is nearer one in every 1,000. Total blindness, with no perception of light whatever, affects only 3.4 percent of those registered as blind. Most of those on Britain's blind register are elderly; only a quarter of them are younger than 60.

At the other end of life, only ten of Britain's totally blind are less than a year old, and only 2,000 are under 15. Females outnumber males by three to two, but women live longer than men, and a gross deterioration of vision is a frequent companion of old age. Unfortunately, although cataract, for example, is less a cause of blindness than it used to be, the number of blind people is not being reduced. Medical science is advancing, but it is also permitting more people to live to an age likely to be accompanied by blindness. Unfortunately, no one predicts any marked decline in blindness in the near future.

In the poorer and tropical parts of the world, the situation is far worse. There is no register of the world's blind population, and estimates fluctuate much like estimates of global malnutrition, but onchocerciasis (caused by a fly-borne worm parasite), trachoma (a form of conjunctivitis, discovered to be caused by a virus by Peking scientists in 1957), smallpox, and malnutrition in the young all add millions of blind people to the total. The World Health Organization has produced estimates that the nematode worm of onchocerciasis has affected 200 to 300 million people, with perhaps 10 percent blinded as a result of the affliction. A recent report from India gave a total of 4.4 million blind people in India alone, and added that this number was about 25 percent of the world's total. So, whether there are 17.5 million blind people in the world or even more, as the latest WHO figures indicate, this means that at least one in 175 of the world's citizens is without competent sight.

Although there is no immediate hope of reducing the blind population markedly in advanced countries, because so many of the causes are linked to the general problem of old age, the worm of onchocerciasis and the virus of trachoma are far less intractable. Also, quite apart from the blindness resulting from these two, they cause plenty of misery long before they cause loss of sight. Each has been accused of affecting 300 million people, making a joint total of nearly one-sixth of the world.

Hearing and Balance

The prime purpose of the ear is not that of hearing. Without the ability to detect sound waves a man is undoubtedly in a silent world of his own. Without the ability to assess the position of gravity or the rotational movements of his head a man would be without equilibrium, and in a disastrously topsy-turvy world. To some extent, as in all higher animals, the eyes could compensate for the loss of balance and orientation, and they always assist anyone's appreciation of his situation; but such a full-time addition to their major role of vision would be entirely abnormal. A man can walk fairly well in total darkness; he would walk far less well in broad daylight if his ears were destroyed. The so-called auditory organs of the earliest vertebrates were probably quite unconcerned with hearing; they were more probably totally concerned with the detection of changes in spatial orientation. The fish ear is without an external ear, such as the flattened pinna of human beings, and without a middle ear with its membrane and bony ossicles; only the inner ear exists. It is this basic ear structure of all vertebrates, including man, that has more than one job to do.

The inner ear consists of three quite distinct sensory systems. There is a relationship among them in that they are all dependent upon small mechanical forces, but this does not alter their entirely separate functions. First, there are the three semicircular canals, each set in a different plane, all three acting as a receptor system for detecting rotational movements of the head. The acceleration and deceleration of fluid within these canals gives the ability to record head movement. Second, there are the saccule and the utricle. A combination of hairs and chalky particles called otoliths inside these containers permits the detection of the position of gravity; a person, or a fish, can therefore tell which way is up in relation to Earth. Both these systems, the fluid and the chalk, the canals and the containers, are termed the vestibular apparatus, and without them any vertebrate would be far more incapable than one merely deaf to sound waves. Tortoises are without hearing and have done pretty well.

The third function of the inner ear is hearing. The organ of Corti, which lies within the 2¾ turns of the snail-shaped cochlea, is the receptor system for sound waves. It can measure the intensity and the frequency of sound waves oscillating between 20 and 20,000 cycles per second. Unlike the two organs of the vestibular apparatus, which are self-sufficient, the hearing part of the inner ear has to work in conjunction with devices for the amplification of sound waves; hence the mechanical complexities of the middle ear and the larger but less crucial shapes of the outer ear.

The squashed-up shape of the human outer ear is a poor remnant of the mobile catchment cups of many other mammals. Probably the outer ear has more to do with the location of sounds than with mere amplification. (It is also concerned with heat loss as North American rabbits have smaller ears in rising latitudes.) Nevertheless, even a human being can tell to within three degrees the direction from which a sound is coming. An owl, blessed with the possession of one ear slightly forward of the other, can locate a sound to within one degree while still looking straight at it. A human being tries to achieve the same accuracy by cocking his head on one side, and a blind man can demonstrate many human abilities previously only latent. For instance, if placed a few feet from a disc, blind men have shown their skill at assessing any changes in its area; the minimum changes they could detect, just by making noises and listening like sonar for alteration in echo, varied from only 7 to 23 percent.

The middle ear is fascinating partly because of the straightforward way in which it achieves its amplification, partly because of its curious origins. Throughout evolution, the process of making do with inherited characteristics and transforming them into novel requirements has been continuous. Stabilizing fins became legs, and two of these legs then became arms. Similarly, the air bladder of fish, a buoyancy device, became the lungs of terrestrial animals, a respiratory device. In just the same fashion, what are gill bars for fish (used in breathing) became jaw-articulation elements in reptiles (used in eating), then the auditory ossicles of the middle ear (used in hearing).

Hearing occurs when sound waves, gathered in to a very slight extent by the external air, enter the ear and cause the tympanic membrane to vibrate. (Anyone unfortunate enough to have some modest and scarcely visible insect invade his ear through the protective wax and hairs will be astounded by the deafening heavy-footed tread as it steps lightly onto the membrane. It will sound much like an elephant on corrugated iron and give a deafening idea of the delicacy of the system.) The membrane's oscillations are directly transmitted to three bones, lying one after the other, named the malleus, the incus, and the stapes because their shapes bear fleeting resemblances to a hammer, an anvil (both very fleeting), and a stirrup. They are the principal contents of the middle-ear cavity, an air-filled hole about ⅓ in. wide, ⅙ in. deep.

It is this pocket of air that can cause trouble in flying; its pressure has to be constantly adjusted to the outside air pressure. Normally, this is done effortlessly through the 1½-in. Eustachian tube, which leads from the cavity to the upper part of the throat behind the nose; but, when the nose is congealed with the mucus of a heavy cold or when an aircraft changes height too rapidly for swift personal adjustment, the result can be curious squeaks as pressure levels are sorted out or temporary deafness. Within this cavity, the middle ear's three ossicles, by their own jostling, pass on the tympanic membrane's vibrations to a far smaller membrane, which effectively seals off the liquid-filled compartment of the inner ear. It is the organ of Corti within this inner ear that transforms the vibrations into nerve impulses, and these are interpreted by the brain as sound.

The human ear's ability to detect frequencies from 20 to 20,000 cycles per second is beaten at the lower end by, for example, the grasshopper and at the upper end by, for example, the dog. Whereas middle C is 256 cycles per second, and top C on a piano is four octaves higher—4,096 cycles per second—the sound at 20,000 cycles per second is heard as little more than a hiss. The fundamental tone of the human larynx is of course much less—about 100 cycles per second with men, and 150 cycles per second with women. But speech makes use of high-pitched hisses as well; the lack of these, as in all telephone conversations, can make speech less intelligible.

The sensitivity of a good ear is remarkable. It can pick up sounds that deflect the tympanic membrane by only .00000001 mm. (Small wonder an insect is so audible when treating that membrane as an entomological trampoline.) Also a good ear can assess about 1,600 different frequencies between the highest and the lowest, about 350 different intensities between the quietest and the loudest. Senile deafness affects the highest tones first, and birdsong can be quickly lost after the age of 60.

Just as the organ for seeing light can be damaged by too intense a light, the human ear can be damaged by noise. The middle ear possesses muscles that dampen the membrane's excessive vibrations, but either short bursts of very loud noise or prolonged exposure to noise well below the painful level can cause permanent loss of hearing. A survey before and after New Year's Eve in Denmark gave audiologists reason to believe that the impaired hearing of half all Danish children can be traced to the firework festivities of December 31. Riveting, drop forges, pneumatic drills, and big guns have long been known to be capable of causing deafness and the jet engine is now the loudest industrial noise; but less fearsome noises are perfectly capable of causing damage. Some visiting ear specialists in the Sudan noted that the ears of remote Sudanese groups, accustomed to nothing louder than human speech, suffered if they were subjected to sounds that many of us tolerate throughout our lives.

Although noise can also be irritating, even painful to the system as a whole, the only damage that can definitely be confirmed as a result of it (according to F. I. Catlin, who recently reviewed the literature) is hearing loss. Intensity of noise is measured in decibels. The bel is named for Alexander Graham Bell, who gave the world the telephone but unaccountably only one "l" to the unit of loudness, and the threshold of sound when it is just audible is called 0 bel. A whisper is about 1,000 times more powerful; therefore, as 1000 is 10^3 and as bels are measured logarithmically, a whisper has the loudness of 3 bels. Conversation is 1,000 times louder than a whisper, namely 6 bels. A loud shout is 9 bels, and noise becomes unpleasant at 12 bels, causing pain when of greater intensity. As bels are too large a unit of measurement, the decibel is used instead, with each decibel equal to 1/10 bel. Therefore, a whisper is 30 decibels, conversation is 60.

Deafness

There are two main types of deafness: conductive, caused by any trouble to the conducting apparatus (as, for example, a punctured eardrum), and perceptive, caused by any trouble to the cochlea or its nerve. Hearing is made adequate with conductive deafness if sounds are made louder. With perceptive deafness, this may be true up to a point, but beyond that the greater the amplification the greater the confusion—notably with speech. It was Thomas Willis, the sixteenth-century physician, who drew attention to the advantage of loudness for conductive deafness. He told of a deaf woman who could hear speech only if a drum was beaten simultaneously, "wherefore her husband kept a drummer on purpose for his servant, that by that means he might have converse with his wife."

The first hearing aids were ear trumpets, giving a gain of 20 decibels. Electrical aids arrived in the last century, and they were radically improved first by the thermionic valve and later by the transistor. All such aids fail to achieve the selective ability of the human ear, which tends to hear what it wishes to hear. Without selection the environment is incredibly noisy and raucous.

According to a British health survey made after World War II, almost 2 million people were thought to be deaf, but in markedly different degrees. The majority, 1.6 million, were classified as hard of hearing, although half of those had difficulty in hearing normal speech unless they had a hearing aid. The hard-core minority included 70,000 deaf to all ordinary speech (although some could hear abnormal speech designed to assist them, such as the exaggerated movements helpful to the lip-reader), 30,000 who were totally deaf, and 15,000 who were deaf and dumb. Therefore, a total of 115,000 were grossly deaf in Britain at that time, and another 14 times as many suffered from deafness, but less severely. According to the figure customarily quoted for the United States, 3 million Americans suffer from hearing loss.

In 1965, a new machine was announced in Canada capable of testing children for deafness within a week of birth. The development of such a device is the culmination of mounting pressure to take note of deafness as early as possible. After all, a baby starts taking note of sounds from the day it is born, and there is no point in delay. A deaf child has to be fitted with a hearing aid before he is a year old if he is ever to speak properly, and children only three months old have been fitted with them.

The custom in former days was to disregard the deaf child's right to the power of speech and permit him to become a deaf-mute. Suzanne de Parrel, the French expert on speech disorders, has written that "the use today of the term deaf-mute revolts the conscience. It should be banished from the vocabularies of the medical and teaching professions. True muteness is a symptom of aphasia, damage to the brain. . . . The deaf are not mute. Also very few deaf people are totally devoid of residual hearing." She has recommended that exercises in remedial education for the deaf child should begin at the age of eight months. Children in general begin to speak later, but they have been listening, making noises, and preparing for speech long before. A generalization, with exceptions (Einstein, who did not speak until aged four, being one of them), is that a child who does not speak by the age of two is either backward or deaf. Most certainly, a child with late speech should be tested for deafness, as high-frequency deafness on its own is a very important cause of late speech. The ability to hear bangs or the radio or footsteps does not preclude forms of deafness crucial to acquiring proper speech.

The Canadian machine discovered that newborn infants initially have a hearing loss of 40 decibels. As with swimmers who can suffer temporary deafness from the presence of water in their ears, the formerly aquatic neonate has fluid in his auditory meatus. By 10 or 12 days this has all gone. Young babies can react alarmingly to quite modest sounds, behaving as if hand grenades rather than milk bottles were falling nearby. Gradually, this reflex hearing becomes inhibited, and by five months an infant may not respond to a very loud bang, particularly if it is familiar. Later, he will start smiling when he does hear a bang or a loud noise if he can associate that sound with pleasures like food or company.

Britain's first school for the deaf and dumb, many of whom had been traditionally assumed to be idiots as well, was established in Scotland in 1760, and London followed suit in 1792. Three United States institutions—the American School for the Deaf in West Hartford, Connecticut, the Clarke School in Northampton, Massachusetts, and the Lexington School in New York—all founded in 1866, contend for the American honors. Some causes of congenital deafness are known, such as German measles, syphilis, and Rh incompatibility; most children born deaf have a failure in their perceiving rather than their conducting apparatus. Some causes of deafness after birth, apart from the human and environmental cuffs to the ear, are diseases like meningitis, mumps, syphilis, and scarlet fever. Senile deafness, responsible for the great rise of deafness with age, is due to an atrophy of the nerve fibers.

Finally there is malingering deafness. The art of pretending not to hear can be practiced with considerable success, but it can also be confounded by an equally cunning procedure. The malingerer is asked to read a piece of prose. His words are picked up by a microphone and then fed back at him through a loudspeaker one-tenth of a second later. Much like some rapid echo this near-instant repetition of one's own words will transform the normal person into a confused and stammering dunderhead. The deaf person, on the other hand, unhearing and unconfused, will be able to read happily on.

Smelling and Smells

The human body possesses strong powers for evoking phrases of wonderment and awe, as if it had no visible faults, as if no aged, acne-ridden, asthmatic with myopia, and high blood pressure had ever been watched running for a bus. Clearly, it does have imperfections, and it does break down; but some of its systems are outstandingly skillful. Such a system is smell. No other receptor has the sensitivity of the olfactory sense. It is exceptionally precise and accurate, and a smell is extremely memorable. Although they are so readily identifiable and each one of us can distinguish thousands of different odors, the problem of passing on information about any single smell to someone ignorant of that particular smell is insuperable. Burning rubber, wet dog, new earth, old books, ripe cheese, fresh rain, cut grass—they are all unique, entirely distinctive, and quite indescribable except with vague terms like acrid and pungent, which also embrace a few hundred other odors. Describing color to a blind man is one impossibility; describing a new odor, say, whale breath or palm wine, even to someone with a perfect sense of smell is another.

Amazingly, the ability to smell is conveyed by very small organs that are not even in the mainstream of breathed-in air. They are in a blind alley, and as soon as they detect the whisper of an interesting smell, the nose is wrinkled into a sniff. These olfactory receptors are cells with long hairlike cilia attached to them. The cilia do not wave about in the air like a field of corn; instead they are embedded in a mucus layer that rests on the cells, and so they are more like reeds beneath the surface of a lake. No one knows how the cilia detect smells, but all odors have to be soluble in the mucus before they can be detected. Somehow, these submerged cilia have the power of sending differing impulses to the brain, so that a certain assortment of impulses is recognizable instantly (i.e., within a second) as rubber, dog, grass, or moldy cheese.

As a species, mankind is not good at detecting smells. A dog, for example, has its olfactory receptors more sensibly placed with regard to the incoming airflow; its receptors can take note of a wide variety of smells and its brain is better equipped to record and interpret olfactory stimuli. Much of mankind's success in the world can be attributed, loosely speaking, to his disregard for smells and his development of that part of the brain for other purposes. Consequently, from our less efficient point of view, a dog's powers of smell are nearly miraculous. With some odorous sources, a dog's nose is over one million times as sensitive as a man's. Acetic acid, for instance, can be detected by man if there are 500 billion molecules of it in a cubic meter of air. A dog needs only 200,000 molecules in a cubic meter for the smell to be detectable. Man's ability is incredible; a dog's is over a million times more so.

Canine abilities at following human masters have been scientifically investigated. Two minutes are sufficient time for the fingertips alone to touch a stick or a few seconds of a whole grasp, if that stick is to be positively identified by a dog with a particular person. It does not matter how many other people have handled the stick before or after the dog's master.

There have been other experiments. If 11 men set off in single file, with the master leading and everyone else treading in his footsteps and if that single file then divides to form two files with the master still leading one, a good dog will have no difficulty in following the right group, whether the trail is over grass or earth, asphalt or rock. Nevertheless, a dog can be muddled by identical twins. Even if the twins are married, living apart, eating differently, and doing different jobs, a good dog can confuse the two scents. It will tend to pick up one glove, for example, out of a whole pile of gloves provided that it belongs to one twin even though the other twin may be its master. New Scotland Yard reported that police dogs had never been concerned in the tracking or arrest of identical twins, but research had proved that the odor of twins could be distinguished by a well-trained dog. If the experiment is so arranged that the dog knows it has definitely to distinguish between two gloves from the twins it will pick out the correct one.

A science that cannot be neatly classified is always vexing, and this encourages many to try defining its categories. No one has been able to delineate a few primary odors equivalent to the three primary colors, but H. Zwaardemaker drew up a list of smells that did not appear to influence one another confusingly. He considered there to be nine distinct groups, and he therefore postulated the presence of nine types of receptor. No one accepts the list as much more than an intelligent attack upon the problem, but it is still quoted even though it was first published in the nineteenth century. Its nine divisions are:

Ethereal (such as fruits)	Empyreumatic (burned odors)
Aromatic (camphor, almonds)	Caprillic (cheese, fat, sweat)
Fragrant (flowers)	Repulsive (bedbug, deadly nightshade)
Ambrosial (musk)	Nauseating (rotting meat or plants, feces)
Alliaceous (garlic, sulphur, chlorine)	

Nowadays, although the existence of primary odors is still elusive and no definitive classification can be made, it is suspected that each olfactory organ has more than nine kinds of receptor. The human nose is thought to have at least 14 kinds, the dog nearer to 30. The reason for these estimates is that the nose is believed to be working (much like a computer) on a yes-no basis: a particular smell will either trigger or fail to trigger an impulse in a particular receptor. Therefore a group of, say, five receptors will perhaps record yes-yes-no-yes-no in the presence of a certain odor, and this batch of stimuli will then be passed to the brain. Another odor will cause another message to the brain, such as no-no-no-no-yes. As mankind can detect thousands of odors, more than 10,000 with practice, and as each nerve fiber is limited in the number of impulses it can transmit per second, and as a smell is discernible in less than a second, the problem of assessing the actual number of receptor types in the human nose is considerable. Perhaps 14 is the answer. Probably it is higher. At present, no one knows. It is also unknown why some substances have an odor and others do not. If so many things have, why not the rest?

The act of smelling is carried out at the molecular level. It has been calculated that eight molecules can trigger an impulse in a nerve ending, and about 40 nerve endings have to be triggered before a smell can be detected. When observed from this molecular standpoint, the procedure of smelling, with its remarkably low threshold levels, becomes more comprehensible. For instance, take the ability of a dog at tracking a man's invisible footprints. A man produces over a pint of sweat a day, but the bulk of it is ordinary water, and certainly only a small fraction of sweat passes through the sole of each shoe; yet, at the molecular level, the amount of odorous substance passing through each sole at each step is enormous. Butyric acid is a smelly constituent of sweat and, following suitable assumptions, it has been estimated that 250 billion molecules of this one substance are deposited in each footprint. For a dog, a millionth of that quantity would be detectable; hence the dog's ability to follow an old scent when so many of the original molecules have evaporated. Even a man can follow a fresh human foot trail if he is prepared to get on his knees and if the trail has been made—invisibly—over blotting paper on a firm floor.

An animal's ability to smell other animals is much aided by the presence of smell-creating, or scent-producing, glands. The elephant has a scent gland on its forehead, the rhinoceros on its feet, the rabbit near its anus, a lemur on its arms, the marsupials (generally) on their necks. Mankind has no such glands, but modified sweat glands produce characteristic smells in the armpit and in the genital area.

It could be that the racial groups of mankind also have specific group odors. A Japanese anatomist visiting Europe said he found the body odor "objectionable, strong, rancid, sweetish, sometimes bitter." Later on, happily, he found it sexually stimulating. Food and mode of living rather than racial inheritance may have caused this European smell, but both are probably important. The smell of an animal is important at the social level, the sexual level, and the individual level. Not only can dogs recognize their masters solely by smell, but mice will fail to maintain their former pregnancy if remated with mice of a different odor. The experiments with human twins show that everyone has a unique smell, genetically determined. Presumably, the ability to smell others and other things is also genetically determined. Certainly, albinos, who start with more than a fair share of disadvantages, have a weak sense of smell. And so do smokers.

Tasting and Tastes

Taste and smell are often spoken of in the same breath, but incorrectly, for there are few similarities. However, to twist the phrase, an actual breath may stimulate both types of sense organ because smell and taste are associated in most minds. A common cold is said to destroy the taste of things, but it only blocks off much of the attendant smell; the taste remains. The true seeker after taste truth should therefore consume everything with a heavy cold and his nose quite closed.

There are four fundamental or primary sensations of taste, namely sweet, bitter, sour (or acid), and salt. Sometimes alkaline and metallic are added, but it is generally believed that only four types are involved. All tastes are either a combination of effects upon these four types or upon these four plus the various ordinary nerve endings in the mouth. A curry has a taste, but it also has a burning effect upon the normal nerve endings; it would not taste like curry but it would burn like curry if placed elsewhere, for instance, in the sensitive places around the eye.

The four types of taste receptor are located in taste buds, and these are mainly on the front, back, and sides of the tongue's upper surface. Sweetness and saltiness predominate at the tongue's tip, sourness predominates at the sides, bitterness at the back. The center of the tongue is virtually without the ability to taste. Not all taste buds are on the tongue; some are on the palate, pharynx, and tonsils. Nothing solid can be tasted unless part of it is dissolved, and without dissolving saliva on the tongue, a solid substance is wholly without taste.

As with smell, no one knows how the taste receptors collect their information. And as with smell, different substances have quite different thresholds, with the general threshold for taste much less sensitive than those for smell. While bitterness can be detected at the back of the tongue, where some of the taste buds are raised on very long nodules, at a dilution of one in 2 million, sourness needs a dilution of one in 130,000, saltiness of one in 400, and sweetness of one in 200. Odors, by comparison, need dilutions of only one part in a billion or more.

Mankind has about 3,000 taste buds. The crude and insensitive pig has about twice as many. Teleost fish have their taste buds extending the length of their bodies as well as in their mouths. Taste and smell sensory organs, or an indistinguishable blending of the two, certainly arose in evolution earlier than hearing or sight, but the present purpose of taste is much less positive than that of smell, and much, much less of the brain is concerned with it. Some harmful plants and foods can be detected by their taste, and therefore some selective advantage exists; but taste as an ability is completely outclassed by the sense of smell.

Touch, Pain, and Itch

Sometimes called the fifth sense, the sensation of touch is five senses on its own—touch, pressure, pain, heat, and cold. Unfortunately, having said that and having delineated five functions, the five can then become blurred and cease to be five neat, separate, distinct types of receptor. Sometimes they seem to be, and the different receptors have been described—corpuscles of Ruffini for detecting warmth, end bulbs of Krause for detecting cold, Meissner's corpuscles for touch, and Pacinian corpuscles for pressure. At other times they seem to be far less definite, as the external ear contains no such receptor endings for the nerve fibers; yet the ear is perfectly capable of detecting temperature, touch, and pressure. Presumably, as in most discussions, both sides are partly correct—sometimes the nerve fibers end in special end organs, sometimes they do not; sometimes a nerve ending is sensitive to more than one type of sensation, sometimes it is not. By no means, as with the entire story of sense organs, has anything approaching a full understanding of the mechanism of the sense of touch yet been worked out.

Taking the body as a whole, there are many pain endings or receptors, there are fewer touch endings, far fewer heat receptors, and even fewer cold receptors. Proportional to these numbers is the ability to describe the locality of a particular sensation; the feeling of cold or warmth is much less precise in any area than either touch or pain. As is well known, the various parts of the body are also unequal for any given sensation. The tip of the penis, the clitoris, the tongue, the lips, and the fingertips are all highly sensitive to touch. The hairy parts of the body, which include almost everywhere except the soles and the palms, are made more sensitive by the leverage of a touched hair. The touch receptors grouped around the base of each hair are efficient at detecting hair movement, and hairs are moved by the gentlest of forces. In animals the whiskery vibrissae attached to most mammalian snouts are extensions of this ability.

The simplest way of proving the closeness of touch receptors in different areas is to measure two-point discrimination: how far apart do the two stimuli (say from pencil points) have to be before two separate stimuli are in fact felt? In the middle of the back the distance is 2½ in., on the forearm it is 1½ in., on the hand's palm it is ½ in., on the tip of the nose ¼ in., on the fingertips $\frac{1}{10}$ in., and on the tongue's tip $\frac{1}{25}$ in. Similarly, any minute slit-shaped wound to the tongue seems to possess the dimensions of a canyon.

Pain, the sense of injury, the warning system that damage is in progress, is a mixed blessing. Not only does it sometimes arise when damage is not in progress, but it can entirely fail to give warning of, for instance, a lethal tumor. There is also the very rare congenital absence of pain that gives to a few the mixed blessing of having no toothache but no warning of decaying teeth. The usefulness of pain is also limited by the fact that it does not correctly indicate the severity or amount of damage; a pinprick gives a ludicrously impressive quantity of pain. A headache may be either associated with physical damage or not.

There are, according to C. A. Keele and others, three layers in the skin from which quite different pain sensations can be evoked. The epidermis produces itch, the dermis a sharp pain, and the deep, or lower, dermis an aching pain. The dermis and deep dermis can be distinguished by some personal efforts with a pin. Provided some masochistic force is put into the experiment, there will be a sharp stab of pain followed by a deeper and prolonged throbbing. Itching is quite different from both. The successful itching powder of schooldays is made up of the spicules of cowhage, and they are extremely adept at inducing the curious and apparently valueless tingling. While pain is not always beneficial, the capacity to itch (the "unpleasant cutaneous sensation which provokes the desire to scratch," as S. Rothman defined it) seems markedly less so.

A girl called Rosa Kuleshova achieved considerable distinction in the early 1960s for her reported ability to see with her fingertips. For a long time, first in her hometown of Nizhni-Tagil and then at Moscow, she astounded groups of investigators by her ability not only to see but to read when blindfolded, with her fingertips running over the type. Here, according to Dr. Isaac Goldberg, a Soviet psychologist, was a modern exponent of a feat that had repeatedly been achieved since first reported in the eighteenth century. Many other girls then did as well or better than Rosa; eyeless vision was all the rage. Some girls said they could read in the dark or see a picture in the middle of a book.

Then, suddenly and sadly, the whole tower came toppling down. *Literaturnaya Gazeta* reported in 1965 that the skillful readers had merely been doubly clever with their own two eyes either before or after being blindfolded. It was a shame, for undoubtedly there are many latent and unused abilities in fingertips. They could, it is frequently assumed, be trained to detect colors by the differing warmth they radiate, and various claims at doing this have been made, or to take more subtle note of textures, or to read big print as if it were braille; but it is asking too much to consider them capable of reading something in the middle of a book.

The Sixth Sense

It is remarkably easy to understand how it was first postulated that a sixth sense might exist because so many animals demonstrate abilities that seem blatantly beyond the range of the five ordinary senses. A hawk, scarcely visible to our eyes, looks for and sees brown mice on the brown earth. An owl does the same trick at night. Bats fly listening for their squeaks and miss cotton threads hung in their paths. Seals return from a 6,000-mile Pacific migration, never once in sight of land, to the small speck of, for example, the Pribilof Islands. Birds fly to Africa and return to the same eave. Huge flocks of birds maneuver with drill-team precision. Salmon find the same river. A dangerous scent, days old, can cause animals to stop as if they have run into a brick wall. Birds navigate over the ocean by night. Bees hurry off to a new source of honey.

In general, as is reasonable, mankind is most astounded at abilities demonstrably beyond him. He is also amazed when the long arm of coincidence strikes home and when some talked-of person chooses that very moment to enter the room. His traditional beliefs in the supernatural foster a desire also to believe in inexplicable events, in telepathy, mysticism, the paranormal, the psychic. Moreover, animals have demonstrated a brilliant exploitation not only of the five senses but also of abilities quite untapped, or seemingly so, by man. The horns of snails retract from ionizing radiation. Rats seem to smell it. Planarian worms can ingest and make use of the memory of chopped-up ancestors. Both snails and worms are affected by magnetic fields. Paramecia swim along mild electric currents. Other single-celled animals line themselves up at right angles to electromagnetic fields. And some puzzling things happen to man, frequently linked to the supposition that minds can influence other minds without going through the normal channels.

How telepathy could possibly have originated among neurons customarily dedicated to transmitting impulses along nervous pathways is entirely puzzling, but might be entirely irrelevant. The first problem of extrasensory perception is the need to prove both that perception is occurring (as against chance, wishful thinking, etc.) and that it is extrasensory. The present state of ignorance about so many aspects of the body in general, which include countless unknowns about the senses in particular, make it hard for anyone to be totally dogmatic that all human perception must come through the five senses. Such evidence as does exist for other forms of sensation weakens the dogmatic case still further. In the meantime ESP workers gain and lose ground steadily, with the entrenched prejudices on either side swaying much as the front line swayed in the First World War. The biologist W. H. Thorpe made a cool summing up when he wrote: "It does seem to me that [the evidence from psychical research] has shown that it is possible for separate minds to influence one another in a manner which is totally inexplicable for any present day theory of the physiology of mind, and is perhaps in principle inexplicable by science as we know it."

✑ 3 0 ✑

The Skin,
Hair, and Teeth

Dermis and Epidermis · Skin Patterns and Prints ·
Sunbathing · Tattooing · Beauty · Hair ·
Bristles and Soap ·
Teeth, Deciduous and Permanent ·
Decay · Cleaning and Fluoride

The skin, taken as a whole, is the human body's largest organ; it is enormously versatile; it keeps foreign agents out and body fluids in; it shields against harmful rays and takes steps to improve its shielding should the rays increase—as in sunbathing; it is associated with body cooling and with heat conservation; it helps to regulate blood pressure; it contains the sense of touch; it forms an individual's shape; it is the main organ of sexual attraction, linked as it is with shape and touch; it is constantly and efficiently renewing itself; it is occasionally and less efficiently having to repair itself when wounds occur; it can differentiate itself into the structures of hair, spines, horns, hooves, claws, scales, feathers; and it lasts fairly well throughout life, although it loses elasticity to a marked degree in later years.

Dermis and Epidermis

Essentially it is a two-layered system made up of the dermis and epidermis. The outer layer is epidermis, and all the outer cells of this layer are dead. Living cells cannot survive exposure to air; and however beautiful a living mate may appear to be, he or she is externally a vista of quite dead cells. The death of each epidermal cell is not caused by the external air but is a deliberate act of self-destruction by each cell. As it is forced nearer and nearer the surface by steady replacement from beneath, each cell produces keratin within itself, a horny substance that is also the principal constituent of nail and hair. By the time the cell reaches the surface it is dead, packed with fibrous keratin, and ready for its share of defensive action. It will soon flake off to be lost as yet another fragment of dried skin.

The dermis, beneath the self-sacrificing epidermis, is seen only when the skin is cut. As the dermis contains both nerves and blood vessels, any small cut produces pain and blood. The dermis also contains fat cells, the roots of hair, erector muscles for each hair, sweat glands, sebaceous glands, and much loose connective tissue. A woman has just as many hair follicles as a man, although less conspicuously, and each human being has about as many as his more visibly hirsute primate relatives, such as the chimpanzee and gorilla. Melanocytes, the pigment-producing cells, are scattered equally in the skin of white and black people; the difference between dark and fair people is the productive capacities of each melanocyte rather than their number.

There is a predictability about the amount of skin that can be lost, as in burns: above a certain percentage of the total body area, anyone would die; below a certain percentage, no one would die. Age is highly relevant to these predictions. Until the age of 30 it is generally reckoned that death is inevitable if over 75 percent of the skin is burned. Below 22 percent death is improbable, with the chances of survival gradually deteriorating as the area increases from 22 to 75 percent. For the middle aged (45 to 49) the figures for probable survival and probable death have dropped to 12 and 58 percent. For the aged (80 to 84) they have dropped even further, with death probable above 23 percent, survival never a certainty; even a 2-percent burn has a 20-percent chance of causing death to the very old. The skin area injured can be rapidly assessed by the law of nines: each leg is 18 percent of the whole (9 percent for the leg's front, 9 percent for its back), each arm is 9 percent, the head is 9 percent, the front torso and back torso are each 18 percent, and the final 1 percent is, for convenience, attributed to the genitals.

Skin Patterns and Prints

The dermis and its fibers principally determine the pattern of skin, the entirely distinctive assortment of shapes, ridges, loops, and whorls laid down for life by the third or fourth month of fetal existence. The uniqueness of fingerprints was first shown by the anatomist J. E. Purkinje in 1823, and no authenticated case of different persons with the same finger patterns has yet been found, although identical twins come very close. The Chinese, who have a habit of beating western records by ludicrous margins of a millennium or two, were using fingerprints as legal identification in A.D. 700.

The four main types of finger pattern are the arch (which resembles strata beneath a hill), the loop (which normally has the rounded or sealed part of the loop toward the thumb), the whorl (which is rarer in women than men; women have more arches), and the composite (which is a muddle of loops and forks). It is not just finger patterns that are individually unique, but palmprints, soleprints, toeprints, and even the pattern of the palate ridges; it is the convenience of fingerprints that has made them most important. The Federal Bureau of Investigation has a file of 141 million fingerprints, and one day a computer will be competent to sift through this collection to make the necessary comparisons. Britain will probably soon start collecting prints from people other than criminals, particularly as prints are becoming increasingly important—X rays can now seek them out on rough or difficult materials like paper or skin.

The habit of fortune-telling from the palms is venerable only for the length of time it has happily engaged both teller and told; but the science of dermatoglyphics has recently become useful. About 30 years ago, it was first suspected that palm prints might be associated with disease, and by 1965 some 40 disorders had been linked with abnormal palm prints. As palm prints are indelibly engraved five or six months before birth, the disorders are congenital and predominantly decided at the moment of conception; but in 1966, abnormal palm prints were linked for the first time with a virus infection. The catching of German measles by mothers early in pregnancy had been known for a quarter of a century to cause large numbers of congenital malformations; but its infection was suddenly linked with abnormal prints. Three New York pediatricians, having first devised a better system for recording the prints of new, tightly fisted wriggling babies than the policeman's inky pad, found that about half the babies affected by their mother's infection also had abnormal prints. Normally, and in babies without noticeable malformations, the proportion of strange prints is 14 percent. A typical palm abnormality is the presence of a simian crease, namely one fold traversing the palm from the area at the base of the forefinger, instead of the conventional two. The mere existence of a palm abnormality is certainly not diagnosis of a larger congenital abnormality elsewhere, but it is a striking hint that one is more likely to exist than in a baby whose pudgy palm is normal.

Sunbathing

Ultraviolet radiation, present in sunlight, was discovered in 1801. It is the presence of ultraviolet that makes so many people go down to the sea, for it is the causative agent both of sunburn and of suntan. Sunburn results from the increased blood flow to the small blood vessels in the dermis. Suntan, upon which many Mediterranean, Caribbean, and other coastal economies are based, results from the change in position and the increase in quantity of melanin pigment in the epidermis. Pigment darkening appears within a few minutes of exposure to sunlight; pigment production takes a day or two to show itself.

Current addiction to suntan, presumably enhanced by long winters spent largely under lightbulbs, is scarcely influenced by the possible harmfulness of solar grilling. L. Dudley Stamp, in *Some Aspects of Medical Geography,* having stated that skin cancer is four times as prevalent on the Black Sea coast as on the Baltic coast, concluded that "voluntary exposure to the sun's rays may be more dangerous than fall-out." Certainly skin cancer in white races occurs predominantly on the face, and another important area is the back of the hand. The *British Medical Journal* wrote in 1964 that "sunburn and sun-tan are the early manifestations of injury to the skin by noxious radiation that is eventually carcinogenic. The only significant beneficial effect of sunbathing is the production of vitamin D." This vitamin is amply supplied in a normal diet, and the writer added that sunbathing and its attendant lubrication "can be regarded as a harmless manifestation of narcissism that one day may interest sociologists, anthropologists and the like."

Harold F. Blum, the radiation biologist who has written an excellent review of the subject, concluded that it is undesirable to instill fear of exposure to sunlight (party because skin cancer is still a rare cancer even under conditions favorable for it, such as those in the southern United States) although good to recommend certain prophylactic measures, such as moderation. Anyone possessing skin changes recognized by dermatologists as precancerous, he adds, should avoid the midday sun and know that ordinary window glass offers good protection against carcinogenic radiation. Finally, everyone except albinos tans on exposure to sunlight, and even those born black may become twice as black—or at least possess double the amount of melanin—after prolonged exposure.

Tattooing

Tattooing is an ancient art. The word itself was brought from Indonesia by Captain Cook. China (yes, China again) practiced it 4,000 or 5,000 years ago, and the custom still thrives throughout much of the world despite the fact that the Koran forbade it. Leviticus condemned it, and Pope Hadrian I called it barbaric. Many peoples have found it convenient. The Greeks and Romans tattooed slaves and criminals; the British and French tattooed their convicts even in the nineteenth century; the British Army marked BC on bad-conduct soldiers until 1879; and the Germans indelibly numbered concentration camp inmates in World War II.

Despite a long association with punishment, most tattooing has been for entirely voluntary reasons. The young or the newly enlisted in the Armed Forces have been particularly prone to the custom. Although in Britain physicians have to obtain parental consent for some entirely beneficial injections and can be accused of assault if consent has not been obtained, the tattooist can inject his nearly immortal particles into any skin, old or young, without fear of subsequent action. Tattooing is easy. It is no more than the injection of an insoluble dye such as carbon black into the dermis; about .04 in. is deep enough. Carbon lasts a long time. The colored pigments are more likely to fade, but the evidence of tattooing often lasts longest in the lymph glands of the armpits. However much dermatologists may deplore the practice, it is unlikely to die out, but at least it could be an offense to tattoo children.

Beauty

Allegedly skin deep or a matter of bone structure, but obviously neither one nor the other, what on earth is beauty? The British journal *New Scientist* once had a lengthy correspondence on the subject, which ended with a suggested yardstick—the unit of beauty should be a millihelen, or enough beauty to launch one ship. Presumably, a microhelen would launch just one plank. Science has been notoriously deficient in this subject. Even its language cannot be used. How can the eye, the window of the soul, be described in its anatomical terms? Externally, its folds of skin are entirely beautiful; anatomically, these are the orbital fold, the superior and inferior orbitopalpebral sulci, herniation of orbital fat, and the malar and nasojugal folds. "For where is any author in the world teaches such beauty as a woman's eye?" asked Berowne in *Love's Labour's Lost*. Plainly, any author would use other language than the one science provides.

Is beauty a matter primarily of the face? The reversal of the traditional animal mating position, which accompanied man's increasingly upright stance, changed his viewpoint. This new attitude, to quote C. D. Darlington, "directed man's interest to the face of his mate, and led to the change from an older to a newer version of Venus." Conversely, it is reported that some African tribes still make their choice of wives from those who project furthest behind. Without doubt, beauty is no one thing among the peoples of the world, and equally without doubt these concepts change with time. Is it rarity? In a country of the beautiful does the ugliest reign as queen? After a while, as Charles Darwin pointed out, the preferred choice of female influences the characteristics of the male. Choose long-legged women, mate with them, and second-generation males will be longer in the leg. Darwin ascribed human hair loss to man's steady preference for women without bodily hair; their own woolliness withered as a result.

Is beauty a breaking of the conventional rules? Francis Bacon said, "There is no excellent beauty that hath not some strangeness in the proportion." Greta Garbo is customarily regarded as the beauty of the western world; and she showed strangeness. The magazine *Nova* reported that "her looks were not pretty. Her expression was of an aching sadness. She moved awkwardly. Her feet were big. Her mouth, down-turned and pessimistic. She rarely laughed." Perhaps it is entirely right that beauty should be inexplicable. It needs mystery. It would be destroyed by delineation. It is haunting, eternal, most temporal, and can suffer no yardstick. "Real is what can be measured," said Max Planck. "That which cannot be grasped quantitatively is scientifically invalid," added J. Schorstein. Better so.

Hair

The hairs develop from the epidermis, but then penetrate through the dermis to the tissue beneath the skin. The root of the hair is a knob called the bulb, and the socket containing each hair shaft is called the hair follicle. To each hair is attached a muscle, and with gooseflesh each muscle makes its power visible. Hair follicles are gradually formed between the second and fifth months of fetal life, and all races and both sexes have a similar number. Each individual produces three types of hair in sequence—lanugo, vellus, and terminal hair.

Lanugo, seen on premature babies, is normally prenatal. It can be quite long, it grows a lot on the face, it is without pigment, it is very soft and silky, and it is usually lost by the seventh or eighth month of pregnancy. Its place is taken by vellus, which is traditionally the first postnatal crop of hair. It is also soft, occasionally with pigment, and hardly ever longer than an inch. The changeover from lanugo can sometimes give babies a two-tone appearance at birth.

Vellus gives rise, sometimes gradually, sometimes blotchily, to terminal hair, the coarser, longer, pigmented hair of later life. The changes are not necessarily immediate; the fineness of a baby's hair can slowly grow coarser, and change color just as slowly. The change can be quite sudden in, for example, the rapid growth of coarse, terminal pubic hair. On the face the change from vellus to terminal hair occurs first on the upper lip, then on the chin, the cheeks, and elsewhere.

At the other end of life, vellus is liable to occur again. Even lanugo can occur again and obscure a person's face with hair, but this change is entirely pathological. Terminal hair is lost with age, not only from the head but also from all other parts of the body. It tends to depart in the reverse order of its arrival, and so goes from the shoulders, arms, chest, abdomen, forearm, thighs, and armpits—roughly in that order. Pubic hair also goes, more so in women than men.

An average scalp contains 100,000 hairs. While new hair follicles do not in general arise where they did not exist before, it can seem as if they do because all hair follicles follow a cycle; they are active, then wither, then rest. It is after the resting phase, which lasts some three to four months, that the hair grows again and continues to do so for a few years. The period of withering is a matter of a couple of weeks, and during this period each hair shaft falls out. Daily loss from a full scalp of hair is about 30 to 60 individual hairs, but the follicles that grew them are not lost. Only with baldness do the follicles not spring to life again.

The speed of hair growth during its active period varies according to its position on the body. On the scalp and beard it is fast; on the limbs and back it is slow, although the occasional rogue hair, especially with males, can suddenly grow out of all proportion to its sluggardly neighbors. Scalp hair growth, according to Dr. Arthur Rook, of Cambridge, proceeds at about .012 in. daily, beard growth at .15 in. and limb-hair growth more slowly. Therefore, barbers make their living out of a steady increment of 4¾ in. of hair per year. Assuming a similar rate of growth, and men and women are equal in this regard, it would take a girl (or a man these days) some six years before the hair grew long enough to sit on. At this rate, even though the speed slows in later life, a person produces about 25 ft. of hair in a lifetime, but the cycle of growth and rest prevents anyone from possessing such lengthy bird-of-paradise locks. The follicle cycle and the regular molting of each shaft every few years mean that no one shaft produces anything like 25 ft. of hair continuously. As the cycle lasts from one to six years, a maximum shaft length is likely to be nearer 2½ to 3 ft. Some women can grow their hair longer and can even stand on their hair, but the regular molting prevents lengthier ambitions.

Baldness is customarily a male attribute, and it appears to be genetically determined. Girls unhappy at the thought that their prospective husbands may go bald in later years should study the family album (and see the earlier chapter on inheritance). A bald father and grandfather are a heavy-handed pointer toward baldness in their offspring and her spouse. Women can grow bald with just as much severity as many men, but it is far rarer and usually starts later. Cures for baldness are legion, which in itself is a kind of indictment, considering their high sales and the persistence of so much baldness. Without doubt, there is one treatment that either prevents it or arrests it if it has already begun— castration removes the predisposing male hormones and almost always is a cure.

Bristles and Soap

The *Journal of the American Medical Association* in its questions-and-answers column recently gave an interesting reply to a query about beard softening and how best to prepare the bristles. "The most effective beard softener in preparation for shaving is water" was the reply, which must have cut across an entire nation's early-morning prejudices and preferences. Two minutes' contact with warm water is all that is necessary for bristles to become hydrated and softened, and the warmer the water the shorter the time. Soap and cream merely maintain the softness achieved by the water. Reputedly, Albert Einstein used only water. So, reputedly, he was right once again.

A last skin custom, totally different but equally ingrained and therefore probably impossible to change, also fails to have the wholehearted support of the medical profession. It concerns a baby's skin and how to wash it. Not only are there many who discourage the traditional soap and water, but also it is frequently advocated that newborn babies should not be bathed at all. Soaping has many disadvantages: it takes time; it makes the baby slippery, thereby increasing nervousness all around; it can get into the baby's eyes, thereby causing yelling and an early displeasure with the whole wet business; and soap can readily form unwelcome scum. The substance hexachlorophane is gaining ground as a soap replacement in the wards, but soap has a strong hold on the home however chancy a hold it causes on the baby.

Teeth, Deciduous and Permanent

Mammalian teeth are formed in two series. The first milk, or deciduous, teeth are lost and are replaced by the permanent teeth. Many primitive vertebrates possess a different system with marked advantages. They produce series after series of new teeth. Sharks are particularly adept at this. The mammal man, envious of sharks while so-called "permanent" teeth fall out and decay with extreme impermanence and without hope of replacement, could well do with a third set in middle age. Such third sets have been recorded, for seemingly every possible aberration is described somewhere, but the condition is extraordinarily rare. (So, too, with complete absence of teeth, although congenital absence of individual teeth has been amply recorded for every tooth position.) The most curious anomaly associated with teeth, painfully so, is that no other structure in the human body is as likely to perish during life and yet no other structure is as resistant to decay after death. As castration is a remedy for baldness, death is a cure for caries.

Most human babies are born without visible teeth. Julius Caesar, Louis XIV, Napoleon, and Richard III possessed a tooth at birth, as do one in 2,000 of the general population. Usually, this early dentition is loose and is one or both of the central lower incisors. First teeth do not normally appear until the age of 7½ months, and the customary range is 5½ to 10 months. For the next 20 months or more, as there is great variance in the timing of teeth, the child produces its full complement of 20 deciduous teeth: four incisors, two canines, and four premolars on each jaw. The final order, starting from the center of each half of each jaw, is central incisor, lateral incisor, canine, first premolar, second premolar. According to Harold Stuart, the customary order and age of arrival for the milk teeth are:

Order of Arrival	Average date of arrival
Lower central incisors	7½ months
Upper central incisors	9½ months
Upper lateral incisors	11½ months
Lower lateral incisors	13 months
Upper first premolars	15½ months
Lower first premolars	16 months
Upper canines	19 months
Lower canines	19 months
Lower second premolars	26 months
Upper second premolars	27 months

Arrival times many months earlier or later than these dates can be entirely normal. Only two-thirds of children produce their upper second premolars within five months of that average age of 27 months. And only two-thirds produce their first tooth between the ages of 5½ and

10 months. The teeth of girls appear earlier than those of boys, but boys tend to lose their deciduous teeth earlier than girls. Although teething is now an excuse for mothers and a presumed unpleasantness for children, it used to be listed as a major cause of death. In 1842, 4.8 percent of all London babies who died before their first birthday had been killed that year by teething.

The permanent teeth by no means mimic the deciduous order of appearance. Although permanent teeth do not appear for six years or so after birth, the buds for them are formed six months before birth. These small protuberances, developed on the tongue side of the deciduous teeth, lie dormant until their sudden growth and activity help to push out the relatively short-lived deciduous teeth. (An alternative plan to three series of teeth would be to have two series of equal duration, say 35 years and 35 years rather than half a dozen years followed by half a dozen decades.) Children acquire their first permanent teeth, the first molars (after the Latin for millstone), before losing any of their deciduous teeth. Girls get them at 70 to 72 months, boys at 73 to 74 months. These permanent molars are not replacements for the deciduous premolars, but the first of the extra teeth, the many-cusped molars possessed by an adult. The deciduous premolars are replaced by two-cusped teeth, the bicuspids or premolars, and these erupt during the child's ninth or tenth year. (Again there is wide, entirely normal variation from the average.)

The first deciduous teeth to be replaced are the incisors, during the seventh or eighth year, followed by the premolars, and then by the canines in the twelfth year. While the first permanent molar appears in the sixth year, the second does not arrive until the thirteenth year. The third—or wisdom tooth—is most casual, arriving perhaps at 17, perhaps at 25, perhaps never. The permanent teeth are entirely leisurely about their onset. The first series of 20 deciduous teeth takes less than two years to be completed, but the second series of 32 permanent teeth takes at least six times as long from first to last appearance.

A mature tooth consists predominantly of enamel and dentine. The surface enamel is the hardest bodily tissue, and is 96 percent mineral. The inner dentine—also called ivory—is much like bone, but harder; 70 percent of it is of inorganic material. Not only are human permanent teeth not replaced, but they do not grow permanently. The incisors of a rabbit, for example, grow steadily, and wear is continually replaced, while the tusks of an elephant grow more and more formidable year by year. Mankind's set of teeth, remorselessly fixed and limited, can deteriorate only with time. This they do, but never so determinedly as in this twentieth century.

Decay

Modern food has been described as overcooked, soft, sticky, and apparently designed for a nation with ill-fitting dentures. Without doubt the quality of today's diet has much to do with today's tooth decay; so have the refined carbohydrates and the frequent consumption of sweet things between meals. Neolithic and Iron Age man would be astounded to hear modern dental advice, that food should both be chewed and eaten only at mealtimes, but even Paleolithic man suffered from tooth decay. Over 1 percent of South African australopithecine teeth had been affected by caries. A survey of 12,000 Stone and Iron Age teeth from France and Belgium showed that decay frequency was sometimes as high as 8 percent, although rotting teeth were normally an affliction of adults. Teeth from the more recent Middle Ages cannot be dug up and examined with such impunity, but one survey found that a quarter of all medieval teeth had been lost before death and 18 percent of the remainder were victims of caries. Poor Anne Mowbray, unearthed by an excavator in 1965, who had lived as a Plantagenet without reaching her ninth birthday, had four milk teeth rotten and even two permanent teeth already bad. Perhaps a fifteenth-century royal diet had much in common with twentieth-century commoners' food, although she could not have encountered much sugar and certainly no refined white flour.

Today Anne would be no exception. In Britain 84 percent of five-year-olds have at least one decayed tooth, and eight years later a third of British juvenile teeth have been damaged by caries. There was an improvement in World War II, but peace restored the decay rate. Some 5,000 children under 20 are now fitted with complete upper and lower dentures annually. (A letter to the *British Medical Journal* erroneously reported in 1964 that 90,000 children a year left British schools with false teeth. The report was reprinted in the newspapers, but even its shockingly false total did not cause national alarm.) In the United States, 18 percent of all adults up to the age of 79 have no natural teeth at all, and a further 9 percent have natural teeth in only one jaw. Whites lose their teeth twice as frequently as Negroes. According to the Public Health Service, 97 percent of American children suffer tooth decay. By the time they reach high school, 11 of their teeth are either decayed or lost.

George Washington himself helped to found the national American tradition of bad teeth. One of his ill-fitting sets of dentures had been carved from hippopotamus ivory. Animals and other donors, such as slaves, helped to fill the gaps in wealthy jaws, and Waterloo teeth were in plentiful supply for many years; but 24 years after that battle Charles

Goodyear discovered a process for vulcanizing rubber. Not only could dentures then be made to fit accurately, but they could be kept in place by suction. Nowadays, dentures may look good and feel good but they can still not permit the pressures of chewing and biting exerted in a normal mouth: the 150-to-250-lb. pressure of biting is reduced to 10 to 30 lb., because, although jaws are just as strong, the tissue beneath the dentures is less capable of withstanding the load. On biting, Albert Schweitzer told John Gunther that a human bite is the most dangerous, then serpents, then monkeys.

Cleaning and Fluoride

How to clean teeth? At a 1964 dental conference held in London, Professor R. D. Emslie described an experiment in the Sudan that assessed various methods. The results, in order of their cleansing abilities, were:

1. Chewing stick. (Dominant in Africa. Referred to by Mohammed).
2. Towel on finger. (Part of Muslim code involves washing out mouth with finger and thumb. Not good for mouth areas inaccessible to the towel.)
3. Tooth brush and paste. (Dominant in industrialized western world. Various forms of brush and paste have been proved highly abrasive. Electrical brush now popular.)
4. Chewing luban. (A natural resinous chewing gum.)
5. Eating dom. (A fibrous fruit.)
6. Eating sugarcane.
7. Eating orange.

The reduction in debris varied from 80 percent with the chewing stick to 40 percent with the orange. This debris (or plaque) is important; without it tooth decay would be less rampant. No one is entirely positive about all the reasons for caries, but there must be acid in adequate concentration and there must be time. The starches are generally swallowed before they are broken down; the simple sugars not only stick around but also are easier to break down into acid. Saliva would be able to buffer this acid were it not for the plaque, which tends to be neutral on the surface where the saliva can get at it, but more acid with depth. Given sufficient acid for sufficient time, even enamel, the hardest tissue of the body, capable of lying in the earth for thousands of years, is eaten away voraciously.

For some reason, the addition of fluoride to the diet prevents decay.

Decay is not stopped, but fewer cavities develop—perhaps one-third fewer, perhaps two-thirds—if fluoride is present in drinking water to the minuscule tune of one part in a million. The fact was discovered by an American dentist, Frederick S. McKay, in the early years of this century, and it has frequently been confirmed since then. Some towns have a natural abundance of fluoride in their water—and less caries; others have added it to the supply, changed their minds, and then added it again—with the incidence of caries going down, then up, then down again in consequence. Antigo, Wisconsin, seesawed in this fashion, having been worried initially about tooth decay, then about sodium fluoride (which is a poison if taken in large doses), and then again after the decay rate had shot up. Other arguments against the addition of fluoride to the water, described as contamination by opponents, are leveled against the allegedly unproved beneficial effects, against the proved harmful effects (modest overdoses cause teeth staining), and against tinkering by the state with the freedom of the individual.

So far, about 60 million Americans drink water to which fluoride has been added by man, and a further 7 million drink water to which it has been added naturally. In Britain, only 2 million people drink the tasteless, colorless, odorless, and inexpensive fluoride in their water. Dr. Luther L. Terry, former Surgeon General of the United States, has called fluoridation the most recent of the "great mass preventive health measures of history"; the three others were the pasteurization of milk, the purification of water, and immunization against disease.

⟡ 31 ⟡

Digestion and Nutrition

Summary · Enzymes · Food · Actual Requirements ·
Protein · Fats · Carbohydrates · Minerals ·
Vitamins · Water · How Much Food? · Obesity ·
Starvation · Cooking · Food Poisoning

Fate cannot harm me—I have dined today.
The Reverend Sydney Smith

On the one hand, the process of digestion is entirely elementary; the
hollow tube of the digestive system stores food temporarily, prepares it
for absorption, absorbs what is absorbable, and rejects the rest as feces.
On the other hand, such simplicity has challenging riddles within it.
How is it that the stomach can digest meat without digesting itself?
How does it consume tripe, or the intestine wall used as casing for
some sausages, or even bone, without the cannibalistic self-destruction
of its own tissue? The stomach contains hydrochloric acid, and in quite
a concentration (gastric juice consists of about 0.6 percent). The popular appraisal of its strength is that a stomach's contents could burn a
hole in the carpet. So why does the stomach not burn a hole within
itself? And how can glands of living tissue actually manufacture such a
corrosive substance as hydrochloric acid?

There are further problems. The human being, traditionally called
an omnivore, can indeed eat a bewilderment of foods; yet he can starve
to death with remarkable ease. Basically, the human system cannot
cope with plants, trees, mosses, and most of the botanical world; it
can cope only with the botanical end products, such as fruits, seeds,

[391]

nuts. The few plants known as vegetables are exceptions. The plant world, so suitable for all the herbivores and consumed so avidly by well over half the world's animal species, is virtually forbidden to man. Forbidden too, despite our digestive ability to break down so many chemical compounds, are a few substances that have the power to poison us, to destroy our lives or merely to affect our well-being disastrously. Eating earth or leaves or old newspapers will not do us good, and may do us harm, but poisons are in a different category. A substance is said to be a poison if less than 2 oz. of it will either kill us or be seriously harmful. (Everything is harmful if consumed to excess, even bread and water. Poisons are harmful if consumed minutely.)

Proteins are a further complexity. The body must have them within the diet and certainly absorbs them, but the body is normally resentful of foreign proteins, and brings its powers of immunity to bear upon any such invasions by amassing antibodies to counter the antigens. However, foreign proteins taken into the intestine are, customarily, absorbed, transformed, and utilized without any disturbance whatever.

Also, what is hunger and what is thirst? In general we eat what we need in that we stay reasonably constant in weight. We drink without too much thought of the need for liquid, and yet do not dehydrate ourselves. We say "Enough" and scarcely pause to marvel at our precise comprehension of requirements.

A final conundrum, more perplexing to the chemist than the ordinary consumer, is that the body performs with speed and precision large numbers of chemical reactions that would normally take far, far longer if carried out in a laboratory at the same temperature and pressure. Anyone who has ever wielded a test tube or a frying pan will know that chemical reaction is faster with heat; yet the body breaks down molecules, combusts them with oxygen, and builds up the molecules at the modest 98°F. temperature of the human frame. This is less than the temperature of bath water, and the chemistry both of cooking and of the test tube would be immeasurably slow if confined to such a heat. A partial answer to the body's abilities is the profusion of enzymes, those natural catalysts that assist and promote biochemical reactions and are not used up in the process. But to define a catalytic enzyme is one thing. To explain how it achieves its remarkable role of initiating or accelerating any reaction, without being unduly involved, is quite another.

Summary

Unfortunately the language of digestion is largely indigestible, but as this barrier does exist, it might as well be encountered right at the start. Food consists of proteins, carbohydrates, fats, salts, vitamins, and water. Some of each are essential, but only the first three have to be altered by digestion.

Proteins (after the Greek word for primary, or fundamental) are large molecules made up of chains of amino acids. These amino acids are joined together by what is called the peptide linkage, whereby each amino group (NH_2) is attached to a carboxyl group (COOH). Some enzymes can break the linkage and can add a molecule of water at the same time—hence the action is called hydrolysis. Some links, as might be expected, are easier to break than others; so the long protein molecules become broken, first into shorter lengths (polypeptides), then into very short lengths consisting of three amino acids (tripeptides) or two amino acids (dipeptides). Finally, there will just be the single amino acids. Traditionally called the body's building blocks, the 20 different kinds of amino acid that build up protein are indeed, when fully digested and broken down into single units, the raw material for the manufacture of the body's tissues. The human body, apart from its bone and its fat, is rich in protein, a fact appreciated by the occasional carnivore; but all proteins have to be broken down into their amino-acid components before they can be built up again into useful protein. Digestion does the breaking down.

Carbohydrates (after the Latin for coal and the Greek for water) are compounds of carbon, hydrogen, and oxygen. These three are joined together to form the three kinds of monosaccharide—glucose fructose, and galactose—and all carbohydrates are built up of monosaccharide units. Once again, the problem of digestion is to break down big molecules into smaller ones. The big polysaccharides, often called starches, have to be broken down. They too have linkages, called glucosidic linkages, and the big polysaccharides are attacked by enzymes at their linkages until they form disaccharides (two units) and monosaccharides (one unit). Unlike the proteins, which are all big and have to be broken down, some of the carbohydrates are small. Glucose is composed of just single monosaccharide units, but glucose has to be made artificially. There are two disaccharides present in food: sucrose, found in cane sugar, and lactose, found in milk. Whether artificial or natural, such carbohydrates need little or no breaking down, and therefore next to no time is necessary for their digestion; hence their use for those with disrupted digestions or the need for instant energy.

Fats (an Anglo-Saxon word) are, like proteins and carbohydrates, combinations of simpler units. These units are glycerol (or glycerin) and the fatty acids, such as stearic acid, palmitic acid, and oleic acid. All such fats are, like the carbohydrates, made up of carbon, hydrogen, and oxygen, but in different proportions—the fats have very little oxygen. A typical carbohydrate has equal amounts of carbon and oxygen and twice as much hydrogen. A typical fat has twice as much hydrogen as carbon, being made up principally of CH_2 units, but only an atom or two of oxygen at one end of the molecule. Another major difference among fats, carbohydrates, and proteins in the body is that fats can be easily stored. The body's available stores of protein and carbohydrate are very limited, but the body's willingness to store up supplies of fat bedevils large portions of the population. Fat is easier to store, and the fact that honey (a carbohydrate) lasts and so does pemmican (a protein) while butter (a fat) goes rancid does not destroy the generalization. Fat is easier to store and, weight for weight, has twice the fuel value of protein or carbohydrate.

Enzymes

The all-important and all-skillful digestive enzymes, which act so effectively upon the casual assortment of foods consumed by the average human, make a long list. Their names and their products also tend to be lengthy. Nevertheless, the most crucial enzymes in digestion ought to be mentioned, if only briefly. Their products follow in parentheses.

From the salivary glands:	Salivary amylase	(maltose, a disaccharide)
	Maltase	(glucose)
From the stomach:	Pepsin	(peptides)
	Rennin	(Casein, a milk protein)
From the pancreas:	Trypsin	(peptides)
	Lipase	(glycerol and fatty acids)
	Amylase	(maltose)
	Ribonuclease	(nucleotides, proteins of cell nucleus)
	Deoxyribonuclease	(nucleotides)
From the intestine:	Carboxypeptidase	(amino acids)
	Aminopeptidase	(amino acids)
	Enterokinase	(trypsin, same as the pancreatic enzyme)
	Maltase	(glucose)
	Sucrase	(glucose and fructose)
	Lactase	(glucose and galactose)

Those from the salivary glands work best in neutral conditions, those from the stomach work best in acid, and those from the intestinal glands work best in neutral or alkaline conditions (or possibly slightly acid conditions—there is dispute about this). The stomach's acidity is partly neutralized by an intestinal secretion of sodium bicarbonate, the same chemical so many people pour with such enthusiasm into their stomachs.

Food

Perhaps there was a time when humanity existed in luxuriant gardens of Eden, plucking fruit here and there; but one wonders. The human digestive system can never have had an easy time. Instead, subjected to trial and error, it must have been the steady recipient of good and bad, of beneficial and disastrous. Countless unsung heroes of the past must have noised it abroad, painfully, that deadly nightshade berries, henbane, wild hyacinth, bluebell, deathcap toadstool, monkshood (wolfsbane), water dropwort roots, cowbane roots, yew berries, ivy leaves, and the fresh anemone were not for eating. Other heroes, having gobbled gristle greedily from some freshly hunted creature, must have come up with the idea of roasting or boiling food to render it more digestible. Still others must have realized that fat, by boiling at a higher temperature, can break down food most effectively.

Even had they been presented with a Garden of Eden stripped of all poisons, one suspects that our human ancestors would not have been content with the dull diurnal round of fruit gathering. For one thing, virtually every tribal group in the world has known how to make alcohol. For another, few people just pluck fruit and harvest nuts; they do things to the food, chop it up, store it, preserve it, flavor and pickle it, and let it rot to the right degree of putrefaction. They want variety, they want the exotic and the rare, the strong-tasting and the rich. The human digestive system, ably equipped with enzymes, has just had to cope with the very mixed assortment of commodities sent down to the stomach in each esophageal bolus.

Nowadays, such naturalness as ever existed is being diminished still further. Take this declared analysis of a particular cracker: "Wheat flour, processed Cheddar cheese solids, cotton seed and soya oil, non-fat milk solids, cornflour, cheese flavour, artificial flavour, salt, sugar, mono and di-glycerides, egg yolk, baking soda, mono-sodium glutamate, butylated hydroxyanisole, butylated hydroxytoluene, certified colour, propyl gallate." Standard flavorings, although kept under constant vigilance in Britain by the Food Standards Committee, still sound unpleasant. Popular ones include Tartrazine, Ponceau MX, Ponceau 4R, Red 10B, and Amaranth. Ponceau 3R, found to act as a carcinogen in rats, was recently recommended for withdrawal by the committee. However, neither food adulteration nor coloring is new. Think of saffron, turmeric, cochineal, and carmine.

Today's average Britons spend 27 percent of their disposable income on foods. Not only are they spending more on food than a few years ago, but they are spending a greater proportion of their actual income on it. A typical Englishman consumes 3 lb., 5 oz., of potatoes a week, 18½ oz. of sugar (plus jams and other preserves), 4 eggs, 2 oz. of sausages, 1½ oz. of fresh fish, 2 lb., 11 oz., of bread (it was 4 lb. in 1950), 5 oz. of cookies and crackers, 3 oz. of tea, and much else besides. The average diet more than meets the nutritional standards set by the British Medical Association, although by no means does every individual eat adequately.

A major victory of World War II was the satisfactory nourishment of the British people, and the distribution of a food supply that had much to be said for it medically over today's excesses. Food rationing began in January, 1940; and 18 months later, when at its most severe, the weekly allowance for each civilian adult was 4 oz. bacon or ham, 8 oz. sugar, 2 oz. tea, 8 oz. fat (of which only 2 oz. were butter), 2 oz. jam, 1 oz. cheese, and about a shilling's worth of meat. In addition, there was a modest supply of milk (with priority for children and expectant mothers), roughly one egg a week, and canned meats and fish, although such desirable extras were included in a rationing system that enabled everyone to select his preferences, provided they were both available and within his allocation. Nevertheless, many a dietitian would long for Britain to be restricted to wartime food supplies, were such an enforced method of national abstinence feasible.

Globally, the food picture is both unsatisfactory and obscure. While many Britons eat too much, and Americans carry so much of their food surplus around with them (Dr. Hugh Sinclair has calculated this transported excess to be 2 million tons of fat), there is obviously great undernourishment in the world; but there is also great uncertainty about its extent. The traditional figure, constantly quoted, is that two-thirds of the world suffers from malnutrition or hunger. In 1964, Colin Clark, director of the Agricultural Economics Research Institute at Oxford, said, "This extraordinary misstatement . . . is believed by almost everyone, because they have heard it so often." It was first made in 1950 by Lord Boyd Orr, formerly director general of the United Nations Food and Agricultural Organization, a body once described as "a permanent institution devoted to proving that there is not enough food in the world." Colin Clark drew attention—at a Ciba symposium on the subject—to the estimate given in May, 1961, by Dr. Sukhatme, director of statistics at FAO, that 10 to 15 percent of the world's people were hungry. Of course, people can be well fed, but malnourished. Accurate estimates of the extent of poor nourishment are even harder to make, for adequate nourishment depends on ambient temperature, sex, body weight, pregnancy, lactation, exercise, and work.

Three generalizations are possible. First, scientific estimates of human calorific requirements have been falling in recent decades; the original calculations put our needs too high. Second, world food production is definitely not keeping pace with world population. Third, all manner of people will inevitably continue to reiterate that two-thirds of the world suffers from malnutrition or hunger.

Whatever the actual fraction of people who would like to eat more, there is quite a big fraction constantly trying to eat less. Diets abound, and for every scheme, however ridiculous, there are loyal devotees—nuts at night, no fats, lots of nibbles, no nibbles. Prescription slimming drugs sold in the United States cost $60,000,000 in 1965, or double the figure for 1960. Stipulated low-calorie foods worth $300,000,000 were sold in 1965, or five times the 1960 figure. Low-calorie soft drinks are accelerating their sales even faster. It is bizarre that so many now grab at foods whose labels proudly proclaim their virtual lack of calories and their nutritional pointlessness, while so many others are dying from a lack of calories; but at least the eating nations are trying to trim their appetites. In the United States, the annual per capita consumption of all foods is now down 197 lb. from the 1909 figure, the year totals of this kind were begun.

Actual Requirements

For every living creature food has a twofold purpose. It must supply the raw materials for the construction or replacement of human tissue, and it must act as fuel for supplying energy to the body. Generally speaking, the first purpose requires the intake of a small number of basic substances, the second requires the intake of sufficient calories. It is possible to eat more than enough calories and still die owing to the lack of some essential substance. It is equally possible to ingest a fully representative tally of essential nutrients but die owing to an insufficiency in the total bulk and a lack of calories necessary for the maintenance of life.

Nutritional needs are also a compromise, for any given species, of what is available, what can be digested, and what can be manufactured against what is actually required. Chemically, a zebra and a lion and a vulture would yield similar analyses; but the zebra lives on grass, the lion can live on zebras, and vultures can live on the decaying corpses of both of them. They all have similar requirements, but they attain them differently. The zebra makes grass fit for lions to eat, and the lion produces meat fit for vultures to eat, and all three produce flesh fit for bacteria to consume eventually.

The human being, like any other creature, has a limited range of foodstuffs and a limited power of converting digested materials into actual needs. He or she does not have to eat meat to make the meat of muscle tissue, but he or she does have to eat the right vitamins, for example, and the right kinds of protein to stay alive. Food is the supply of raw materials, but when broken down by digestion these are still partly constructed for our needs. A housebuilder requires neither trees nor sawdust to make a house, but needs the intermediate plank form. The body requires neither meat nor its elemental constituents of nitrogen, hydrogen, carbon, and oxygen, but the intermediate amino-acid form. As the housebuilder needs more than one type of plank to make his house, so the body requires some 30 to 40 essential nutrients.

These essentials consist of about a dozen vital minerals, about a dozen vitamins, some ten amino acids, a lot of water, and a sufficiency of fats, carbohydrates, and proteins. From these, the countless profusion of different bodily constituents will be manufactured, such as the hemoglobin of blood (with each molecule possessing 64,500 atoms), the nucleic acids (possessing even more), and the digestive enzymes (which can break down still larger molecules). Yet all this profusion also consists of just a very few elements. If a human body (of 156 lb.) were analyzed completely in a test tube and all its complexities were rendered into its constituent elements, it would be found to consist of oxygen (100 lb.), carbon (28 lb.), hydrogen (15 lb.), nitrogen (4.6 lb.), calcium (2.3 lb.), phosphorus (1.6 lb.), potassium (8.5 oz.), sulphur (6 oz.), sodium (3.7 oz.), chlorine (3.7 oz.), magnesium (1.25 oz.), iron (0.15 oz.), zinc (.07 oz.), copper (.008 oz.), manganese (.0008 oz.), molybdenum (.0006 oz.), some cobalt, some selenium, and some still smaller fractions of other elements. Chemistry teachers sometimes comment facetiously that, chemically, the body is worth about a dollar and certainly there is nothing exotic about its main constituents, although some of the trace elements might bring more money these days. Nevertheless, no body could survive were it to be presented, like a chemical Pygmalion, with a ready supply of its constituent elements in elemental form. It has to have them as protein, fat, carbohydrate, vitamins, and water, and only to a limited extent can it have them as salts and simple inorganic chemicals.

Protein

Every cell contains proteins, and about 18 percent of body weight consists of protein. They are the most complex compounds found in nature and consequently have large molecular weights varying from a few thousand to several million.* However big, the structure is always built up of amino acids, the small constituent units of every protein. Egg albumin, for example, the ordinary "white" of egg surrounding the yolk, is a small-sized protein of molecular weight 45,000. It consists of 418 amino-acid units bonded together to form each molecule of albumin. Each amino-acid unit has of course a smaller molecular weight than the large built-up protein, and amino-acid weights vary from 75 (glycine) to 240 (cystine).

The list of amino acids makes dull reading, but their totally vital role demands that they should be heard. Some are more vital than others, and the ten found to be indispensable in the diet of a young growing rat have been underlined. Without every one of these ten essential amino acids the laboratory rats suffered; with sufficient supplies of all ten, the young rats were able to make the remaining amino acids necessary to the buildup of their own proteins. There are several variants in the list of amino acids, but the basic types include:

Glycine $C_2H_5NO_2$	(19)	Glutamic acid $C_5H_9NO_4$	(52)
Alanine $C_3H_7NO_2$	(35)	Hydroxyglutamic acid $C_5H_9NO_5$	
Serine $C_3H_7NO_3$	(36)	Arginine $C_6H_{14}N_4O_2$	(15)
Threonine $C_4H_9NO_3$	(16)	Lysine $C_6H_{14}N_2O_2$	(20)
Valine $C_5H_{11}NO_2$	(28)	Phenylalanine $C_9H_{11}NO_2$	(21)
Norleucine $C_6H_{13}NO_2$		Tyrosine $C_9H_{11}NO_3$	(9)
Leucine $C_6H_{13}NO_2$	(32)	Tryptophan $C_{11}H_{12}N_2O_2$	(3)
Isoleucine $C_6H_{13}NO_2$	(25)	Histidine $C_6H_9N_3O_2$	(7)
Cystine $C_6H_{12}N_2S_2O_4$	(6)	Proline $C_5H_9NO_2$	(14)
Methionine $C_5H_{11}SNO_2$	(16)	Hydroxyproline $C_5H_9NO_3$	
Aspartic acid $C_4H_7NO_4$	(32)		

Like carbohydrates and fats, proteins consist largely of carbon, hydrogen, and oxygen; but, unlike carbohydrates and fats, proteins are distinguished by the presence of nitrogen. Every single amino acid contains some nitrogen, and a couple contain sulphur as well. The proteins in human diet are practically the only source of new nitrogen. Constant replenishment of nitrogen is necessary because irreversibly damaged proteins lead to the loss of nitrogen; it passes out of the body in urine

* A molecular weight is relative to that of an atom of oxygen, which is taken to be 16.

as urea. Proteins are also the chief source of sulphur. The figures listed in parentheses after the chemical formulas are the number of each of these amino-acid units present in egg albumin.

This one example of the constituents of one fairly simple protein should give some idea of the hideous complexity of organic chemistry, particularly with regard to proteins. Ordinary inorganic chemistry seems infantile when set beside the interactions of molecules so large. Every schoolboy is taught basic inorganic reactions, like sulphuric acid acting upon zinc when $H_2SO_4 + Zn = ZnSO_4 + H_2$. The production of zinc sulphate and hydrogen is straightforward and entirely elementary compared with the changes that must take place when, for example, egg albumin is merely heated. Everyone knows it changes irreversibly with heat from transparent and fluid to opaque and stiff (in four minutes, if you like your egg done that way), but the chemistry of that change, the manner in which heat affects those 418 amino-acid units, is formidable. Even writing down the 418 constituent formula units of just one albumin molecule would be a major endeavor.

Proteins, in short, are complex. However, it is not their complexity that is vital to our diet, but their amino acids (plus their nitrogen and sulphur). Digestion breaks down the large molecules into these amino acids, and the body then builds up its own vast protein molecules, its albumin, its hemoglobin, its nucleoproteins, its enzymes, collagens, and keratins. As might be expected, animal proteins are, when broken down, nearer to human requirements than plant proteins, but our normal human diet contains a bit of both.

In Britain, the average consumption per person per day is 3 oz. of protein, almost 2 oz. of which are animal protein. In the United States, as in New Zealand, Canada, and Australia, the consumption is nearer 4 oz. daily, with nearly 3 oz. of animal protein. Conversely, India eats less than 2 oz. of protein a day, of which only ⅕ oz. is of animal protein. If all these figures, even for North America, seem low, it should not be forgotten that water is the main weight of most foods. There is only ¼ oz. of protein in a pint of human milk and 3 oz. or less of protein in every pound of beef.

Anyone's intake of either total or animal protein is a very fair guide, and often an extremely precise one, to his or her income in the world. The U.S. Food and Nutrition Board recommends 2½ oz. a day for a 156-lb. man. This is less than the average American eats, but probably more than he needs, decidedly more than most people in the world achieve.

Vegans, the vegetarians who eat no animal products, not even the eggs or cheeses that are entirely acceptable to other groups, have to subsist wholly on plant protein. This can lead to dietary difficulties, but plant proteins can be mixed in such a way that the amino-acid content of the mixture is adequate. Many strict vegetarians have adopted the diet for ideological reasons, but tend to look upon the whole business of eating as a slightly sordid necessity. Consequently, they can be lax about diet, and there can be deficiencies in it. Vitamin B_{12} is an additional complexity, for it is short in a vegan's diet. It can easily be supplemented, but its lack may also encounter a general lack of enthusiasm for caring about the unpleasant demands of mere food.

Where to find proteins? All flesh, whether of fish, fowl, or mammal, is rich in protein. Cow's milk has nearly three times as much protein as human milk, and dried or condensed milks have a still greater proportion by weight. Cheeses tend to have even more. Cereals contain some protein, roughly 5 to 10 percent by weight, with rice and rye less good in this respect than wheat and maize. Sugars have no protein, but nuts, beans, lentils, and all such firm botanical end products are good. Fruits also contain protein, but only 1 percent or so by weight, as so much of their bulk is water. The same also applies to vegetables although, with their water content usually less predominant, the protein proportion is greater.

Where to acquire more protein? The world is short of it, and this lack is the greatest single cause of malnutrition. Kwashiorkor (which in South Africa means the "disease of a child when another is born") is protein deficiency and generally occurs after weaning. Even today, with so much chemistry applied to the food industry, no protein is produced synthetically for food. Attempts to short-circuit traditional gastronomic procedures have generally been frustrated by human conservatism. "The force of habit of millions of people is a terrible force," said Lenin. N. W. Pirie, of the Rothamsted Experimental Station, has constantly produced new schemes for stepping up protein supplies. His "mechanical cows" have extracted it from leaves, from grass, from cereal waste; and yet people are still suffering from lack of it. The wealthier countries, with enough protein to eat, are more tolerant of new foods than the poorer countries who are in greater need of supplementary—and novel —foods.

Most traditional methods of protein production are wasteful and lengthy. In 24 hours, a half-ton of beef will make one pound of protein; in 24 hours half a ton of yeast will make 50 tons of protein. One wonders how long the world will permit itself to be semicarnivorous. It is so much more economical not to process available protein through creatures like the cow, the sheep, and the pig before eating it.

Perhaps future protein supplies will be largely artificial anyway. Alfred Champagnat and others, working at a French institute of the British Petroleum Company, have in recent years used certain microorganisms to make protein out of petroleum. Equally improbable, coal and natural gas are now being investigated as protein sources. So, what next? Even a human protein—insulin—has been artificially made. Anything seems possible in organic chemistry—except possibly the ability to persuade malnourished people to forget their traditional longings and to consume the synthetic marvels manufactured in their place. What would Lenin have done?

Fats

Broadly speaking, fats have two roles in the body. First, they are essential ingredients of every cell, vital to innumerable cell mechanisms. As such, they weigh about 1 percent of the body's total and are not appreciably consumed during periods of starvation. That kind of consumption is limited to the second role of fats, their use as a store of energy. Weight for weight, a pound of depot fat—as it is called—will yield over twice as much energy as either a pound of protein or a pound of carbohydrate. The ratio, roughly 9 to 4, is due to the somewhat boring nature of the typical fat molecule. Essentially, it is just a chain of carbon atoms tied, except at one end, to an unvarying series of hydrogen atoms. Except for the occasional oxygen atom at the end there are no more; hence no water is locked up within the molecules, hence its greater capacity to act as a fuel. The H_2O of water cannot serve as a fuel, and molecules rich in H_2O are less effective as energy liberators when oxidized. Fortunately for creatures like the camel, not only is fat such a well-compressed store of energy, but when it is oxidized it also liberates water. Nature is frequently adept at gaining from both means, and the camel rides on both. (The animal can also allow its body temperature to rise, thus obviating some water loss.)

Depot fat—and more about it under starvation and obesity—is not a fixed entity, like a spare can of shortening in the kitchen. However constant an abdominal outline may in fact be, the fat within is being perpetually removed and replaced. Only about half of depot fat is stored beneath the skin. A lot is attached to the mesentery, the membrane supporting the small intestine, and a lot more is around the kidneys. Some depot fat is entirely normal; obesity is often defined as the condition where over 30 percent of the body weight is fat. This depot fat also acts as a good insulator because of the relative lack of blood vessels ramifying through this kind of tissue. It consists essentially of cells, which are just droplets of fat each surrounded by a thin membranous shell of protoplasm.

Unlike beef fat and other animal fats, human fat melts at quite low temperatures; its melting point is normal room temperature, much less than body heat, as against 121°F. for beef fat. Although many fats liquid at normal temperatures are called oils, there is no distinguishing difference; olive oil is strictly olive fat. Fats also have a low specific gravity. Consequently, fat people float in water more readily than thin people. This is one advantage of growing old, a time of greater fatness, for one's specific gravity decreases as the proportion of fat increases. Even thin old people have more fat in them than in their youth, and therefore float more readily without the exertion of swimming.

Fat needs are very obscure. They are mainly hidden by the organic changes going on within the body. It is all very well to talk of proteins, fats, and carbohydrates as if they were entirely separate from one another, but to some extent they can be made from one another. Potatoes have only .1 percent fat, but they are undeniably fattening; much of their carbohydrate is turned into fat by the body. Similarly, some fat can be turned into carbohydrate and many proteins can be turned into sugar. However, although carbohydrate and fat can go some way toward forming proteins, the essential amino acids already referred to are essential to the formation of new proteins; the fats and carbohydrates cannot do all the conversion by themselves.

Such interchangeability complicates the issue of dietary fat needs. Certainly, some mammals survive on outstandingly little fat, and the human species as a whole is remarkable in its ability to eat either a little or a lot of it. In Britain, the average fat intake is 4 oz. per person per day. A Kikuyu of eastern Africa eats less than a quarter of this, while an Eskimo eats double on average. Extra fat is not always beneficial. Too great an intake of fat with insufficient carbohydrate in the diet can lead to ketosis, a dangerous affliction that is a kind of internal poisoning. The general opinion on fat intake is that, while a high carbohydrate intake can do much to maintain high fat stores, it is probably necessary to eat at least a small amount of fat, particularly if it contains what are called unsaturated fats.* Quite apart from actual fat needs, but integral to them, is the need for vitamins. Animal fats to a large degree, and vegetable oils to a smaller degree, are rich in vitamins A, D, and E.

There is next to no difference between animal and vegetable fats in their energy value, but there is eternal dispute over their respective

* They are called unsaturated because not every carbon atom has its full potential of hydrogen atoms around it. Instead there are some double bonds in the carbon chain.

merits. The principal villain is alleged to be cholesterol, a sterol* found in animal fats and which can also be manufactured by the body. Each of us has about 6 oz. of cholesterol within us at the best of times. Gallstones are largely cholesterol (up to 97 percent), and evidence of an association has sometimes been found between high cholesterol levels in the blood and the incidence of heart disease and arterial degeneration. However, an association between two factors does not indicate a causal relationship. The cholesterol may well be in the blood because of some breakdown in fat metabolism that also affects the arteries. Whether cause or effect, the proportion of cholesterol is at the center of the storm and of countless contradictory statements about animal and vegetable fats.

In 1961 the American Heart Association said, "There is no final proof that changing the fat content of the diet will prevent cardiovascular disease. . . ." In 1965 the association turned around and said, "Atherosclerosis could originate as a result of high-fat diets." It recommended an increased consumption of vegetable oils and a decrease in foods and fats rich in cholesterol. Conversely, only a few months before, a professor of food science from California had said that too great a reliance on vegetable oils would greatly increase aging and decay. Conversely, again, the National Academy of Sciences produced a report in 1966 recommending no general decrease in fat consumption: "Any drastic reduction . . . would alter the body metabolism in unpredictable, possibly deleterious ways." With a subject so complex and little understood as the ingestion of polyunsaturated fatty acids, triglycerides, and all the rest and with the equally tricky problem of arterial decay, it is small wonder that no hard-and-fast answer can be given. In summary, therefore, cholesterol had bad publicity in the late 1950s, but its reputation is now better; vegetable oils boomed in the 1950s and are still booming.

Where are fats found? Roughly speaking, in meats there is a comparable weight percentage of fat and protein, although something like lean pork has more protein and something like rump steak has more fat. Rabbit, duck, and chicken all have extremely modest amounts of fat. Fish vary considerably, with quite a bit for eel, salmon, and herring, virtually none at all for cod and haddock. Human and cow milks have a little, and all condensed milks and cheeses have far more. Egg white has scarcely any (about 1 percent), egg yolk has a lot (over 30 percent). Substances like lard, dripping, olive oil, and fish liver oil have 100 percent; butter and margarine have less since they contain some water. Most cereals are extremely low in fat, and sugar, jams, molasses, and

* Sterol is Greek for "solid." As *chole* is Greek for "bile," the word "cholesterol" means "solid bile," or gallstone.

honey have none. Nuts have a lot, Brazil (70 percent), hazel (62 percent), walnut (60 percent), and peanuts (48 percent). Fruits and vegetables have less than 1 percent.

Carbohydrates

Carbohydrates include all sugars and starches. Chemically, they are built up of carbon, hydrogen, and oxygen, and they follow a general rule: there are two hydrogen atoms for each atom of oxygen—as in water. The general formula can be written as $C_x(H_2O)_y$, and this is called a hydrated carbon, or carbohydrate.

In advanced societies, like Britain, carbohydrates, fats, and proteins are consumed in roughly a ratio of 4:1:1. This means, bearing in mind that a given weight of fat yields over twice as much energy as a given weight of either protein or carbohydrate, that 55 percent of British energy comes from carbohydrate. Many other societies, because of the universal cheapness of carbohydrates over fats and proteins, eat an even greater proportion of sugars and starches. It is customarily recommended that carbohydrate should not supply more than 66 percent of anyone's energy; but it frequently does so.

The total weight of carbohydrate in a 156-lb. man is about 13 oz., some two-thirds of it in the muscles. Carbohydrate is steadily used by the body, but can be stored only to a very limited degree. Within 13 hours of the last replacement, even among those of sedentary occupations, all available supplies have been consumed, and fat stores will be called upon to bridge the gap. Basically, the body's method of dealing with the various forms of ingested carbohydrates is to try and turn them all into glucose. No starches can be absorbed into the blood. The enzymes amylase and maltase must work on them to produce glucose. The sucrose of cane or beet sugar is turned by sucrase into glucose and fructose, and the fructose is turned into glucose by the liver cells and other cells. The lactose of milk is turned by lactase into glucose and galactose, but the liver soon turns the galactose into glucose. There is a stubborn persistence about the body's attitude toward carbohydrates. Glucose is always the end result.

Unfortunately, ability does not always match this persistence. A notable exception is cellulose. Were the human body able to absorb this sugar, the world would not go short of carbohydrates because cellulose is omnipresent in the vegetation all around us. We do eat cellulose in large quantities with leafy vegetables and most forms of plant food; but nothing happens to it, and the undigested raw material is expelled in the feces. It may have suffered somewhat from decomposition by bac-

teria, but they have not had time to break it down into a form that
human enzymes can work upon. The greater length, capacity, or complexity of the herbivore's alimentary canal permits greater opportunity
for the bacteria and therefore an absorption of the valuable glucose
locked within cellulose. Some human beings claim to have the key and
eat a lot of grass, and possibly they do extract some nourishment from
their lawn mowings, but the human being is, in general, incapable of
benefiting from the universality of cellulose. He can starve in a forest
of vegetative profusion.

There is an argument that cellulose supplies beneficial roughage. No
such argument can be applied to the refined sugars, which form an
increasingly large lump of our diet. In fact, sugars have been receiving
bad publicity recently. A writer to *The Lancet* in 1964 said, "The
refining of sugar may yet prove to have been a greater tragedy for civil-
ized man than the discovery of tobacco." Refined sugar used to be listed
with spices as a rare and expensive delicacy. Colonization of the New
World with cheap labor from the old led to huge sugarcane plantations,
and by 1837 the average consumption of refined sugar in Britain had
risen to 20 lb. per man per year (or about 1 oz. a day). By 1850, it
was 30 lb. per man per year, by 1900 82 lb., by 1936 100 lb.; then
came World War II, with its enforced ration of only 26 lb. per man per
year, but by 1961 it was up to 118 lb. (over 5 oz. a day), and it is now
even higher. In the United States, the recent rise has been steeper still,
going up 120 percent in the last 70 years.

On July 4, 1964, Professor John Yudkin and Mrs. Janet Roddy published a paper called "Levels of Dietary Sucrose in Patients with Occlu-
sive Arteriosclerotic Disease." It was an exceptionally important paper.
For years, fats have been harangued for their suspected role in arterial
disease, and for years sugars have been relatively free of such insinua-
tions. The joint paper presented current evidence that "sugar rather
than fat is responsible," and it added that sugar was the more likely
culprit on evolutionary and historical grounds. Not only had the authors
discovered evidence of association between high sugar intake and arterial
and heart disease, but also the increasing consumption of sugar mirrored
the increasing incidence of cardiovascular diseases. The rise in fat consumption—where such a rise even exists—is much less positive than
the meteoric rise in sugar intake.

Many authors supported Yudkin and Roddy with similar findings of
their own. Others (for such is the meat and drink of scientific argument)
took issue either with the paper's conclusions or with the manner in
which the evidence had been collected. All in all, with sugars now
indicted, fats still criticized, protein always expensive, and any form of
gluttony deplored, the latest revelations add weight to a remark made

by Alistair Cooke about the U.S. Food and Nutrition Board. He pictured it "haunted by the fear that someone, somewhere, may be happy eating."

Where to find carbohydrates? Meats, in general, do not possess any, but there is some in liver and quite a bit in pork pies, sausages, and fish paste. Milk is about 5-percent carbohydrate; therefore, by weight, condensed and dried milks possess much greater percentages of carbohydrate, although cheeses either contain the same amount as milk or less. Egg contains a little (less than 5 percent) and chocolate a lot (some 55 percent on average). Of course grains contain massive amounts; white flour is 75-percent carbohydrate, rice even more, and sago and tapioca more still. Sugar is 100-percent carbohydrate, but brown sugars contain 2 percent or so of impurities, such as a few minerals and possibly some vitamins, which do not contribute any significant advantages to a normal diet. All nuts contain carbohydrates. So do all fruits and vegetables—it is their greatest constituent after water. As a generalization, albeit with exceptions, there is starvation when carbohydrate supplies are exhausted, and malnutrition where carbohydrate is available but either protein or fat is not.

Minerals

Carbon, hydrogen, oxygen, nitrogen, and sulphur are elements necessary to life, but are always liberally contained in the carbohydrate, fat, and protein of the diet. The remaining elements necessary to life are customarily grouped together under one heading: minerals. Unlike the first five, which *have* to be eaten as part of a molecule, the remainder can be eaten in their ionic form. Most elements are eaten along with the food and there is no chance of inadequacy. But in certain areas, certain elements can be in short supply, notably calcium, iron, and iodine. Minerals are not used in the production of energy, but are eaten solely —except when the body is actually growing—to replace the minerals that are lost, principally by excretion. Even such minerals as calcium and phosphorus, which are needed in greatest quantity by the body, are required in very small amounts. Others, just as vital, are needed in microscopic fractions. No man can be deprived of iodine in his diet, but his needs are measured in millionths of an ounce per day. The extreme modesty of mineral requirements demands their measurement in grams rather than ounces (28.35 gm. equal 1 oz.).

Calcium. Daily needs are roughly 1 gm. for children, 1.6 gm. for pregnant or lactating women, .68 gm. for adult men. Most calcium eaten is not even absorbed through the intestine, but passes straight out with the feces. The chief roles of calcium are associated with bones and teeth, blood-clotting, muscle contraction, and nerve impulses; and there must always be a certain level of calcium in the blood. Calcium is plentiful in food. Milk has about a gram a quart. There is little in meat, quite a lot in egg yolk, and it is present in most cereals and some vegetables, although generally in a form less suitable for absorption. Countries with poor milk or cheese supplies are most likely to suffer from calcium deficiencies—small stature, poor teeth. One percent of the edible part of cheese is calcium, but less than .1 percent of wheat and rice.

Phosphorus. Daily needs are 1 gm. for children, 1.9 gm. for pregnant or lactating women, 1.3 gm. for adult men. This element can be used either in an organic form, such as part of a protein, or in an inorganic form, such as part of a salt. Phosphorus is used in the body in association with bones and teeth, with the fat content of every cell, with enzymes, and with many intermediates in metabolism. It is found in most foods. Good sources are meat, fish, milk, cheese, eggs, many vegetables, and many cereals. Normally, provided someone is getting enough to eat, he is getting enough phosphorus.

Iron. Daily needs, although vital, are only about .012 gm. This means the loss and the replacement of 1/250 of the body's iron content every day. Iron's chief role is in the formation of blood (about 60 percent of the body's iron is in the hem portion of hemoglobin), but there is some in enzymes and in the liver. A normal diet has more than enough iron in it to satisfy the body's milligram requirements, and good sources are liver, kidney, egg, many vegetables, and cereals. Unfortunately, there is little iron in human milk and even less in cow's milk. Therefore, babies fed lengthily and solely at the breast or the bottle are liable to suffer from an iron-deficiency anemia. This is no problem for six months or more because the baby is born with a modest store of iron and does receive a little in its milk. There is varied enthusiasm and considerable debate about giving additional iron to pregnant and nursing women.

Iodine. Daily needs are .00005 gm. (or slightly over .000001 oz.). Most areas have more than sufficient iodine in water and vegetables to provide this modest intake, but there are iodine-deficient regions, such as Michigan, Derbyshire, and some Swiss valleys. Goiter, or neck swelling due to overactivity of the thyroid gland, can result, and disruption of the thyroid can lead to stunted growth. Women are far more affected than men, and treatment generally consists of the addition of minute fractions of iodine to the table salt. The thyroid gland contains over half of the .025 gm. of iodine normally in the body. As Iodine 131 is a radio-active fission product, happily short-lived with a half-life of eight days, nuclear explosions or accidents (as in Windscale, Cumberland, in 1957) can lead to a sudden rise in iodine contamination of local water, milk, and vegetables. Conveniently, most of this radioactive iodine will, as with ordinary iodine, be absorbed by the thyroid gland, thus localizing the radiation and helping Geiger counters to measure the dose that has been received, although it is medically unsatisfactory that the dose should concentrate in just one area.

Sodium. This element can hardly be mentioned without its principal salt, sodium chloride. Man cannot exist without sodium and without sodium chloride, the dominant salt of common salt; yet he cannot con-sume too much salt, as everyone knows, thirsty ancient mariner or not. Normal daily intake of sodium chloride is 20 gm. per adult, well above actual needs. Although bulk salt is not found everywhere (the sea, saline springs, and salt mines are the principal sources), the normal diet contains quite enough salt without any extra sprinkling either at the cooking stage or at the table. Such additions are for taste; but in areas accustomed to food preserved in salt the acquired craving for it can be considerable.

When abnormal quantities of salt are lost in sweating, the losses have to be made good, but one aspect of acclimatization to hot places is a reduction in the amount of salt lost both by sweat and urine. Salt intake does not have to be much higher in the tropics, particularly as most individuals normally consume more than enough either for temperate or tropical conditions. Of the 60 gm. of sodium customarily found in the body, one-third is in the bones, two-thirds are in the extracellular fluids.

Potassium. This element is chemically very similar to sodium, and its lack can be just as fatal to a body totally deprived of it; but, whereas most of the body's sodium is outside the cells, 99 percent of the body's potassium is inside them. There are about 150 gm. of potassium in the body, and daily turnover is about 3 gm. Potassium deficiency is unlikely, but possible.

Magnesium. It plays a similar role to calcium, but is scarcely ever de-ficient in diet. Most of the body's magnesium is in bone.

Chlorine, bromine, and fluorine. These are grouped together chemically, but they have few similarities for the body. Chlorine is mainly present as the chloride of sodium chloride, and therefore plays a vital part in the osmotic regulation of the body's water content. Normally about 15 gm. of chloride are lost and replaced every day. Bromine is a mystery. It is distributed throughout the tissues, there is more bromine than iodine, and its importance is quite unknown. Fluorine has achieved distinction because of its association with tooth decay. There is convincing evidence that fluoride in drinking water inhibits dental caries. There is doubt about the actual role of fluoride in the body, as the lack of it causes no detectable effect beyond increased tooth decay, but there is absolute certainty that it can be harmful in excess. A mere 2.5 gm. of fluoride is lethal, and the compound sodium fluosilicate can be fatal if only .2 gram is eaten (or .007 oz. for Bond aficionados).

Copper, cobalt, zinc, manganese, and molybdenum. These five are the small five, the essential trace minerals. An average man possesses .96 gm. of zinc, .15 gm. of copper, .018 gm. of molybdenum, .012 gm. of cobalt, and .011 gm. of manganese—a total weight of scarcely more than a gram, but he *has* to have them. They play vital parts in the creation of vital enzymes. Strangely, there is more copper in the brain and liver of a baby than an adult.

The rest. Twenty elements have been mentioned. Of the remaining 72 naturally occurring elements, a good many are both eaten and customarily present in the body, but what they do or whether they have to be present is unknown. Take aluminum. Since the manufacture of aluminum saucepans, there has been controversy whether the extra quantities of this element now inevitably added to human diet were harmful, beneficial, or totally irrelevant. According to existing knowledge, the human body manages with about one-fifth of the Earth's natural elements, and the remaining four-fifths are considered quite unnecessary—at present.

Vitamins

Give a man only the correct amounts of fat, carbohydrate, protein, minerals, and water, and he will surely die, probably within a few months, certainly before long. The understanding of vitamins has a long or short history, according to your outlook. The word itself is less than 60 years old, having been coined by the Polish Jew Casimir Funk when working in England in 1912. His word "vitamine," used to describe what had been called accessory food factors, was a union of vital and amine. They are still vital, but between the World Wars it was realized that few were amines. Therefore, the spelling was adjusted to something less blatantly inaccurate.

The idea of vital substances existing surreptitiously in foodstuffs is much, much older. Hippocrates was recommending vitamin A when he suggested liver for night-blindness. The Indians were recommending vitamin C when they produced a leafy brew in Quebec for Jacques Cartier's scurvy-ridden men. Two centuries later, when Captain James Cook received accolades owed more accurately to various nautical predecessors for insisting upon lime juice for his crew, he was only recommending vitamin C. In that same century, cod-liver oil, rich in vitamins A and D, achieved fame in industrial England as a cure-all primarily because it was making up dietary inadequacies. A century later, the Japanese were fighting beriberi in their sailors by giving them barley. By the turn of the century, scientists were doing important experiments proving the same sort of point, and in this century's first decade the subject of accessory food factors started to open up. The food deficiencies of World War I were a great spur to research, but the work took time. In 1921, the magazine *Discovery* reported, "It is at present generally accepted that there are three distinct vitamines. . . ."

Now there is evidence that some 40 vitamins exist, at least a dozen essential to the human diet. Unfortunately, despite the similarity of the roles of vitamins, in that we cannot get by without their presence, there is no similarity among the vitamins themselves. They are a hodgepodge of chemicals the body must have but cannot manufacture. Professor A. S. Romer has called them "the odds and ends of vitally needed materials." Others have called them "hormones produced outside the body." Unlike the vital amino acids, which also cannot be made by the body, the dominant characteristic of vitamins is the pathetically small amounts needed to keep a person healthy. A man, for example, needs .003 gm. of vitamin A per day (or .0001 oz.). If totally deprived of this vital speck in his diet, he will suffer visually, he will be more easily infected, he will suffer internal lesions, and—if still growing—his growth will be disturbed. In his whole lifetime, he will need to consume only 3 oz. of this entirely necessary substance. He needs even less of some others. For instance, less than 1 oz. of thiamin, distributed over his seventy years, will be ample.

To cope with these minuscule requirements, the League of Nations in the 1930s defined International Units (IU's) of vitamins in a suitably small fashion. For example the IU of vitamin B_1 is defined as "the activity of 3 micrograms [.000003 gm.] of the International Standard Preparation of pure vitamin B_1." Consequently, due to these minute definitions, any vitamin dose seems fairly hefty when it refers to thousands of units encased within a single vitamin pill; but the scale of things is again shrunk to its proper size when it is remembered that a few thousand millionths of a gram are still only a few thousandths of a gram, i.e., very little.

All animals, not just man, require vitamins, or so it seems, because even the smallest microorganisms require groups of vitamins fairly similar to our own. Naturally, not too much work has been done on the dietary refinements of 99 percent of the animal kingdom; but, from the work that has been done, it is probable that all animals require vitamins, that requirements vary widely, and that some animals are capable of making common vitamins for themselves. Of course, as soon as a vitamin can be manufactured by an organism it is no longer a vitamin, but just one more complex organic molecule created as part of an organism's biochemisty. And if some animals and plants were incapable of making vitamins for others to consume, the natural supply would soon expire. Vitamins are what each creature cannot make but can normally find in its diet. Only when diets become grossly abnormal, as in forced-labor camps, on long sea voyages, or when rice grains are polished, does avitaminosis manifest itself in its various unpleasant ways.

The haphazard classification of vitamins reflects to some extent the manner of their discovery. The alphabetic listing of each new discovery was upset by subsequent discoveries (J. B. S. Haldane made use of the word "covery" to describe work that upset or corrected an earlier "discovery"). The single vitamin B was subsequently found to contain more than one vitamin, so B_1, B_2, and so forth were coined. Later, various "coveries" made it clear that some subdivisions were one and the same. Today the numbered B vitamins are B_1, B_2, B_6, and B_{12}, and these four—like most vitamins—have proper names as well.

The characteristics, names, functions, and peculiarities of the leading vitamins are listed below.

Vitamin A. Certainly all mammals, probably all vertebrates, and possibly large numbers of invertebrates need either vitamin A in their diet or some similar substance that enables them to manufacture it. Lack of vitamin A causes blindness in rats and deficiency in humans causes night-blindness, a dry and inflamed eye, lack of resistance to infection, and bad skin. The major source of vitamin A in human diet is liver, and there is huge disparity of vitamin-A content in food. International units per ounce are sardines, 25; milk, 75; peas, 200; carrots, 550; butter, 725; rose hips, 2,100; beef liver, 4,600; calf's liver, 13,000; and cod-liver oil, 14,000. Excessive intake of vitamin A can be poisonous, causing painful swellings, rashes, and loss of hair.

Vitamin B. Every animal needs vitamins of this group to carry out vital reactions within the cell. (One wonders why such a vital component of living matter has to come from outside.) The four numbered B vitamins are called thiamin (B_1), riboflavin (B_2), pyridoxin (B_6), and cobalamin (B_{12}). Various other vitamins, all water soluble, are often classified in the B complex. The important ones are nicotinic acid (niacin, or vitamin PP), biotin (vitamin H), pantothenic acid, and folic acid.

B_1 was the first of the group to be isolated—by the American Robert Williams, who died in 1965 at the age of 79. In 1910, he forced some rice-bran syrup containing B_1 into a victim of beriberi (after the Sinhalese word for weakness). Victims of alcoholism often suffer from a form of beriberi—called alcoholic polyneuritis—due to poor diet. The tales about an alcoholic's suffering liver should often be applied, more correctly, to the alcoholic's suffering body as a whole. All B (and C) vitamins are likely to suffer during boiling because they are soluble in water and therefore can diffuse into the cooking water.

B_{12} is the most spectacular since it is the largest vitamin and the only one that contains a metal atom (cobalt). It can only, so far as is known, be manufactured in nature by microorganisms, and it is the most potent of known vitamins—the daily human requirement is a few millionths of a gram. B_{12} is deficient in the strict vegan's diet and needs to be supplemented. The source of dietary B_1 is largely the germ of cereal grain; hence the rash of beriberi when this was polished away, but the richest source is yeast.

The other B vitamins are obtained in a normal diet from a great variety of foods including meats, cereals, and vegetables. During World War II, National Flour was introduced in Britain. This had to have a certain percentage of wheat germ, therefore more B_1. White flour is now again permitted in Britain, but is still subjected to beneficial additions, such as B_1, nicotinic acid, iron, and calcium carbonate. Pellagra, a disease suffered occasionally by the American and European poor, is caused by a lack of nicotinic acid—7,000 Americans died from it in 1930, the peak year for this fatality.

Vitamin C. Also known as ascorbic acid, vitamin C prevents scurvy. It is amply supplied in fruit and vegetables, and only a couple of ounces daily of black currants, brussels sprouts, strawberries, or peppers, for example, would be sufficient for each human being. Fresh fruit and uncooked vegetables are much richer than old fruit or cooked vegetables. The famous lime juice may either be rich in vitamin C or totally devoid of it—a polar expedition of 1875 relied upon lime juice and suffered scurvy. The disease has a venerable history on expeditions, and a Spanish galleon was once found with every man on board dead of it, but it now survives in a less romantic fashion; the old and the lonely are its current victims. Lazy bachelors, widows, widowers, and the poor are likely sufferers.

Many old people eat a lot of potatoes, but stored potatoes have lost a lot of their vitamin C, and boiling will destroy much of the remainder. There may be hundreds of thousands of scurvy sufferers among the elderly in Britain, reported Dr. Geoffrey Taylor in 1965, most of the cases undiagnosed. Babies fed entirely on cow's milk have also suffered, and need additional vitamin C because boiling or even heating milk destroys much of it. Human milk contains enough vitamin C, provided the mother is getting enough, but even breast-fed babies are generally offered supplementary spoonfuls of orange juice these days. In many households the elderly could well imbibe a sip or two of that vitamin-C-rich orange juice.

Vitamin D. Called the antirachitic vitamin because it protects against rickets, vitamin D was first proved in the 1920s, although an association between the bandy, stunted legs of rickets and bad nourishment had been known only too well. Good sources of vitamin D are fish-liver oils, but there is colossal variance. There are 40,000 international units per liver-oil gram from bluefin tuna, 1,000 per gram from halibut and mackerel, 100 from cod, and none from sturgeon. There is some vitamin D in egg yolk and some in milk, but the cheapest source by far—although still unavailable for many—is sunshine. Solar radiation, although it has a great capacity for doing harm, can also turn sterols (including the cholesterol linked with heart disease) into vitamin D. Eskimos, who see little sunshine, get their vitamin D from fish oil. Unfortunately, some slum children experience neither sufficient sunlight nor sufficient vitamin D in their diet. Even in the 1960s, with cod-liver oil supplies available at Britain's welfare clinics and with cheap foods such as dried milk fortified with vitamin D, there have been 40 cases of rickets in five years from just one Glasgow slum area.

Conversely, there have been cases of hypercalcemia, an unpleasant assortment of disorders including mental retardation of babies blamed —by some—upon excessive vitamin-D intake. In 1957, due to these suspicions of guilt, the D-content of British welfare foods was halved. No one blames this reduction for the cases of rickets that now appear in welfare Britain. The United States, alarmed at the huge intake of vitamin D by many pregnant women and its possible effect upon their babies, has sought to cut the quantities of the vitamin in nonprescription foods. The Food and Drug Administration proposed in 1965 that the normal daily dose should be limited to 400 units from all sources. Some pregnant women had been taking 2,000 to 3,000 units a day, causing, according to some of their doctors, greater likelihood of disastrous results to their babies.

Vitamin E (the tocopherols). Like some magic elixir, vitamin E has had wide-ranging claims made for it. It has been used as cure and treatment for infertility, menopause, heart disease, lupus, diabetes, and muscular dystrophy. Unfortunately, although it is generally agreed that vitamin E does none of these things, there is much uncertainty about what it does do. No optimum human requirement can be given, since a human lack of the vitamin is extremely rare and the lack does not manifest itself in any clear-cut fashion. This is not so for animals. Without vitamin E, chicks die from cerebellar degeneration, pigs develop liver disease, rats fail to multiply. The rat story helped to found the tale that vitamin E is the sex vitamin, for without it rats suffer progressive reproductive deterioration—first, gestation is prolonged, then stillbirths occur, and finally, the unborn young perish.

The vitamin is found in a wide range of vegetable foods, and some is even found in animal foods, although there is no evidence that the animal has actually manufactured the vitamin itself. In the 40 years since its discovery, due one suspects to the very positive effects upon animals, the research for the vitamin's role in humans has never abated. In 1966, for example, two more major claims were made. Work in the United States indicated an association between hemolytic anemia and the lack of vitamin E as well as an abnormality of fat metabolism in red-cell membranes. Perhaps vitamin E is vital to the red cells. Perhaps such a basic disturbance is why animals suffer in such varied fashion. Perhaps a positive answer will come very soon. In the meantime, vitamin E, called everything from a will-o'-the-wisp to the "shady lady of nutrition," will have to suffer such nomenclature, as well as its alleged but unfounded association with fertility in particular and sex in general.

Vitamin K. A human baby is born with virtually no bacteria in its intestine. This fact can be highly relevant both to decay and to vitamin lack. A stillborn child is likely to mummify because decomposition does not start from within as with longer-lived bodies, and a newborn baby can die from lack of vitamin K. This vitamin is divided into K_1, abundant in any normal diet, and K_2, which is amply produced by the intestinal bacteria. Unfortunately, some babies receive inadequate supplies of vitamin K from their mothers and are born with a major need of it;

they can then suffer hemorrhagic disease of the newborn. If blood loss or hemorrhage does not kill them within the first two or three days, the disease will rapidly recede because the bacteria invading the intestine start their production of K_2 within a few days of birth. The critical first three days can be made safe by daily doses of vitamin K in the sort of quantity that makes sense only in the world of vitamins—.001 gm. every 24 hours.

Lack of vitamin K in older children and adults is unlikely, but it may occur during starvation or when antibacterial drugs, such as the sulphonamides, have killed off the bulk of the intestinal bacteria or, as in obstructive jaundice, when bile is not getting into the intestines. (No vitamin K can be absorbed without the help of bile.) Vitamin K is extremely important in birds and the poultry industry; without it in their diets they die rapidly.

The novelty of vitamins and their fearful revenge when inadequately absorbed have led to great respect for their powers. Sometimes this respect has overflowed into a belief that, while some vitamins are good, more must be better. They are not. Each vitamin is required to a degree, but no more, and much more can be harmful. One also suspects that the full vitamin story has yet to be told, and not every essential organic chemical in the human diet has yet been identified.

Water

There is nothing quite like water. It has no equal in the number of functions it carries out in living tissue. It is the best solvent in existence. It is extremely stable, carrying many chemicals either in suspension or in solution without being changed itself. It is the most efficient cooling agent because it needs so much heat to evaporate each gram. It vaporizes easily at human temperatures. It is by far the most abundant chemical in the human body, and it is also the most abundant chemical in the human diet. It dominated mankind's evolution; it is still dominating progress. Its own chemistry is simple—it is made easily by the meeting of hydrogen and oxygen and is less easily parted. Its absence from the diet will cause a quicker death than if every other dietary need is withheld. There is, in short, nothing like it.

An average human being doing light work in a temperate climate loses nearly 5 pt. of water a day. Therefore, he has to replace it. As about half of ordinary food is water, he can take in .6 pt. at each meal without drinking at all. He also creates about .75 pt. of water a day within himself in oxidizing his food; both energy and water are by-products of this combustion, notably of the combustion of fat. The remaining 2.5 pt. or so he needs to maintain the balance are drunk as liquids. The daily 5-pt. loss of this average man is made up of .2 pt. in his feces, nearly 1 pt. from his lungs, some 2.5 pt. of urine, and about 1.25 pt. from his skin. Sweating is often spoken of as if it begins only during strenuous exercise; instead, it is customarily only visible during such exercise, when evaporation fails to keep pace with perspiration, but even a man at rest is losing over .5 oz. of water through his skin every restful hour.

Intake and output are both highly variable. Diarrhea can step up the fecal loss greatly. While a sedentary European is consuming only some 5 pt. a day, a miner may lose 13 pt. in a day's shift, and an Indian working in the sun may have to replace over 20 pt. every normal day. Dehydration and sweating can each cause a great drop in the excretion of urine. Tropical conditions can cause urine loss to be less than 1 pt. a day, often much less. On occasion, sweat loss in the heat can even be 3.5 pt. an hour, and 1.5 pt. an hour can be lost for several hours in succession, provided that the fluid is replaced in drinks. The maximum possible daily loss—and replacement—ever recorded is about 50 pt. Even under normal sedentary conditions in a temperate climate, there is a rapid turnover in the body's water supply. A 156-lb. man possesses 70 to 80 pt. of water within his frame, and half of it will have been lost and replaced every ten days. Incidentally, a woman has less water within her than a man of equal weight. The reason is her greater abundance of fat, and the low water content of all fatty tissue. (Female water content also oscillates with the menstrual cycle.)

Man is not a good desert animal. His organic system squanders its precious liquid. The kangaroo rat, which never needs to drink water, is far more careful. It has, for example, a cunning system within its nose for cooling expired air so that much of the water this inevitably contains is condensed as a kind of nasal dew; therefore, it is not lost to the system. Man just breathes out, and wastes nearly 1 pt. a day by doing so. The kangaroo rat may still lose 13 percent of its modest 3½-oz. weight in an hour by water loss; a human being is dead or dying after such a loss, whether after hours or days. Given cool conditions, a totally inert existence, and neither food nor water, a man is dead when he loses 15 percent of his body weight, and such a loss would usually occur within ten days. (A camel can last for two weeks with no water at all, it can lose up to 30 percent of its body water with no ill effects, and it can then drink 30 gal. of water in ten minutes and return to normal.) Given water and no food, a man can survive far longer, for two months or more, and despite prolonged starvation he can live after having lost over half his weight. With water, therefore, a 168-lb. man can drop to less than 84 lb.; without water, he is dead well before he has reached even 140 lb. Although acute hunger fades away after a few days, acute thirst is continually rampant.

Thirsty mariners, unable to drink seawater, may well have looked enviously at seabirds drinking it. The human system cannot absorb large quantities of seawater because the salt it contains can be excreted only by the use of even greater quantities of water. The body's capacity for salt is strictly limited, and the cycle is therefore as vicious as any. Most seabirds possess nasal glands. These lie above each eye, and they secrete a fluid extremely rich in salt. Like thick tears, these secretions are shaken off, and the bird is therefore able to make use of the desalted water it has drunk. Those who stress the perfection of the human being should ponder for a moment upon the advantages of this nasal gland.

How Much Food?

Most human food goes to produce energy; only a small fraction is used for growth, repair, and replacement of tissues. Vitamins, water, and minerals in the diet produce no energy. Instead, it all comes from the burning of the carbohydrate, protein, and fat fuel in the ratio of 4:4:9 for any given weight of these three. It is entirely correct to refer to them as fuel. Just because something is eaten, digested, and then acted upon during metabolism in the presence of oxygen does not make it basically any different from a lump of coal burning in the grate. In fact, 1 lb. of coal produces about as much energy as a man needs from his food in one day. The energy potential of a piece of food, say, a sandwich, can be discovered in a most physical fashion by placing it inside a calorimeter (essentially just a can), burning it in the presence of oxygen, and measuring the amount of heat produced by the combustion. Both sandwich and coal will be ash at the end of the experiment, and an eaten sandwich will have been just as emphatically consumed by the body.

The energy of coal and of sandwiches are both measured in heat units, namely calories. A single calorie is the amount of heat required to raise the temperature of 1 gm. of water 1°C. This is too small a unit of heat for most measurements of the energy of food; therefore the kilocalorie is used. This unit, 1,000 times larger, can heat 1 kg. of water 1°C. Unfortunately, the precise term kilocalorie is forgotten in nearly all discussion about food, and Calorie is used. Its initial capital stands for kilo, an abbreviation that is universal and causes constant confusion.

The daily human requirement of some 3,000 Calories is truly 3,000 kilocalories, or enough to heat 3,000 kg. of water 1°C., or 30 kg. of water 100°C.—or enough to maintain an active human being throughout 24 hours.

Human needs have a touch of economics about them; there seem to be as many opinions as there are experts.* Essentially, there is the basic metabolic need, the actual cost of maintaining the warm, healthy, and resting body. On top of this comes the cost of doing physical work, whether sewing or coal mining.

The basic need has been calculated as 3.7 Calories an hour for roughly every square foot of a man's bodily surface area, and 3.5 Calories for every female square foot. The difference in surface area between a lissome young girl and a stevedore is not so great as might be expected. It can be determined if both weight and height are known. Some examples follow.

Weight	Height	Surface area of body Sq. feet	Basic needs per hour Man	Woman
98 lb.	4 ft. 10 in.	14.5	54	50
112 lb.	5 ft. 2 in.	16.2	60	56
126 lb.	5 ft. 6 in.	17.7	66	61
140 lb.	5 ft. 8 in.	18.9	70	65
154 lb.	6 ft. 0 in.	20.5	76	71
168 lb.	6 ft. 2 in.	21.7	81	75
182 lb.	6 ft. 3 in.	22.7	84	78
196 lb.	6 ft. 4 in.	23.6	87	81

Therefore, between the short, light girl and the 6 ft., 4 in., heavyweight who could carry her off with ease, there is double the weight but only 63 percent more surface area, a mere 9 sq. ft., or the top of a card table of 3 ft. by 3 ft. The actual disparity in basic energy needs between the two is marginally even greater, owing to the more demanding metabolism of the male. She, if 98 lb. and 4 ft., 10 in., needs a basic 1,200 Calories a day, while he, if 194 lb. and 6 ft., 4 in., needs a basic 2,090, quite apart from the energy needed to lift her up and carry her off. Work done usually demands at least as much energy as the basic need.

Calories become liable to a more flexible interpretation in assessments

* Perhaps there are not enough experts. In 1965, only one German university had a chair for human nutrition, while 11 German universities had chairs for animal nutrition.

of their extra supply according to work done. Coal mining, for example, is often said to demand an extra 120 Calories an hour, or one and a half times the basic needs of a fair-sized person; but there must be coal miners and coal miners, even assuming an equal task. Some people do a job with a minimum of energy expenditure, bending down only when it is an absolute necessity. They cut corners, lift a shovel with a foot rather than reach for it, and never squander their resources. As it was said at an obesity conference, not only do some persons get less exercise than others but also they exercise less energetically when they get it. Some fat girls were once filmed playing tennis, and even during singles they were motionless 60 percent of the time. A fat person is usually expert at such maneuvers, thereby adding to his or her fatness.

Similarly, defying all the rules, some people eat like giants and remain like rakes; others eat like sparrows and expand like balloons. Also, people with large frames are more likely to grow heavy. As the *British Medical Journal* once put it: "To him who hath, it seems, weight shall be given." Fat men do in fact need more food; not only do they have more to maintain, but they need more energy to transport themselves around, and yet they still tend to fatness more than thin men.

Plainly, calories do count, although a book sold well by saying the opposite (despite the author's subsequent legal entanglements), but by no means is calorie theory reconciled to calorie practice. Suppose, for example, a man eats the correct amount. Suppose he is then permitted some minor indulgences, such as a banana with his breakfast, a bottle of beer, and one more slice of bread with his lunch, a cup of lemonade and 2 oz. of cake in the afternoon, and then a 2-oz. chocolate bar on the way home. These humble additions to his fare, not everyone's taste admittedly, nonetheless add up to 600 Calories in that one day. In theory, he would have to walk fast for over two hours or row more than three miles to burn up the extra calories. If he fails to do something of the sort and continues to consume the additional items, he will have put on 1 lb. of fat by the end of a week. And to get rid of 1 lb. of fat means walking 34 miles.

However, despite theory, people do often eat more than they should, they often get less exercise than they should, and yet their weight stays reasonably constant. There is no other way of acquiring calories except in food, and yet there seem to be ways of disregarding calories without putting on fat or doing anything positive to counter their rapid intake. One wonders, for example, about the calorific content of feces from different people at different times: there must be great variation. Nutritionists are, in general, agreed that the former straightforwardness of calories tends to grow more complex year by year. An American, for example, has listed 27 different types of obesity. He would also, one presumes, agree that there is more than one reason why some people get too many calories and yet remain eternally thin, and others are perversely the other way around.

Recently and suddenly, the Food and Nutrition Board of the U.S. National Research Council has lowered its estimates of calorie needs. Hitherto, the standard man and the standard woman had been permitted 3,200 and 2,300 Calories daily. In 1964, these allowances were abruptly dropped to 2,900 and 2,100 respectively. The board is still noncommittal about the means of providing these calories. Apart from alcohol,* which is certainly a food and can certainly add to a drinker's fat (even though there exists a "drinking man's diet" that recommends a lot of alcohol), an American receives 47 percent of his energy from carbohydrate, 41 percent from fats, 12 percent from protein. British figures are higher for carbohydrate energy, and poor countries receive two-thirds or more of their energy from this one source, a source undeniably rich in energy but inadequate in so many other needs.

A baby and a young child both need much less food than an adult. However active the infant, he has to move much less bulk, and requires less energy to move his smaller frame from A to B. By the age of 10 or 12, a boy starts to need as much food as his father. By 14, he probably needs one-third more and by 18 one and a half times as much. The ages depend upon the timing of his growth spurt and his actual size at any time, for it is his size and his work output that are most relevant. Growth itself is not very demanding of calories. The average growth rate of both boys and girls between 11 and 16 is about 9 lb. a year, requiring only 44 Calories extra a day, allowing 4 Calories per gram of protein.

Mankind is an increasingly idle being—his latest title is Homo sedentarius. Only a few centuries ago, everything was done by muscle power. This is no longer so, but there is still great variance in activity and consequently in fuel needs. To swim, demands 550 Calories an hour; to run, 500; to saw wood, 400; to work stone, 330; to walk fast, 240; to dance, 240; to bicycle, 175; to walk slowly, 140; to sweep, 100; to drive, 60; to dress, 50; to stand, 40; to write, 30, and to think demands none whatever. These averages are wild averages, for some dance with the vigor of sawing wood, and some saw wood with the zest of a sweeper. The brain does indeed cause no measurable increase in energy output, although muscle tension accompanying the anxieties of cerebral activity consumes energy on its own separate account.

* Alcohol yields 7 Calories per gram, i.e., more than protein, more than carbohydrates, less than fat.

All in all, no one runs, dances, bicycles, or thinks all day long, and minimum requirements become more uniform. Comparative estimates for sedentary, light, moderate, and heavy work have been assessed as requiring at least 2,500, 3,000, 3,500 and 4,000 Calories a day. Should anyone in fact run, dance, or ride all day long, his needs would be far greater; long bicycle races can burn up 10,000 Calories in 24 hours, and even some lumbermen can regularly consume and use 8,000 Calories a day. For the most part, twentieth-century man in advanced countries is increasingly transported to work, increasingly sits down when he gets there, and is increasingly in need of less than 3,000 Calories, although he probably eats more than that, and so is fatter than he should be.

Obesity

Who is overweight? Or, rather, what is overweight, and might not average weight itself be overweight? Is it normal or correct for middle-age spread to occur, and how heavy should heavyset people permit themselves to be? The most telling definition takes as its premise that the right weight to be is the one associated with maximum longevity. No one is so single-minded about survival as the insurance companies, and no insurance company is so good as the Metropolitan Life Insurance Company at producing fascinating biological statistics. Desirable weight, according to its figures, is within 10 percent of one's weight when 25 years old. To be 20 percent heavier means definite overweight, and anything greater is defined as obesity. Therefore, three people weighing 125 lb., 155 lb., and 180 lb. at 25 will have reached the 20 percent category when their respective weights have crept up to 150 lb., 186 lb., and 216 lb. Similarly, to be within 10 percent of the 25-year-old weight means that the maximum permitted additions to those three people are, respectively, 12½ lb., 15½ lb., and 18 lb.

There are other more subjective definitions. One is to look in a mirror. Another is to stand naked before wife, husband, lover, or mistress and demand a genuine opinion. A third (for men) is to make certain that waist measurement is at least 2 in. less than deflated chest measurement. A fourth is to squeeze a fold of skin from fat-potential areas, like the side of the lower chest, the back of the upper arm, or just below the shoulder blade; if the fold is more than an inch thick it is bluntly said that you are fat.

Finally, there are charts, usually compiled with the aid of insurance morbidity data. The charts divide humanity into ectomorphs, meso-morphs, and endomorphs (see page 280), or small, medium, and large frames, and allow for the disparity among the three. The desirable weight, for example, of a 6-ft. man is permitted to vary between 148 lb. (lightest limit for small frame) to 184 lb. (heaviest limit for large frame). What is not permitted is for either a small-frame man or a medium-frame man to regard himself as being suddenly in a larger frame category merely because he has put on weight. The frame will not change in life; it is the poundage hanging on to it that differs.

Women are overweight more frequently than men. There are figures suggesting that one-third of all American women over 30 are at least 10 percent heavier than the standard weight, and 75 percent of women between 45 and 55 are said to be overweight. Men tend to become heavier later than women, but between 45 and 55 half of them are said to be overweight. There is thought to be less fatness in Britain, and the sex difference is less marked. Of course, men in offices put on weight more decidedly, roughly 30 lb. more decidedly, than manual workers; but women are contrary, for the manual-worker woman is fatter than the professional woman—on average. (As a digression, I wonder if women really see themselves as those very long, thin, and elegant creatures dressed so beautifully in shopwindows. One maker of these dummies produces a standard size—5 ft., 8 in. to the hairline, 34 in. bust, 24 in. waist, 34 in. hips. There must be extraordinarily few real women so long and thin.)

Fat children are more than likely to grow up into fat people; 80 percent of them do. Similarly, 30 percent of fat adults can remember having been fat in childhood. A recent survey showed that when both parents are overweight three-quarters of their children will be; when neither parent is overweight, 9 percent of their children will be. Once again, heredity and environment must play an interwoven part. Is this child fat because his genes promote fatness or because his household customarily fattens up its inhabitants? The problem is not simple; most children in Britain, as in the United States, consume more calories and more carbohydrates than they require, yet only a few of those British children become obese. Mothers generally welcome rotund children and deplore skinny ones. At the Institute of Child Health in London, more visiting mothers express anxiety about possible underweight than possible overweight. Baby-show prize-givers tend to favor the round babies over slim ones, and the prize-winners chuckle into their deep-set dimples.

Making young children thinner is a distinct problem, with a general feeling that any treatment before five is unprofitable. Even then, diets are liable to be unsuccessful unless the whole family takes part. The best hope of success, according to an article in the *British Medical Journal,* is to persuade the mother to reduce the calories in general, by giving meals richer in protein, poorer in carbohydrate. The older the fat child, the greater the chance of persuading the child to take personal steps to reduce his or her intake.

The control of appetite and the acquisition, retention, and disposal of food is, despite some obesity, remarkably well controlled. An individual is likely to process 30 to 40 tons of food through his system in his adult lifetime, and yet remain within 5 or 10 lb. of a certain figure on his bathroom scale. The so-called appestat, or appetite-control center, is presumed, with good reason, to exist in the hypothalamus, the small portion of brain that lies underneath the cerebrum. If a small central portion of a rat's hypothalamus is deliberately attacked with needles, the animal recovers from the anesthetic to start voracious eating. Sure enough, within a few weeks the rat is very fat. Should two lateral portions of the hypothalamus be destroyed instead, the animal will not eat at all. Occasionally, a human being will suffer injury to his hypothalamus, notably when a tumor is growing nearby, and obesity may follow. However, most very fat people reveal no such detectable lesion at postmortem, and the appestat's mechanism or method of control is a long way from being fully understood. How can it possibly know when a meal has proved sufficient? What information can it possibly acquire that leads it to interpret so accurately one's needs of the day?

Medically, fatness is to be deplored. Not only is there an association between extra weight and shorter lives, but it is also linked with a great incidence of high blood pressure, arterial disease, liver and kidney disease, varicose veins, and a small regiment of other ailments, including obvious associations such as tiredness and shortness of breath.

Journalistically, fatness is to be welcomed. Articles on dieting are very popular, and there is more than a battalion of diets in circulation. Professor John Yudkin, the London nutritionist, has written that he is astounded at the way new dieting nonsense bobs up as soon as he believes he has scotched the previous batch. He has written pungently of diets that slim you only where you wish to slim, diets that surround you with marine plankton, diets that allegedly work while you relax in the bath. He has himself summed up the whole dieting question by dividing it into three.

1. Low-fat diet. Likely to lead to hunger, irritability, bad skin, poor concentration, and a possible unhealthiness.
2. Low-protein diet. Average American intake of protein is about 125 gm. daily. The authorities agree it should not be less than 70. Therefore, a saving of 55 gm. a day—a little more than 200 Calories— is possible, but ineffective.

3. Low-carbohydrate diet. The easiest kind. An average consumption
    is 400 gm.—or 1,600 Calories—a day. Refined sugars are responsi-
    ble for much of the excess. Some slimming schemes remove sugar,
    replacing it by glucose, honey, or sorbitol. These three give, weight
    for weight, the same calories as sugar, but are less sweet. Therefore,
    more is taken, and therefore more calories than before are absorbed.

Finally, many people say it is easy to slim. They have done it time and
again!

The real slimmers are quite a different matter. These are the huge
people who try to get weight down to a level where they will again
require only one chair to sit on. Recently, instead of giving them modest
diets, some have been given nothing at all—just vitamins, minerals, and
water. Sometimes the routine is only marginally less severe. Take the
case of William J. Cobb, born in Georgia. In 1962, he weighed 802 lb.,
and his struggling circulatory system was failing to supply enough
oxygen; every few steps, he had to stop and rest awhile. In a sense, a
200-lb. man was carrying an extra 600 lb. around with him; small wonder that the load proved excessive.

He decided to diet. Manfully, he reduced his weight to 644 lb. and
then volunteered for obesity research in an Augusta hospital. This meant
a far stricter regimen. He was permitted no exercise and merely 1,000
Calories a day. (Don't forget he was four or five times normal size, and
therefore had a far greater basic need of calories.) The diet varied
between high-protein, high-fat, and high-carbohydrate diets, and every
eight weeks he was shifted from one to another. After 83 weeks, he left
the hospital and was soon working as a shoe repairer: his weight—a
dainty 232 lb., proving a weight loss equivalent to the combined weights
of three large men or five slim women.

At least he left the hospital. A different story, from San Francisco in
1965, told of a 38-year-old, 5 ft., 2 in., woman who was rushed to a
hospital. Twenty men helped to carry her in, since no stretcher or ele-
vator could accommodate her, but she was to die within 24 hours. Her
weight, on arrival and on departure, was registered as 675 lb.

Starvation

Starvation is accompanied, apart from loss of weight, by a senile appearance of the skin, a slow heartbeat, a shortness of breath if exercise is
attempted, increasing urination, and a general swelling, or edema, of the
tissues. This retention of liquid is a feature of most starved people and
occurs mainly in the legs, ankles, feet, and abdomen. It often gives a

reasonably well-nourished look to the lower half of the body compared with the skinny chest and spindly arms. Diarrhea may follow or accompany the edema. Normally, and starvation is so frequent in the world that average findings have been easily evaluated, a person can shrink to half his or her weight and still be perfectly capable of putting on all former weight if given food. When weight is less than 50 percent of its original amount, death is much more likely. Its actual cause will probably be some infection, permitted by a lack of resistance to infection, caused in its turn by a deficiency of protein.

C. J. Polson in *The Essentials of Forensic Medicine* has listed some of the postmortem findings of starved people. Body weight is usually well below half normal weight (on average 38 percent). A 155-lb. man and a 110-lb. woman may therefore have been reduced to 59 lb. and 42 lb. They look old. All organs except the brain have shrunk in size and weight. No fat is visible, and all muscles have atrophied. There has been demineralization of bone.

Between the starved human being and the obese lies a fantastic margin of viability. If a starved man of 155 lb. can fall to 59 lb. and live, and if William J. Cobb can swell up to 802 lb. and also live, there is a gap of 743 lb. between these two living adult human beings. One is over 13 times the weight of the other. Between a highly emaciated woman and Mr. Cobb, the differential factor is nearer 19. There is a huge range in the potential weight of Homo sapiens.

Cooking

The Hadza of Tanzania are a small tribe living near Lake Eyasi. All their food is either gathered or hunted. They cultivate nothing and store nothing. However, they do cook, crudely, briefly, and badly. They throw a piece of meat into the fire, remove it later, and chew away at it. As a tribe, they are probably typical of countless tribal people who existed in the days before agriculture and animal husbandry and who were our ancestors. They were primitive, nomadic, casual, and yet they did cook. The practice was initiated, it is believed, virtually as soon as fire was controlled.

Cooking performs various roles. It can improve flavor, as with meats. It can help to liberate substances that stimulate the secretion of digestive juices. It can break down and loosen connective fibers, as with the collagen fibers of meat and the cellulose framework of vegetables. It can also kill bacteria and parasites within the food; think of "measly pork" and trichinosis. It does not always increase digestibility; raw meat is said to be most easily digested if kept raw but well disintegrated.

Cooking helps to achieve that disintegration; but overcooking, which causes a shrinkage of the coagulated protein, can decrease digestibility. Some foods, like meats, have less water in them after cooking; some, like rice, have more. A general estimate is that 10 percent of the energy value of foods is lost by cooking, but many contend that the loss is much less. Undeniably, some vitamins are lost in cooking, notably B_1 and C. All B and C vitamins are soluble in water, and so are likely to be lost in the surrounding water. All other vitamins are soluble in fat. Vitamin C, the fruit vitamin, is particularly liable to destruction by heat. Because vegetables possess enzymes that can destroy vitamins and because these act more speedily if warmed up, the slow warming of a vegetable can lead to much vitamin loss. A better practice is to plunge the vegetable into boiling water (or hot fat), thereby destroying the enzymes.

The Hadza do indeed cook. However, throwing an impala's head onto an open fire, and then peeling off the charred meat a few minutes later, is about as different as could be from the near-religious devotion that the art of cooking evokes in some households. It had to start somewhere, and that burned antelope head is clearly nearer to tradition for mankind's stomach than a delicate soufflé that threatens to tremble into humiliating collapse.

Food Poisoning

There are three subdivisions of food poisoning. The food can be contaminated with a poison; it can be a poisonous food; it can have been contaminated by pathogenic bacteria. The first is customarily considered willful malevolence on someone's part. The second, with so much advisory folklore, is generally obviated these days. The third is almost always the fault of staphylococci, streptococci, and salmonellae—and of the person who permitted them to grow or who failed to kill them off.

Their presence is insidious. They do not change the taste or smell of food (although other nonpathogenic forms may have simultaneously caused detectable putrefaction). They can all give rise to direct, emphatic, and short-lived attacks of food poisoning. Mere decay, without a corresponding density of the three pathogenic forms, is generally harmless. Many foods are intolerable without some putrefaction; fruits have to ripen, so do cheeses, so does game that is best eaten high, and—for Eskimos—so does fish. Many inland communities also prefer their fish with a tang to it, accustomed as they are to well-traveled cod and herring.

Clostridium botulinum is a big exception to all the rules. For one thing it can often kill. Its virulent poison is always referred to in discussions of biological warfare (for instance, it has been stated that a cubic inch of botulinus toxin would be sufficient to kill everybody in North America). Some 65 percent of botulism cases are fatal. Fortunately, the bacillus cannot usually multiply without liberating a noxious smell, and, equally fortunately, 15 minutes of boiling will destroy all the toxin and the bacteria. The spores are made of sterner stuff, but even they yield to steam under pressure. Commercially, botulism has been defeated—the last industrial contamination in the United States and Britain occurred in the 1920s—but the home-canning and -preserving business can still lead on occasion to a modest, but fatal, proliferation of Clostridium botulinum.

⊸§ 3 2 §⊷

The Alimentary Canal

Beaumont's Window · The Stomach · Acidity · Ulcers ·
Vomit · Intestines · Appendix · Liver ·
Pancreas · Spleen

De temps en temps, il faut étonner l'estomac.
Marcel Proust

Beaumont's Window

Quite the most famous (and astonished) stomach of all belonged to a French-Canadian. His name was Alexis St. Martin, and the contributions made to digestion knowledge by his one stomach were enormous. Behavior of his gastric juices is still quoted today even though the famous accident that opened up the subject so dramatically took place 145 years ago. It was on June 6, 1822, that the 18-year-old Alexis was unfortunately only three feet away from a musket that accidentally went off. He received the shot and wadding in his chest on the left side. Part of his sixth rib was destroyed, the fifth was fractured, his left lung was damaged, and his stomach was pierced. The other principal in this story, William Beaumont, surgeon in the U.S. Army, was quickly on the spot. He found the victim's lung and stomach protruding from the wound, and he pushed them back in again.

Remarkably, in an age when a severely wounded man was usually just a dead man who had not yet died, after nearly two weeks of giving every indication that he would not do so, the young Alexis began to recover. One week later, the wound was quite healthy and the patient was enthusiastically eating, but with one snag—everything he ate came out of the open wound. He was given nutriment through his anus, and Beaumont naturally made every effort to close the stomach wall. Alexis refused any kind of operation that would attempt to suture the wound

[429]

and instead preferred bandages that served in place of a stomach wall. He ate regularly and well, his digestion was effective, his whole alimentary canal behaved as it should have done, and provided the bandage remained unmoved, all was well. By the following summer, when Beaumont finally gave up all hope of "closing the orifice," it was 2½ in. in circumference, 2 in. below the left nipple, and apparently a permanently open reminder of the accident. All food and drink still poured out unless some suitable bandage plugged the gap.

Two years later, Beaumont started his experiments. This army doctor was among the first Americans to make an important contribution to medical science, and he achieved his fame by realizing the splendid opportunities afforded by Alexis's stomach: the annoying hole was an excellent window into the physiology of a vital organ. It was little good just looking; so he devised experiments. He weighed morsels of food, tied them with silk, and then let the stomach do its work on them. At hourly intervals, he removed them, noted the degree of digestion, and then replaced them. He also took specimens of gastric juice, and it was from such a specimen that hydrochloric acid was first positively identified. Beaumont also noted that a fasting stomach was empty and contracted, and that it became flushed with blood when its owner became angry. It also moved about with anger. (A woman in St. Louis who, much later, had a stomach that could also be inspected was made similarly angry, but her stomach then grew pale and motionless. If she is characteristic, this fact may explain the greater proportion of peptic ulcers among males.)

Of course, once Beaumont realized the remarkable value of his physiological window he wished to make full use of it. He therefore had to follow his patient—expensively—from place to place. Alexis is frequently called "uncooperative" and "difficult" by subsequent authors, and plainly the relationship between the two men had its ups and downs. When having either an up or a down, one can imagine Beaumont longing to taste the accompanying gastric acidity (as was frequently his custom) in the interests of science. Anyway, he published his *Experiments and Observations on Gastric Juice and the Physiology of Digestion* in 1833. Douglas Guthrie, the medical historian, has called it "a fine piece of research in the face of unusual difficulties." Meanwhile, Alexis, the difficult Alexis, lived his life and was eventually left alone with his orifice, his perforated stomach, and his well-renowned gastric juices. His burial place was kept secret, but in 1960 his granddaughter revealed it to be at St. Thomas de Joliette, forty miles northeast of Montreal.

Serendipity in science is common, and gunshots have frequently been revealing, but none so conveniently as that of Alexis St. Martin. So much of what is known today has its origins in that one French-Canadian stomach, and many of those involved in today's perpetual debate on ulcers would dearly love to watch the rise and fall of peptic ulceration, or to have so intimate an acquaintance with practically any aspect of the organs of the digestive tracts.

The Stomach

The human stomach (after the Greek for throat*) is, apart from the mouth and esophagus, the initial recipient of human food. It is the first important organ of the alimentary canal. Its capacity is about 2½ pt., and a heavy meal takes some six hours to pass through it. It is regularly referred to as being J-shaped—which I personally think a poor description, since it is more like a boxing glove. The constricted wrist end is the pyloric region, and the bulbous end is the fundus, which has the esophagus leading into it from above. Its walls secrete digestive juices, and waves of contraction, roughly three to the minute, cause the food to move into the duodenum, the next section of the alimentary canal. The stomach is storage container, digester, and mixer. Both its movements and its fluids render food more suitable for the duodenum and intestines than the casually chewed lumps and varieties of food and drink that pass down the esophagus.

There are also many things the human stomach is not. It is not vital —many ulcer victims have had two-thirds of it removed, and many others have experienced its total removal. It is not particularly important in digestion, in that the bulk of the digestive enzymes are mixed with the food after it has passed through the stomach. It does not absorb much through its walls; some water and some alcohol may go through, but nearly all absorption occurs later. Quite a few vertebrate species normally have no stomachs.

In fact, the evolution of the stomach gives a clue to its current role in man. Almost certainly, its primary function, when developed with the early jawed fishes (earliest fishes had no jaws), was for food storage; the jaws could bolt food, which then had to be retained. The rapidly bolted and chunky food also had to be prepared so that the main alimentary tract could act upon it. The introduction of digestive enzymes to these storage and preparation functions was presumably, as A. S. Romer put it, "a phylogenetic afterthought." The human stomach, now some 500 million years after those first storage stomachs of early fish, is still dominantly a storer and a preparer. Consequently, its total or partial absence can best be gotten around by sending down prepared food frequently. Complete removal of the stomach has been successfully inflicted not only on humans but also on laboratory animals such as

* It is the Greek word for stomach that is responsible for the stem gastero-.

rats, dogs, pigs, and monkeys. Of course, life is not the same without it, but all, with the possible exception of the rat, find the stomach dispensable.

Animals, such as the carnivores, which always bolt their food, tend to have large stomachs relative to the alimentary tract as a whole. In dogs and cats, for example, the stomach's capacity is between 60 and 70 percent of the total digestive capacity. They also tend to empty their stomachs between meals. Herbivores, who tend to eat again before the stomach is empty, generally have long and complex digestive tracts, and the horse's stomach capacity is only 8 percent of the whole; but some herbivores have exceptionally elaborate stomachs, with extra pouches that prepare the cud they chew. An ox's stomach is 70 percent of the whole digestive system. The actual capacities of some animal stomachs are: large dog, 5 pt.; pig, 1½ to 2 gal.; horse, 2 to 4 gal.; sheep, 4 gal.; cow, 30 to 40 gal. (although, strictly speaking, only those parts of the ruminant stomach that secrete gastric juices ought to be called stomach). The human 2½-pt. stomach is a relatively modest possession, as well as dispensable if need be.

Some digestive juices are produced by the stomach. The salivary glands have already mixed the digestive enzymes maltase and salivary amylase into the food, and the stomach then adds the enzymes pepsin and rennin. (As with the stomach, the saliva plays other roles, such as helping in the food's preparation and making speech possible, and a man secretes over 2½ pt. of saliva every 24 hours. As a horse secretes 9 gal., a cow 12 gal. a day their occasional drooling is entirely reasonable.) The stomach's pepsin is a protein-splitter and creates so-called proteoses and peptones. However long the food stays in the stomach—and two to four hours is a likely time—these proteins will be broken down no further; so far as the stomach is concerned, they are then indigestible. Rennin (familiar in the kitchen as rennet, the junket maker, which is extracted from calves' stomachs) has just one task—it converts the caseinogen of milk into casein. This solidification of milk is definitely caused in a baby's stomach by rennin, but, as the acidity of a stomach changes with age, the rennin becomes progressively less useful, and the pepsin can and does do its job. No one knows much about the role and presence of rennin in the adult stomach.

Acidity

The stomach's acidity poses problems all its own. Fairly strong hydrochloric acid (it is .17N) is produced by living tissue and is then poured into the stomach. There is nothing particularly resistant about living tissue, for a snake's living meal starts to suffer digestion as soon as it has been ingested, but the hydrochloric acid is diluted by the food in the stomach, and the stomach walls are protected by alkaline juices. The actual manufacture of hydrochloric acid is still surrounded by theoretical notions, and the available evidence is inadequate. Somehow or other, it seems, the acid glands have a membrane permeable only to water, hydrogen ions, and chloride ions. Even so, this is far from explaining how an acid capable of dissolving iron is produced, collected, and secreted by human tissue.

The stomach's acidity is in fact responsible for a great deal of personal medication. Americans spend 85 million dollars a year on substances to neutralize acid. There are innumerable notions about foods that are thought either to be acid or to promote or discourage acidity. Sodium bicarbonate, because it is cheap and easy, has been poured repeatedly into suffering stomachs, and their acidity has often been instantly turned into alkalinity. Alkalosis (or alkalemia), which can be fatal, is the result of excessive alkalinity in the blood. Unlike sodium bicarbonate, which can be absorbed into the bloodstream, there are other antacids that cannot be, and there is also food, often underrated but an extremely effective neutralizer of stomach acid. Without doubt, the stomach is guilty of imperfection, and without doubt it can be upset by the circumstances of life; it just so happens that acid is customarily indicted by possessors of upset stomachs as the guilty agent. Punishment with swift doses of antacids is therefore summarily meted out.

Ulcers

Nevertheless, there is positive correlation between the secretion of a lot of acid gastric juice and the origin of peptic ulcers. These open wounds are almost always single, usually ½ to 1 in. in diameter, and about 60 percent of them occur in the duodenum. The remaining 40 percent are in the stomach but near its exit (near the wrist of the boxing glove). Contrarily, few ulcers occur in the acid-producing area of the stomach, the bulky fundus. Men get ulcers more than women, by a ratio of 3 or 4 to one, and those with blood group O are more likely to suffer from duodenal ulcers than the general population. There is a less marked correlation between group-O people and the formation of gastric ulcers. (Peptic ulcers include both gastric ulcers—in the stomach—and duodenal ulcers—in the duodenum.)

A recent excellent study of peptic ulcers in the English county of Kent investigated 265 sufferers, 212 with duodenal ulcers (83 percent men) and 53 with gastric ulcers (53 percent men). There were 4.2 new victims per 1,000 of the general population every year. Duodenal ulcers in the Kent study were more likely to appear first, between the ages of 30 and 39 for men and between 40 and 49 for women. Gastric ulcers were more likely to be later, in the 50 to 59 decade for men and 60 to 69 for women.

Unfortunately, ulcers are no will-o'-the-wisp, here today and gone tomorrow. The degree of disablement they cause tends to increase as the years go by, but this reaches a peak after some 5 to 10 years and then recedes. Average peak times for duodenal men in Kent occurred 8.1 years from the start of symptoms, 7.1 years for duodenal women. Gastric peaks were after 6.5 years for men, 6.8 years for women. After 15 years, only 2 percent of the victims were still severely disabled by their peptic ulcers. The two most usual complications of ulcers were hemorrhage and perforation, and one-fifth of the Kent sufferers suffered one or the other, but only a single person of the 265, a man of 70, had a death attributable to his ulcer. Perforation normally accounts for two-thirds of all ulcer deaths. Only 16 percent of the 265 men and women of Kent were treated surgically for their ulcers.

Surgery for ulcers is a world of argument in itself, with individual and regional preferences for cutting the vagus nerve and where to cut it, for cutting out stomach tissue and how much, for enlarging the stomach's exit and by how much, and even for freezing part of the stomach. Someone once said that the surest way to empty the room at a medical meeting was to announce that the next subject would be the surgical treatment of peptic ulceration. Someone else's ulcers also have the power to empty countless other ordinary rooms if embarked upon as a subject with any determination by the ulcerous owner.

Vomit

Similarly, and possibly even more rapidly, another stomach subject has powers of evacuation; yet vomiting has its interesting characteristics. Herbivorous animals and rodents seldom or never vomit. When a horse does, and it is extremely rare, the vomit usually comes out of the nostrils. Carnivores and omnivores, except rodents, vomit easily. The process of vomiting is not caused by the stomach and is not a reversal of the customary procedure in which food moves down the throat and through the stomach. Instead, coordinated by the brain, both abdominal wall and diaphragm contract together and squeeze the stomach lying between them. The cardiac sphincter at the esophagus end of the stomach opens, the pyloric sphincter at the other end stays shut, and the stomach's contents have nowhere to go but up and out. Simultaneously, the larynx is raised so that no vomit gets into the air passages. The stomach may have contributed marginally to the general effect by reversing its modest peristaltic flow; but, except for infants, this probably does not happen. In any case, most babies have a vomiting ability of their very own. It is often not so much a mere outpouring with them as something akin to the firing of a projectile.

The act of vomiting can be triggered by any number of causes. There is an arresting book called *Understanding Your Symptoms* (by Dr. Joseph D. Wassersug), with an index that contains repeated mentions of vomiting because it is associated with drugs, stomach diseases, many other abdominal complaints, pregnancy, smells, poisons, unpleasant movement, visual disturbances, brain tumors, cerebral abscesses, meningitis, smallpox, scarlet fever, typhus, cholera, too many green apples, or too much alcohol, tobacco, or salt water, or with reasons that are never identified: people can just get up in the night, vomit, and return to bed feeling much better. Vomiting has been called God's gift to the hypochondriac. The frequent and customary event can be dramatically allied to a bewildering battalion of diseases, any one of which may be the cause. Or none.

Mere expulsion of air from the stomach is known as eructation. Such belches can have an electrifying effect in the wrong company; but they are not customarily explosive. Nevertheless, some surgical operations have been rendered dangerous by a patient's sudden eructations of inflammatory gases. These mistimed and chemically hyperactive belches have caused explosions. The true tale is also told of a parson who had every reason for emotional alarm: his breath caught fire each time he blew out the altar candles. No one cynically told him to pinch out the candles instead, but an operation was performed to enlarge the constricted opening at the far end of his stomach, the fault of an ulcer. "Following which," according to the man who performed the surgery, "he was able to carry out his duties in a more decorous fashion."

Intestines

Named after the Latin for "internal," the intestines are a continuous tube leading from the stomach to the anus. An average figure for mammals is that the tube is eight times the animal's length, but some herbivores have intestines proportionately much longer. Man has 28 to 30 ft. of intestine.

Various names have been somewhat arbitrarily attached to its various sections. The first 10 to 12 in. (or twelve finger widths) are the duodenum, the next 8 or 9 ft. are the jejunum, and the slightly longer subsequent length is the ileum. The ileum joins with the large intestine, but not very accurately; the actual joint is more like a T-junction at a main road, with the left-hand portion of the large intestine nothing more than a cul-de-sac called the cecum. The right-hand turn is the true large intestine, or colon; it leads after 6 ft. into the rectum and the anus. Little of nutritional importance, apart from water absorption, happens in the large intestine. Attached to the cecum is the appendix, a thin structure like a flexible pencil, and, like pencils, it is from 2 to 6 in. long.

Due to the convolutions and folds and twists in the intestinal tube, the actual absorptive inner layer of the 28-ft. tube has an area of over 100 sq. ft., five times the skin area of the body as a whole. Practically all human digestion is carried out in the intestine, and an even greater proportion of the actual absorption of food takes place through its walls. The stomach plays only a small part in digestion, an even smaller role in absorption.

From the moment a piece of food is eaten it has a restless time; yet the pace of its travels is by no means constant. William Gladstone, the nineteenth-century British Prime Minister, is alleged to have chewed every mouthful 32 times, but most people are more hasty; they soon have the food descending toward the stomach. Some four to six hours later, all of a large meal is out of the stomach and into the intestine. The constant jostling by the waves of peristalsis hurries the food—now called chyme—along the intestines at about an inch a minute. Within five hours of leaving the stomach, it is entering the far wider tube of the large intestine, and about 12 oz. of liquid chyme enter the large intestine every 24 hours. The pace then slows down, as the chyme takes perhaps two dozen hours to pass along the half-dozen feet of the large intestine. It takes a swallowed dye 15 to 25 hours to pass through the alimentary canal from start to finish before it first begins to appear at the rectum, but several days before the last of it has disappeared.

Nevertheless, there is always movement. The peristaltic waves are slower in the colon, and the movement of the rectum is slower still as that is customarily filled and emptied only once every 24 hours. The increasing pressure and the steady accumulation of feces cause the rectum to fill, thereby causing a desire to defecate. When the feces have been permitted to be expelled (the adult voluntarily opens the sphincter, but the child has to learn how to do this) the rectum is once again empty, and the accumulation can begin anew.

The relatively slow rate of progress through the large intestine occurs primarily because that tube has a larger bore—2½ in. in diameter as against a maximum of 1½ in. for the small intestine. But the quantity actually flowing through the large intestine is also steadily decreasing. Throughout its 6-ft. length, water is absorbed into the bloodstream, making the flow less urgent and the chyme less bulky. Of the 12 oz. of chyme that flow daily into the large intestine only about 4 oz. of feces pass daily out of it.

Like almost everything else in the body, these figures are highly variable; a rich vegetable diet will produce 13 oz. a day, and a starvation diet will produce less than an ounce. Feces are continually produced even throughout starvation. Children produce a relatively large amount of feces, ranging from 2½ to 5½ oz. a day. Even though so much water has been extracted from the chyme to make feces (after the Latin for dregs), water is still 65 to 80 percent of its bulk. Of the remainder, of the dry matter that it contains, a third to a half is bacteria, mainly dead. The rest consists of secretions from the intestine itself, of cellular remains from the alimentary canal, and of very small amounts of food residue, all of which (except for the food residue) helps to explain how it is that feces are still produced even during starvation.

Not much that is digestible, except in certain diseases, reaches the feces. The food residue is mainly indigestible items, such as cellulose—hence the large feces of a vegetable diet—and fruit skins and seeds. Feces smell most on a meat diet, less so on a vegetable diet, and least of all on a milk diet.

Intestinal gases also vary in their potency. Essentially, they are a mixture of swallowed air and of gases produced by the intestinal bacteria; the actual composition changes as diet and degree of constipation and bacterial activity are themselves changed. Flatus—the correct term for the more widely used expression, fart*—has been analyzed, and an average finding is nitrogen 59 percent, hydrogen 21 percent, carbon dioxide 9 percent, methane 7 percent, and oxygen 4 percent. Occasionally, there is a little hydrogen sulphide, a gas responsible for the well-known odor of the rotten egg. Hydrogen and methane are always combustible but, given the right mixture with oxygen, they can be explosive. On rare occasions, notably when using diathermy or cautery, disastrous explosions have resulted when surgeons have opened up intestines containing dangerous proportions of air and the inflammable gases.

Appendix

Finally that appendix. It can still be dangerous. The U.S. National Center for Health Statistics estimated 1,850 appendicitis deaths for the year

* Assumed to have arisen from the Old English "feortan."

1966. There were 606 in England and Wales in 1962, but there had been 1,045 in 1952. Next to nothing is known about the causes of its inflammation, but the main cause is certainly not orange seeds, grape seeds, apple pips, date stones, or other hard objects that might find their way into it. Occasionally, relatively solid objects *are* found in the appendix, but only very occasionally. For the most part, the complaining tube contains nothing but some hardened feces or fragments of lime, but these are thought to be the effects of appendicitis, not its cause.

No one knows the purpose of the appendix, but many other primates have it and so do many rodents. Appendicitis commonly affects the young (half the cases are of patients under 20) and males are more frequently afflicted than females. It may be less dangerous these days, but 125,000 appendix patients in England and Wales are still admitted to hospitals for treatment annually, and at any time, one of every 50 general-hospital beds is occupied by someone who has every reason to wonder what on earth the human appendix is all about, and why, even if it has a point, it is so painfully unreliable.

Liver

The liver is the largest gland in the body. In an infant, it weighs 4 percent of the total body weight, occupies 40 percent of the abdominal cavity, and is largely responsible for the distended silhouette of the abdominally pudgy child. In an adult, it weighs 3 to 4 lb., according to the adult's size, and represents about one-fortieth of the total body weight. It lies on a person's right side, close up against the diaphragm, and roughly matches the smaller stomach's position high on the left side. At rest, a quarter of the body's blood is within the liver, but a pint or two will suddenly leave it when exercise is taken or imminent.

Frequently called the chemical factory, the liver performs innumerable roles—some 500 or more have already been counted—in the body's metabolism. It plays only a minor role in intestinal digestion, even though it arises in embryology as a gland leading from the gut wall in the duodenal area. The liver (the word is Anglo-Saxon, possibly linked with the verb "to live") has a double blood supply; its oxygen comes primarily in the hepatic artery, but it also receives the portal vein. It is this vein that brings to the liver all the absorbed materials from the intestines. No one can live without a liver. The experimental removal of the organ from laboratory animals leaves them with apparent well-being for a little while, but thereafter deterioration is rapid.

No vertebrate is without a liver, but many are without gall bladders, the small, often troublesome, containers of bile that man can dispense with and frequently has to. Lampreys, many birds, horses, deer, rats, for example, never have one. Strangely, the striped gopher has one, and the pocket gopher does not. Stranger still, the giraffe sometimes has one and sometimes does not.

Whether or not there is a gall bladder, there is always bile. In the human being this contains no digestive enzymes. Its production is over a pint a day, but the gall bladder can store only about one-tenth of that amount. Bile does include some substances that assist digestion, but it also includes a lot of waste products. Gallstones, observed only in man and domesticated animals, are usually made of cholesterol, the fat so frequently maligned for its association with circulatory failure and disease. It is estimated that one-quarter of all women and one-tenth of all men will develop gallstones sometimes before they reach 60. "Fair, fat, and 40" is the old tag for possible victims, and the complaint is even older, being recorded in the earliest medical writings. There may be one gallstone, even up to hen's-egg size, or there may be several hundred minute grains. No one has learned how to dissolve the stones away, and almost all operations for their extraction remove the gall bladder as well.

In the past, the liver was called the seat of life. A cult of liver investigation and interpretation seems to have started in Mesopotamia, spread westward, reached Greece, then the Etruscans and the Romans. When viscera were examined for propitious signs, the liver was the most carefully inspected organ. Ezekiel (21:21) tells of the king of Babylon who, at a parting of the ways that called for a decision, "looked in the liver." Fortunately for hepatoscopy, as this form of divination was called, and for the diviners, the loose structure of the liver, its varying appearance, and its susceptibility to disease presented each investigator with sufficient changeable evidence on which to base his imagination and his predictions. The right half of the liver was allegedly relevant to the questioner, the left to everyone and everything else. (Palmistry draws a similar parallel between the two hands.)

The belief that the liver was also the origin of the veins lent additional authority to the organ's importance, and the later view that it was the source of two of the four cardinal humors (choler and melancholy, leaving only blood and phlegm) added even greater prestige to the liver's position of power. As remnants of these previous beliefs there are many current words—lily-livered, choleric, bilious, melancholic, gall—that make unintentional obeisance to the liver's ancient authority and none to medical accuracy. The liver is certainly important, but it is neither the origin of veins nor the creator of anger or sadness any more than it is soothsayer to all who consult its five-lobed oracle.

The multifarious functions of the liver make a formidable, wide-ranging, and awe-inspiring list. They include the destruction of red blood cells, the manufacture of plasma proteins and of blood-clotting agents, the storage of carbohydrates in the form of glycogen, some storage of fats and proteins, the conversion of fats and proteins to carbohydrate, the change of galactose—milk sugar—into glucose, the extraction of ammonia from amino acids, the conversion of ammonia into urea, the production of bile salts for the digestion and absorption of fat, the storage of fat-soluble vitamins, the conversion of depot fat into the more combustible ketone bodies, and the modification of various drugs and poisons—the short-acting barbiturates, for example, are destroyed by the liver. The organ, therefore, is vital and is emphatically the central organ of metabolism.

It is more than capable of replacing its tissues. A dog with 90 percent of its liver cut away is still able to produce bile at the normal rate; and if three-quarters of its liver is removed, the remaining quarter will undergo extremely active cell division until the entire organ reaches its original dimensions six to eight weeks later. The liver's powers of regeneration are so good, particularly when much of its substance has been destroyed by some hepatic poison, that it has been called the immortal organ. If any organ has to be called the seat of life, perhaps the liver most deserves the title, even if its importance is now seen in biochemical terms rather than those of mood and prophecy.

The pancreas and spleen are frequently spoken of in the same breath, presumably because they lie fairly near each other, they are about the same size, and they are both in the abdominal cavity. However, they are as unalike as chalk and cheese. One of them is little understood, and not essential to life. The other has two distinct roles, both thoroughly investigated, both essential to normal life; no surgeon removes the pancreas without an urgent reason, and life without it needs careful supervision. While both organs are customarily similar in weight (one is 3 oz., the other 5 oz.), the spleen can swell up to 20 lb. during infectious and other diseases. One is a gland; the other is not. The pancreas and the spleen are therefore two most distinct neighbors.

Pancreas

Named after the Greek for "all-meat," due to its boneless and fatless substance, and known gastronomically as sweetbread, the pancreas is a dual organ, the second largest gland in the body (after the liver). Not only does it produce crucial digestive enzymes (trypsin, lipase, amylase) and pour a pint or two of its pancreatic juice into the duodenum every 24 hours, but also it manufactures insulin in the minute and vital quantities necessary. Total removal of the pancreas was first carried out in man in 1944, and this is still a rare operation. The loss of the pancreatic juice to the digestive system means that much food, notably fat, cannot be digested; therefore large quantities of undigested matter are passed out in the feces; therefore the feces are some three times bulkier than normal. The loss of insulin that follows removal of the pancreas means the existence of yet another diabetic, although the disease of diabetes customarily arises naturally without this brutal interference with the pancreas's function.

Normally, the organ weighs 3 oz., it is soft, it is at the back of the abdomen behind the lower part of the stomach, and it looks pink or yellowish-gray. Along the pancreatic duct, which connects the gland to the alimentary tract, flow the pancreatic juices. In every hour of flow, these secretions weigh almost as much as the gland itself. Although vital for sound digestion the pancreas's fame in the eyes of the world is primarily associated with its importance for the diabetic.*

The great year for diabetics was 1922. Those who suffered from the disease before then had little hope, but in Canada in that year Sir Frederick Banting, with C. H. Best and J. J. R. Macleod, discovered insulin. The story really began over three decades before the momentous discovery. Two German physiologists, von Mering and Minkowski, had wanted to know more about the pancreas. So they removed the organ from a dog and later on observed the attraction that particular dog's urine had for flies and wasps. Contrary to Samson's riddle, where the buzzing bees had caused the sweetness, the buzzing flies were being attracted to the urine by its sweetness. (Others had noted the presence of sugar in a diabetic's urine, but they had not caused it to be there.) Later it was realized that sugar was excreted into the urine because it had reached high levels in the blood, and later still it was assumed that the pancreas was liberating something that somehow kept the sugar level in check.

Banting, Best, and Macleod managed to extract the insulin, an extraction made more complex by the fact that the pancreas produces large quantities of protein-splitting enzymes in its pancreatic juices as well as the insulin, which is itself a protein. Fortunately, calves secrete insulin before they secrete their enzymes, and some insulin was obtained from calves' pancreas in sufficient quantity to quell the rising glucose levels

* When the term "diabetes" is used on its own, it always means diabetes mellitus. Diabetes insipidus is quite a different and unrelated disease.

in the blood of a diabetic dog. The Canadian team also tied off the pancreatic ducts of dogs, thereby causing atrophy of the pancreas's enzyme production and thereby permitting the safe extraction of the insulin. The calf and the dog were to save diabetic man. (The name "insulin," from the Latin for "island," was coined because it is produced in the pancreas's small and scattered endocrine glands called the islands of Langerhans. The name "diabetes" is after the Greek for "a passer-through," and was given to the disease by Aretaeus in the second century.)

Insulin is a small protein whose production (or, for the diabetic, injection, since it cannot be swallowed, for the digestive enzymes pepsin and trypsin would destroy it) has to be correctly balanced. Too little, and there is too much blood sugar, fatigue, and loss of weight. Too much, and there is insufficient blood sugar leading eventually to irritability, sweating, hunger, and coma. There is a fairly narrow margin between too much sugar in the blood and too little, and the normal range is between .1 and .18 percent. Above .18 percent, there is likely to be sugar in the urine, and Minkowski noted that the sugar level in his dogs without a pancreas rose to .3 percent. The tightrope control of insulin, and thus of sugar levels, cannot swerve very far from normal without disastrous consequences.

The disease is common. There are 300,000 sufferers in Britain, and it is assumed there are tens of thousands more undetected—random surveys always uncover more. Surveys in the United States suggest that 9 people in every 1,000 are undiagnosed diabetics. It is suggested that the figure of 2 million known diabetics in the United States is possibly matched by just as many still undiagnosed. Diabetes is increasing all over the world, primarily in well-fed communities. African Negroes, who frequently have a low-fat, low-calorie diet, do not suffer from it, but the disease or lack of it is not a racial characteristic. Negroes in the United States suffer as much as white Americans, and Europeans suffer less only when there is a war on. This beneficial effect of food rationing was first noticed in the Franco-Prussian War, and was still being confirmed during the Second World War.

There is also a hereditary risk. If one identical twin gets the disease, the other twin will get it in seven cases out of ten, although possibly not for ten years or more. People with the disease are more likely to have diabetic relatives than those without it, and diabetics wishing to marry diabetics and produce children should be aware of the greater likelihood that their children will follow suit. Overweight predisposes people to diabetes, and diabetic women have greater problems with pregnancies. There is also considerable discrimination against the ½ to 1 percent of the population who are diabetics; many jobs are denied them, and there has been mounting pressure recently to eradicate the injustice.

Spleen

This organ has no right whatever to appear in a section dedicated to digestion and its allied organs, except that the pancreas and spleen—strange bedfellows that they are—are so frequently bracketed together. On the other hand, it is possible to hold a slightly splenetic view that the spleen (sometimes called lien; "spleen" is Greek, "lien" is Latin) has no right to appear anywhere, so vague and unassuming is the organ. It is 6 in. long, and it weighs about 6 oz. Its form is roughly fist-shaped. Its position is high up behind the stomach. Its appearance is a ruddy red, its texture much smoother than the pancreas. Its function—well, that is the problem, for it is certainly not essential to life. Its total removal can be carried out with minor changes to the blood the only detectable aftereffects.

In some animals, such as the cat and the dog, it is an important reservoir of blood, a built-in transfusion system against times of stress or oxygen lack. In man, since it weighs just a few ounces, the addition of just a few ounces of blood—assuming it contained nothing but blood —to the 12 lb. of blood in a normal body would be of negligible assistance. Therefore, it is scarcely identifiable as a storehouse, any more than is a cupboard containing just one can of beans.

However the spleen does act upon blood cells. In the fetus it is important in manufacturing both red and white blood cells, but after birth it loses its ability to make red cells although it perseveres with the white cells. In adult life, it reverses its fetal role and helpfully destroys old blood cells. It also prepares old red cells for their destruction elsewhere. Normally, the spleen cannot be palpated, or felt from the outside, unless it is three or four times its ordinary weight, say over a pound. The spleen usually enlarges when it is suffering from disease, and it also often enlarges when the body itself is afflicted with disease, notably with malaria. In extreme cases, the spleen can grow from 6 oz. to 20 lb., a fiftyfold increase. One distinct disadvantage of a large spleen is its vulnerability; engorged as it is with blood, disastrous internal bleeding can follow quite trivial bumps or knocks.

Although malaria is characterized by a lack of red blood cells and although the spleen's traditional malarial enlargement can be linked with the need for more blood, the organ's expansion in most diseases is associated more precisely with its role as a producer of antibodies.

It plays a part in the defensive system, in which, as soon as foreign protein or infection invades the body, some matched protein is manufactured to counteract the foreign material; antibody is produced to counter the antigen. However, even here the spleen's role can competently be carried out elsewhere in the body.

Is the spleen therefore totally valueless? No, but it just so happens that whatever it does seems to be better done elsewhere. The poor organ was not even granted a positive role in the early and more imaginative days of medicine. Andrew Boorde, the sixteenth-century medical monk, diplomatically said it "doth make a man to be merry and to laugh, although melancholy resteth in the spleen if there be impediments in it." (But then, Andrew Boorde was never at a loss for a definition and, in those Latin days, even called himself Andreas Perforatus, assuming "bored" to be near enough.) Neither happy nor sad, the organ is still viewed equivocally, and Boorde's casual definition is virtually valid today.

33

Excretion

The Kidneys · Urine · The Bladder

The excretory system has several dual aspects to it. As a process, it is inextricably involved with the reproductive system: ducts and organs are shared, and the amalgam of interests is customarily known as the urinogenital system. The kidney has two distinct jobs to do; it has to eliminate waste products via the urine *and* it has to regulate the salt and liquid content of the body. Although the kidneys are the organs of excretion, and without them a man would quickly die, the kidneys do not do all the excreting; the sweat glands, the lungs, and the intestines excrete waste products. And, as if to emphasize the duality, the two kidneys are not situated evenly in the human body; the left kidney is a little longer and narrower and slightly higher up the back than its partner on the right. When one kidney fails to develop, as happens on rare occasions, the missing kidney is more likely to be the left, and the condition affects males to females in the ratio of 2 to 1.

It is for the removal of waste products that the kidney is principally renowned. Fats and carbohydrates are made up of carbon, hydrogen, and oxygen. When these two types of food are broken down during their combustion, or oxidation, the end products are carbon dioxide and water. Carbon dioxide is removed from the lungs, and water—if this vital requirement can ever be considered a waste product—can also be removed by the lungs, and is so to the extent of about a pint a day.

Excretion thus far is no problem, but it becomes so when proteins are broken down. Their main constituent, after the big three of carbon, hydrogen, and oxygen, is nitrogen. Unfortunately, nitrogen is quite different. Unlike carbon dioxide, it cannot be removed as a gas, for there are energy problems about nitrous oxide (NO_2) that only some bacteria have mastered, and it cannot be turned into something simple, such as ammonia (NH_3), because this is extremely poisonous to all tissue. A few marine animals excrete their nitrogen as ammonia, but hastily and into a big wide sea. The land-based compromise is to form

urea, a far less poisonous substance whose molecule contains two atoms
of nitrogen, four of hydrogen, one each of carbon and oxygen. Frogs
skillfully blend their two existences; when free-swimming as tadpoles,
they excrete ammonia, and when adult, they excrete urea.

Birds and reptiles encounter a third problem, solved neither by the
immediate removal of ammonia in water nor by the slightly more leisurely
removal of urea, also in water. Their eggs, developing and experiencing
metabolism (and therefore creating waste products for weeks at a time
without any extra supply of water), have no means for excreting anything. The excellent compromise is to produce uric acid, a larger
molecule (4 nitrogen, 4 hydrogen, and 3 oxygen atoms) than either
ammonia or urea and quite insoluble. Therefore, crystals of it can be
produced and stored here and there within the egg. These are then
incapable of doing any harm to the developing creature whose egg it is.
A human embryo, when within its mother's uterus and seemingly egglike,
is by no means comparable with the constricted, prepacked prisoners of
the reptilian and avian eggs. The human is bathed in ever-changing
liquid and continually refreshed with blood that happily yields the waste
products collected from the embryo to the mother's blood supply, and
therefore to her kidneys.

The Kidneys

In human beings, kidneys* are each about 4½ in. long, 2½ in. wide,
1½ in. thick, and weigh 5 oz. They are not in the small of the back,
but higher up, in front of the 12th rib, where they lie close to the spine.

Basically, each kidney is nothing more than a collection of filter
units, each of which initially absorbs virtually everything small from
the blood—broken-down food molecules, water, waste products—and
then a similar collection of tubes whose dominant function is to put
back into the blood everything still required. (One way of tidying a
desk is to remove everything and then replace only objects still of value.
Another is to pick out the valueless objects without disturbing the
remainder. The kidney makes use of the first system.) Therefore, as
actual urine production is only 2 to 3 pt. a day, and as the initial extraction of fluids and solids is about 100 times greater—perhaps as much
as 50 gal. a day, it must be the fate of much liquid and solid matter
to pass through the kidneys very many times every 24 hours. Moreover,
some 2¼ pt. of blood are pumped through the kidneys every minute—

---

* The word's two syllables are taken from two Anglo-Saxon words meaning uterus
and, oddly, kidney. As extras, the Latin for "kidney" is *ren*, plural *renes*, and is
thus responsible for renal; the Greek *nephros* is the stem for nephritis, etc.

or one-quarter of the heart's resting output, and therefore much of the blood is going through the kidneys a mere five minutes after its previous passage. Of the 1/5 pt. of water filtered by the kidneys every minute, over 99 percent is passed back again to the blood and less than 1 percent goes into the urine.

The filter units responsible for all this activity are called nephrons, of which there are more than a million in each human kidney. Consequently, despite the enormous quantities filtered all the time by the kidneys as a whole, the work done by each minute nephron is appropriately modest—roughly 2 cu. mm. an hour. The first person to see a glomerulus, the bulblike part of each nephron that does the initial extracting, was Marcello Malpighi, the seventeenth-century Italian who was accustomed to small-scale work (he also saw the capillary network of blood vessels, thereby putting final proof on William Harvey's theory of blood circulation). It is through the tube connecting each glomerulus to the main ducts of the kidney that the wanted substances, like that 99 percent of the water, like glucose, like amino acids, are returned again to the blood system through the renal vein. In a sense, each glomerulus is a crude filter, just sorting according to size; the tubule is more refined, highly specific about what it does and does not pass through its walls to the blood.

Study of the kidney is highly relevant to an understanding of evolution. Paleontology is a great subject for personal idiosyncrasies, and for refusals to submit to a prevailing view, but paleontologists (in general) believe that the earliest fishes lived in rivers and lakes and only later took to the seas. Kidney study, again according to almost everybody, clinched this point.

Living in a fluid less salty than their own body fluids, as freshwater fish do, requires quite a different kidney system from that necessary in the sea, where the surrounding water is saltier than body fluids. Osmosis, that process encountered in school biology when water is shown to flow through a membrane to dilute the saltier side, is also encountered everywhere in living tissue. A marine fish is threatened with dehydration by osmosis; its fluids are trying to dilute the saltwater all around it. Conversely, a freshwater fish is saltier than fresh water, and is therefore threatened with dilution. In both cases, the kidney system reflects the particular threat, even with animals such as salmon—which can happily swim from one to the other—and the conclusion is that primitive fish, our ancestors 500 million years ago, struggled into their vertebrate existence in rivers and lakes rather than in the sea. Their osmotic problem is thought to have been too much water rather than too little, therefore caused by life in fresh water rather than salt.

Urine

Normal daily production of urine is 1¾ to 3 pt. Disease can cause the quantity to go up, as in diabetes insipidus and various kidney ailments, or down, as in conditions causing fever and diarrhea. Of course, heavy drinking causes a rise, and so do diuretics such as tea, coffee, and cocoa, as well as excitement or nervousness. Hot weather causes production to go down. Normally, whatever the actual liquid output, a day's urine contains 2 oz. of solids. These make it slightly heavier than water, for urine has a specific gravity of 1,010 to 1,025, but this will fall with a lot of drinking or rise with a lot of sweating.

The color of urine is proportionate to the specific gravity, but color is no one thing because many pigments are involved. Also, some diseases can bring about coloration of their own, ranging from the orange of many fevers, to the brown of blackwater fever—an early hazard of West Africa—to the brownish-black of alkaptonuria, and to the greenish-blue of cholera and typhus. The dyes of some foods can produce garish and somewhat hair-raising effects. Beetroot, blackberries, and quite a few drugs can change the color, but even without the senna and methylene blue of drugs, the urine can be kaleidoscopic, whether the cause is a different diet or disease.

In medieval times, the study of urine had a high status, and early woodcuts frequently show some vial receiving careful examination while the unfortunate victim of plague, childbirth, syphilis, or whatever lies nearby, blatantly in need of help.

Nothing is known about the ordinary smell of urine, but this usual odor can change, notably after eating asparagus. That urine smells of ammonia is really only true of stale urine, when bacteria have had time to act upon the urea to produce far more ammonia than exists in fresh urine. Urine is virtually bacteria-free when liberated and has even been used as a disinfectant in extreme conditions, such as in the battlefield. Feces, whose bulk is largely bacteria, and urine are therefore entirely distinct in this regard.

The composition of urine is a bewilderment of organic and inorganic chemistry. It also varies widely, as is reasonable, with all changes in diet. On an average day, it contains an ounce of urea and far smaller amounts of differing acids, bases, salts, and organic compounds, all adding up to another ounce. Some glucose is always present, but not in the 3 to 5 percent proportion of the diabetic. Some protein is present, but if easily detectable may be a sign of one of a plethora of diseases that can put it there.

The medieval medicine men were right in a way, in that the composition of urine is a valuable guide to the condition of the patient, but holding a vial to the light is a poor substitute for today's microanalysis. This can, for instance, tell of a person's stage of starvation, for so long as fat is available, fat will be consumed to produce energy, but when fat is exhausted, it is the turn of tissue, of protein, to supply the energy. Twice as much protein as fat has to be used to produce a similar supply of energy. Therefore, as protein contains nitrogen and fat does not, the sudden extra metabolism of tissue means the sudden presence of more nitrogen in the urine. This is known as the premortal rise, and the urine is giving warning of possible death from starvation.

Kidneys have achieved considerable notoriety due to the efforts to transplant them from one person to another, from a donor or a corpse to someone with renal disease. The surgery has been successfully worked out, but the problems of immunity have been and still are formidable. Up to June, 1966, over 600 human kidney transplants had been performed, 500 of them since March, 1963. Most of the patients have since died, but survival time is improving. By the end of 1965, some 37 percent of all recipients had lived more than a year after the operation.

The success depends largely upon the relationship of the person giving the kidney to the person needing the operation; the nearer the genetic relationship, the better. Until the end of 1965 88 percent of the grafts from identical twins had been successful for at least a year, 53 percent of the grafts from brothers and sisters, and 51 percent of the grafts from other blood relatives. Remarkably, a chimpanzee of the right blood group is of more use as a kidney donor than an unrelated human being of a different blood group. Suitable matching of donor and recipient is the best that can be done at a time when the process of immunity frustrates so many efforts at transplantation, but at least it is slightly less frustrating with the nearest of blood relatives, whether human or simian. Just as nineteenth-century surgery had to wait for the development both of anesthesia and antisepsis, modern surgery—not just of kidney transplants—is impatiently waiting for the conquest and understanding of the barrier of immunity.

A radically different approach is being used for kidney failure, which kills 7,000 people in Britain every year. (U.S. figures, more specialized, give 9,850 deaths from kidney infections for 1966.) Given a low-salt and water diet, with a lot of carbohydrate and moderate amounts of protein, and given a dialysis machine twice a week or so to adjust the blood's composition, a victim of renal failure can be kept alive in a manner that would never have been possible a few years ago.

The Bladder

"Of Pissing in the Bedde," as Thomas Phaire called it in *The Boke of Chyldren* in 1553, I have already written in the section on child growth. However, this is also a problem for the old. In one group of 500 elderly people, all waiting to go into a hospital for the aged sick, 70 were incontinent. It was not so much a lack of control with them as of bladders that emptied themselves long before the stage at which conscious control had previously been exercised. The sphincters were relaxing before any feeling of fullness was made manifest.

A normal bladder appears thick and stratified when empty, but it is only a layer or two of scale-shape cells when full. Customarily, no sensation is felt at first as the bladder fills and its pressure rises, but the pressure rise is small at first because the bladder expands to accommodate the extra urine. The pressure is about 4-in. water gauge, or some 2½ oz. per square inch of bladder, until the contents start nearing a pint. The bladder still expands to accommodate increasing urine, but reflex contractions give rise to a conscious desire to urinate (or micturate). This can be suppressed for a time, but suppression fails when the internal pressure has built up to around 40-in. water gauge (or 1½ lb. per square inch—about one-tenth of normal atmospheric pressure).

Like any flexible container filled internally with a positive pressure, the bladder tries to assume a spherical shape. This means that ½ pt. of urine, the normal level for emptying, distends the bladder into a sphere 3.2 in. in diameter. Should there be a whole pint within, when the pressure is likely to be either rising or painfully seeming to, the diameter will be a fraction over 4 in. Therefore, because a sphere's volume goes up proportionately to the cube of the radius ($4/3\pi r^3$), the doubling of the contents from ½ pt. to a pint pushes up the diameter only another .8 in., although the subjective impression is of a far greater increase. Were it possible to double even that accumulation of a pint up to 2 pt., the diameter would increase by only another inch. If relief is impossible, as may happen in unconsciousness or paralysis, or if relief is strongly suppressed, the swelling bladder may cause a visible fullness in the lower part of the abdomen. Normally, no change in external shape is detectable.

The process of relief is straightforward, but involved. The full bladder causes contraction waves. These are regular and can be timed subjectively with a stopwatch. They stimulate pressure receptors in the muscles of the bladder wall. From them, nervous impulses travel to the spinal cord and the brain. The desire for relief is caused by these messages, and nothing more will happen—beyond the dispatch of reminding impulses—until it is convenient to micturate. The brain then starts to cancel various automatic controls. Nervous impulses from it cause a relaxation of the bladder's internal sphincter plus a contraction of the bladder muscle. Similarly, the bladder's external sphincter is relaxed. Then the breath is held and the diaphragm is forced down, while the abdominal wall is contracted. Both acts increase the pressure on the bladder and help it to get rid of its accumulated urine.

Such an assortment of nervous control, inhibition, and relaxation makes it entirely comprehensible why a child takes time to learn the act, and most children walk before they can urinate with any degree of controlled competence. Even an adult, maturely adept at such control, can find it impossible to initiate both micturation and defecation simultaneously. The problem is likely to be resolved only by initiating one process and then the other, but the attempt should indicate the complexity latent in both systems.

An interesting extra complexity, more a matter of hydrodynamics than nervous physiology, is the twist imparted to the masculine urine stream. Obviously, with hygienic advantages, the system ensures a compactness of flow, which must be preferable to the widespread spraying that might overwise result.

Adult females are generally credited with the ability to micturate less frequently than the adult male. There is no greater bladder capacity in the female; instead it is assumed there is greater suppression of the emptying reflexes. The urethra, the tube leading from the bladder to the exterior, is of course far longer in males than females, roughly 8 in. as against 1½ in., and the male urethra goes through the enlarging prostate gland, which can be a source of masculine suffering in later years. In fact, the bladder then has a tendency to revert to a second childhood of its own; not only is there increasing incontinence with age, but also the business of having to get out of bed in the middle of the night is an additional chore for many over 55.

Respiration and Blood

The Need for a System ·
The Lungs · Breathing and Breath Control · Altitude ·
Drowning and Pollution · Choking, Coughing, Sneezing ·
Laughing, Yawning, Hiccups · Oxygen, Excess
and Lack · The Heart · Harvey and Galen ·
One Pump into Two · Heartbeat · Blood Pressure ·
Blood Distribution · The Pull of Gravity ·
Blood, Corpuscles and Platelets ·
Plasma · Blood-letting

If man were a single-celled animal, there would be no need for a respiratory system; oxygen would be able to diffuse through the cell wall in ample quantities. If man were a small multicelled animal, there would still be no need, provided his dimensions were modest and the distance from oxygen source to remotest cell was short, perhaps .02 in. at most. The vital gas could still diffuse through the intermediate tissues in sufficient quantity. Even if man were an insect, there would also be no need for lungs and pulmonary arteries because insects are small enough to rely upon air-carrying tubes, which ramify throughout their bodies. No part of the insect is more than a small distance from a branch of one of these tubes, and therefore no part is without oxygen. (Such a system can supply only small animals. H. G. Wells's giant wasps, however godlike their nourishment, could never have existed—for which, great thanks.)

The Need for a System

Man is a large animal, too big by far for simple diffusion, too big for the insect's tracheal network. Consequently, there has to be a better method of distributing oxygen around the body. In all the higher vertebrates, this advanced system consists basically of one air pump and two liquid pumps. The air pump, a combination of the diaphragm and the chest, draws air into the passive lungs and then forces it out again. The two liquid pumps are the two ventricles of the heart. They have quite separate functions. The right ventricle pumps its blood into the capillary network of the lungs, and so brings blood short of oxygen into the proximity of air that possesses oxygen. The left ventricle pumps its blood, now rich with oxygen, into the capillary network of the body, and so brings rich blood to the tissues needing oxygen. The system is only an extension of the simple diffusion mechanism acceptable to the smallest creatures. Blood has to be brought near to the surface so that the oxygen of air can diffuse through into it. The blood is then moved near to all tissues so that the oxygen can then diffuse through into them. The diffusion is similar; it is only the distances that are greater, and blood is the transport agency that eliminates the distances.

Some measurable facts about the respiratory system:

A relaxed adult breathes in and out some 10 to 14 times a minute, with each breath therefore lasting 4 to 6 seconds.

In each minute, a resting adult breathes in 9 to 12 pt. of air.

Should this person then leap into violent physical exercise, his demand for air will increase perhaps fifteenfold, perhaps twentyfold, and he will pant in and out some 20 gal. of air every minute, with only a second or so for each breath.

The urgency for more air is great because the relaxed body carries slender reserves of oxygen. Within 20 seconds of starting hard work all the reserve capacity will have been consumed, but long before that the panting will have begun.

A normal day's breathing involves about 3,300 gal. of air, or 530 cu. ft., or a cube of air roughly 8 ft. by 8 ft. by 8 ft. In one night, therefore, a person's lungs will require a third of that amount—namely a block 6 ft. by 6 ft. by 5 ft. Although replenishment with fresh air is necessary, the traditional gale that blows through so many English bedrooms is more than adequate compensation for the quite moderate requirements of a night's respiration.

In a lifetime of nights and days, each human being will have breathed in a phenomenal quantity of air, say 13 million cu. ft.

A lot of people can use up the available oxygen in any unventilated hall or shelter in quite a short time, particularly if they are active or even walking about. For instance, assuming no removal of carbon dioxide and no replenishment with oxygen, 650 people could stay in a shelter of 42,000 cu. ft. (say 45 ft. by 45 ft. by 21 ft.) for only three hours even if they were sitting down. If moving about, the time would be halved. A black hole of Calcutta is easy to create without ventilation. The necessary oxygen replenishment is about a cubic foot of oxygen per person per hour if the people are sitting or lying down, 2 cu. ft. if they are active. At the same time, carbon dioxide and other noxious accumulations such as smoke have to be removed. Telephone booths—in England, they have tight-fitting doors and no effective ventilation—contain about 37 cu. ft. of air. On the figures quoted above, allowing a small displacement bulk for the person telephoning, a call ought to be no longer than 30 minutes, certainly no more than 45. Otherwise the caller will faint and fall foul of the built-in curtailment system for excessive private use of a public service.

Lungs

A pair of human lungs weighs about 2½ lb. The right lung is heavier than the left, and both extend upward to an inch or so above the collarbone. In various aspects, the lungs are inefficient organs; they are a brilliant execution of a poor design. The exit and the entrance are at the same place; the air both enters and leaves by the mouth. Consequently, there is only a partial interchange of gas with each breath, and about five-sixths of the air present in the lungs is still there when the next breath begins. The next breath again leaves five-sixths, and so on. In fact, due to molecular minuteness, it could even be argued that some molecules present in the lungs at the start of life are still there at the end of it; the relentless removal of one-sixth of their number at each breath has been insufficient to ensure their total extraction in a lifetime of breaths. Not so with fish. They use a flow system, and water passes over their gills in a steady stream. The human mechanism, which had to make do with and adapt the air bladder developed as a buoyancy device by fish generations before, is far less attractive in theory, although some awkward valving would be necessary were we, too, to possess outlet vents on the sides of our chests.

The dominant reason why mankind and any large animal have to possess a respiratory system is that bulk becomes so much larger than skin area with any increase in size. However good the diffusion of oxygen through the skin, the area for diffusion would be inadequate, but this area for diffusion has to exist somehow. It is, in fact, created by the architecture of the lungs, and human lungs have an area some 40 to 50 times greater than the surface area of the body's skin. (Traditionally, this huge lung area of 800 to 1,000 sq. ft. is referred to as being the size of a tennis court. I personally find it hard to equate the ramifying delicacy of the human lung with a flat slab, quite apart from the difficulty that courts can be two-sided and bordered or not.) The alveoli of the lungs, the round endings of each culmination of all the subdivisions of the one original windpipe, cause this huge area. There are said to be 300 million of them, and they are spots where gaseous diffusion most readily occurs. (The number of alveoli fluctuates wildly in the estimates, and a figure of 750 million is also often quoted. This must be a prime example of follow-the-leader, for any thought of personally checking the astronomical number is highly intimidating.)

Each alveolus is covered with a tracery of blood capillaries. Each capillary is just wide enough to let the red blood cells pass through one after the other, just as a narrow street permits cars only in single file. Each blood cell is jostled along by pumping from the heart's right ventricle, and it stays in the capillary for only three-quarters of a second. In that time, aided by the fact that the walls of the alveolus are .00004 in. thick, the red blood cells have picked up their oxygen atoms, and the blood's content of carbon dioxide will have been yielded up to the lungs. Should the heart be pumping vigorously, as during exercise, the blood will be in the pulmonary capillaries for only one-third of a second, but the time is still adequate for the exchange. The hemoglobin molecules of each red blood cell, it need hardly be said, have a great affinity for oxygen.

Pumping 17 pt. of blood a minute through the capillary network of the lungs, and over those 300 million alveoli endings, is quite a task, but this act requires one-tenth of the pressure necessary for pumping oxygenated blood through every other capillary network in the body. The left ventricle's more powerful role demands a pressure of 10 cm. of mercury, but both its pressure and the centimeter of mercury needed for pulmonary circulation seem ridiculously small when it is borne in mind that hundreds of miles of capillaries are involved in each instance. Part of the explanation lies in the fact that all blood vessels are slightly elastic (an elasticity that diminishes with age) and that there is only a small volume of blood actually in the capillaries at any one moment. The huge network of pulmonary capillaries, for example, contains only about 5 cu. in. of blood, an amount roughly equal to the output of each single pump of the right ventricle.

Breathing and Breath Control

Breathing in, with the inrush of air through the nostrils, the mouth, or both, gives the impression that some system within the nose or

mouth sucks the air in. Not so. To expand the lungs, which are themselves elastic and prone to collapse upon themselves—as in operations
—the diaphragm pulls itself downward and the rib muscles enlarge the
rib cage. In quiet breathing, the diaphragm moves downward about ⅔
in., but in deep breathing it moves nearly 3 in. When the diaphragm
is pulled down and the chest wall expands, the lungs are pulled downward and outward. Air then rushes in with nature's customary abhor-
rence of vacuums. The reverse action causes a slight increase of
pressure within the lungs. Therefore, as nature has to balance pressures,
air leaves the lungs to join the atmosphere again. Normally, the pressure
differentials are small, and breathing is quietly carried out without
anything more than a gentle flowing to and fro.

Diaphragm and chest wall can each maintain breathing on their own
should one fail, although the diaphragm is normally responsible for
three-quarters of the tidal respiration. The diaphragm, in particular,
is capable of creating quite considerable pressure, as in exercise or in
blowing up balloons. A pressure of about 2 lb. per sq. in., or one-
seventh of an atmosphere, can be made to force air out of the lungs,
but a smaller pressure differential is involved when air is breathed in.
The forces associated with breathing seem quite powerful, as someone
puffs and blows, but their actual levels can be demonstrated by attempting to emulate those film heroes who submerge themselves in
the swamp with only a straw as an air link to the surface. As everyone
knows, the pressure of water increases with depth, and at only nine
inches below the surface the pressure is sufficient to stop breathing.
Some heroes might be able to go a fraction deeper, and the depth does
depend upon the position adopted beneath the surface; but no hero,
however strong the straw, can submerge himself to any great extent
beyond nine inches. The pressure of water around him is too much for
his powers of respiration.

The iron-lung kind of respirator also works upon the outside of the
chest, but beneficially. Instead of raising the pressures to a point where
breathing becomes impossible, it lowers the pressure surrounding the
patient's chest. This has the effect of expanding the thorax, of enlarging
the lungs, and of drawing air in through the mouth. A slight reversal
of the system will cause the reverse procedure, and the patient breathes
out. Naturally, there has to be sealing to prevent air from entering
or leaving around the patient's neck.

The normal automatic control of the rate of breathing depends mainly
upon the level of carbon dioxide in the blood, and therefore in the
expired air; but there is some uncertainty. Mild exercise neither reduces
the amount of oxygen in the arteries nor increases their content of

carbon dioxide, and yet the breathing rate goes up. Severe exercise certainly depletes the oxygen levels and raises the carbon-dioxide levels, and the breathing rate increases considerably. Therefore, it does seem logical to presume that the changing levels are linked with the changed breathing.

Normal air possesses virtually no carbon dioxide—perhaps 3 parts in 10,000. Expired air may be 4 percent carbon dioxide, and breathing may become twice as fast when this proportion goes up to 4.2 percent. Should the inspired air also be rich in carbon dioxide, we start feeling faint and probably pass out if the proportion goes up to 5 percent. There may still be the normal 20 percent of oxygen in the inspired air, but the abnormal quantity of carbon dioxide getting into our blood is more than a match for us.

Altitude

Although high levels of carbon dioxide can cause panting and an unpleasant swimming feeling, the reduced quantity of oxygen at high altitudes can cause unconsciousness without any consciousness of its approach. In World War II, RAF pilots were placed in pressure chambers to demonstrate the insidiousness of oxygen lack. At simulated altitude, both unconsciousness and recovery could be effected by cutting off the oxygen supply without any awareness of either event by the individual pilot. Of course, mountaineers are well aware of the thinness of the air through which they climb, as their lungs are made to gasp for more, but pilots have little physical work to do and can quietly pass out. It used to be the regulation that they switched on their oxygen supply at 15,000 feet, when atmospheric pressure is nearly 40 percent lower than at sea level, but recent work suggests that a person's ability to cope with a novel flying situation is impaired if he is breathing ordinary air at any pressure level above 5,000 ft.

Much of humanity lives above 5,000 ft. It is roughly the height of Nairobi and many other regions of the African continent. In the Andes, there are many settlements three times as high, and the limit for permanent acclimatization, according to the physiologist L. G. C. E. Pugh, is between 15,000 and 17,500 ft.—roughly three miles up. Mountain climbers have spent many weeks at higher altitudes, and early Everest attempts reached 28,000 ft. or thereabouts. F. S. Smythe, for example, spent three nights at 27,400 ft. in 1933, an altitude where the pressure is less than one-third of that at sea level. All the successful climbs of Mount Everest have been with the aid of oxygen cylinders, but it is an odd coincidence that the earth's highest mountain just about represents the highest peak man could achieve solely with the aid of his lungs.

Condors fly over the Andes and geese have been seen at 30,000 ft. but birds have a different lung system from mammals. Also, one assumes, soaring flight is less of an effort than stumbling along some windswept mountain ridge. Human beings already fly higher, of course, and with even less effort, in their pressurized airliners. Cabin pressure is generally equivalent to a height of 6,000 to 8,000 ft., according to the height of the aircraft. Therefore, the altitude is already substantial and can be disturbing for some people. Should an aircraft flying above 30,000 ft. suddenly lose its cabin pressure and become in equilibrium with the outside air, and should the passengers fail to breathe through the emergency oxygen masks carried on board, their lungs would reverse their traditional role. The pulmonary capillaries would then start giving up oxygen to the lungs rather than taking it from them. Naturally, such a procedure will be short-lived, and so too would the passengers unless their oxygen was boosted either artificially at altitude or by swift descent to denser regions of the atmosphere.

Drowning and Pollution

At a postmortem, the lungs can have much to say about life and death. For instance, the lungs of a newborn infant that never took a breath will sink in water. After a few breaths, any portion of the lung will have been sufficiently inflated to float. Not all who drown have water in their lungs; some 10 to 20 percent of them are asphyxiated quite simply when air is prevented by water from getting to their lungs. There is a great difference whether someone drowns in fresh water or in saltwater. Fresh water is less salty than blood; therefore, if it reaches the lungs, it rapidly invades the blood, and, quite apart from blocking off the oxygen supply by its existence in the lungs, so much extra water in the blood can cause paralysis of the circulatory system. Saltwater is more salty than blood; when it is in the lungs, it extracts water from the blood, causing what is known as hemoconcentration. This, too, produces heart failure but for quite a different reason and after a longer time.

Between the lungs of an Eskimo, who has lived his life in clean air, and of a coal miner, who has not, there are the lungs of the rest of us. An Eskimo's lungs stay clean and can easily be cut with a knife. A miner's lungs can be black, rich in mineral matter, and hard to cut. An ordinary city-dweller, according to Professor Julius Comroe, of the University of California, breathes in 20 billion particles of foreign matter on an average day. It does not matter that the air may be very cold or hot or dry because it will be warm and moist by the time it reaches the alveoli, but it does matter that it is polluted, although less than might be imagined.

Experimental animals have breathed in dirty air at 500°C. and at −100°C., and in both cases the air was at body temperature or nearly so before it had penetrated very deeply into the lungs. At the same time, it was rendered virtually free of particles before reaching the delicate alveoli. Of course, some particles are breathed out just as they were breathed in, and some are vehemently sneezed out if particularly irritating, but a large number do land on the trachea, the bronchi, and the huge branching network of bronchioles. All these tubes are lined with cilia, minute hairlike structures that can row back and forth. Their rowing is all coordinated, much like the leg movement of a millipede, and it has the effect of wafting particles up and out of the lungs. The cilia work within a thin layer of mucus, and it is this mucus sheath, with all its trapped particles, that is pushed out of the lungs at the astonishing speed of about ⅔ in. a minute. This means that a particle that has penetrated a foot into the lungs will have been evicted about a quarter of an hour later. The moving staircase of mucus and particles eventually reaches the junction with the pharynx. It can then be quietly swallowed or accumulated and spat out.

The alveoli have neither mucus glands nor cilia. Particles that reach this far can still be removed either by the bloodstream or by being forced into contact with the mucus sheath of the bronchioles; but some stay there forever. It is these that can stridently testify at a postmortem whether the lungs in question belonged to Eskimos, to coal miners, or to city-dwellers on the wrong side of town.

Choking, Coughing, Sneezing

Large particles of noxious substances result in immediate coughing and choking. Any attempt by food to go down the wrong way, into the lungs rather than the stomach, is met with explosive protests from the lungs. Customarily, the procedure of swallowing blocks off the glottis, stops respiration for a moment or two and ensures correct division of air and food. An unconscious person generally has no such reflex. The forcing of a drink between his clenched teeth, however well intentioned, may lead to the pouring of this drink straight into his lungs. Even during consciousness, the system is not always perfect. Fruit pits, nails, bits of toys, parts of false teeth, and of course food have all found their way into the bronchi. Respiratory distress is generally instantaneous, but often the objects cannot be choked out, and they remain within the lungs for decades or forever.

One of the most famous chokings was suffered by Isambard Kingdom Brunel, better known for engineering Britain's Great Western Railway. He swallowed a half sovereign coin in 1883, and it chose to go the way of his lungs rather than his stomach. For two days, he suffered and was then summarily strapped onto a plank. It was raised nearly to the vertical, with Brunel's head at the lower end; his back was then hit. This rough approach failed entirely. It caused much more choking to arise, but no half sovereign. Further treatment in the same sledge-hammer manner three and a half weeks later did in fact budge the coin from his right bronchus, but not far enough. His trachea was then cut open, but unavailingly. Two more weeks passed, and he again submitted to the upside-down shock treatment—it sounds as if it was entirely of his own devising—and the coin dropped from his mouth. Richer then by a half sovereign, worth ten shillings, and an unpleasant six-week experience, Brunel was a lot luckier than some who never lose the impediment in their lungs.

The force of a cough can be exceedingly powerful. It involves a slight breathing in, a closing of the glottis, a forcible respiratory effort to build up pressure, and then a sudden release of the trapped air. Speeds up to 500 ft. a second have been recorded. A sneeze can be even more explosive, and supersonic speeds have been alleged for the expelled gust. Unlike a cough, the glottis stays open before and during the sneeze. There are different varieties of sneeze, some modified by a desire not to douche the immediate environment, but, basically, a sneeze is always initially accompanied by a raising of the tongue to block the mouth. This causes the nose to receive, and pass on, the first blast, with only the second part coming from the mouth. According to a report from Dr. David Mezz, of New York, polite sneezes, or internal attempts to muffle the approaching storm, can lead to nosebleed, a ringing in the ears, sinus trouble, and much else. He recommends an open mouth, a natural sneeze, a temporary disregard of popularity, and a handkerchief if there is time. Not only the obvious and inhaled irritants and approaching attacks of influenza, measles, colds, and hay fever can initiate sneezing, but also more bizarre phenomena like changes in external temperature or exposure to bright lights. They too can trigger paroxysms of supersonic sneezing.

Laughing, Yawning, Hiccups

There are other oddities of respiration. Laughter is a deep breathing in followed by a succession of short and spasmodic breathings out. Crying, right at the other end of the pleasure scale, or sometimes right next to it, is caused by similar respiratory movements. Yawning, a deep breathing in with the mouth opened exceptionally wide, seems curiously pointless, as has already been pointed out. Sighing is the opposite, for it is a breathing out, but it is equally vague in its reasons. Hiccups are spasmodic inspirations that end with a click due to the sudden closing of the vocal cords. Here, it is the diaphragm that is at fault, or probably the nerves controlling it. There are innumerable home remedies, such as drinking out of the wrong side of a glass (which concentrates attention) or breathing into a paper bag (which must concentrate carbon dioxide) or eating sugar lumps (which is nice— for some) or drinking gin.

Every now and then, someone gets the hiccups and keeps them. Lucy McDonald, an Atlanta waitress, got them in 1963 and still had them in 1965. Naturally, she tried all the old remedies, some 2,000 of them, and she saw over a hundred doctors. Finally, 40 lb. weaker and millions of hiccups after the attack had begun, still dosed with tran- quilizers and unable to get work to feed her three children, she under- went surgery. Her right phrenic nerve was deadened with a drug, and the hiccups immediately stopped. So the nerve was crushed, and the hiccups did not come back even when the drug was no longer effective. The result—a cure. The cost—a loss of a quarter of her breathing capacity due to the loss of that nerve. The conclusion—entirely satis- factory, as a normal person's breathing capacity is more than enough in normal circumstances. In fact, men have lived long lives with only one-fifth of their lungs.

Oxygen, Excess and Lack

Holding the breath is possible to a certain extent, say, for 45 seconds, but thereafter becomes impossible. Breathing is resumed before the lack of oxygen has been damaging. Should someone take either a few puffs of pure oxygen first or gasp deeply solely with ordinary air, the time of breath-holding can be extended by perhaps two minutes. Should he first breathe pure oxygen for a minute, he may thereafter be able to hold his breath for five minutes. In all these cases, the voluntary restric- tion does not cause any damage due to oxygen lack.

Although oxygen is vital to almost every living thing on this planet (there are exceptions, such as the anerobic bacteria), it can also be a poison. Animals kept in pure oxygen for several days have suffered lung damage as a result. American astronauts, who have been living off pure oxygen when in orbit, have been receiving it at much less than atmos- pheric pressure. This is known to be safe—at least physiologically, although prone to disastrous fires. Should men be given pure oxygen at four-atmospheres pressure they will generally suffer severe symptoms, such as convulsions or faintness, in less than an hour. Four atmospheres is equivalent to a water depth of 130 ft. As men have already lived quite extensively in seahouses at that pressure or even deeper and will certainly go deeper still very shortly, the problems lie jointly in seeing that they get enough to breathe, yet not too much oxygen.

Asphyxia was probably the cause of Christ's death, and of all who were crucified. Dr. Jacques Bréhant, of Algiers, who has examined the subject and reviewed reports of crucifixions from World War II, believes suffocation resulted when the victim's arms carried the whole weight of the body. This made breathing difficult and later, when exhaustion set in, impossible. Temporary relief could be gained by using the nail through the feet to take some of the body's weight; but, again, exhaustion would intervene or, as in the case of the two thieves, the legs would be broken making such relief impossible. Therefore, the correct anatomical picture of the dead Christ on the cross should show, according to Dr. Bréhant, the head tipped forward—not upward or to the side—and the nails through the wrists—not through the palms, through which they would tear. Had Renaissance painters been as familiar with this method of execution ("the most cruel and horrible of all," said Cicero) as the Romans and their subjects were, they would probably have been more strict in their interpretations.

The Heart

The heart weighs less than a pound, is the size of a fist, and has scant resemblance to the simple arrow-pierced emblem carved on trees. It pumps the body's entire blood content through its chambers every minute, beats throughout life, grows from less than an ounce at birth, starts work months before that, and continues to beat thereafter. In short, the heart is a formidable pump. In fact, it is two pumps, each having similar output. One sends the blood through the pulmonary network; the other sends it through the body, the systemic network. Each pump produces its 2,000 gal. a day, or 50 million gal. in a lifetime. Considering its continuous labor and responsibility, it does seem entirely reasonable that failure of the heart and its blood vessels is the major cause of death in many countries.

Harvey and Galen

Like Charles Darwin two centuries later, William Harvey, the seventeenth-century physician whose *De Motu Cordis* so shook the world, knew he was right, and knew many would think him wrong; he therefore polished and verified his ideas year after year. In 1616, he wrote: "The movement of the blood is constantly in a circle, and is brought about by the beat of the heart." It was this—to us—innocuous thought that had to be proven beyond disbelief, and it was 12 years until he published this thought, then expanded to 72 pages. To us it seems incredible that Harvey's work should have encountered opposition. Many men other than anatomists had seen arms lopped off and had seen rich arterial blood gushing forth in great jets, but the belief was that these portrayed the ebbing and flowing of the vascular system. Galen, the second-century know-it-all of medicine, had laid down the law about blood flow and had mentioned nothing about circulation. Even 1,400 years later Galen was still commanding unswerving respect in most quarters. Jean Riolan, professor of anatomy at Paris, countered Harvey by saying that if dissections no longer agreed with Galen it was because nature had changed and not because Galen had been wrong. Guy Patin, professor of medicine at Paris, said Harvey's theory was paradoxical, useless, false, impossible, absurd, and harmful.

Harvey was, of course, quite right. Blood does go "as it were, in a circle." He was right even though no one had then seen blood capillaries, the minute links between the outgoing arterial system and the incoming venous system. He was right even though he knew nothing of oxygen and not much about the reason for circulation—"whether for the sake of nourishment or for the communication of heat, is not certain." Marcello Malpighi, of Bologna, was to see capillaries later in the same century; but Joseph Priestley, of Leeds and America, was not to isolate oxygen and Antoine Lavoisier, of Paris, was not to name the gas or discover its nature until the second half of the eighteenth century. However, Harvey's attackers had been vanquished long before either capillaries or oxygen had set their seals upon the argument.

The heart's two pumps consist of a total of four chambers. Unhelpfully for clarity, the primitive vertebrate heart is also of four chambers, but for quite a different reason. Fish, having no lungs and using a more primitive pumping system, have their chambers arranged in a line. The blood flows through all four chambers consecutively, and then leaves the heart to make its circuit through the gills and around the body. With the development of lungs, in those vertebrates that struggled on land to make use of air, a complexity arose. Venous blood returning to the heart first had to be pumped through the lungs, and the subsequent arterial blood had to be pumped around the body. It was plainly unsatisfactory if the two streams were to be mixed in the heart; therefore —and this is loose teleological speaking of a high order—the heart's single pump had to become two pumps, the pulmonary pump and the systemic pump. The wall between the two main pumping ventricles had to be a total barrier. (Galen was so wide of the mark in his theory of the blood's tidal flow that he had to assume that this wall, the ventricular septum, was somehow porous, even though its porosity was impossible to demonstrate.)

One Pump into Two

The complexity of making one pump into two was not solved overnight during evolution. Both in the lung fish and in the later amphibia there is still mixing of the blood. In reptiles, there is less mixing, as a wall exists between the two parts of the pumping ventricles; but the wall is not quite complete, and so mixing of the two types of blood still occurs. Only in birds and mammals is the wall complete. Only in these two classes of the animal kingdom is the venous blood pumped entirely separately to be oxygenated, and the oxygenated blood is then pumped just as separately to the body. The dual role of a single heart is thus satisfactorily accomplished.

Venous blood returning to the heart first enters the right auricle (named after its alleged resemblance to a little ear). It is then pumped by this auricle into the right ventricle (the name means a little stomach). This ventricle pumps the blood around the lungs, and it flows back from them into the left auricle. This third chamber pumps it into the most powerful chamber of all, the left ventricle. It leaves this ventricle through the aorta, a vessel an inch in diameter, which receives the heart's output of 1/5 pt. in every beat. In mechanical terms, this means the relentless exertion of between 35 and 50 foot-pounds of pressure every minute, or the exceptional exertion of 500 foot-pounds or more during strenuous exercise.

Heartbeat

The human heart beats roughly 70 times a minute, or four times for every breath. It will therefore have beaten 2.5 billion times before it finally calls it a day at the end of an average life. In general, the bigger the animal the slower the beat. An elephant's 48-lb. heart beats only 25 times a minute. The mouse's heart trips along at 600 to 700 times a minute. Birds tend to be faster for their size; a chicken's beat is between 200 and 400, and a canary's is 1,000 times a minute. The dog species varies according to the size of the dog; big dogs are 80, small dogs are 120. Each individual slows down his heart as he or she grows; the human infant has a pulse of about 130, which will slow down to the adult 70. Before birth it was even faster. These infantile speeds are matched again only during strenuous exercise or anxiety or both, when the pulse rate may triple its customary pace.

When increased demands are being made upon the heart and its beat quickens, it also pumps more with each beat. Many machines become less efficient as they go faster, but the heart's output—its stroke volume—can be nearly doubled from the normal resting output. Consequently, with both more beats and more blood per beat, the heart can pump five times the quantity of blood that it normally pumps when at rest. If a large output is maintained, as in a long-distance race, the heart shrinks during the race by about 15 percent; the larger the heart, the greater the shrinkage. Often, athletes have large hearts, as might be expected both by virtue of their proven abilities and of their training, but their hearts are not abnormally large and are well within the ordinary range of human variation. Most mammals, including humans, have hearts that weigh from less than .5 up to 1 percent of the total body weight. An ordinary dog's heart is 1 percent of the total body weight; those of sedentary dogs are .5 percent. The human proportion of heart to body is nearer that of the sedentary kind of dog. An ordinary horse has a 9-lb. heart; the famous English thoroughbred Eclipse had a 14-lb. heart.

The human heart does not lie entirely on the left side, as is frequently alleged. It lies fairly near the midline with about one-third of its bulk on the right side, two-thirds on the left. An anatomical awkwardness is that the flatter base of the heart faces backward, and the sharper apex of the heart faces outward and downward. It is this apex that reaches out to a person's left side, almost to the nipple, and because the apex pulses with every beat, the heart has a reputation for being at that spot, rather than stretching to it with its pointed end. This apex beat can both be seen and felt. Its location in a standing person is 3½ in. to the left of the midline, between the fifth and sixth ribs. (As a helpful nearby reference point, although not for everyone, the nipples are between the fourth and fifth ribs.)

While this apex is seen to beat at the normal 70 or so times a minute and while the pressure waves of the pulse can be felt to possess an identical rhythm, the heart itself makes a twofold sound for every beat. Listen to it with a stethoscope or just by placing your ear in the vicinity of someone else's heart (since personal auscultation demands excessive contortion), and the noise of a beat is distinctly double. Spelled as lip-dup, lub-dub, or even lub-dup, the first sound is louder, lower, and longer than the second. That first lip or lub is itself a mixture of sounds: the ventricles contract, then the valves between them and the auricles slam shut. The dup or dub, the second sound, is caused when the valves in the big blood vessels leading to the lungs and the body each slam shut after the pulse of blood has gushed past them.

These four valves are all passive one-way valves. They are of varied shapes. Between the auricles and the ventricles lie the mitral and the tricuspid valves, so called because they have two flaps (like a miter) or three, and they permit the blood to flow in the direction of the ventricles but prevent it from flowing back again into the auricles. The two valves in the aorta and the pulmonary artery are called semilunar, and they shut to prevent the blood from flowing back again into the ventricles. Canal lock gates also work in this one-way fashion; they slam shut to keep the water from flowing back. It is this steady shutting, of necessity twice for every beat and of necessity with a time lag between them, that contributes the remorseless lip-dup of the active heart. Should a valve weaken or leak, there will be an equally steady rhythm of gurgling or backwash as the blood flows backward past the faulty valve.

Blood Pressure

Contrary to heartbeat, blood pressure does not fall between infancy and adulthood, but rises throughout childhood and then continues to rise in later life. The first man to demonstrate and measure arterial blood pressure was an eighteenth-century clergyman named Stephen Hales. He also found time to devise a windmill for ventilating London's Newgate Prison to reduce disease, but his principal claim to renown came after he used a horse, a goose, and a tall glass to examine blood pressure. In 1733 he tied the horse to a post, removed a goose's windpipe in lieu of flexible tubing, and inserted a small glass tube into one of the horse's leg arteries. By means of the goose's windpipe he connected this small tube to a very tall and vertical tube, also of glass. The blood then shot up it to a height of 9 ft. The pressure of arterial blood caused this high level and it then oscillated steadily with every heartbeat. Soon blood-clotting curtailed the experiment.

Nowadays, the more ordinary human practice is to use a sphygmomanometer (a pulse-pressure measure) in conjunction with a stethoscope. By listening to an artery's beat and applying variable pressure to the arm, it is possible to estimate both the pressure of each beat and the residual pressure between each beat. The two are known as systolic and diastolic respectively, with the systolic always greater than the diastolic and the two always written down in that order, such as

180/110. The figures are a measurement of the pressure in millimeters of mercury, as is the 760 of normal atmospheric pressure.

Systolic pressure for a newborn baby is about 40. At ten days it may be 70, and at the end of the first month it may be around 80. By ten years, it is still under 100. An average young man at rest has a systolic pressure of 120, a diastolic pressure of 80. Nearly all mammals, large or small, have adult systolic pressures between 100 and 200, and man is not one of the few exceptions. The human combination of 120/80 stays reasonably constant for a time, but after the age of 25 it may creep up by .5 a year. By the age of 60, it will be near 140, and by 80 it will on average be about 160. No one asserts that it ought to rise like this, any more than middle-age fatness ought to happen. It is just that blood pressure does rise with age, and a modest rise is better than a steep one.

Insurance companies are enthusiastic to discover the blood pressure of potential customers, and insurance statistics are cold-blooded in showing how the odds lie against the hypertensive population, although not necessarily against the hypertensive individual. In general, the higher the pressure the greater the risk of death. There are always exceptions, but a high blood pressure in a middle-aged man is more dangerous than the same blood pressure in an elderly one; for instance, 160/90 men in their 40s are nearly three times more likely to die than average men of the same age, while 160/90 men in their 60s are only twice as likely to die as average sexagenarians.

The lack of any blood pressure is of course more rapidly fatal than the mere excess of it. For those whose hearts stop beating and whose pressure slumps in consequence, irreversible brain damage follows within a few minutes. Until 1960, the treatment for such a condition was to cut open the chest, expose the heart, and massage it manually; but in that year a method of external massage was first published. W. B. Kouwenhoven, of the United States, and his colleagues excited the world by describing how an internal circulation could be maintained by rhythmic pressure from outside. Just by leaning heavily on the sternum 60 times a minute, they achieved blood circulation and considerable blood pressure despite the heart's failure. Simultaneous efforts were made to start the heart again, and first reports indicated considerable success. Other attempts have not always been so satisfactory, and the firm pummeling has frequently led to broken ribs and sternums; but the 1960 report, coupled with the resurgence of interest in mouth-to-mouth artificial respiration (which has a venerable, even Biblical history; see II Kings 4:32), has helped to open up the subject of starting stopped hearts without the hazardous extra of opening up the chest.

Artificial pacemakers, which deliver regular electric shocks to hearts no longer capable of beating correctly on their own, have also kept hearts going in recent years. Between 1958 and 1964, over 3,000 patients in the United States had these devices implanted in their bodies. In fact, modified pacemakers, beating much more frequently than the conventional 70 times a minute and implanted in the neck rather than near the heart, have even been capable of lowering the blood pressure. William Harvey was undoubtedly the first man to prove the blood flows "as it were, in a circle." Now, nearly three and a half centuries later, mankind is making great efforts to make it continue to do so instead of letting it come prematurely, as it were, to a stop.

Blood Distribution

So far as the heart is concerned, blood distribution is an elementary business. It pumps it all into the aorta, and that is that. At a customary speed of 15 in. a second, the blood is received by the aorta, from which the branches almost immediately begin to distribute it around the body. With all this ramification, the speed slackens, mainly because the cross-sectional area of all the arterioles and then of the capillaries is so much greater than that of the inch-thick aorta. Within a capillary, the blood flow is only about $\frac{1}{50}$ in. a second.

The heart, as has already been said, can boost its delivery of blood almost fivefold if need be. From over a gallon a minute it can rise to 5½ gal. a minute at times of maximum output. Such a delivery means pumping the body's entire blood supply several times around the body every 60 seconds. However, even this flow is inadequate. The muscles need more. They are bearing the brunt of strenuous exercise and need increasing quantities.

In fact, they do get more, but at the expense of other organs. Blood is diverted away from these other organs, and the muscles receive 18 times as much blood in times of extreme exertion even though the heart's output is only five times as great. The organs that suffer are the kidneys, which receive about one-quarter of their normal supply; the skin, which gets more initially with moderate exertion, although this is severely cut back with extreme exertion; and the digestive system, which gets only one-fifth of normal. The heart, being muscle itself and undeniably working harder, receives about four times as much during the exertion. The brain, it seems, is totally unmoved by all exertion, diversion, and increase. At rest, it receives 1⅓ pt. of blood a minute; at peak demand it still receives 1⅓ pt. per strenuous minute. In the meantime, the blood flow to the muscles, excluding the heart, has been boosted from some 2 pt. a minute to almost 40 pt. At this time of top exertion, the muscles receive 88 percent of the heart's furious output; at rest they receive only 20 percent. Conversely, the abdomen normally gets 24 percent of the supply; during exertion its share of the greater output is only 1 percent.

The Pull of Gravity

An extra work load for the heart, never encountered in nature—at least not to any marked degree—but developed by man, is caused by artificially increasing the normal gravitational pull upon the system. When a man leaps out of bed in the morning, moving from the horizontal to the vertical, his heart suddenly has to pump blood upward to his head rather than along to it. This represents a greater effort than pumping it horizontally. Sometimes the leaping man finds himself sitting dizzily down on the bed when the load has proved too much or too sudden. Aircraft pilots became extremely familiar with increased work load when steep turns caused them to black out. The heart could no longer adequately pump blood to the brain against the extra pull involved in the turn, a pull equivalent to a few times that of normal gravity. An astronaut, subjected to the tremendous accelerations of rocket travel, suffers still greater pulls upon his system—and upon his heart. To help counter them he lies facing the direction of travel; therefore, his heart pumps mainly horizontally. A recent report from the Soviet Union suggested that a man could withstand 26.5 times the pull of gravity and not black out, if he was inclined at 80 degrees to the direction of acceleration. A 200-lb. man at that acceleration could therefore be said to weigh 2¼ tons.

Blood, Corpuscles and Platelets

The transport medium of the body, the principal fluid of the circulatory system, is blood. Slightly heavier than water, three times as viscous, half plasma and half corpuscles, human blood is pushed around the body once every minute even under quiet conditions. It is squirted out of the heart, it falls back to the valves, it is squeezed through the capillaries, and then sucked and forced along the veins to start the whole cycle once more. During its tempestuous circulation it carries water, vital to every cell, it takes oxygen from the lungs and carbon dioxide to them, it carries nutrients to the cells and waste products from them, it transports heat from the hotter to the cooler regions, it distributes hormones, it is a circulator of antibodies—the anti-infective agents—and of its own white cells, and it carries its own self-sealing mechanism for occasions when its essential fluidity has to be congealed to block an open wound.

The average human body, weighing 156 lb., contains 13 pints of blood, or a pint for every 12 lb. Blood weight is about one-twelfth of total body weight. Although one pint can be given in a transfusion with equanimity,* the loss of blood from, say, a wound can never be regarded casually, even though the body has proved itself capable of losing at least one-quarter, possibly one-third, of its vital transport fluid without any apparent severe physiological consequences. However, although one-quarter can be lost with equanimity and one-third generally without serious effect, the loss of half is likely to be fatal. Transfusion must intervene to prevent death in such cases. Experiments on dogs have shown that an occasional dog can lose two-thirds of its original blood volume without dying and without transfusion.

At any ordinary moment three-fifths of a person's blood is in his veins and returning to his heart. One-fifth is in his lungs, and the final one-fifth—say two pints for the average man—is in his heart, arteries, arterioles, and systemic capillaries. The universal color of blood, bright red in the arteries and dark blue in the veins, is belied if some blood is taken and allowed to stand awhile. Provided something is added to the blood to stop its clotting, all the color will sink to the bottom. This part contains the red corpuscles. On top, forming 55 percent of the whole, will be the blood plasma, a straw-colored liquid. Between the two, as a very thin boundary layer, will be the white corpuscles, not so heavy as the red but heavier than the plasma.

The white corpuscles are not only lighter than the red, but also far less numerous. In each pinprick of blood measuring a cubic millimeter, there are only between 4,000 and 10,000 white corpuscles. In the same pinprick there will be about 1,000 times as many red corpuscles, perhaps 5 million for men, 4.5 million for women. (By no means are distinctions between the sexes solely confined to chapters on reproduction.) There are about 250,000 platelets in each pinprick; these play a part in stopping bleeding after injury.

For those to whom large numbers are comprehensible, 10 pt. of human blood therefore contain between 20 and 50 billion white corpuscles, 1.25 trillion platelets, and 25 trillion red corpuscles: they all fit into the 45 percent of blood that is not plasma. Furthermore, to remain a little longer at this level, each red cell has a short life. Some say a month, some say four months. A month will have involved 43,000 journeys around the body; four months will have involved 172,000

* The amount given is usually ¾ pt.

journeys. Even allowing the longer period, this means a replacement every day of 20 billion red cells by the bone marrow. In fact, only 9 oz. of bone marrow is sufficient to carry out this task. Although probably meaningless, these large numbers, by their very hugeness, ought to give some meaning to the statement that a capillary is only the diameter of one red cell, and therefore help to stress the minute size of the transport network at the opposite end to the heart. Every minute, the heart's pumping squeezes all the 26.3 trillion corpuscles and platelets through this ubiquitous filigree of blood vessels.

It is the red corpuscles that contain hemoglobin, and hemoglobin both picks up oxygen from the lungs and delivers it to the tissues. When carrying oxygen, it is, for some reason, bright red. Without oxygen, it is dark blue, almost black. "Blue babies" suffer from oxygen lack, and whenever pulmonary function is unsatisfactory, a person will appear blue. Hemoglobin has been the subject of much research in recent years, leading both to Nobel prizes and an understanding of the molecule. There are about 280 million molecules of hemoglobin in each red corpuscle. Each molecule is very big, having 10,000 atoms and a molecular weight of 64,500, but it can readily pick up and give up four molecules (eight atoms) of oxygen. Therefore, this figure of eight, multiplied by the number of molecules in a corpuscle, multiplied by the number of corpuscles flowing through the lungs will indicate the body's ability to transport oxygen—or 56 sextillion atoms of oxygen per average minute. If a carrier such as hemoglobin were not available and if the oxygen were to be dissolved in blood much as it is dissolved in water, the amount of blood would have to be 70 times greater than it is. (But that is quite enough of astronomical figures.)

White cells, or leucocytes, are of different kinds. None of them is plate-shaped, like the red corpuscles, and they are all fairly transparent. They have the power of movement, unlike red cells, and they progress in an amoeboid manner, pushing out part of themselves and then advancing into it. Customarily, they move along the sides of blood vessels, rather than being bowled along in the middle like the pulsing tide of red cells, and they can even intrude their way through the walls of the capillaries. They can advance upon solid particles or upon bacteria, and they can ingest them by flowing around them. For a time the 20 or so bacteria imprisoned within a white corpuscle remain alive, but this is not a one-sided battle. The corpuscles can die from the effects of the bacterial toxins, and the subsequent pus is an accumulation of dead leucocytes. It is also not one-sided in the sense that bacteria can win, however vigilant and active the leucocytes; but most bacterial invasions—and they are constant—come to nothing partly because of the omnivorous leucocytes. These cells can also absorb the polluted particles that stick in the lung, they can slowly ingest splinters, and they do attack practically anything foreign to the system. Too many white cells can be as disastrous as too few. In leukemia, which is an overproduction, there may be 60 times as many white cells in the blood as normal. By no means is everything understood about the different kinds of leucocyte, why they are different, why their numerical proportions are so dissimilar, and how many roles each type can play.

Blood platelets, or thrombocytes, smaller than the red cells but even smaller and much more numerous than the leucocytes, are also elusive about their many tasks. They are concerned with the clotting of blood and with the immediate needs at the site of an injury—such as constriction of the blood vessels. Like the red blood cells, but unlike the white, platelets have no nucleus. They are just broken-off fragments of the large marrow cells that made them.

Plasma

Finally, blood plasma. This 55 percent of the whole blood, the part that is not cells, is itself 91 percent water. The rest of it is proteins, salts, and most of the blood cargo, such as those nutrients, hormones, waste products, and antibodies that have already been mentioned. The proteins are crucial to the maintenance of blood pressure, to the regulation of blood volume, to the clotting of blood, and to the manufacture of antibodies. A recent and dramatic benefit of plasma has been its use as a substance for transfusion. Quite often, a patient needs the plasma part of blood more than all the corpuscles; death from blood loss is more a matter of loss of blood bulk than of loss of cells capable of carrying oxygen, vital as oxygen is. Unlike whole blood, which has to be of the right blood group, plasma can be mixed from all donors and is then useful for all those in need. It can also be dried, unlike whole blood, which cannot and which has a short shelf-life, and dried plasma requires only the addition of sterile water to make it fit for a needy recipient.

Blood-letting

Quite the most remarkable aspect in the history of blood, this revered and vital fluid, was mankind's willingness and enthusiasm to rid himself of it voluntarily and often disastrously. Every major civilization has practiced blood-letting. Every region seems to have had a different rationalization for opening the veins, whether it was a form of sacrifice, a necessary outlet for the fourth bodily juice, the calming down of an overexcited metabolism, a driving out of the sickness and fever, an evacuation of malevolence, or a precaution against malaise. In Europe the practice of derivatio flourished, both with ancient support from Hippocrates and with medieval argument from the doctors. It entailed the letting of large amounts of blood from the center of disease. A rival system had been the modest extraction of blood from a spot opposite to the diseased area, but derivatio won the day in the fifteenth and sixteenth centuries. A liter—about a quart—was the customary letting. Louis XIII of France once suffered 47 bleedings in six months. Louis XIV was bled 38 times. Charles II of England was a victim of countless lettings and purges, no less so when on his deathbed. Frederick the Great even had his veins opened during battle to calm his nerves.

Then, suddenly, the old idea of leeches became popular. Instead of cutting blood vessels and often encouraging septicemia, millions of leeches were dragged from ponds and made to do the work in their own quiet way—½ oz. of blood per leech. The leech trade reached its zenith, not in some Aztec period of ancient history, but in Paris in the first few decades of the last century. The fiercest enthusiast of this practice, France's Dr. Broussais, was alleged to be shedding more blood than all the bloody wars going on at that time. The allegation is not unfair for, according to the medical historian H. S. Glasscheib, Broussais instigated the letting of some 20 to 30 million liters of blood in France alone.

Suddenly, in the middle of the last century, a scant 100 years ago, blood-letting fell out of favor. It failed to overlap by only a few decades the medical revolution of blood transfusion. The total reversal of policy, from pouring it out to pouring it in, was extremely abrupt, and extremely welcome.

ᕦ 35 ᕤ

Skeleton and Muscle

The Bone Total · Development · Sex
Differences · Growth · Function of Bone ·
The Hand · The Number of Muscles ·
All or None · The Working of Muscle ·
ATP and ADP · Cramp, Stiffness, and Stitch

The Bone Total

The traditional complement of bones in each human being is 206, but this is a general rule, not a law. About one person in 20, for example, has a 13th pair of ribs, and mongoloids frequently have only 11 pairs. A baby is born with about 350 bones, some of which fuse in later life, some of which retain their individual identity throughout life. All bone fusion is over by the end of the growth period, perhaps in the 25th year for men, younger for women. An old person will, accidents apart, retain his or her mature complement of bones, but many—notably women—will have lost half their bone content by the time 70 is reached. Bones not only provide skeletal support for muscles, but also perform other roles. In fact, there is even argument that the structural and protective tasks of the skeleton should be considered secondary to the more important bone duty of providing a mineral reservoir. It is hard to contemplate a pudding of a human being, totally without a rigid framework, but it is harder still to imagine the proper function of metabolism without extra supplies of calcium and phosphorus always readily available.

The total of 206 is achieved more from the limbs than from the main axial skeleton of trunk and head. Each arm has 32 bones: one collarbone, one shoulder blade, one humerus, one radius, and one ulna, eight wristbones in two rows, five metacarpals in the palm, and 14 phalanges, three to each finger and two to the thumb. Each leg has only

[474]

31 bones: one hipbone, one femur, one kneecap, one tibia, and one fibula, seven tarsals in the instep and heel, five metatarsals in the foot, and 14 phalanges, three to each ordinary toe and two to the biggest toe, the hallux. With two legs and two arms, this means a limb total of 126 bones. The axial skeleton has 80 bones. There are 29 in the skull, of which eight are in the cranium, 14 are in the face, six are in both ears (the ear ossicles), and one—the hyoid bone—is in the throat between the lower jaw and the upper larynx. The spine has 26 bones, of which— in descending order—seven are cervical vertebrae, 12 are thoracic vertebrae, five are lumbar vertebrae, one is the sacrum, and one is the coccyx or tail. The chest has 25 bones, of which one is the breastbone and 24 are ribs.

Unlike all other apes (as was mentioned in the chapter on the male), the human species has no bone in its penis; it has to make do without such an aid. Also man can acquire bone during life according to his mode of existence. Cavalrymen have been known to acquire bones in their buttocks and thighs, quite distinct and separate objects from the traditional hip and femur bones. As these extra bones have arisen entirely as a result of the cavalryman's continual riding this makes one wonder again about humanity's lack of an os penis.

Mammals, despite unevenness in size, ranging as they do from shrews to whales, are remarkably consistent in their bony skeleton. The quaintest example is the system of cervical vertebrae. These bones are quite distinct from the thoracic vertebrae that follow them, and yet the long-necked giraffe has only seven and the no-necked whale also has seven. Exceptions to this rule of seven are manatees and tree sloths. The horse, able to transport a man with ease, has 205 bones as against 206 for the man. The horse has 18 pairs of ribs (against 12) and 54 bones in the backbone (against 26) but, because the manner of its evolution forced the modern horse to be prancing around on its middle fingers and middle toes, there has been considerable bone loss; horse limbs have only 20 bones each, against 32 and 31 for human limbs.

Development

As everyone knows but tends to disregard, the fact that two children both happen to be the same chronological age is relevant but frequently misleading. Neither intellectual nor sexual maturation pays so diligent a regard to the calendar as human beings do. Skeletal maturity is equally casual about birthdays, but its degree of development can be of terrifying importance to some children. Does this girl's above-average size mean that she will end up taller than average and therefore useless for ballet?

Does this girl's current height indicate that she may be over 6 ft. when 18 and ought she to try to slow down her growth while there is still time? An X ray of the wrist will probably give the answer. Bone development follows a definite routine, and the stage reached indicates the proximity of the final stage, the end of growth.

On average, growth in height has virtually ceased at 17¾ for boys, 16¼ for girls. However it has not entirely ceased. The vertebral column increases by .1 to .2 in. between the ages of 20 and 30, a fraction of an inch that should worry neither ballet dancer nor too-tall girl. After 50 stature diminishes.

Sex Differences

Sex differences in adult size and shape come about in different ways. The longer male legs result from the greater time spent by boys growing before puberty, a time when the legs are growing faster than the trunk. Conversely, the longer male forearm is established at birth, and it continues to be longer than the female forearm throughout life. Similarly, the female tendency to have a longer second finger (index) than the fourth finger (ring) exists from birth. Yet another cause of sex differential is direct intervention by male and female hormones. This happens both in the shoulders (broader for men) and in the hips (broader for women) when androgens and estrogens respectively stimulate cartilage growth.

Growth

Bone growth and form is undoubtedly genetic, but is influenced by the demands made upon it. Unlike some structural girder, it is altered and improved, provided the load is insufficient to cause damage, by any increased demands made upon it. Both volume and density of bone can be made to increase by work. For example, two groups of growing rats were fed differently. One group received hard food, which needed chewing, and the other group received soft food, which did not. Not only did the soft-fed rats acquire slightly smaller heads and faces —by 1 to 2 percent, but also the bones of their head and jaw were lighter—by 12 percent. One wonders, in consequence, whether the prevalence of steak in the American diet helps produce the thickset jawline characteristic of the well-fed Americans, or whether it is just the good feeding in general.

Mice have been kept in centrifuges at four times the force of gravity and have thicker and differently shaped bones as a result. Human beings kept in bed promptly lose bone; this is not just decalcification but loss of bone itself when the skeleton is abnormally idle. For the same sort of reason, the sudden change and call-up from a sedentary life to Army training can lead to certain types of fracture. Demands are made on a skeleton unprepared for relentless effort. One wonders too about astronauts. For long periods they will be weightless and will suffer an idleness of effort even worse than a bedridden patient. Then, suddenly, gravity will be restored, plus the full rigorous effort of existing again in a world of weight.

Remarkably, bone grows to a large extent where it ought to grow, where the stresses demand that it should be grown. Should a child break a femur and should the bone fracture be wrongly aligned, the healing will look unsightly at first as a large callus is formed, but the site of the fracture ought to be invisible a couple of years after the break. Bone-construction cells will have combined with bone-destruction cells not only to join the break but to erase the broken outline of the faulty alignment. Unfortunately the repair system grows increasingly inefficient with increase in age, and faulty alignment is more likely then to lead to permanent thickening.

The word "skeleton" is derived from a Greek word meaning dried up. Bones are most frequently seen when dried up, but their living strength depends upon their not being dry. Chemically, bone tissue is 70 percent inorganic matter, 30 percent organic matter. Dissolve away much of the inorganic component with an acid, and the result is like a dog's rubber bone; in fact, a long bone like the human femur can be tied in a knot. Remove the organic component, either by burning it or by letting decay seek it out, and the result will be a dry, brittle, hard object with more of the properties of cast iron than the flexible and stronger steel of the living tissue.

Although the body's 206 bones are long (like the femur), short (as in the wrist), flat (like the shoulder blade) or irregular (like the vertebrae), all bones have an outer, denser layer of compact bone and an inner meshwork of porous material. The outer layer benefits from the principles that cause a tube to be almost as strong as a solid rod of the same diameter. The inner layer, often called spongy because it looks that way, is phenomenally strong. It is more like hard coral than sponge, and its strength also follows from the engineering principles that explain why many meshworks, such as a honeycomb pattern, can be so strong and yet apparently so delicate.

Both inner and outer strength are necessary. When a parachutist touches down or when someone jumps from a wall, the traditional loads are exaggerated many times. The leg bones are capable of withstanding compression of a ton or more. Later, particularly in postmenopausal women, bones can be unfortunately vulnerable to far smaller loads, and the neck of the femur is then a frequent victim of quite modest accidental burdens imposed upon it.

Function of Bone

The function of bone is diverse. Its rigidity provides a shape and support. It protects. It acts as an anchor point for muscles. Its internal marrow manufactures all red blood corpuscles. It also produces other constituents of blood, as well as destroying old red cells. It contains minerals, chiefly calcium and phosphorus, but also some magnesium, fluorine, chlorine, iron. More important than their mere presence, the bone's minerals are frequently being removed and replaced. For all its structural solidity, bone is remarkably changeable.

In the earliest fish, the skeleton was external, much like the armor of a medieval knight. Not only is this external plating a restriction to movement but also it can have little to do with the body's metabolism. Like teeth, it was probably deposited in a one-way process; and, once deposited, the minerals were as good as lost. The calcium carbonate and calcium phosphate of bone can be deposited, then removed, then replaced, and so on. This ability to have a supply of phosphorus readily available is vital, considering the huge number of chemical processes in which this element takes a crucial part. The ability to have a supply of calcium equally available is also necessary for many other chemical reactions and for the correct balance of the body's fluids. Animals living in salt or fresh water, a mixture of the two, or moving from one to the other have to be able to cope with the changing osmotic situation. Adjusting the level of calcium in bodily fluids is an essential part of keeping the internal environment stable whatever is happening to the external environment. Bone acts helpfully both as a storehouse and as a dumping ground. At different times the two aspects have equal merits, but the ability to control these vital elements, both so crucial to metabolism, has created the argument that bone's metabolic functions outrank its functions of structure and support. Admittedly each is vital, and pride of place is therefore entirely hypothetical, but at least the argument makes the point that bone is not the static framework of structure and support that a skeleton might seem to be. The skeleton is not comparable to the permanent frame of an office building.

Moreover, unlike most structures, the skeleton has to provide not only firm rigidity but also extreme flexibility. The muscles have to be strongly anchored, and yet there has to be articulation. As with so much else dictated by all the opposing forces of natural selection, the result is compromise. Man is a mixture of stiffness and relaxation, restriction and freedom, joints without movement and joints with great versatility. The wrist is free, the ankle far less. The thumb is opposable, the big toe is not. Just as an architect indicates on his drawings how a door will open, so have attempts been made to indicate all possible human movement. The result is always a muddle. The hand can touch everywhere else on the body, even the middle of the back for most people, but it is hard to show this. It is harder still to show how a child's ability to squat, with an apparently total disregard for any knee- or ankle-joint limitations, gradually loses this rubbery simplicity and is transformed into the more awkward posture of the typical adult. A child's elasticity is particularly important at birth, when even its cranial bones can be molded, and the narrow passage of the birth canal is not so restrictive as would otherwise be the case.

The Hand

Considering that the hand of man has played an integral part in man's development and that both its structure and nervous connections are more highly advanced than in any other creature, it still has great limitations. Nothing much can be done with any of its fingers except flexion and extension. The thumb has slightly greater freedom, and the customary explanation of the human hand's dexterity is the capacity for that thumb to oppose itself to every finger. With a little cooperation from each finger, both thumb tip and fingertip can be made to touch. However, the fact that the hand possesses two distinct grips is believed to be even more remarkable. Two billiard balls, for example, can be picked up, and each held independently by two parts of the same hand. One is held between the last two fingers and the palm; the other is gripped between thumb and forefinger. Being able to hold two billiard balls in this manner may seem a poor asset, but it is certainly not unimportant that these two grips exist. Try taking the cap off a fountain pen with the hand that is holding it, and imagine doing it without two grips. Try doing anything with only the single, clawlike grip of a baby's hand, and imagine such restriction.

Incidentally, with regard to the hand, the professions have been confused by nomenclature for the five digits. Elsewhere in the body, the anatomists never seem to have been at a loss, but the medical and legal professions, as well as the ordinary citizen, do not agree about nomenclature. Courts of law, insurance documents, doctors, and mere people should at least be referring to the same digit, but such unanimity is frequently lacking. Is the thumb the first finger, or is the forefinger? Do we have four fingers or five? Is the order thumb, index, middle, ring, and little? If so, where is the forefinger, and where the first finger, and do all people wear rings, and on the left or the right hand?

By the end of 1965, every single one of the fifty states except for California had adopted standard systems of naming the five (or four) fingers, but in their collective attempts at standardization they had made use of ten different systems. The British journal *The Lancet* said every system had its drawbacks and wondered about a man "who has lost one digit from a hand showing a six-fingered polydactyly but having no properly differentiated thumb." The dictionaries, in attempting to clarify, underline the problem. In general they say a finger is "one of the five terminal members of the hand, or one of the four other than the thumb."

Finally, some of the earliest human-type skeletons give strong indications of human-type behavior. According to *Bones, Bodies and Disease,* by Richard Fiennes, skulls of australopithecines have been found showing a form of fracture consisting of two depressions close together. The humerus bone of antelopes has been discovered nearby. The end of such a bone fits well into the skull depressions. In other words, a million years ago people were already being hit on the head by people. Burial grounds and skeletal remains of more recent date give permanent evidence of mankind's perpetuation of this custom.

The Number of Muscles

All animal movement is the work of muscles. Muscles can work only by pulling, never by pushing, and however much a man may be pushing down a wall, every single muscle doing work is doing it by pulling; the body's engineering sees to it that the pulling becomes pushing. Human muscle tissue is laid down before birth or shortly afterward. In this aspect, it is similar to nervous tissue. An infant's complement of muscle fibers is its complement for life; it will probably acquire no more. Strength comes after the expansion of each fiber and after it has been made to do work. For the same reason, the limbs of a blacksmith and of a girl contain a similar number of fibers, although he may have several times her strength. Big people are customarily stronger than small people but, per pound of body weight, bantam-class champions can lift about a pound more than heavyweight champions. In terms of maximum energy output, it has been calculated that the theoretical limit for man is about 6 horsepower, that the highest recorded is 4.5 horsepower, that .6 horsepower can be sustained for five minutes, and that .5 horsepower can be sustained indefinitely. (Which makes one wonder about the sustained horsepower of one horse.)

Muscle fibers can be long—up to 1½ in.—and they can be minute —.04 in. or less—but their diameter is always far smaller. Most fibers are from .004 to .0004 in. across. Many individual fibers make up each distinct anatomical muscle, and there are about 656 muscles in the body, or over three times as many muscles as there are bones. Some 42 percent of male weight is muscle, some 36 percent of female weight. Most muscles attached to the skeleton are linked to a bone either at one end by a tendon or, less frequently, at both ends. In man these tendons (or sinews) may be very small or more than a foot long. Ligaments are also composed of strong fibrous tissue, but their role is to bind bones together.

All or None

Each muscle fiber obeys the same all-or-none principle as the nerve fiber; it either does contract or it does not. However, movement is not a series of robotlike jerks, because each muscle contains innumerable fibers and each separate fiber has to be triggered to effect its pull. Should the stimulus be strong, as when a hand touches a hot surface, every fiber will pull, and the result will be a jerk. Should the nervous stimuli to contract continue to arrive very rapidly at the muscle, it will not contract and relax again, as generally happens, but will remain contracted in a state of tetanus.

The impulses that can cause a fiber to twitch are electrical, mechanical, thermal, and chemical. The time between the arrival of a stimulus at the fiber and the start of that fiber's contraction is between .002 and .004 seconds. A muscle works by the conversion of chemical energy into mechanical energy; only about 25 percent of the potential energy is correctly converted, and the remaining 75 percent is assumed to be lost as heat, assisting the rising temperature of someone suddenly doing strenuous work. A maximum efficiency of 25 percent is similar to the efficiency of an internal combustion engine; that, too, loses most of its energy as heat, and systems are necessary to dissipate this heat.

However much a muscle may either contract or fail to contract on an all-or-none basis and however much this rule may be generally applicable, there is no such uniformity about the total time taken either for a contraction or between regular contractions. On heartbeat alone there is great diversity: an elephant's will contract every 2.5 seconds, a canary's will contract 17 times every second. The human heart, as everyone knows, can change from a solemn beat of 45 a minute to the furious pace three or four times faster during extreme exercise. Even the fast heart is not the fastest muscular rhythm achievable by the body. Finger-tapping can be far faster—for a time—and the tongue and the teeth and the eyelids can all be made to move with a far swifter tremor. Such human speeds are completely outclassed by the wing beats of many insects. Butterflies are ponderous as they flap their casual course, but the wings of beetles can oscillate up to 175 times a *second,* of bees up to 247 cycles a second, of mosquitoes up to 587 cycles, and one midge has been recorded with a wing beat faster than 1,000 cycles a second.

Such vibrations are possible only because the wing muscles do not conform to the conventional relationship between nerve and muscle. Almost always a voluntary muscle twitches once in response to a single nerve impulse. The remarkably high-speed insect wing is twitching many times in response to each stimulus. It is unique in this respect, for the muscle is not going through the normal routine of relaxing after contracting. This phenomenon means that, weight for weight, the wing muscle of some insects generates more energy than any other animal tissue, certainly more than human muscle tissue.

When a human fingertip, for example, is tapped rapidly on a table in a feeble attempt to emulate the insects it will soon tire. Eventually, suffering a paralysis of its own, the finger becomes immobile. The muscle, it seems, can do no more. In fact, if that muscle is then stimulated electrically and externally, as with those massage machines used by therapists, the finger will start tapping again. It is therefore not the muscle that is tired, for it is still responsive; nor is it the nerve that is tired, for it is still capable of transmitting the customary stimuli; rather it is the gap between the two, the synapse, that fails to conduct the stimulus any more from nerve to muscle. Of course, finger-tapping paralysis is short-lived. Within a few moments, the synapse will have had its capabilities restored, and tapping can begin again. Muscular fatigue itself exists quite independently of any synapse fatigue and is believed to be due to an accumulation of lactic acid, which has arisen as one result of the temporary lack of oxygen.

The Working of Muscle

How does muscle work? The subject was opened up notably after World War II and is still in the state of exciting development. Basically, the decade of the 1950s ended with a generalization that muscle contracts because it possesses two kinds of filament. One is thick and the other is thin, and they slide past each other to produce the shortening. It was known that this contraction is extremely rapid—each fiber shortens at a speed equal to several times its length in a second—and it was known that the power of its tension is 40 lb. per sq. in. of muscle cross-section. It is now known that the thin filaments (composed of the protein actin) are drawn further and further in between the thick filaments (composed of the protein myosin), and it was considered valid in the 1950s to compare the system to a ratchet action. Those doing this work still like the comparison. They like it because it appears that the sliding action progresses in a series of distinct notches.

ATP and ADP

The biochemistry is extremely complex, but it is understood that the energy for pushing each filament on a notch comes from ATP (or adenosine triphosphate), which itself gets energy from glucose. ATP uses up its energy in the notch-advancement process and becomes ADP (or adenosine diphosphate) when it does so. Probably, myosin has been the protein that acted as an enzyme to split off the phosphate group, the act that turned the triphosphate into the diphosphate. Such a remark is easy to make, but how proteins act as enzymes—which they are doing all the time in every bodily activity—is another matter. Anyhow, glucose, the simplest sugar, then supplies the energy to reverse the process and assists in putting that phosphate group back again—another easy remark of hideous complexity. Each molecule of glucose can recharge many molecules of ADP to form ATP.

Even if this oversimplified version is comprehensible, it is by no means the whole story. The full story is really the full story of how proteins work, how they catalyze biochemical reactions, how they are affected yet unchanged. Such questions are not just unanswered problems of muscular contraction. They are among the fundamental questions of the chemistry of living tissue. ATP is not just another set of initials; it stands for the molecule that is the universal carrier of energy in the living cell.

Work on muscular contraction has taken such a leap forward since its critical strides in the 1950s (which led also to Nobel prizes) that it may solve not only many of its own problems but others equally fundamental to all forms of tissue. The biochemical examination of contraction and of the two proteins myosin and actin has already shown itself to be a favorable platform for the examination of protein as a whole. As with some tortuous knot, the careful unraveling of one small part can suddenly expose the simplicity of the remainder. However, it has not done so yet.

Cramp, Stiffness, and Stitch

Cramp, stiffness, and stitch have been painfully encountered by most people. Although common, they are certainly not fully understood. Cramp, for example, is certainly a muscular contraction and may well be caused by the nervous system, notably without recourse to the higher control centers; but there is cramp and there is cramp. It frequently comes during sleep, or when there has been discomfort, or when a body is starved of salt, or when cold and exertion—as in swimming—combine to induce it. There must be many possible causes, each leading either to different varieties of cramp or to the same punitive and spasmodic kind of contraction.

Stiffness is equally clear-cut in its symptoms and equally vague in its causes. It may affect joints, ligaments, tendons, or muscles. It usually occurs after exceptional exercise, it may be either an accumulation of products of contraction, whatever they may be, or merely the manifestation of slight injury. The tissue between muscle fibers may have been torn or pulled causing the modest pain and modest impairment.

A stitch can give the sharpest pain of the lot. Generally, it is felt below the ribs and on the left. It is frequently the accompaniment of jolting exercise, as in running with a loaded stomach. Cross-country running, with all its irregularities, is more of a jolt. Sir Adolphe Abrahams, in *Fitness For the Ordinary Man,* says that exposure to cold can help bring it on, that wearing mittens has sometimes proved beneficial, that it helps if the stomach is empty, that disappointment usually follows attempts at prevention, and some people just do seem to have a constitutional tendency for stitch.

~§ 3 6 §~

Radiation

Ionizing Radiation and Its Effects ·
Death and Injury · Safe Levels · Fallout ·
Sensing Radiation · A Glossary

Ionizing Radiation and Its Effects

Ionizing radiation is no new thing. It has been bombarding this planet ever since the world began, partly from the sun, partly from space. And Earth has been bombarding itself from its own naturally radioactive materials. What is new is man-made radiation. Man has been indulging in this type of bombardment for slightly over seventy years. In 1895, Röntgen demonstrated his newly discovered X rays. In 1898, the Curies isolated radium. By 1900, in one way or another, 170 cases of radiation injury had been reported, but no one was alarmed. X-ray machines were used almost like toys, and certainly without restriction.

By the 1920s, owing to the mounting toll of radiation injuries, with fingers and toes eaten into and turned cancerous, there was increasing alarm, but little understanding. Lord Rutherford was gathering a brilliant team of men around him at Cambridge, but even he could see little future for the atomic energy they were starting to unleash. Between the world wars, atoms were split and transmuted, but only experimentally in the laboratories. Scarcely anyone had any idea of the nuclear holocaust to come or of the sudden explosive flowering of man-made radiation. People were being urged to drink radioactive waters. Watches and clocks glowed brightly from their highly radioactive luminous paint. The girls who painted it on used to lick their brushes to make the job easier. Some trichologists used to get rid of surplus hair by subjecting it to X rays. The hair fell out all right, but subsequent malignancies were common. (The last such depilatory machine in the United States was working until 1949.) X-ray machines in shoe shops used to keep the children happy. Pregnant women were routinely X-rayed. No one worried very

[485]

much about "maximum permissible doses." Those days were still to come.

In August, 1939, Albert Einstein wrote his famous letter to President Roosevelt warning him of the possibilities of nuclear energy. The Manhattan Project, dedicated to the exploitation of nuclear energy, got under way, and, at the end of 1942, a disused squash court at the University of Chicago became the site for man's first nuclear chain reaction. Enrico Fermi, born in Italy, watched over the "pile" of uranium as it went critical, as atom after atom of uranium split more and more atoms of uranium and left the radioactive products of all this fission in their wake. That first chain reaction was carefully monitored and controlled; but later, once over New Mexico in July, 1945, and twice over Japan the next month, the chain reactions were permitted to do their damnedest. This time, the fission products were violently scattered over the land and into the atmosphere. Eighty percent of the Hiroshima and Nagasaki victims died from blast and heat, much as millions have died from blast and heat since high explosives were first unleashed, but the remaining 20 percent died quite a new death from radiation.

The testing of nuclear weapons began modestly enough, then accelerated as first the United States, then the Soviet Union, then Britain, then France, and then China loosed off their devices. The fission products rained down as fallout, increasingly as the bombs increased in number. In 1961, the fallout rate in the Northern Hemisphere for strontium 90, the long-lived radioactive element that settles in bone, was about 3 microcuries per square mile. By 1962 it was closer to 15. By 1963, it was about 25. Fortunately, the escalation was stopped by the Nuclear Test Ban Treaty of December, 1962, signed by all the nuclear powers except France and China. By then, the United States had set off some 250 nuclear devices of one kind or another, Russia about 140, and Britain 23. The fission products of all this atomic splitting, the famous isotopes, like strontium 90 and cesium 137, were then part of every one of us, rich or poor, old or newborn.

Despite the huge destructiveness of these weapons, the amount of radioactive fission products released by them was very small. The Hiroshima bomb, although it exploded with the power of 20,000 tons of TNT, was all the work of 2 to 3 lb. of uranium. More uranium is actually necessary to set the thing off, but most of it is scattered in the explosion. A mere 2.2 lb. is equivalent, in explosive energy, to those 20,000 tons of TNT.

When uranium splits, many of its resulting products are harmless to man. They lose all their radioactivity either too quickly or too slowly for it to be harmful. Some, like strontium 90 and cesium 137, are definitely harmful, or have the power to be. But these two products account for only about 6 percent each of the weight of the split uranium, of those 2.2 lb. In other words, Hiroshima's huge bomb left, as a residue of its splitting, a couple of ounces of harmful strontium and another couple of cesium. The scale of the atomic world is incomprehensibly minute.

No one knows quite how much fission product has been produced by the nuclear total of over 400 devices, for they were all secret and some were dirtier than others in producing radioactive residue. This number of bombs could have gone off leaving only 900 lb. of fission products, or 45 lb. each of strontium and cesium. Even if those 45 lb. are multiplied by ten or 100, the total is still seemingly small when compared with the thousands of millions of square miles of the Earth's surface. Yet, despite the huge dilution, despite the great oceans and the atmosphere, despite the size of the continents, those fission products were more than sufficient to be present in every one of us. Take any fragment of bone, take a sliver of that fragment, whether from Eskimo or a New Yorker, and it will instantly record on a suitable instrument the amount of man-made radioactivity that it contains. We all possess fallout. We all drink it and eat it. No one can escape.

But then neither can we escape from all the natural radiation. It is just that man has added to it since the nuclear age began, gently with Röntgen's X rays, explosively with the bombs of 1945.

It was after America's Pacific Island nuclear tests of the early 1950s that the world suddenly woke up to the dangers of fallout. Before that, there had been sympathy for the Japanese. After the Bikini test and after the huge clouds of radioactivity had encircled the earth to deposit active iodine in the milk and strontium and cesium in the soil, the sympathy became more introspective. What will this radiation do to us? Since then, pronouncements, official and otherwise, have either soothed or frightened. Usually the pronouncers have had more then one ax to grind. In 1964, the director of Britain's Atomic Energy Authority's Health and Safety Division gave a skillful summing-up of the conflicting axes when he wrote: "Firstly, the public should be protected from unnecessary and harmful exposure to ionizing radiation; secondly, from unnecessary and harmful propaganda about it; thirdly, from unnecessary and harmful interference with the ability to enjoy the many benefits that radiation can bring now and in the future."

Ionizing radiation exists. It can do great good. For instance, in 1957, 13 million X rays were taken in Britain alone. Seventy radioactive chemicals are regularly used in diagnosis. Over 200 kinds of radiation source (for killing cancer) are manufactured. Ionizing radiation can also do great harm, and the extent of this harm is the subject of continuing debate. To try and clarify this current wrangle, I have split the harm story into three. There is obvious harm when it kills, there is conspicuous harm when it suddenly causes a particular disease, and there is suspected harm if sufficient people receive a dose appreciably higher than normal.

Death and Injury

Radiation deaths, apart from those in the two Japanese cities, have been extremely rare. The first accidental death by radiation occurred in the United States a matter of days after Hiroshima and Nagasaki. On August 21, 1945, Harry Dagnian accidentally gave his right hand a huge dose. Apart from a slight tingling sensation in his fingers, he felt well. Three and a half weeks later, he was dead. On May 21, 1946, in another American laboratory, the screwdriver of Louis Slotin slipped. After the blinding flash, caused by two masses of uranium coming temporarily too close together, Slotin coolly calculated the dosage that everyone in the room had received. He sketched in their positions on the blackboard, and realized that his own dosage had been fatal, but not that of anyone else. The whole group went to a hospital, and nine days later Slotin was dead. Since then, a small handful of other nuclear fatalities have occurred, one in Yugoslavia, and once three men in an American reactor when its control rod was inexplicably removed. In fact, these three died instantaneously from the blast, although they would also have died from the amount of radiation they received, from the insidious manner in which a lethal shower of atomic particles kills a man.

Such a death hit a worker at the Rhode Island uranium-recovery plant in July, 1964. This was the world's first fatal industrial accident from radiation (which is not too bad a record considering that coal mining has regularly killed 200 to 300 men a year in Britain alone). For some reason, the nuclear worker poured enriched uranium into a small tank. Once again, there was a sudden flash of neutrons and gamma rays. The man received 8,800 rads, or ten times the lethal dose (more about rads and dosages in this chapter's glossary). Two hours later he was in the hospital with a slight headache and normal temperature and blood pressure.

The clinical report in the *New England Journal of Medicine* skates over the man's personal feelings at this time, but suffering massive radiation must be emotionally akin to swallowing poison irretrievably.

The body feels well temporarily, but the mind knows a little of what is in store for it. In the case of this Rhode Island man, his blood pressure suddenly dropped after four hours, and steps were taken to keep it up. Eight hours later, it was still falling, and his temperature was up to 120°F. Parts of his body, those that had been nearest to the tank, were red and swollen; but he still felt physically well. Thirty-six hours later, the swellings were worse, his blood pressure was becoming more difficult to maintain, and his blood was increasingly full of the products of decay. After 44 hours, his blood pressure was falling too low for it to be maintained, and after 49 hours he died.

Death had been inevitable throughout those two days. Its immediate cause was circulation failure, but the destruction of tissues could equally well have caused death in several other ways. A man just cannot take more than a certain amount of radiation, just as he cannot take more than a certain amount of poison, injury, blood loss, fever, or cold. There are limits, and somewhere between 500 and 1,500 rads is the limit for nearly all of us. A Yugoslav who suffered 1,350 rads in a reactor accident near Belgrade holds the world record in this respect because he survived. Bone-marrow grafting in Paris was vital to his survival. Current thinking is that no treatment would be effective for doses higher than 1,500 rads. The Mol (Belgium) reactor accident at the end of 1965 helped to confirm this view. One man received up to 5,000 rads on his left foot, but only 200 rads on his trunk. Six months later he was discharged from the hospital, but with a mid-thigh amputation of his left leg.

Apart from killing, radiation can also maim or cause definite injuries. The injuries may prove fatal in time or hinder life in the meantime, but they come into a different category from the inevitably fatal class. Mrs. Mijjua Job, of Rongelap, came into that nonfatal category following the events that began one sunny day in March, 1954. Rongelap is one of the Marshall Islands of the Pacific; so is Bikini. She saw the flash and then the huge growth of cloud following the detonation of an American hydrogen bomb. The 120 miles between her atoll and the one pulverized in the explosion had been considered sufficient, particularly as the forecast wind would take all radioactive debris to the west and away from Rongelap. The wind, unfortunately, did nothing of the kind. It blew to the east, and then subjected Mrs. Job and 81 Rongelapese to two days of intensive fallout. Radioactive iodine, strontium, cesium, and other isotopes all came their way and landed silently on the inhabited atoll.

Consequently, nearly everybody suffered radiation burns; these are much like ordinary burns, but harder to heal. Ninety percent of the children and 40 percent of the adults suffered hair loss. Practically everybody's white-blood-cell count slumped to half its former level. Something like 175 rads of radiation dose had been suffered by these people from the direct consequences of fallout. They had also suffered further rads when they drank water and ate food contaminated by the Bikini debris, perhaps 160 rads extra for the adults and even more for the children. The wind miscalculation had turned the island, as one American bluntly and accurately put it, into a unique human-laboratory colony.

In the years since 1954, the colony's thyroid glands have been of particular concern. By 1965, 18 of the 82, including Mrs. Job, were found to have thyroid abnormalities. Six of the islanders, again including Mrs. Job, were flown to Boston for surgery. Fortunately, most of the thyroid nodules were thought to be benign, but one turned out to be a carcinoma of the gland. Seventy-five of the Rongelap children were on another island at the time and significantly not one of them has developed a thyroid nodule. Other deleterious changes to the 82 have been that the bone-marrow status of some of them was still below normal even ten years after the mishap, that more miscarriages occurred in the first four years, that some benign lumps appeared near some of the burned-skin areas, and that the children who were younger than five at the time are slightly smaller or less developed than normal. Admittedly, the explosion was not even 15 years ago, and cancers frequently take longer to manifest themselves, but many investigators of the Rongelap disaster are already beginning to sigh with relief that doses so huge have led— so far—to consequences no worse than those already recorded. Mrs. Job, for example, has had one miscarriage since March, 1954, but four of her nine children have also been born since then. Fertility at least, despite fears to the contrary, does not seem to have been impaired.

Safe Levels

There is no such thing as a "safe level" of radiation, a threshold below which no harm can be done. Radiation is harmful. It does damage. It comes in various forms, all with variously damaging potentialities, but all do harm. Whether as alpha or beta particles, gamma rays, neutrons, or X rays, all do harm, but differently. Energetic gamma rays pass, bullet-like, straight through the human body. Alpha particles are stopped in the skin. None of them are detectable by the five human senses (although some animals seem to be aware of them). A lethal dose is painless— until its effects start showing up as painful symptoms hours later. Sub-lethal doses are equally painless, but even quite high doses, such as 100 rads, produce no symptoms at all. Between 100 and 200 rads, the symptoms are mild, if obvious at all, and they really become apparent only after doses of more than 200 rads. However, symptoms are quite different both from long-term effects and from genetical effects upon subsequent generations. It is these effects that cause so much reasonable concern. High doses, of the sort received at Rhode Island or Rongelap, will—one hopes—be rare. Low doses are with us all the time; and so, presumably, are their effects.

There is a maximum established in Britain for the dose permitted to the whole body for an ordinary member of the public—½ rem a year. (In this connection, rems and rads can be considered equivalent.) For ordinary workers at atomic-energy establishments in Britain, the maximum dose is 1½ rems a year. For workers actually dealing with radioactive materials, the maximum is 5 rems a year, with a subsidiary maximum of 3 rems in any period of 13 weeks. Such doses are minute when compared with the 175 rads received by Mrs. Job as the direct consequence of the fallout and the 160 rads extra that she received indirectly.

This total of 335 rads in a few weeks is about one and a half times as much as an atomic worker would be permitted to receive in a working lifetime of 50 years. It is almost 700 times as much as the average member of the public, subjected to his or her share of natural radioactivity, X rays, and fallout, is permitted to receive as a maximum in any one year. And this maximum dose was still not reached by a long way even during the worst fallout year, 1963, or during the year for greatest contamination of food by strontium, 1964. The Rhode Island worker received 8,800 rads and was dead 49 hours later. Mrs. Job received a total of about 1/25 of that and had to have her thyroid gland removed ten years later. Each ordinary man in the street receives much less than 1/700 of her dose from fallout in any year, let alone in a few weeks, and yet there is great concern.

So there should be. There is a tremendous lack of knowledge about the effects of radiation both genetically—upon future generations— and somatically—upon the current generation. There are men who stress the dangers; there are also those who belittle them. *Time* magazine has reported that in "almost all argument involving fall-out and its potential hazards, equally reputable scientists can be found on both sides." Despite this lack of knowledge, or perhaps because of it, there is more concern about the genetic than the somatic possibilities. From the genetic point of view, there is no such thing as a safe level, because at any level radiation is likely to increase the number of mutations, the irreversible changes between one generation and the next, and almost all of them will be harmful. J. B. S. Haldane once likened this harmful inevitability to a crude attempt at watch-repairing. If you take an erratic watch and jab a finger into its mechanism, there is just a chance that this jab will improve matters. There is a far greater chance that it will not. So too with mutations. They are almost always harmful. Radiation causes more of them. Therefore radiation is harmful.

Long-term experiments are being carried out to discover just how harmful it is. Some mice at Los Alamos, New Mexico, for example, are being subjected to 200 rads of gamma radiation (roughly Mrs. Job's direct dose and some 5,000 times the amount customarily received from natural sources) and are then being allowed to breed. By 1967, this mouse colony was nine years old, and had produced 44 generations. There were by then two visible effects—one good, one bad. There were fewer mice per litter, but more litters per female lifetime. The result so far is just as many mice as in the control group and a growing conviction that nothing short of sufficient radiation to bring about complete sterility will cause the genetic death of a mammalian population. Admittedly, mice are not men, but one past fear had been that in an irradiated world so many genetic monstrosities would result that breeding would be impossible. Although only mice, the Los Alamos colony helps to dispel this fear.

Future generations are also in jeopardy when young embryos and fetuses are X-rayed. When X-ray machines were new and obstetricians were reveling in their new-found ability to check on fetal development, on twins, and on the correctness of fetal posture, the wombs of pregnant women were regularly pierced with ionizing radiation. Now, this is less true. The maximum permissible dose to be given to any fetus in its nine-month gestation is a single rem (again virtually equivalent to a rad), and the mother's abdomen is not to receive more than 1.3 rems.

Obstetricians today use X rays whenever they feel the radiation risk is more than outweighed by the advantages to be gained from seeing the X-ray picture. Suppose that X-rayed fetuses are more likely to suffer in consequence from leukemia—which is the general belief. Suppose that one in 5,000 of them will eventually die from this disease—which is a ratio that has been postulated. Such long odds can be immeasurably longer than the very short odds against a baby's survival if the obstetrician does not know all that he wishes to know about its position in the womb. Infant mortality is still two per 100. It would be markedly higher without X rays.

In May, 1966, almost 21 years after the first atomic bombs, 12 years after the large Bikini tests, and 3½ years after the test-ban treaty, Britain's Medical Research Council's Committee on Protection against

Ionizing Radiations summed up the situation. It concluded that "as a result of the atmospheric tests that have taken place up to the end of 1965 it is estimated that by the year 2000 three additional cases of leukemia, two of all other types of fatal cancer, and two of thyroid cancer per million of the population exposed may, at worst, have been caused in the United Kingdom."

Only France and China have been conducting atmospheric nuclear tests since the treaty, and the number of their detonations has, so far, fortunately, been small.

Fallout

Radioactive fallout, which first became a major issue after the American nuclear tests of 1954 (although the word was actually coined back in 1945), is still falling and will fall in significant amounts for many years to come. Far more forcibly than the early Röntgen rays and even the holocaust over Japan, it was fallout that alerted the world to the dangers inherent in increased levels of radioactivity. Yet even at its worst time, the amount of radiation suffered, on average, by anyone as the consequence of fallout has always been less than the amount suffered as the result of medical radiology. And the amount of radiation from such X-ray equipment has always been less on average than the inescapable amount to which we are all subjected from natural sources, from space, from the rocks of the earth. Fallout sounded the shrill alarm, but proved to be less alarming than had originally been feared.

A major fallout scare was concentration. It is all very well to talk in general terms about whole-body doses, but radioactive materials can be concentrated in very small areas. There is 30,000 times as much radiation in some foods as in others. Brazil nuts are outstandingly high. So too are some cereals. Various plants and animals collect it in amazing amounts. Certain fish swimming in the waters near the Bikini atoll staggered the scientists by their ability to concentrate radioactivity within them. One fish collected radioactive zinc, which could only have come from the casing of the exploded bomb. Many seaweeds collect radioactive iodine, a major product of nuclear fission.

Mrs. Job's thyroid trouble was undoubtedly due to radioactive iodine, for iodine will always collect in the thyroid, whether radioactive or not. If radioactive, it can do harm primarily in that area. Other common radioactive substances have other propensities. Radium, soluble plutonium, strontium, and calcium settle in the bone, insoluble plutonium in the lungs. The kidneys accumulate gold, uranium, and other heavy metals. The bone marrow collects phosphorus, tritium, sodium, and chlorine. Radioactive cesium, after strontium the most notorious product of nuclear fission, is much more general and gets carried around in the blood. Therefore, it can come more into contact with the precious gonads than, say, strontium, which settles in the bone. Strontium is worrying enough, being superbly placed to induce bone cancers and leukemia, but cesium presents the extra genetical worry of the future.

Sensing Radiation

Professor Wilhelm Röntgen first demonstrated the power of his discovery to himself on November 7, 1895. He told the world about it in his article "A New Kind of Ray" that Christmas. The world found it difficult to comprehend something that could not be felt or seen. Several firms made much money by exploiting this bewilderment and selling X-ray-proof underclothes for women. To a large measure, the incomprehension still exists. Sight, sound, touch, taste, or smell cannot detect ionizing radiation under ordinary circumstances. So the Japanese fishermen of the *Lucky Dragon,* liberally dusted with fallout in the Pacific, swept up the stuff to put it under their beds and in their lockers, thereby storing up inevitable disease and sickness for themselves. The Mexican family who died in 1966 when one member brought back a lump of cobalt felt and saw nothing strange; but it was strongly radioactive cobalt 60, a powerful emitter of gamma rays, and it killed them. One measuring instrument could have saved their lives. Geiger counters stammer away audibly as they count the nuclear disintegrations hitting them and give warning of levels of radioactivity. They are extraordinarily efficient, detecting in each ounce of ordinary rainwater some fallout from a quite modest explosion on the other side of the globe. Human beings are quite incapable of doing this. Like aircraft flying in cloud they are totally dependent upon their instruments.

Nevertheless, certain creatures have smelled out X rays and the like. No one knows how they do it. Rats have proved their ability to detect minute doses, such as 1/50 rad. Cats can detect X rays, and it has been proved that their eye is not involved; they seem literally to smell them out. If small beams of radiation are aimed at the delicate and receptive horns of snails, these horns will retract. Barnacles withdraw their tentacles in the presence of undue radiation, worms change course, fleas hop away. Even plants, like the sensitive Mimosa pudica, which collapses when touched or irritated in any way, will react under the invisible, inaudible effect of a modest beam of radiation. How? It is not known, but it is suspected that cats and rats may be smelling the extra ozone in air caused by the irradiation.

In this nuclear age, when a built-in Geiger counter of a sense organ would be an invaluable asset, it would be nice to know. In the meantime, like miners carrying canaries to detect firedamp, we might well carry snails. Their delicate horns could then be induced to give warning of high levels of radiation.

A Glossary

Finally, the nuclear age has caused a nuclear language of its own. Some words likely to be encountered follow:

Curie	The principal unit of radioactivity. One gram of radium has the activity of one curie. It emits 37 billion disintegrations a second.
Millicurie	One-thousandth of the activity of a curie.
Microcurie	One-millionth of the activity of a curie.
Picocurie	One-billionth of the activity of a curie (i.e., 37 disintegrations a second). Levels of strontium 90 in human bone, for example, are measured in pico-curies per gram of calcium.
Rad	The unit of absorbed ionizing radiation. It is defined as the energy absorption of 100 ergs per gm. of tissue. Between 500 and 1,500 rads will kill most people.
Röntgen	The unit of radiological dose. Defined as the dose that corresponds to the release of 83.8 ergs of energy in a gram of air.
Rem	The unit of biological dose of ionizing radiation, being an abbreviation of Röntgen Equivalent Man. (The differences between rads, röntgens, and rems are real, and not just the hair-splitting of physics. Röntgens are always measured in air. Rads measure the radiation that has been absorbed by something. Rems measure the radiation absorbed by man. For practical purposes, rems and rads are the same for all of us who receive our radiation predominantly from X rays, fallout, and natural background activity. Rads are likely to be less than rems, perhaps only one-tenth as much, for those people involved in reactor accidents, who survive atomic-bomb attacks, and who either eat or breathe the very heavily radio-

active elements, such as radium and plutonium. To use another language, rads are similar to rems for beta particles, gamma rays, and X rays. They are much less than rems for alpha particles and neutrons, particularly the energetic kind.)

Radiation An all-embracing word taking in all the ways in which energy can be given off by an atom. It thus includes X rays, gamma rays, all charged particles, and all neutrons. (Radiation is also used with other meanings, such as radiators and radiating heat, that are distinct from the word's use in atomic energy.)

Radioactivity Most atoms are stable and nonradioactive. Those that are unstable and radioactive will give off either particles or gamma radiation. Although a piece of radioactive material is continually active and emitting radiation, each atom in it is either about to emit energy or has already done so.

Half-life All radioactive substances form stable substances in time. Their half-life occurs when they have lost half their activity. Half-lives can vary from less than one-millionth of a second to millions of years. The substances in fallout whose half-lives pose the greatest harm biologically are neither the very short nor the very long. The very short have lost all their activity before falling out. The very long take so long to lose their radioactivity that their gentle smoldering is virtually inactive. Iodine 131 has a half-life of 8 days, cobalt 60 of 5.2 years, strontium 90 of 28 years, cesium 137 of 30 years, and carbon 14 of 5,600 years.

Decay An atom decays when it distintegrates, when it changes from instability to stability. Half of the atoms have decayed in a half-life.

Isotope Two atoms are isotopes if they are of the same element but have different masses. Less accurately, but more frequently, an isotope means a radioactive element.

Disintegration It occurs when an atom's nucleus emits a particle.

Fission This is the splitting of an atom's nucleus into fragments, which are called fission products. Fission is always accompanied by the release of energy.

Gamma rays Electromagnetic radiation similar to X rays.

Ionizing radiation Radiation that knocks electrons from atoms, thereby leaving ions behind. Conversely, ions are charged atoms that have lost or gained an electron.

Nucleus The heart of the atom. About a millionth of a millionth of a centimeter wide.

Postscript

"If we could first know where we are and whither we are tending, we could better judge what to do and how to do it." Abraham Lincoln's remark, already used in this book, should be used time and time again. But where on earth are we?

In the past we led our hazardous lives with a mixture of fear, common sense, and superstition. We watched our children die, and we ourselves died—probably—before our time. In the recent past the hazards have diminished (save for those of our own making), much of the superstition has faded away, and we can expect to live to a decent age; the triumphs of hygiene, sanitation, medicine, and science have caused such expectation wherever a country's economy allows these triumphs to be applied. In a sense they have merely put the balance right. Man's body has a life of 70 years; hygiene and the rest are permitting it to achieve those 70 years. And that is where we are.

But whither are we tending? With every chapter of this book, there will obviously be quite a different tale to tell by the end of the century. I do not mean solely that fewer babies will be dying, that ulcers may be a thing of the past, or that athletes will run a mile in 3 minutes, 30 seconds. I believe the differences will be revolutionary. Also, while the ethics of today impel society to prolong life wherever feasible, the ethics of tomorrow will be vastly more complex.

Take abortion. Today, we are destroying fetuses of two, three, and four months as a form of contraception. Today, we can keep some babies alive who are born after only six months in the uterus. Skills in the prematurity wards will grow more skillful, and even younger babies will survive. An abortion can then no longer be called contraception but will be the killing of a baby that could be kept alive, like denying a transfusion to a bleeding man. Perhaps transfusions should be denied more to some bleeding men. Perhaps euthanasia should have wider applications.

[498]

Perhaps the plug should be pulled out more readily, as is discussed in the chapter on death. Perhaps grossly malformed babies should be deliberately killed at birth. And should steps be taken to prevent their production? Should certain marriages and matings be forbidden?

Conversely, should positive eugenics, which aims to create better stock, be actively encouraged? Should man breed men as he breeds his animals? Should woman, who has her imperfections as a breeding chamber for fetuses because she smokes, takes drugs, falls, and succumbs to illness, be supplanted by the test tube? Should children be entrusted to parents who, according to George Bernard Shaw, are the last people who should have children? Should growth be adjusted? Should mental development? Should senility, or the age of death? All such questions could well be the chapter headings of a book such as this in a few years' time.

On a different level, and bearing in mind that food production may frequently be inadequate, should man permit himself the inefficient luxury of nourishment like beef? And what will he do in a world of leisure? In a cosseted community will his virtues decay? La Bruyère wrote: "Liberty is not idleness; it is the free use of time, the choosing of work and exercise. To be free, in short, is not to do nothing; it is to be the sole arbiter of what one does or does not do." Just as retirement today seems frequently to hasten death, will the automated life of the future be disastrous when man is free? Will we merely prolong senility, and remember Somerset Maugham's address on his 80th birthday: "There are many values in growing old. . . . For the moment, I cannot think of one of them."

Drugs have already become today's problem. If a newspaper headlines "Youth Takes Drugs" as against "Drugs Sent to Marooned Youth," our ambivalence at least is clear. "The desire to take medicine is perhaps the greatest feature which distinguishes man from animals," wrote Sir William Osler. Drugs have enabled us to survive so well; they are wonder drugs, miracle drugs. Will mankind's propensity for self-medication continue to be mainly beneficial?

Spare-part surgery did not come within the compass of this book, but it will surely grow more and more crucial. Not only will artificial replacement of valves and joints become more widespread, but one can imagine a young accident victim providing the organs for a number of ailing patients. Will people be allowed to bury their dead? Will many of the current dignities of life be assaulted when they interfere with the new ethical wave?

"Life," said Blaise Pascal 300 years ago, "is a maze in which we take the wrong turning before we have learnt to walk." Few would disagree. And still fewer would disagree that the maze ahead of us is infinitely more complex than anything encountered so far.

Index

[501]